SCIENCE
Third Edition

Matter and Energy

Mortimer L. Bloom
Brooklyn College

The Macmillan Company, New York / Collier-Macmillan Limited, London

The Macmillan Company
866 Third Avenue, New York, New York 10022

Collier-Macmillan Canada, Ltd., Toronto, Ontario

Library of Congress catalog card number: 79-155266

FIRST PRINTING

Preface

Our belief that science is not only "the soul of the prosperity of nations and the living source of all progress" but also one of the great achievements of the human mind has caused us to make this attempt to deepen the understanding of the physical sciences by the non-science college student. We agree with Glenn T. Seaborg, 1951 Nobel Laureate in Chemistry, that the problems posed by science enter into the fabric of our whole society in many ways.

If it has been important for knowledgeable laymen of the past, particularly the recent past, to know some of the elementary principles of science, it is now far more important since *ecology,* a term almost completely unknown even by well-informed laymen four or five years ago, has become a household word. A truly meaningful fight against pollution calls for considerable knowledge that is physical, chemical, and geological, as well as biological. Although scientists and government officials will make the necessary decisions, ordinary responsible citizens need to make their views felt. They will be unable to do so unless they comprehend what is going on. Science will give mankind a better world given the proper mental climate. For this mental climate to prevail, there must be people with knowledge and

understanding. Unfortunately, there are not enough such people. Our concern about this low level of understanding of science among otherwise well-informed and thoughtful laymen leads us to say that it is one of the most critical problems confronting higher education in the United States today.

There is a widely held misconception that the sciences are far beyond the comprehension of the average person, even beyond that of the average good college student. That this is a fallacy is well demonstrated by the interest in things scientific displayed by children, most of whom have a natural curiosity regarding things and events. Unfortunately, the questions they ask to satisfy this curiosity most commonly go unanswered by parent and elementary school teacher alike, with the result that not only do they stop asking questions but many even become indoctrinated with the belief that the answers are beyond their comprehension. As Albert Einstein put it, "There exists a passion for comprehension. That passion is rather common in children, but gets lost in most people later on."

This book is primarily an exposition of the major concepts and theories of physical science, but it is also an attempt to set these concepts and theories into a broad historical and philosophical context. A proper understanding of the origins of theories and their relationships to one another and to the observational evidence that supports them should help the student to appreciate the scope and limitations of science. This in turn should introduce him to the inherent uncertainty and the role of probability and truth in science. The result should be some understanding of the influence that science has on the philosophy that underlies our culture.

The selection of the major topics has changed little from the previous editions, but their order and organization have been modified, sometimes drastically. This we believe has improved the continuity and the integration of the various topics. It has also allowed us to give better and more complete explanations of many phenomena. We have adhered to the premise that the purpose of science is *explanation* rather than description. We cannot, of course, abandon description, nor can we dispense with facts and measurements. But to be content to limit our discussions to these would make the book intensely boring to most students and cause us to fail utterly in achieving our major objective.

That there are fewer chapters in this edition does not mean that the coverage is less. It simply means a different grouping of topics. We have, in fact, introduced a new chapter on relativity and added other new topics, chief among them sections on continental drift and on nucleic acids.

No mathematics beyond elementary algebra is presupposed, and nothing beyond that and a bit of plane geometry is presented in this book. We have deferred the chapter on mathematics to the end of Part I to avoid giving students the impression that the book is frighteningly mathematical.

We are indebted to many of our colleagues at Brooklyn College for their advice, general and specific. We thank particularly Professors David E. Goldberg, Evan Williams, Wilbur G. Valentine, and Peter J. Brancazio. We also are indebted to Dr. Bernard Fryshman of the New York Institute of Technology for assistance, to Mrs. Helen L. Feldman for typing the manuscript, and to Mrs. Elisabeth H. Belfer of The Macmillan Company for careful attention to manuscript and proof.

V. H. B.
M. L. B.

Contents

Part III Molecules, Atoms, and Heat Energy

Part IV The Electrical Nature of Matter

Chapter 17 Electric and Magnetic Energy 265

Chapter 18 The Fundamental Unit of Electricity 298

Part V Structure of Matter

Chapter 19 Divisibility of Atoms 319

Chapter 20 Electromagnetic (Radiant) Energy 332

Chapter 21 Relativity 361

PART I

The Solar System

The Rise of the Ptolemaic System of the Universe

Chapter 1

Astronomy compels us to look upwards and leads us from this world to
another.
PLATO

Primitive man's attempts to explain those parts of the physical world closest to him were probably feeble at best. Like the majority of modern men, he took the commonplace things about him for granted. Actually the different kinds and shapes of the matter that we see in our everyday lives are not simple; to our early ancestors they must have seemed nearly infinite in number and utterly random in their occurrence and behavior. To seek basic relationships between them must have seemed futile to all but a few.

To most primitive peoples the easiest explanation of natural phenomena seems to have been to invent gods who were assumed to be the creators and the rulers of the universe. These gods were assigned human attributes, particularly those of love and anger. Earthquakes, volcanic eruptions, eclipses, violent storms with their flashing lightning and crashing thunder, floods, droughts, and so on, were interpreted as evidences of the anger of one or more of the gods. Rites to appease the god's anger commonly followed these sometimes catastrophic events by the making of a blood sacrifice of some sort.

Attempts were (and still are) made to control nature or to appease the gods by magic. Some primitive peoples tried to cause rain by performing certain dances; an example is the rain dance of the Hopi Indians of Arizona. Others of us keep the sale of rabbits' feet and other good luck charms a thriving business; some search for four-leafed clovers or visit fortune tellers, astrologers, spiritual mediums, or others who prey upon those who are prone to invoke the supernatural to explain natural phenomena.

The practitioners of magic became the "medicine men" still common in many tribes today. In some of the more "advanced" societies the medicine men became the priests, who commonly banded together to form entrenched priesthoods dedicated to the control of men's intellects and the preserving of the status quo. The inevitable result has always been the inhibition of the furtherance of scientific ideas. The occurrences of earthquakes, violent thunderstorms, floods, eclipses of the sun and moon, and other such phenomena, in a random order and without apparent natural causes, were not conducive to the development of a belief that order and regularity exist in the universe, that a particular set of effects is always preceded by a particular set of causes. The tendency to ascribe certain events to wrong causes because the events happen in a particular sequence is common among all peoples of the earth. For example, the dog star, Sirius, rose at dawn in Egypt at the time of the Nile floods; the belief that Sirius caused the floods was thus perhaps inevitable. Even scientists are not entirely immune from the choice of an incorrect causal sequence, but the true scientist is forever consciously trying to distinguish cause from effect, and both from

accidental coincidence insofar as natural phenomena are concerned. He believes that the universe is comprehensible to man, and so can be described in an orderly way.

Order and Regularity in the Natural World

From earliest times man has pondered the stars of the night sky. Early man eventually discovered that celestial movements could measure time—and the science of astronomy was born among the Babylonians, Egyptians, Chinese, Hindus, and (probably somewhat later) the Mayans of Central America. Hundreds, and even thousands, of years before the development of the other sciences, these peoples realized that the arrangement of the heavens was not chaotic but orderly; the stars formed systematic patterns. To nomad and seafarer alike the stars were signposts that told direction. To farmer and herdsman the moon's phases and the sun's annual northward journey in springtime foretold the coming of the annual floods of certain rivers, the rains, and the times of planting. Such information was of the utmost importance to the farmer, particularly where the seasons were alternately wet and dry, with the wet season much the shorter. This early study of astronomy was a thoroughly practical endeavor before it earned the name of a science.

Babylonian and Egyptian Astronomy

A calendar based on the two astronomical cycles—the phases of the moon and the changing points of sunrise on the eastern horizon, farthest north in summer, farthest south in winter (Fig. 1-1)—was devised by the Baby-

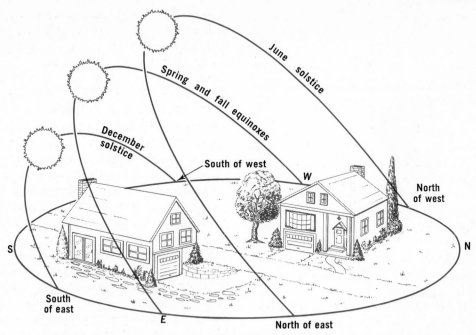

Fig. 1-1   Points of "Sunrise" and "Sunset" at Different Seasons in Temperate Zone of Northern Hemisphere. The sun is shown at the noon position, midway between the two horizons. Note that the sun rises *directly* in the east and sets *directly* in the west only at the times of the two equinoxes.

lonian astronomers, who were also priests, long before 2500 B.C. Remembering groups of stars and their relative positions was found to be easier than remembering each individually. The Babylonians made fanciful groupings of them and gave the groups (constellations) fanciful names. Most constellations are visible in the night sky for only a portion of a year. These times of visibility are different for different constellations (Fig. 1-2), but there are order and regularity in their appearance and disappearance. Certain groups in succession always rose in the east shortly before sunrise. The astronomers thought these particular constellations stretched in a belt across the sky, for they saw that the sun always stayed within that belt as it pursued its daily apparent journey around the earth. This belt is now known as the zodiac (Fig. 2-16). The Babylonian cal-

endar divided the year into 12 months of 30 days each, the week into 7 days (the sun, moon, and 5 known planets make 7 celestial bodies), the day into 24 hours, the hour into 60 minutes, and the minute into 60 seconds.[1]

Early Egyptian astronomy was simpler than that of the Babylonians because the Egyptian astronomers remained essentially astronomers instead of becoming devout astrologers like the Babylonians. Nevertheless, the Egyptians kept excellent records of celestial movements and so were able to devise a calendar that made their year 365 days long—12 months of 30 days each and 5 feast days.[2]

---

[1] Note that all these figures, with the exception of 7, are multiples of 6. To the Babylonians, 6 was a magic number.

[2] Meanwhile the Chinese calculated the length of the year as $365\frac{1}{4}$ days.

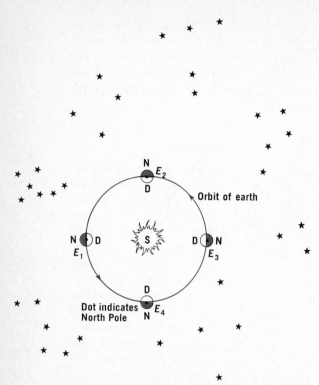

Fig. 1-2. Change of Night Sky with Seasons. The earth revolves about the sun counterclockwise in a nearly circular orbit. Consider the earth at E_1 about July 1 (summer in the northern hemisphere). D indicates the side of the earth lighted by the sun—daytime and not a cloud in the sky. An observer there sees no stars because of the intense light of the sun. Suppose the sun's light could be completely shut out by the wave of a magic wand. The observer could then look out across the earth's orbit and see the stars to the right of E_3—and elsewhere. On January 1 the earth is at E_3 and at night he can look out and see those same stars, but he cannot see those to the left of E_1 because the light of the sun is so much brighter. The constellations he sees in January are not those he sees in July.

The Rise of Astrology

Before 600 B.C. the Babylonians surpassed all the other peoples of antiquity—Egyptians, Chinese, Hindus, Greeks—in the quality of their astronomical observations. The careful

records, some going back to 4000 B.C., kept by their priest-astronomers enabled them to establish apparent relationships—which could be either coincidental or truly causal—between celestial cyclic phenomena and terrestrial cyclic phenomena. All changes in the apparent paths of the sun, moon, planets, and even the stars were slow and cyclical; inevitably each pattern returned to what it had been at some previous time. The Babylonians' records even enabled them to predict eclipses. The correspondence of the seasons with the north-south journeys of the sun was cyclical, alternately bringing summer and winter or wet and dry seasons. If the sun could bring such benefits—or the reverse—perhaps the moon with its cyclical waxing and waning might somehow be related to the success or failure of crops. Perhaps even the planets (the five that are visible to the naked eye—Mercury, Venus, Mars, Jupiter, and Saturn) with their seemingly erratic wanderings among the "fixed" stars had power over earthly affairs. This going beyond the justifiable interpretations of their observations created the pseudoscience of astrology. The priest-astronomers of Babylon became astrologers who gained great economic and political power 500 to 1000 years B.C. Eventually, astrology infected every culture and infiltrated every level of education, down to the present day, despite all scientific evidence of its worthlessness.

The Concept of the Earth in Space

All the early priest-astronomers assumed that the earth was motionless at the center of the universe. Several thousands of years were to elapse before it was recognized that the earth itself was a celestial body that a hypothetical observer out in space would see as another planet. The main reason for the long delay in making such a conclusion is that we make our observations from a moving observation post; hence all motion is relative. The fact of the earth's motion is contrary to common sense, for our senses do not make us aware of it. A second reason for delay in recognizing the earth as a celestial body is our tremendous isolation in space, an isolation that even today is difficult to conceive, let alone perceive. The nearest "fixed" star to our sun (which is itself a star) is Alpha Centauri. It is so far away that its light, traveling at 186,000 mi/sec, takes a bit over four years to reach us. In more understandable terms, a space ship, traveling the entire distance at a speed of 25,000 mi/hr,[3] would take about 130,000 years to reach Alpha Centauri. Even at an average speed of 1 million mi/hr, it would take nearly 3000 years.

Greek Astronomy

Neither the Babylonians nor the Egyptians attempted much in the way of rational explanations of what they observed in the heavens. Their explanations were rooted in the supernatural. On the other hand, the Greeks did not rely upon the supernatural, nor did they waste much effort on astrology. They tried to imagine mechanisms that would make the heavenly bodies move as they do. To use modern terminology they "constructed models" that are sometimes called theories. Their religion was such that they could inquire into the natural order of the universe without fear of punishment by angry gods. Reason liberates man from the terror of the gods, said the Roman poet Lucretius (ca. 60 B.C.).

Thales

Thales (ca. 580 B.C.) was one of the first of the ancient Greek philosophers. Some author-

ities have stated that he was the first known scientist because his school was the first to break away from mythological traditions and assume that the whole universe is natural and could be explained by ordinary knowledge and reasoning.

Anaximander

Anaximander (ca. 550 B.C.) is said to have been the first man of record to note that the heavens (in the northern hemisphere) appear to revolve about Polaris (Fig. 1-3). The simplest explanation of this observation is that the stars are lights embedded in a great overturned spinning bowl—that is, half of a great sphere—with the earth motionless at the center. You would undoubtedly believe the same if you watched the sky for many nights—and had not been indoctrinated to believe otherwise. If you were a genius, you might even extend this bowl to a complete sphere, the other half of which could be viewed from a point directly opposite you on the other side of the earth.

Pythagoras

Pythagoras (ca. 530 B.C.), or some member of his school, pictured a universe with a round earth[4] at the center surrounded by a series of concentric transparent rotating spheres in which were embedded the various celestial bodies.

Plato and Eudoxus

Plato (ca. 400 B.C.) conceived the sphere to be the most perfect of forms and therefore concluded that the universe and each of its parts were perfect spheres. It followed that the

---

[3]This is the *minimum* initial speed a rocket ship must have to escape from the earth's gravitational attraction. See page 139 for a clarification.

[4]A round earth is hard to believe if one has not been indoctrinated when very young. Consider the child trying to picture "upside-down" people on the other side of the earth.

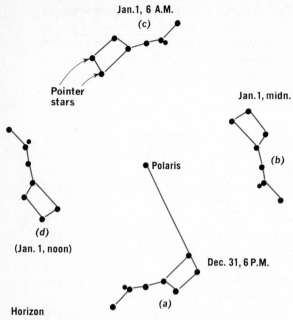

Jan.1, 6 A.M.
(c)

Pointer
stars

Jan.1, midn.

(b)

• Polaris

(d)

(Jan. 1, noon)

Dec. 31, 6 P.M.

(a)

Horizon

Fig. 1-3. Apparent Daily Swing of Big Dipper (Ursa Major) About Polaris. About January 1, when the nights are long in the middle and northern latitudes, the Big Dipper may be observed in three of the four positions shown at the hours indicated. A line through the two pointer stars will always pass very nearly through Polaris. At the equator Polaris is always on the horizon; south of the equator Polaris can never be seen.

circle must be the most perfect two-dimensional figure, and that all moving celestial bodies must move in perfectly circular paths. Adherence to this purely esthetic concept was to cause untold trouble to Kepler nearly two thousand years later. Eudoxus (ca. 370 B.C.), the founder of scientific astronomy and one of Plato's pupils, found that the simple concentric sphere idea did not fit the facts. For one thing a planet does not move steadily along a circle among the stars. Instead, it speeds up, then slows down from time to time, and even appears to stop and move backward for a time before proceeding forward again. The sun and the moon also move at varying

speeds. Only the true stars appear to move as a unit. To explain the observed motions of the celestial bodies Eudoxus conceived a large family of concentric spheres. Each planet had its own group of adjacent spheres spinning about different axes with different inclinations to the axis of the sphere of the fixed stars. The complete system is difficult to visualize even with a detailed diagram, and we will not attempt that here. However, the resultant motions duplicated the observed motions of the planets. Eudoxus needed 27 motions to duplicate those of the whole system—sun, moon, planet, and stars.

This model (theory) was the first ever made that could be called scientific because it was made to conform with the few facts as they were then known. It had comparatively few basic assumptions, and was a fruitful theory for it allowed predictions to be made as to the approximate positions of the planets at any particular time. "But," you might ask, "is it true?" If you had asked that of the Greeks, they would have wondered what you meant by "true." But if you offered them a simpler theory that conformed reasonably well with the facts, they would have welcomed it.

Aristotle

The conceptual scheme of Eudoxus, although good, was not good enough to withstand the pressure of more accurate and additional observations. The easiest solution was to add more spheres. This Aristotle (ca. 340 B.C.) and his students did, and other astronomers followed suit in later centuries. Each addition added to the complexity of the mechanism created by Eudoxus. Eudoxus had nothing in his model to maintain the motions of the heavenly bodies. To remedy this Aristotle added an outermost sphere whose function was to turn all the other spheres, thus becoming a *primum mobile* (prime mover).

Aristotle made strong arguments for a spherical earth, using the chief evidences that we cite today.

Aristarchus

Aristarchus (ca. 250 B.C.) made two simplifying assumptions: (1) the earth rotates, thus explaining the apparent daily motion of the stars, and (2) the earth and the other planets revolve about the sun, thus accounting for the apparent motions of the sun and the planets across the star patterns. This was a truly heliocentric scheme. However, he could observe no *stellar parallax* (Fig. 1-4),[5] so that he was forced to believe that the stars were immensely far away. This lack of observable parallax (Fig. 1-5) doomed his hypothesis in the eyes of his contemporaries; their minds could not conceive of such great distances to the stars, nor can ours. He also arranged the six planets Mercury, Venus, Earth, Mars, Jupiter, and Saturn in order of their distances from the sun.

Eratosthenes

Eratosthenes (ca. 200 B.C.) calculated the circumference of the earth and came up with a figure of about 25,000 mi. His method is shown in Fig. 1-6. It is essentially the method used until artificial satellites were put into orbit about the earth. Eratosthenes was the first great physical geographer.

Hipparchus

Hipparchus (ca. 140 B.C.) was the greatest astronomer among the ancients. Some authorities have called him one of the greatest as-

[5] As an observer moves, the position of distant objects relative to nearby objects seems to change. This apparent change of position of distant objects, due to the actual change of the position of the observer, is defined as *parallax*.

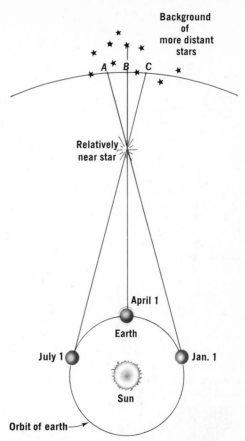

Fig. 1-4. Parallax of Stars. That stars show parallax is proof that the earth revolves around the sun. Viewed from the earth's January 1 position, the relatively near star seems associated with the more distant stars about A, whereas on July 1, the near star seems associated with the stars about C. This apparent change of position of the near star due to a change of position of the observer is called parallax. Because of the enormous distances involved, star parallax is not observable to the naked eye.

tronomers and mathematicians of all time as well as a great physical geographer. He made new instruments to increase the accuracy of his naked-eye[6] observations; he catalogued the positions of about a thousand stars; he intro-

[6] Telescopes were not invented until 1800 years later.

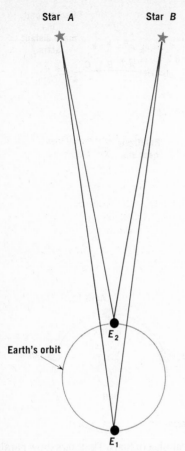

Star *A*   Star *B*

Earth's orbit

E_2

E_1

Fig. 1-5. The Argument Against Heliocentric Hypothesis of Aristarchus. If the earth revolved about the sun, the angle AE_2B should be greater than the angle AE_1B. The Greeks could detect no difference; they could observe no parallax and so concluded the earth was stationary. The explanation is that the distance from E_1 to E_2 is infinitesimal compared to the distances to the stars, and so the angles appear to be the same to the naked eye.

duced the concepts of latitude and longitude.[7] But his greatest discovery was the precession of the equinoxes (Fig. 2-24). He also determined the difference between the tropical and the sidereal years (Chapter 2). His measure-

[7]For definitions see footnotes 2 and 3, Chapter 2.

ment of the length of the former was less than seven minutes from the modern value. He rejected the heliocentric hypothesis of Aristarchus because he could not observe stellar parallax (Fig. 1-5). He altered greatly the geocentric hypothesis of Eudoxus and Aristotle to bring it into line with his more accurate observations. By the addition of his two new geometric devices, the epicycle and the eccentric[8] (Figs. 1-7 and 1-8), he could explain the occasional apparent retrograde (reversal) motions of the planets (Fig. 2-14). These retrograde motions were real to the geocentrists but were only apparent to the heliocentrist, for he could explain them as follows: The earth is closer to the sun than Mars; it takes the earth one year to complete a revolution and Mars almost two of our years. Consequently the earth catches up with Mars and passes it from time to time, causing Mars to *appear* to move backward for a time when viewed against the background of fixed stars, just as does the appearance of a landscape to an observer on a moving train if he concentrates on the train. Hipparchus needed an epicycle every time the earth caught up with and passed a planet.[9] Hipparchus knew that the sun, moon, and planets appeared brighter at some times than at others, hence their distance from the earth must vary in a cyclic manner. He used the concept of the eccentric (Fig. 1-8) to explain this and so "saved the phenomena." He also knew that these celestial bodies appeared to move faster at regular intervals.

By using these corrections to the geocentric theory he could prepare planetary tables from which the positions of the sun, moon, and

[8]These were devices to preserve the Platonian concept of uniform circular motion for all celestial bodies. This is an excellent example of what a preconceived notion, alien in origin to the problem concerned, can do to the thinking of even learned men.

[9]Mercury and Venus are closer to the sun than earth, and so travel not only shorter distances per revolution but also at faster speeds.

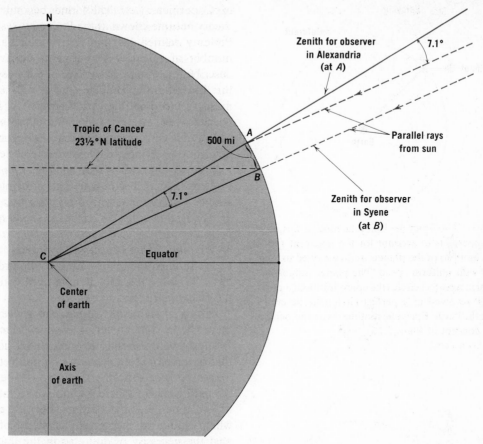

Fig. 1-6. Eratosthenes "Measures" Circumference of Earth. On June 21 the sun is directly overhead at noon at *B*. At the same moment a vertical rod at *A,* 500 mi to the north, makes an angle (*A*) of 7.1° with the sun's rays. The angle at *A* equals the angle at *C. AB* is a measured distance. The circumference is given by 500 mi × 360/7.1 = 25,300 mi.

planets could be predicted for any time with a considerable degree of accuracy.

Ptolemy's Synthesis

Hipparchus failed to organize his ideas into a unified theory. Claudius Ptolemy, the last of the great Greek astronomers, did this about A.D. 140 in Alexandria, Egypt, then the intellectual center of the world. He collected the works of Hipparchus, added the more recent data, did all the necessary calculations involving epicycles and eccentrics, invented the equant (a highly artificial geometric device) to refine the scheme a bit, and published the theory in a great book called *The Almagest*. He included a set of newly calculated planetary tables. These tables were particularly useful in navigation. Similar tables are used today. *The Almagest,* an encyclopedia of astronomy, remained the standard treatise until the time

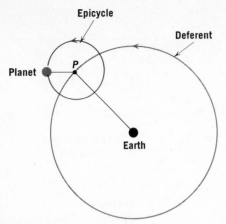

Fig. 1-7. The Epicycle. Epicyclic motion was used by Hipparchus to account for the apparent retrograde motions of the planets as they moved in their orbits with uniform speed. The planet supposedly moved in a perfect circle (the epicycle) about a point *P* as *P* revolved in a perfect circle (the deferent) about the earth. Epicyclic motion saved the perfect circle concept of Plato.

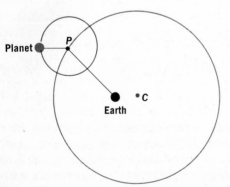

Fig. 1-8. The Eccentric. The eccentric was another "save the phenomenon" device invented by Hipparchus to account for the observed fact that a planet (or the sun) is not always the same distance from the earth. The earth was no longer at the center, *C,* of the orbits of celestial objects.

of Copernicus (A.D. 1500) and beyond; the theory became known as the Ptolemaic system. Ptolemy refined his model by reducing the number of epicycles and equants needed to describe the observed motions. The concept of the transparent crystalline spheres was recognized as incompatible with epicycles by Hipparchus, but later astronomers used them up to the time of Copernicus because they made descriptions of the complex scheme easier.

It is worth noting that in *The Almagest* Ptolemy stated a fundamental principle of science (not original with him): *In explaining phenomena, it is best to adopt the simplest hypothesis that will coordinate all of the known observations.* This concept of simplicity pervades all scientific theory down to the present day. We will encounter it time and again in the following pages.

Let us examine the Ptolemaic geocentric theory (Fig. 1-9) in terms of this principle. Doing so will also help us understand how a theory can be so completely wrong and yet win long-term acceptance by those most expert in the field if it is in accord with the observations of the time. We must always bear in mind when evaluating the accomplishments of the past the necessity of doing so in the light of what was known at the time rather than in light of what we now know.

Ptolemy's system prevailed for 1500 years because

1. It described the observed paths accurately enough considering the fact that the observers had no instruments to help them.
2. It predicted the future paths and positions of the planets with a reasonable degree of success.
3. It explained the lack of observable parallax.
4. It explained the phases of the moon.
5. It coincided fairly well with the philosophical ideas of celestial bodies.
6. It had common-sense appeal.

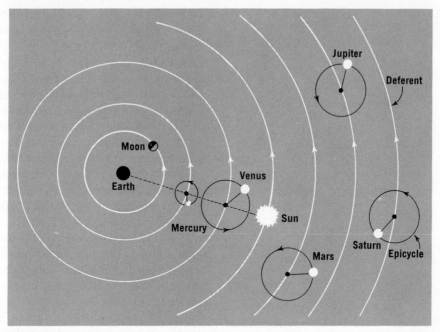

Fig. 1-9. Ptolemaic System of Universe. The dome of the stars lies outside of Saturn. An epicycle and a deferent are associated with each planet. Since Venus and Mercury are never observed far from the sun, the centers of their epicycles must always be on the line of sight from the earth to the sun.

We have already discussed 1, 2, 3, and 5 in sufficient detail. We will now discuss 4 and 6.

Phases of the Moon

Let us consider the phases of the moon to see how this geocentric theory explained them. Eudoxus, in building his original model of the universe, had to provide for the easily observable facts that the moon orbited the earth, that it was closer to earth than the sun (because it came between us and the sun at times of a solar eclipse) and that it exhibited a complete set of phases. He therefore had to adjust the imaginary axes of the domes carrying these three bodies in such a way as to account for these phenomena.

At any one time the sun illuminates one half of the moon's surface just as it illuminates one half of the earth's surface. If the moon is rising in the east as the sun sets, we on earth can see that fully illuminated half (Fig. 1-10, position 5). This is the full phase. If the moon is setting with the sun, the illuminated half is turned away from us, position 1, so that we cannot see the moon at all. This is the new phase. If the moon is high in the sky at either sunrise or sunset, we have one of the quarter phases (position 3 or 7), for then we see only half of the illuminated half. As the moon progresses from third quarter (position 7), toward the new moon, we see the *waning* crescent (position 8), and as it progresses from new moon to first quarter (position 3), we see the *waxing* crescent (position 2).

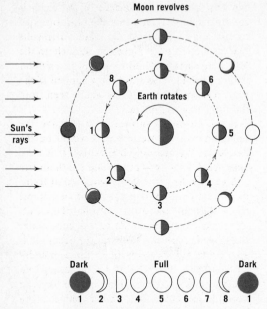

Moon revolves

Earth rotates

Sun's rays

Dark   Full   Dark

1 2 3 4 5 6 7 8 1

Fig. 1-10. Phases of Moon. The inner circle of "moons" shows the left half of the moon illuminated by the rays of the sun coming from the left. Note that only one half is illuminated at any one time. You can see it this way only from a position far out in space beyond the moon and between it and the sun. An observer on earth, however, sees the moon as it appears in the outer circle of moons. Thus in position 1 he sees none of the illuminated side. This is the "dark" of the moon (new moon). Two weeks later the moon is in position 5, where the full illuminated half can be seen (full moon). Halfway between, in positions 3 and 7, half of the illuminated half may be seen; these are the quarter phases. At position 2 we see the waxing crescent, and at position 8 the waning crescent. Positions 4 and 6 show the gibbous phases. Of the infinite number of phases possible, these are the only ones that have special names. As an aid in seeing the relationship between the two circles of moons, try looking along the line of sight at each pair, remembering that you can see only that part of the illuminated half which is turned toward the earth.

Common Sense vs. Uncommon Sense

Let us now consider the problem of common-sense appeal. Ask yourself the question,

"Why do I believe that the earth revolves about the sun?" There is only one answer—because you have been taught so from childhood. Could you have reached the correct answer by your own observations? You see the sun appear to rise in the east, move across the sky and appear to set in the west.[10] If you believe the evidence of your own eyes, you would think that this apparent motion was the real motion. If anyone questioned this observation you would say that your common sense tells you that the sun moves around the earth, and defy anyone to tell you differently. You would be doubly convinced that you were right because you could detect no motion of the earth.[11] You would probably wonder why, if the earth traveled so fast through space, there were no strong winds blowing in the opposite direction, and why birds were not left behind in their flights. The answer is, of course, that our atmosphere moves with the earth. In this respect, it is just as much an integral part of the earth as the soil and rocks. If you watched the sky all night, you would note that the stars

[10]The terms *sunrise* and *sunset* are holdovers from the days of widespread belief in the geocentric theory. They imply a stationary earth. In fact, the whole terminology that we use to describe movements not only in our solar system but also in the whole universe is based on a stationary earth. This is because no terminology has been developed to describe the actual movements. In fact, no simple terminology can ever be developed to describe them, for nothing is stationary in the whole universe; all movements are relative and highly complex. Since apparent movements are comparatively simple, we use an "apparent" terminology. No harm is done so long as we remember that it is apparent motion, not real motion, that we are talking about.

[11]Actually, if you live on or near the 40th parallel, you are moving at a speed of about 600 mi/hr because of the rotation of the earth on its axis. You are also moving at a speed of about 66,000 mi/hr because of the revolution of the earth about the sun. Finally, the whole solar system is moving through space at a speed of about 1 million mi/hr. However, there is practically no danger of a collision with some other stellar body, first because this solar system of ours is tremendously isolated in space, and second, because all the other stellar bodies with which it might collide are also moving in the same general direction and at comparable speeds.

near the North Star would appear to revolve about it (Fig. 1-3) and those farthest from it would appear to rise and set once a day. If you did not know that these apparent motions were due to the earth's rotation, you, too, would believe that the earth was stationary at the center of the universe, a universe that had been created especially for the benefit of man.

Ptolemy's Arguments for a Spherical Earth

You might also believe that the surface of the earth was flat, particularly if you lived in a plains country. The Greeks, however, believed the earth to be spherical. There were several reasons. Plato had conceived the sphere to be the most perfect of all objects, and the sun and the moon, as we see them, appear to be cross sections of spheres. It was therefore natural for them to think the earth spherical, too, although they could present no evidence that it was. Ptolemy had some concrete evidences, however. He made a list of them in *The Almagest,* about A.D. 150. It is instructive to quote directly from him:

> We are best led to the concept that the earth is sensibly of spherical form by the following considerations. We observe that the sun, the moon, and the other heavenly bodies do not rise and set at the same time for all inhabitants of the earth, but rather first for those to the east and later for those to the west. For we find that the phenomena of the eclipses, particularly those of the moon, which always occur at the same absolute time for all people, are not, for all that, seen at the same hour relative to noon; that is, at an hour equally distant from the middle of the day; but that, in every case, the times are later for eastern observers and earlier for those further to the west. Now since the differences between the times when one observer and another see these eclipses is proportional to the [east–west] distances between their respective locations, one

can conclude that the surface of the earth is certainly spherical, and that the uniformity of its curvature extends to the whole; it results that each of its parts makes an obstacle to the following parts, and limits the view in a similar manner for all. This would not happen if the earth had any other shape as can be seen from the following reasoning.

If the terrestrial surface were concave the inhabitants of the western part would be the first to see the heavenly bodies rise; if it were a plane, all its inhabitants would see them rise and set together; if it were composed of triangles, quadrilaterals or polygons of any shape, all of the inhabitants of the same plane face would see the phenomena at the same time; things which are not observed to occur. It is also evident that the earth is not a cylinder whose surface views the rising and setting and whose bases face the poles of the sky, an assumption which one might judge more probable; for if such were the case, there would be no stars which are always visible, but on the contrary, some stars would rise and set for everyone on the earth, and certain stars up to an equal distance from each pole would be invisible to everyone. However, the further we go towards the north, the more stars we discover which never set, and at the same time, southern stars disappear from view in the same proportion. Therefore, it is evident that here too, along the north–south direction, by an effect of the uniform curvature of the earth, each part forms an obstacle to the adjacent parts due to the uniform curvature of the earth, which proves that the earth has in every direction a spherical curvature. Finally, on the sea, if at any point and in any direction, one travels towards mountains or other elevated places, one sees these objects as if coming out of the sea where they were apparently hidden by the curvature of the surface of the sea.[12]

[12] Translated by T. A. Ashford and T. L. Page, and reprinted from *From Atoms to Stars: An Introduction to the Physical Sciences,* by Theodore A. Ashford. Copyright © 1960 by Holt, Rinehart and Winston, Inc. Used by permission of Holt, Rinehart and Winston, Inc.

Exercises

1. How do you know that the earth goes around the sun instead of the sun around the earth?
2. What is the distinction between apparent and real motion? Illustrate.
3. (a) How does a natural satellite differ from a planet?
   (b) What is another name for a natural satellite?
4. In what major respect does a star differ from a planet or a satellite?
5. (a) How many celestial bodies other than the fixed stars did the ancients recognize?
   (b) Name them in order of their supposed distances from the earth.
6. Did the Greeks use the term *fixed star* to mean that these stars did not move? Explain.
7. What is meant by *parallax?*
8. Aristarchus was the first heliocentrist of record. Why did he have so few followers?
9. Many of the astronomical measurements of the ancient Greeks were inaccurate. What one cause best accounts for these inaccuracies?
10. The Big Dipper appears to have turned through how many degrees in (a) 1 hr and (b) 24 hr?
11. What are epicycles? Why were they invented? Are they apparent or real?
12. What is a deferent? Why were deferents considered necessary?
13. What are the relative positions of the earth, sun, and moon at new moon and at full moon? Draw diagrams to illustrate. Why is new moon called the "dark of the moon"?
14. At about what time of day (suntime) would you expect to see the full moon rise? Explain.
15. If you travel northward a distance of 70 mi, the North Star appears 1° higher above the horizon. Assuming the earth to be approximately spherical, what is the length of its circumference?
16. Suppose that the apparent periods of the sun and the moon were exactly the same. Would you see a complete set of phases of the moon? Explain.
17. State one contribution that Hipparchus made to the Ptolemaic system of the universe.
18. List the various pieces of evidence given by Ptolemy for a spherical earth.
19. Did Columbus prove that the earth was round? Explain.
20. What is the chief function of a good scientific theory?

Some Basic Astronomical Observations

We have presented the Ptolemaic system of the universe, which accounted well enough for the motions of the various celestial bodies insofar as they were known at the time of Copernicus and beyond. Top-heavy though it was, and seemingly ready to crash under its own weight, this theory had a common-sense appeal that no heliocentric hypothesis could possibly have. As previously implied, we would all be geo-centrists if we relied exclusively on the evidence of our own senses. Since we are going to have to replace a common-sense universe with one that is very "uncommon-sensical," we are going to postpone the story of this replacement until we learn something about our solar system as we know it today. We will be concerned chiefly with the earth in space.

Science starts with facts and returns to them to prove itself right or wrong.
ANONYMOUS

17

Rising and Setting of Celestial Bodies

If we believe that the earth is stationary, then we have a ready explanation for the daily rising and setting of the sun, moon, planets, and stars; they simply revolve about the earth once a day. But, if we believe that the earth revolves about the sun, then we are most likely to believe that the earth has an axis about which it rotates once a day. This rotation[1] must be from west to east, for all celestial bodies that we observe to rise and set, rise in the east and set in the west. If the rotation were from east to west, then all rising celestial bodies would rise in the west and set in the east. As viewed from a point high above the North Pole, the rotation and revolution of both the earth and the moon are counterclockwise (Fig. 2-1). Note the circular and the straight star trails in Figs. 2-2 and 2-3. They prove one of two things: either the sky revolves once a day above a motionless earth, or the earth rotates about an axis passing through its center and with one end of the axis directed toward a point 1° to 2° away from Polaris (Fig. 2-4). Which is it? Only additional evidence will solve the problem.

Daily Motion of the Earth—Rotation

Rotating Earth or Revolving Sky?

Although such scientists as Copernicus, Kepler, Galileo, and Newton were convinced that the earth rotated on an axis, no evidence, direct or indirect, that indicated the earth was

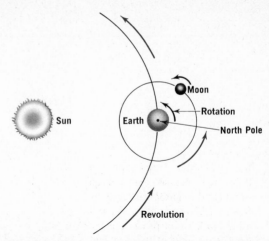

Fig. 2-1. Directions of Rotation and Revolution of Earth and Moon. Note that all four motions are counterclockwise as viewed from a point high above the North Pole, as from Polaris.

actually rotating was forthcoming until about 1735. Sir Isaac Newton, in his great scientific work, the *Principia,* published in 1688, showed that a rotating spherical body should be flattened at the poles. If the earth is flattened at the poles, then the length of a degree of latitude (in miles or kilometers) in the polar regions should be somewhat greater than the length of a degree in the equatorial regions because of the greater radius of curvature there (Fig. 2-5). Evidence that this was so came in 1735–36 when the French Academy sent expeditions to both Peru and Lapland (northern Scandinavia) to measure a degree of latitude[2] in kilometers. They found that it was greater in Lapland than in Peru. This supported Newton's conclusion but did not prove that the flattening was caused by the earth's rotation.

---

[1] It is important to remember that to *revolve* means that one body travels around another—for example, the earth and the planets revolve about the sun—whereas to *rotate* means that a body spins about an axis that passes through its center.

[2] Latitude is normally expressed as distance north or south of the equator, measured in degrees. On globes it is shown by means of lines parallel to the equator. What the French measured was the linear distance between two of these parallels of latitude 1° apart.

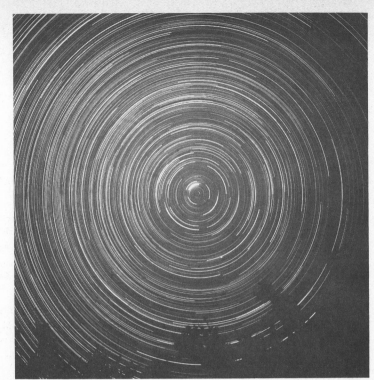

Fig. 2-2. Star Trails About a Point near Polaris. The curved trail near the center was made by Polaris. Exposure time was about 4 hr. The motion producing the trails is not that of the stars but of the camera, which is anchored to a rotating earth. No stars appear to rise or set. Compare with Fig. 2-3. (Photo by Paul W. Davis.)

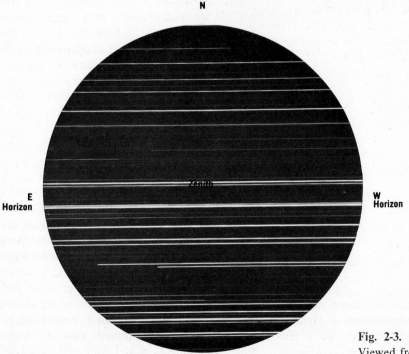

Fig. 2-3. Star Trails at Equator. Viewed from the equator, all stars appear to rise and set.

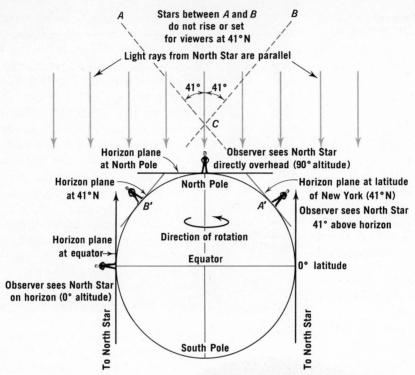

Fig. 2-4. Apparent Rising and Setting of Stars in Northern Hemisphere. Assume a smooth-surfaced earth and a cloudless sky. One's visibility of the sky is then limited only by his horizon plane. As the earth rotates, so does his horizon plane. On a long winter's night at 6:00 P.M. an observer at *A'*, 41°N, will see all stars above (to the right) of horizon plane *AA'*. At 6:00 A.M. next morning the observer is at *B'* because the earth has rotated through 180°, and he sees all stars above (to the left) of horizon plane *BB'*. The stars to the right of *A* but to the left of *B*—that is, those within the angle *ACB*—neither rose nor set for him; instead, they circled Polaris. If the observer moves northward, the angle gets bigger and bigger, so more stars are seen to circle Polaris. When the angle is 180°, all stars appear to do so. If the observer moves southward, the opposite is true. When the angle becomes 0° (at the equator), all stars appear to rise and set.

Foucault Pendulum as Evidence of Rotation

Experimental proof came about 115 years later (1850) when the French physicist Jean Foucault demonstrated rotation of the earth by suspending a large iron ball by 200 ft of wire from the dome of the Pantheon in Paris. The suspended ball constituted a gigantic pendulum that cleared the floor by a few inches. It was carefully started in a swinging motion parallel to a line marked on the floor beneath the pendulum (Fig. 2-6). As time passed the pendulum slowly changed its apparent direction of swing even though there was no force acting on the pendulum except that of gravity.

The explanation is much easier if we perform an idealized experiment in which we suppose that the pendulum is suspended by a frictionless support directly over the North Pole. The time is winter and night lasts six months; we can see that the stars appear to

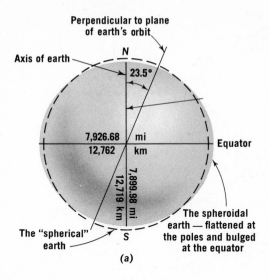

Perpendicular to plane
of earth's orbit

Axis of earth

N

23.5°

7,926.68 / mi
12,762 / km

Equator

7,899.98 mi
12,719 km

The "spherical"
earth

S

The spheroidal
earth — flattened at
the poles and bulged
at the equator

(a)

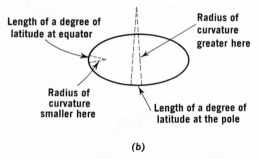

Length of a degree of
latitude at equator

Radius of
curvature
greater here

Radius of
curvature
smaller here

Length of a degree of
latitude at the pole

(b)

Fig. 2-5. Length of Degree of Latitude vs. Shape of Earth. If the earth were truly spherical, the polar and equatorial diameters (in miles or in kilometers) would be equal and the length of a degree of latitude would be the same everywhere. Measurements show that the polar regions are flattened and the equatorial region bulged. The radius of curvature is therefore greater at the poles and smaller at the equator, making a degree of latitude as measured in miles greater at the poles than at the equator. The earth is thus spheroidal in shape, a consequence of its rotation on an axis. Newton calculated the bulging shape of the earth several decades before the bulge was observed (p. 18). His argument is a bit too complicated for us to present here, but you can rest assured that it had nothing to do with centrifugal force (see p. 125 and footnote 9 on that page).

revolve about the pole once every 24 hours. The pendulum is started swinging in a plane that is lined up with the bright star Vega (Fig. 2-7). As time passes we see that the plane of the swing remains lined up with Vega, yet this plane is changing with respect to the marked line on the floor. As seen from Polaris, the line moves in a counterclockwise direction, until it comes back to its original orientation in exactly 24 sidereal (meaning "starry") hours (p. 37).

Did the plane of the swing change or was it the direction of the line that changed? We need to know. We already know that stars in the vicinity of Polaris appear to revolve about it (Fig. 2-2). If the earth did not rotate, then these stars would actually be revolving, and the plane of the swing would not remain lined up with Vega. There is no force—centripetal, frictional, or other—acting on the pendulum except that of gravity, which always acts toward the center of the earth-moon system. This means that there is no force tending to turn the plane of the swing, and so it does not turn. Instead the ground beneath the swinging pendulum turns 360° counterclockwise in 24 sidereal hours, that is, in the direction opposite to the apparent westerly (clockwise, footnote 11) turning of the plane of the pendulum. This proves that it is the earth that rotates, not the celestial sphere (Fig. 2-15c).

At the equator a pendulum set swinging parallel to a meridian[3] continues to swing parallel to a meridian (not the same one) forever (Fig. 2-8). Thus the time needed for the plane of the swinging pendulum to turn through 360° is infinity at the equator; the *rate* at which it turns is 0° per hour, whereas at either pole it is 15° per hour.

[3] A meridian is a half circle extending from pole to pole. There is an infinite number of them. "Our" meridian is the one that passes through the point where we are. Meridians are used to indicate longitude, that is, distance east or west of the prime meridian (which passes through Greenwich, London, England), measured in degrees.

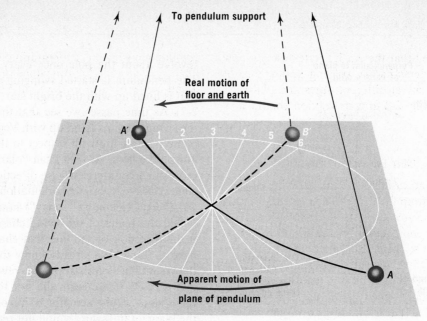

To pendulum support

Real motion of
floor and earth

Apparent motion of
plane of pendulum

Fig. 2-6. Representation of Foucault Pendulum in Relation to Pantheon Floor. The pendulum is started swinging, parallel to a meridian (line 0), in vertical plane *AA'*. After some hours it appears to swing in the vertical plane *BB'*, no longer parallel to the meridian.

★
Vega

Fig. 2-7. A Pendulum Suspended from a "Sky Hook" Directly Above North Pole. The direction of swing of this pendulum apparently changes 360° in one sidereal day (Fig. 2-23).

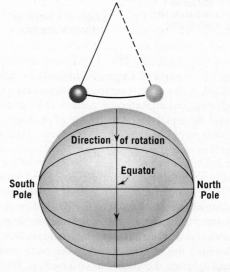

Direction of rotation

Equator

South
Pole

North
Pole

Fig. 2-8. A Pendulum Suspended from a "Sky Hook" Directly Above Equator. The direction of swing of this pendulum makes no apparent change as the earth rotates.

Knowing that the earth rotates we can now better understand the varying appearance of the night sky at different times and places. A study of Fig. 2-4 and its caption should now be made.

Other Evidences of Rotation

Other indications that the earth rotates are obtained from the firing of artillery shells long distances. Since all parts of the spherical earth complete one rotation in the same time, it is obvious that the *linear* speed varies with the latitude.[4] If we neglect air resistance, the artillery shell retains, at all points in its trajectory, the rotational speed *of the place from which it was fired.* If it is aimed at a target directly north of the gun in the northern hemisphere, and then fired, it is moving toward a region of slower rotation and therefore arrives ahead (east) of its target. If it is aimed and fired at a target south of it, the shell is moving toward a region of faster rotation and so arrives behind (west of) its target. In any case, the deflection is to the right of the observer in the northern hemisphere when he faces the target. In the southern hemisphere the deflection is to the left of the observer. Obviously, artillerymen must allow for the deviation by aiming to the left of the target in the northern hemisphere instead of directly at it.

This deviation occurs not only for artillery shells, bullets, missiles, and artificial satellites, but also for the major wind systems of the earth, such as the prevailing westerlies and the trade winds. The rotation of the earth also accounts for the direction of the spiraling of the winds in cyclones (the lows of our weather maps), in hurricanes, and in tornadoes. In conjunction with the configuration of the continents, it controls the directions of the great ocean currents, such as the Gulf Stream.

Annual Motion of the Earth—Revolution

A Revolving Earth or a Stationary Earth?

Almost all of the early Greeks believed the evidences of their eyes, so they argued for a stationary earth. Copernicus had no more evidence than they had. Some of the evidence for the earth's revolution is comparatively simple, some is complex. We need to differentiate here between evidence that can be used to support either the heliocentric or the geocentric theory, and that which supports one theory while denying the other. We will present three pieces of the latter type that support the heliocentric theory.

Parallax

The most direct and easily understood is that of stellar parallax (Fig. 1-4). Parallax is, however, undetectable even with our best telescopes for those stars that are more distant than 300 light years,[5] and even for those nearest, it is so small (less than 1 sec of arc) that it was unobservable until fine telescopes were made. It was discovered in 1838 by Bessel.

Aberration of Starlight

Aberration of starlight was discovered in 1725 by Bradley, an English astronomer, while he was trying to detect stellar parallax. He observed that as the earth moved across the path of light coming from the star Gamma Draconis, the star appeared to be slightly dis-

---

[4] The linear speed of a point on the earth's surface, due to the rotation of the earth, is about 1000 mi/hr times the sine of the latitude. At the equator this speed is about 1000 mi/hr, at either pole it is 0 mi/hr, and at New York City it is 750 mi/hr.

[5] A light year is a measure of distance, not time. It is the distance light travels in one year: 186,400 mi times the number of seconds in a year, or about 6,000,000,000,000 (6 trillion) mi.

placed from the position it has when the earth moves directly toward or away from the star. This slight displacement is in the direction of motion of the earth. In the course of a year, Gamma Draconis appeared to describe a tiny orbit. Bradley interpreted this orbit as the resultant of two motions, one being that of the earth and the other that of the light coming from Gamma Draconis. Consider rain falling *vertically*. If a man wearing a hat is standing still, the brim keeps the rain off his face. If he now starts to walk rapidly, the rain will strike him in the face, thus making it appear that the rain is no longer falling vertically but is falling slantingly and coming from the direction in which he is walking. If he changes his direction the rain appears to come from the new direction (Fig. 2-9). In the same way light entering Bradley's telescope appeared to come from a new direction as the earth changed its direction as it revolved (Fig. 2-10). The tiny elliptical path *apparently* described by Gamma Draconis is about 41 seconds of arc in its major diameter. This is more than 25 times as great as the largest observable parallactic displacement; it can be more accurately measured and hence is more convincing. Since the aberrational displacement depends only on the velocity of the earth and the velocity of light, the size of the major axis of the displacement ellipse is constant for all stars regardless of their distance. However, parallactic displacement depends on the distance of the star and is smaller for more distant stars.

Phases of Venus

Indirect evidence (but not a proof) that the earth moves around the sun is given by the phases of Venus. All open-minded geocentrists from the time of Aristarchus onward agreed with the heliocentrists that Venus, in order to go through a full set of phases like the moon,

Fig. 2-9. Aberration of Starlight Analogy. A man is running around a circular track on a rainy windless day. The rain is falling vertically at all times, but to the runner it appears to come first from one direction and then another as he changes direction in circling the track. Just so, starlight appears to come from a different direction as our observation post (the earth) circles the sun. The difference in direction is very small because the star is so far away. If the earth were stationary, there would be no aberration.

would have to revolve about the sun instead of about the earth. If Venus revolved about the sun, perhaps the earth and the other planets did, too. At any rate, it would be easier to believe so. That Venus actually has a full set of phases has been known since the invention of the telescope (about A.D. 1600). The Greeks used the fact that the phases of Venus cannot be seen with the naked eyes to support Ptolemy's theory.

The pertinent observable facts about Venus are as follows: Venus may be seen in the western sky (as the evening star) up to about 3 hours after sunset, or in the eastern sky (as the morning star) up to about 3 hours before sunrise, depending upon the relative positions of the earth and Venus in their orbits (Fig. 2-11). Venus always crosses the high part of the sky with the sun and so is never seen there during the night. Note that in Fig. 2-11 the angular distance between Venus and the sun as viewed from the earth is never more than

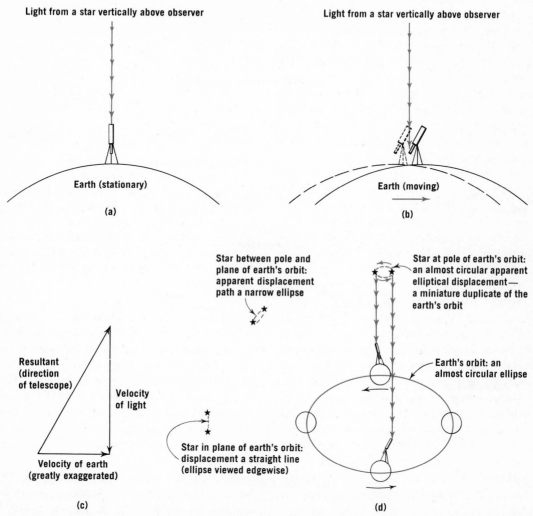

Fig. 2-10. Aberration of Starlight. (*a*) If the earth were stationary, then to see a star vertically above him, an observer would merely point his telescope in a vertical direction. (*b*) However, since the earth is moving (around the sun) and light does take some (very short) time to traverse the telescope tube, the telescope must be slightly tilted so that the starlight that enters the top of the telescope will hit the bottom rather than the side of the tube. (*c*) Vector diagram to show necessary tilt of telescope. (*d*) The various shapes of apparent aberrational paths depend on the position of each star in relation to the plane of the earth's orbit.

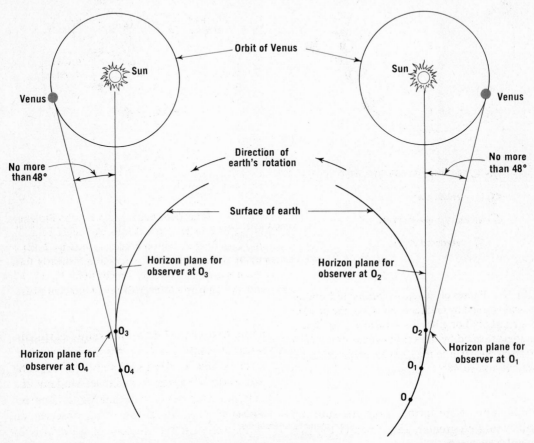

Fig. 2-11. Venus as a Morning and Evening Star. Consider an observer at O (lower right). The time is more than 3 hours before sunrise. As the earth rotates, his position shifts to O_1, and he can see Venus rising as a morning "star." The rotating earth then brings him to position O_2 so that he sees the sun rise. He no longer sees Venus because the sun is too bright. Several months later, as a result of the revolutions of Venus and the earth about the sun, the positions are as shown at the left. To the observer at O_3 the sun is setting ahead of Venus. For the observer at O_4 the sun has set far enough that its light does not obscure Venus, and he sees Venus as an evening "star."

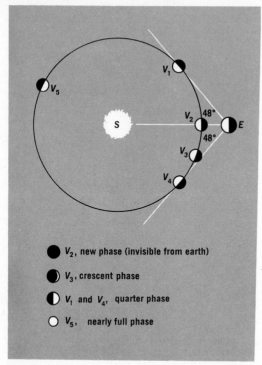

V_2, new phase (invisible from earth)

V_3, crescent phase

V_1 and V_4, quarter phase

V_5, nearly full phase

Fig. 2-12. Phases of Venus. According to Copernicus, and verified by Galileo, Venus is in the position for a nearly full or gibbous phase at V_5. As shown, the angle formed by lines from Venus to the earth and from the earth to the sun (the observed angle) does not exceed 48°.

48°. If Venus were farther from the sun, this angle would be greater, and if nearer the sun, it would be less.[6]

Inspection of Fig. 2-12 shows that the Venus–sun distance is about constant (about

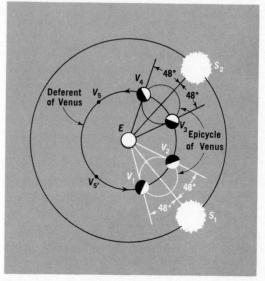

Fig. 2-13. Phases of Venus According to Ptolemy. In the Ptolemaic system Venus can never be at V_5 or $V_{5'}$ as long as the observed angle (Fig. 2-12) is not more than 48°. Hence no gibbous (nearly full) phase would be possible. At positions V_1, V_2, V_3, and V_4 Venus would be seen in the crescent phase.

65 million mi), whereas the Venus–earth distance varies. In Fig. 2-13 it is the Venus–earth distance that is nearly constant, whereas the Venus–sun distance is variable. Modern distance measurements show that Fig. 2-12 agrees with the facts. Moreover, to an observer on earth, Venus at the crescent phase (V_3) is $2\frac{1}{2}$ times as bright as at the nearly full phase (V_5), thus verifying the great variation in the Venus–earth distance.

Apparent Retrograde Motion of the Planets

Like the sun, moon, and the stars, the planets rise in the east and set in the west. At the same time the sun, moon, and the planets appear to drift toward the east with respect

[6]Mercury, nearer the sun, can never be more than about 28° from the sun. At this angular distance the light of the sun obscures our view of Mercury so greatly that few people ever see it. To see it one must look a little above the eastern horizon an hour or so before sunrise (at a time when it is a morning "star" just as Venus is) or a little above the western horizon an hour or so after sunset (at a time when it is an evening "star"). The best time is when the sun–earth–Mercury angle is the greatest, that is, near 28°.

to the stars—except that the planets are observed to reverse their directions periodically to drift westward for a time, and then to return to their normal eastward drift. How can we explain these observations of retrograde motion?

A geocentrist has no choice; he must assume that the reversal is real. A modern geocentrist would then be forced to look for a cause. The Greeks had no such problem, for their methods of scientific reasoning did not call for an explanation of any celestial phenomenon. Hipparchus placed epicycles in the paths of the planets to duplicate the observed motions, but these epicycles did not constitute an explanation for the reversal. The heliocentrist needs no epicycles, for the observed retrograde motion is only apparent, not real (Fig. 2-14). He needs only to assume that the earth is a planet, just as Mars is, and that both revolve about the sun. Mars travels in an orbit considerably larger than that of the earth, and at the same time travels at a slower speed, so that it takes nearly two of our years to complete one revolution. It therefore covers a smaller fraction of its orbit per unit time than does the earth. The result is that if we "let" Mars "start" out a bit ahead of the earth, the earth will catch up with and pass Mars, making it appear that Mars is moving backward for a time. All of the planets with orbits greater than that of the earth appear to retrograde every time the earth catches up with and passes them. Venus and Mercury, with orbits inside that of the earth, appear to retrograde briefly when they catch up with and pass the earth. Given different periods and the slower velocities for planets with the larger orbits, the apparent retrograde motions become inevitable; that is, the apparent paths are just what we would expect them to be. If it were useful to do so, we could plot these apparent paths for centuries to come just as we do their real paths. If prediction is the test of a theory, there can be no question about the heliocentric theory.

Note how much the heliocentrist has simpli-

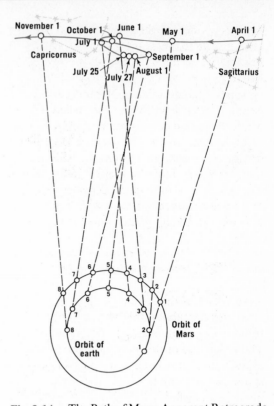

Fig. 2-14. The Path of Mars: Apparent Retrograde Motion of Planets. On April 1, Mars was moving east along the ecliptic at a rate that would carry it into the next constellation (Capricornus) in two months. By June 1 the planet was hesitating at the edge of Capricornus and slowing down so noticeably that by July 1 it had come to a standstill. It now began to move again, slowly at first, but picking up speed toward the latter part of July, only now it was moving backward, returning to the west toward the constellations through which it had moved early in the spring. On August 1, Mars was again slowing down and by September 1 the planet was at a standstill. As if it had finally made up its mind, it began to move again, this time toward the east, with increasing speed, which by November 1 had carried it through Capricornus. Drawing is not to scale. Numbers indicate positions of earth and Mars on the following dates: (1) April 1, (2) May 1, (3) June 1, (4) July 1, (5) August 1, (6) September 1, (7) October 1, (8) November 1. (Modified from Fig. 6, "The Path of Mars," in *The Search for Order* by Cecil J. Schneer, Harper & Row, 1960, p. 36.)

fied his model of the solar system. Just by assuming that the planets revolve about the sun instead of about the earth, he has eliminated a host of epicycles. If Ptolemy had known the planets Uranus, Neptune, and Pluto, none of which is visible to the naked eye, he would have had to add many more epicycles to his system. In the heliocentric system one motion for each planet was substituted for many motions. Ptolemy himself had stated in *The Almagest* a fundamental principle of science: *one should adopt the simplest hypothesis that will coordinate all known observations.*

The Ecliptic

The orbit of the revolving earth is a nearly circular path about the sun, a path that it traverses once in exactly one sidereal year. The projection of this path or orbit on the celestial sphere (an imaginary and very distant spherical surface) is called the *ecliptic*. The plane that includes the ecliptic is called the *plane of the ecliptic* (Fig. 2-15). It is a plane of reference for all other bodies in the solar system. The earth's axis is tilted $66\frac{1}{2}°$ to the plane of the ecliptic. The ecliptic is inclined $23\frac{1}{2}°$ to the celestial equator, and intersects it at two equidistant points called the *equinoxes* (Fig. 2-15). These points are more precisely called *equinoctial points*. The term *equinox* is also used to refer to either of the *moments* at which the sun apparently crosses the celestial equator. The moment of crossing when the sun is apparently going north is the March equinox, the southward crossing is the September equinox.[7]

The Zodiac

The zodiac is a band of the sky about 16° to 18° wide that is centered on the ecliptic (Fig.

[7] The terms *vernal* and *autumnal* are not used here because the seasons are reversed in the southern hemisphere.

2-16). The apparent motion of the sun is within this band (or belt) at all times. As the moon and the planets (except Pluto) travel in paths close to the sun's apparent path, they also appear against the background of the stars composing the zodiac. Hipparchus divided the zodiac into twelve parts (or signs), each spanning 30°, starting with the spring equinox. Each part of this belt contained a group of stars that is called a constellation. The name assigned each part, or sign, was that of the constellation within it *at the time Hipparchus made the division.* Because of the precession of the equinoxes (Fig. 2-24), the constellations are no longer in their namesake signs.

Earth–Sun Distance

The earth–sun distance varies from approximately $94\frac{1}{2}$ million mi (about July 4) to around $91\frac{1}{2}$ million mi (about January 4). This was first reliably determined in 1862 by observations of Mars when it made one of its closest approaches—35 million mi—to the earth. Discovery of the asteroid Eros in 1897 made possible better calculations in 1901 when Eros came within 15 million mi of the earth. The average distance to the sun, 93 million mi, is referred to as 1 astronomical unit (AU). This unit of distance is widely used in comparing the distances of the other planets from the sun. The earth's orbit is therefore 2 AU across. The earth moves more rapidly when it is nearer the sun than when it is farther away. This variable speed contributes to making the apparent motion of the sun a poor timekeeper.

Apparent Migration of the Sun

There is one effect of this annual motion that is easily observable to all people on earth, even in those regions where there are no seasons

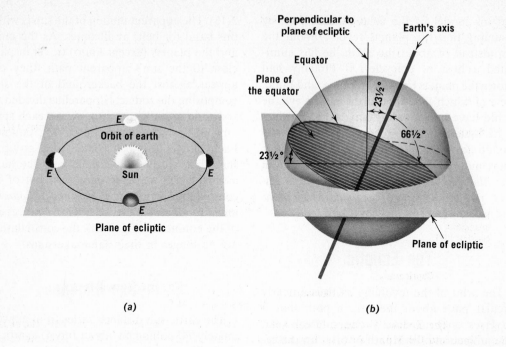

(a)

(b)

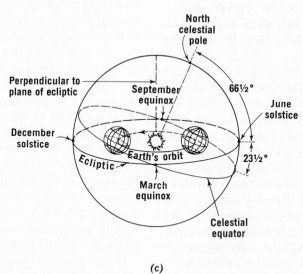

(c)

Fig. 2-15. Plane of Ecliptic; Celestial Equator. (*a*) The ecliptic plane passes through the centers of the sun and the earth (*E*) so that it includes the orbit of the earth. It extends indefinitely in all directions and is a plane of reference for our solar system. (*b*) Note the angles of tilt of both the earth's axis and the plane of the equator to the plane of the ecliptic. (*c*) The celestial equator is the projection of the earth's equator on an imaginary and very distant spherical surface called the celestial sphere. The plane of the celestial equator makes an angle of $23\frac{1}{2}°$ with the plane of the ecliptic.

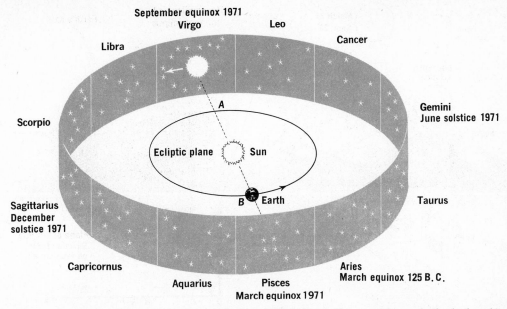

Fig. 2-16. The Zodiac. The band of constellations called the zodiac roughly marks both the plane of the ecliptic and the Milky Way. As shown, the sun is said to be in Virgo (as viewed from the earth) or the earth in Pisces (as viewed from the sun). As the earth revolves, the upper end of the line *AB* shifts to the left (counterclockwise), which is defined as eastward as viewed from Polaris. Therefore the sun appears to drift eastward among the immobile stars.

as we in the middle latitudes know them. The observation is simply that of the apparent movement of the sun northward, which makes it appear higher and higher in the sky during the six-month period beginning (in the northern hemisphere) about December 22 and ending about June 21,[8] and then southward, and so lower in the sky, from about June 21 to about December 22 (Fig. 2-17). The times at which the sun is apparently making the shift from northward to southward, and vice versa, are known as the *solstices*. The solstices also refer to the points on the ecliptic at which these shifts are made.

Those of us who live in the United States (Hawaii excepted) never see the sun directly

overhead. To do that we would have to live somewhere on or between the Tropic of Cancer ($23\frac{1}{2}°$ north of the equator) and the Tropic of Capricorn ($23\frac{1}{2}°$ south of the equator). The sun is directly overhead at the Tropic of Cancer about June 21, at the Tropic of Capricorn about December 22. The time it takes the sun to appear to move from the Tropic of Cancer to the Tropic of Capricorn and back again is called the tropical year. Our calendar is based on it. This annual motion (apparent migration) of the sun is illustrated in Fig. 2-18, which shows this north–south apparent movement of the sun as it would appear to properly placed observers if the earth did not rotate. Thus we visualize the apparent annual motion of the sun apart from its apparent daily motion. If we combine these two motions (annual and daily), we may illustrate the combination as shown in Fig. 2-19.

[8] Since our calendar is not quite synchronized, and never can be, with the apparent movements of the sun, the hour varies so much that the date of any solstice or equinox may occur on either of two days.

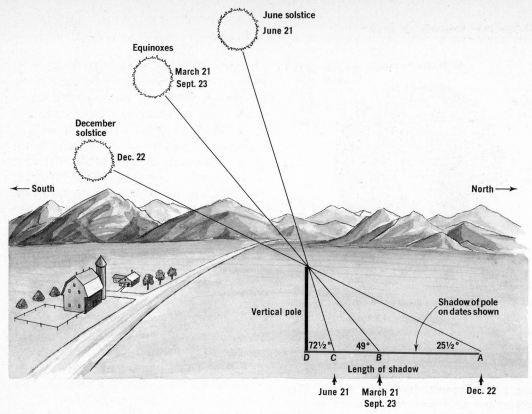

Fig. 2-17. Length of Shadow vs. Angle of Sun's Rays at Noon at Latitude 41°N (New York City). When the angle is greatest ($72\frac{1}{2}°$), the shadow (*DC*) is shortest. When the angle is least ($25\frac{1}{2}°$), the shadow (*DA*) is longest. It takes three months for the shadow to lengthen from *C* to *B* and another three months to lengthen from *B* to *A*.

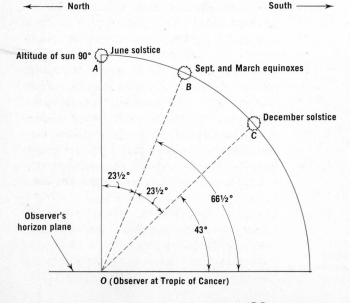

Fig. 2-18. Apparent Annual Motion of Sun. To separate the sun's apparent annual motion from its apparent diurnal motion we need to assume that the earth has stopped rotating. An observer on the Tropic of Cancer would see the sun directly overhead at noon on June 21. He would then observe it to sink lower and lower until it reached *C*. It would then reverse itself and move back to *A*. The time consumed is one tropical year.

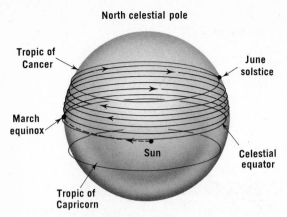

Fig. 2-19. Apparent Path of Sun in Sky. The sun's apparent annual motion combined with its diurnal motion gives the apparent path of the sun in the sky. It is here shown for the period March 21 to June 21 as viewed from the North Pole. The sun is observed to be on the horizon all 24 hours of March 21. Each day it appears a little higher above the horizon until it reaches a maximum of $23\frac{1}{2}°$ above it. The apparent path is thus an ascending spiral of low pitch until about June 21. It then becomes a descending spiral. Remember that the sun never sets at the North Pole from March 21 to September 22.

Tilt of the Earth's Axis

The axis of the earth is inclined $66\frac{1}{2}°$ to the plane of the ecliptic. More commonly we use the complement of this angle (Fig. 2-15*b*) and say the axis is inclined $23\frac{1}{2}°$ to a perpendicular to the plane of the ecliptic. We who live north of the Tropic of Cancer can determine this angle by measuring the altitude of the sun above the horizon at noon suntime[9] on both solstices. The difference between these two

[9] Noon suntime is the time of day when the sun is at the highest point in the sky for that day. The sun is then midway in its apparent path from horizon to horizon. The altitude of the sun for any particular day is defined as its elevation above the horizon at noon suntime, measured in degrees.

altitudes (47°) is twice the angle of tilt. If we were on the equator, the difference in the altitudes of the sun at noon suntime on an equinox and a solstice would give us the angle of tilt directly. If there were no tilt—that is, if the earth's axis were perpendicular to the plane of the ecliptic—the altitude of the sun at noon suntime would be constant the year round for any one place. It is the tilt of the axis that determines the positions of the Tropics of Cancer and Capricorn and the Arctic and Antarctic Circles. It also determines the altitude of the sun at any particular time.

This inclination has important consequences to the human race, for it makes more of the earth's surface habitable than would be without the tilt. The axis maintains this angle as the earth revolves, so that in any one position it is parallel to what it is in any other position (Fig. 2-20). This is called *parallelism of the axis*.

The Seasons

Three of the factors we have discussed, operating together, give us the seasons as we in the middle latitudes know them: (1) the inclination of the axis, (2) the parallelism of the axis, and (3) the revolution of the earth about the sun in about 365 days. Change any one of these significantly and our seasons would change. Of greatest importance to people living in the middle and high latitudes is the inclination of the earth's axis, for when the axis is inclined toward the sun (Fig. 2-21*b*) they have summer, a season that would be absent from the earth outside the equatorial regions if there were no tilt—that is, if the axis were perpendicular to the sun's rays (Fig. 2-22). Also as a result of the tilt, the sun's rays are vertical about June 21 at the Tropic of Cancer, $23\frac{1}{2}°$ north of the equator.

The Tropic of Cancer is the farthest north the vertical rays of the sun ever get (Fig. 2-21*b*)

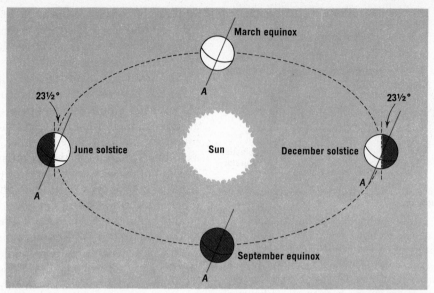

Fig. 2-20. Parallelism of Earth's Axis. As the earth revolves about the sun, its axis maintains a constant angle of inclination to a perpendicular to the plane of the ecliptic. Thus the earth's axis remains parallel to itself in all positions in the orbit.

just as the Tropic of Capricorn is the farthest south the vertical rays ever get (Fig. 2-21c). *The sun is never directly overhead anywhere in the United States, Hawaii excepted.* The tilt affects our seasons not only by increasing and decreasing the angle of the sun's rays (Fig. 2-21) but also by regulating the length of day and night. Thus in the latitude of New York City one has a day of about 15 hours and a night of about 9 hours at the June solstice—15 hours to heat up and 9 hours to cool off. At the December solstice the situation is exactly reversed. The inclination of the axis causes the sun to rise and set once a year at the poles; thus the polar day (the time between two successive sunrises) is equal to a year. The six months of steady sunshine makes the polar regions far warmer during the summer months, and the lack of any sunshine during the winter months makes them far colder, than they would be otherwise.

Rotation, Revolution, and Time

The measurement of time from the very beginning of civilization has been dependent on the varying space relations of the earth and the stars. The rotation of the earth on its axis, with the resultant changing pattern of the stars in the sky, has long furnished the fundamental "clock" mechanism on which the civilized world depended. Thus, our day is defined by the earth's rotation. So accurate is this standard clock[10] that the greatest observed error with respect to the average during the past 200 years was 30 seconds, first in one direction and then in the other. Such fluctuations could be caused by expansions and contractions of

[10] The earth's rotation as a standard clock has been replaced recently by an atomic clock, designed by the National Bureau of Standards. It has a constancy that is far greater than that of the earth's rotation.

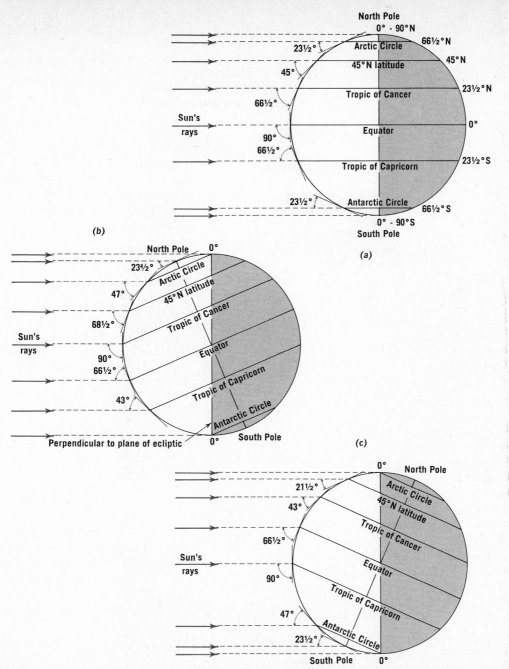

Fig. 2-21. Angles of Sun's Rays at Equinoxes and Solstices. (*a*) At an equinox the angle is 90° with the plane of the earth's surface at noon at the equator, $66\frac{1}{2}$° at either tropic, and 0° at either pole. (*b*) The angle of the sun's rays at noon at the June solstice at any given place is $23\frac{1}{2}$° more than at an equinox in the northern hemisphere and $23\frac{1}{2}$° less in the southern hemisphere. (*c*) The angle of the sun's rays at noon at the December solstice at any given place is $23\frac{1}{2}$° less than at an equinox in the northern hemisphere and $23\frac{1}{2}$° more in the southern hemisphere.

35

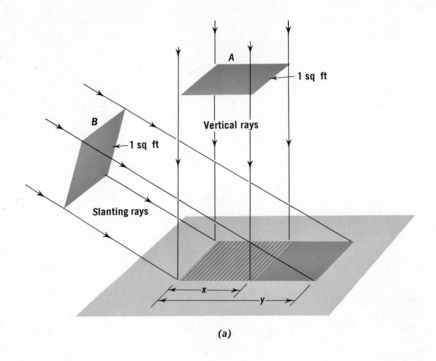

(a)

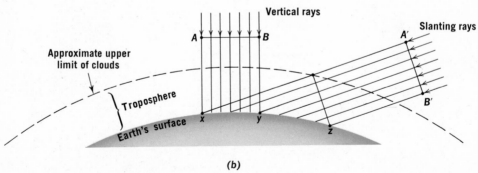

(b)

Fig. 2-22. Vertical Rays of Sun vs. Slanting Rays. In both (*a*) and (*b*) the two bands of rays contain the same total heat energy. The heat of the vertical rays is spread over a smaller area on striking the earth than is the heat of the slanting rays, so that the heat per unit area is greater. Summers are warmer than winters outside the equatorial regions in part because the summer rays are nearer the vertical than are the winter rays.

the earth, which alter the radius of the earth by a few feet. Superimposed upon these fluctuations is a steady retardation of rotation caused chiefly by tidal friction.

The revolution of the earth about the sun and the revolution of the moon about the earth define our calendar, that is, our year and its division into 12 months. Although clocks can be designed to keep precisely in step with the rotation of the earth, our calendar is not, and never can be, truly in step with the revolution of the earth. This is because the time to complete one rotation is a sidereal day (Fig. 2-23), and the time of revolution is not an even number of days. The exact time of one revolution is 365 days 5 hr 48 min 45.68 sec. This is the time that elapses between two March equinoxes, and it is called the tropical year, on which our calendar is based. If, instead of being about 11 min short of $365\frac{1}{4}$ days, it were exactly 365 or 366 days (or, better still, 360), we would not have an extra day every 4 years. This extra day overcompensates, and so we omit a leap year every 100 years. This over-

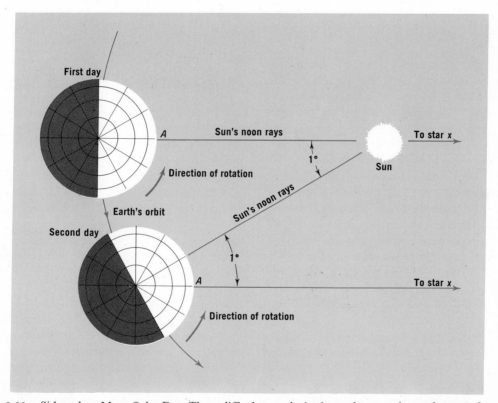

Fig. 2-23. Sidereal vs. Mean Solar Day. These differ by nearly 4 minutes because the earth moves forward in its orbit as it rotates. Assume that at noon (first day) both sun and star X were directly overhead to an observer at *A*. The earth rotates counterclockwise (as viewed from a point above the North Pole) through 360° in 23 hr 56 min to bring the star directly overhead again, but must rotate through another 1° to bring the sun directly overhead again. The angle (1°) is enormously exaggerated in the figure.

compensates the other way, and so we put the leap year back in those years that are divisible by 400. This overcompensates the other way—and so it goes on forever.

The stars make a nearly perfect timepiece because the sun appears to move slowly among the fixed stars, requiring one sidereal year to return to the same position among the stars. Thus the stars that rise in the east appear to rise a little earlier each night; that is, the sun appears to drift eastward[11] among the stars. This was interpreted by the early geocentrists as a faster turning of the dome carrying the stars than that of the dome carrying the sun, enough faster so that the former gained a complete lap on the latter in a full year—the sidereal year.[12]

A difficulty arises because we gear our daily lives to the sun rather than the stars. The sidereal day is the time between two successive crossings of the same meridian[13] by the same star. This time is 23 hr 56 min 4 sec. Sidereal days are all practically the same length. Now the day we use is "hitched" to the sun, the interval between two successive midnights or, more conveniently, from one noon to the next. There are called *solar days,* and they are not all the same length. One reason is as follows. If our earth were rotating but *not* revolving, sidereal days and solar days would be the same. But in revolving, the earth moves forward in its orbit, faster in some parts than in others, and so has to rotate a bit farther—

about 1° on the average—to "catch up" with the sun (Fig. 2-23). This takes on the average about 4 minutes (3 min, 56 sec), but because of the earth's variable speed of revolution—due to the ellipticity of its orbit—the extra amount of rotation is also variable. Since the speed of rotation is constant, the time it takes to rotate this variable distance is also variable, so solar days are not all the same length. A second reason for the variation is that the day from noon to noon (suntime, p. 33) tends to be longer than average at the solstices and shorter at the equinoxes. The length of our conventional day is the average length of our solar days, and we call this the *mean solar day.*

Precession of the Equinoxes

The term *equinox* has already been defined (p. 29). Since the sun is apparently moving along the ecliptic at a speed of about 66,000 mi/hr, it is obvious that it can be at either equinoctial point for only a moment. Thus at the March equinox the sun is at a definite point in the zodiac (Fig. 2-16). It is reasonable to suppose that at the next March equinox, the sun would be at the same point at the same time. This can be checked by the position of the sun with respect to the background of stars in the zodiac. Careful measurements would relate the sun's position to a particular star or patch of stars in a particular constellation.

Hipparchus made these careful measurements and compared them with those made by Alexandrian astronomers during the preceding 150 years and more. He discovered a slow rotation of the whole pattern of stars around the ecliptic axis (which is perpendicular to the zodiac belt). He found that the sun was not quite in the same patch of stars as it was in the previous March equinox. He found that the sun reached the equinox about 20 minutes before it could be aligned with the

---

[11] Here on earth we use the North and South Poles as reference points for our compass directions. When we face north, east is on our right. But this system is meaningless far out in space. Yet we do have need for the easterly and westerly directions out there, although there are no reference points there within our solar system. Therefore westward is arbitrarily defined as clockwise in our solar system as viewed from high above the North Pole. Eastward is therefore counterclockwise as viewed from the same place.

[12] The sidereal year is about 20 minutes longer than the tropical year. This difference is due to the westward precession of the equinoxes.

[13] See footnote 3.

same patch of stars. Thus the March equinox comes 20 minutes earlier each year. In other words, the equinoctial points "slide" westward [14] along the ecliptic and so meet the oncoming sun 20 minutes before the sun has completed a full journey around the ecliptic. This westward sliding of the equinoxes is called *precession*. It is this precession that causes the tropical year to be 20 minutes shorter than the sidereal year.

Minus the mathematics, the cause of the precession may be simplified as follows: The gravitational pull of the sun on the earth's equatorial bulge is unsymmetrical with respect to the earth's center; the pull is greater on the side nearer the sun. The bulge on the average is slightly nearer the sun than other portions of the earth, and so the effect of gravity on the bulge is a bit greater than on the other parts. Any rotating object responds to such unbalanced forces by changing the direction of its axis of rotation (Fig. 2-24). The earth's response is a slow conical motion of its axis about a perpendicular to the plane of the ecliptic, as shown in Fig. 2-24*b*. This motion is the same as that of a slightly inclined spinning top that, instead of falling, precesses in a cone about the vertical. It takes nearly 26,000 years for the earth to complete one precession. One result is that no one star can remain our pole star throughout the cycle of 26,000 years. Vega will be the pole star 14,000 years from now.

It is therefore evident that the previous statement about the parallelism of the earth's axis (p. 33) is not precisely true. However, any deviation from one year to the next or even during a man's lifetime is relatively insignificant, and so what we said is essentially true for all practical purposes. Over a long period of time (12,000 to 13,000 years) the cumulative effects of deviation from parallelism could cause our seasons to be completely reversed, if our calendar were based on the sidereal year instead of on the tropical year.

Precession has caused the March equinoctial point to move westward about 30° since the time of Hipparchus. The signs of the zodiac (Fig. 2-16) have moved with it, away from the constellations after which they were named. Thus the signs no longer coincide with their original constellations. Modern astrologers, however, fail to take these changes into consideration in making their predictions.

Motions of the Moon

The moon is the earth's only natural satellite; it revolves around the earth as the earth revolves about the sun, and so its motions are appropriately discussed with the motions of the earth.

The actual motion of the moon [15] is not a simple revolution in an elliptical orbit about the earth. When we say that it moves in an elliptical orbit we are reverting to the geocentric concept of a stationary earth. Actually the earth is moving through approximately 30° of its orbit, a distance of nearly 50 million mi, while the moon completes one revolution about the earth. We shall, therefore, consider the moon's orbit relative to the earth; that is, we shall, part of the time at least, consider ourselves good geocentrists. This merely means that we are talking about apparent motions rather than real motions.

The orbit of the moon is an ellipse with the earth at one focus. The eccentricity is small, the greatest distance from the earth being about 253,000 mi and the shortest distance about 221,000 mi. The mean distance is about 239,000 mi, roughly 240,000 mi. This is about 60 times the radius of the earth.

Astronomically, the month is the period of

---

[14] See footnote 11.

[15] For a description of the moon see page 67, and for a discussion of its phases see page 13.

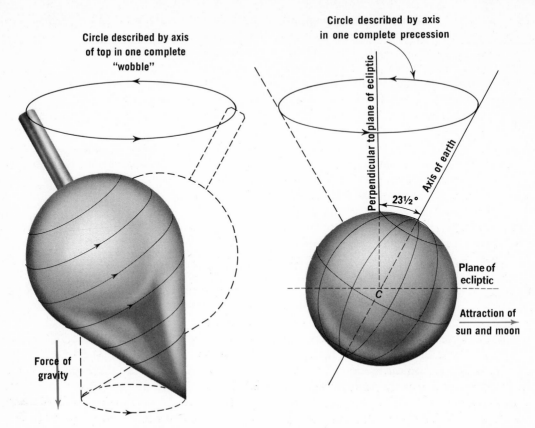

Circle described by axis
of top in one complete
"wobble"

Circle described by axis
in one complete precession

Perpendicular to plane of ecliptic

Axis of earth

23½°

Plane of
ecliptic

Attraction of
sun and moon

C

Force of
gravity

Fig. 2-24. Precession of Equinoxes. Precession of the earth's axis may be compared to the wobbling of a top as it spins. Note that the earth's axis changes the direction in which it points as it revolves about the perpendicular to the plane of the ecliptic. This change is so slow as to be negligible in any one year since it takes the axis 26,000 years to complete one "wobble."

the moon's revolution. There are two kinds of months, depending upon our point of reference. The sidereal month is the time of a complete revolution with any particular star as the reference point. This is about 27.32 mean solar days. The synodic month is the time of a complete revolution with respect to the sun; that is, it is the time from one new moon (or full moon) to the next, about 29½ days. The longer time is due to the fact that the earth has moved forward nearly 30° in its journey about the sun during those 27.32 days, and so the moon

has a longer distance to travel.[16] With respect to the *diurnal* (daily) motions of the earth, the moon falls behind the sun about 50 minutes a day so that moonrise, on the average, comes about 50 minutes later each day. The result is an apparent eastward drift of the moon among the stars, a drift that can be observed on any clear night by checking the moon's

[16]See Fig. 2-23, which shows why there is a difference between the sidereal and the solar day. The cause of the difference between a sidereal and a synodic month is a similar one.

position with respect to a particular star at two different times. The speed of the moon relative to the earth averages a bit over $\frac{1}{2}$ mi/sec. Its actual speed is, of course, much greater, for the earth is moving forward in its orbit at an average speed of about $18\frac{1}{2}$ mi/sec.

The moon rotates on its axis in exactly the same time it takes to complete one sidereal revolution. The result is that the moon always keeps the same side toward the earth; we always see his "face," never the "back of his head."

Eclipses, Lunar and Solar

To us the sun and the moon seem to have the same diameter. Actually that of the sun is about 400 times that of the moon, but the sun's distance from the earth is about 400 times the moon's distance. If the ratios between their sizes and distances were greatly different, solar eclipses as we know them might be nonexistent. Venus and Mercury—both larger than the moon—pass directly between the earth and the sun from time to time but never eclipse the sun.[17]

The plane that includes the path of the moon is inclined about 5° to the plane of the ecliptic. Thus the moon is in the plane of the ecliptic twice every revolution about the earth, or twice a month. These two points of intersection of the plane of the ecliptic with the path of the moon are called the *nodes*. The earth casts a shadow (the *umbra* in Fig. 2-25*b*);

[17]The passages of these planets across the face of the sun are called *transits*.

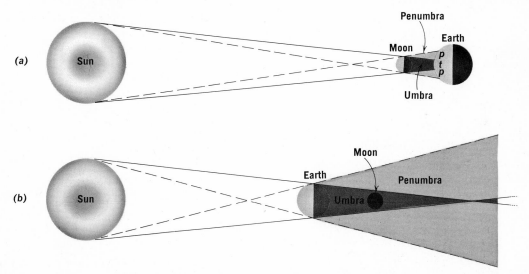

Fig. 2-25. Eclipses of Sun and Moon. (*a*) Eclipse of sun. The solid lines from the sun to the moon meet to form a cone whose tip is intercepted by the earth, producing a total eclipse, *t*. When the moon is farthest from the earth, this tip fails to reach the earth and so there is no eclipse. This explains the rarity of eclipses of the sun as compared to eclipses of the moon. Note also that only a small part of the earth intercepts this tip. Thus a total eclipse of the sun can be seen only in the areas intercepting the tip, but a partial eclipse, *p*, is seen in the areas on either side of the tip. (*b*) Eclipse of moon. Note that the moon is on the opposite side of the earth from that during an eclipse of the sun and that the moon is completely within the cone formed by the solid lines from the sun to the earth. Thus a total eclipse of the moon may at times be seen from all of the dark side of the earth at the same time.

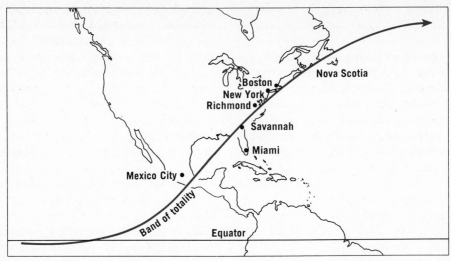

Fig. 2-26. Typical Band of Totality of Solar Eclipse (March 7, 1970). The width of the band of totality never exceeds 167 mi. However, a partial eclipse may be observed up to 1000 mi on either side of this band.

when the moon crosses this shadow, it is eclipsed. Note that the phase must be full, for the moon is on the opposite side of the earth from the sun. But to be in this shadow, the moon must be at (or very near) one of the nodes; that is, it must be in, or very near, the plane of the ecliptic. If the moon's path were always in the plane of the ecliptic, there would be a lunar eclipse each month. Since it is not, the 5° tilt allows the full moon to be as much as 21,000 mi on one side or the other of the plane of the ecliptic. When it is that far away, it misses the earth's shadow completely.

To cause a solar eclipse the moon must again be at or very near one of the nodes, but this time the phase must be new. The moon is so much smaller than the earth that its shadow can never engulf the whole earth (Fig. 2-25a). However, a new moon may be at a node and not produce a total eclipse simply because the tip of the moon's shadow is not long enough to reach the earth. The length of the shadow varies with the distance of the moon from the earth; that distance varies from 221,000 to 253,000 mi, and the length of the shadow

varies from about 228,000 to 236,000 mi. Only when the moon is closer than 236,000 mi will there be a total solar eclipse observed anywhere on earth.

Both the earth and the moon are spheres far smaller than the sun; their shadows are cones with the apexes directed away from the sun. In an eclipse of the sun only the tip of this cone sweeps across the earth, in a belt that is never more than 167 mi wide[18] (Fig. 2-26). To a stationary observer the maximum duration of totality in a solar eclipse is about $7\frac{1}{2}$ min.

At least two solar and two lunar eclipses occur each year, none of them necessarily total. Five of each may occur. At any one place lunar eclipses are seen more often than solar because of the greater area of the earth from which a lunar eclipse is visible. Lunar eclipses may last 3 hr 40 min and may be visible over more than half the earth (Fig. 2-25b).

---

[18]This is the maximum width of the band in which any total eclipse of the sun may be observed. A partial eclipse may be observed in a band up to 2000 mi across.

Exercises

1. Suppose that you are on the equator. You observe a certain star directly overhead.
   (a) Where did it rise?
   (b) Where will it set?
   (c) In what part of the sky would you look to locate the North Star?
   (d) Would you see any stars that did not rise or set?

2. What determines the positions of the North and South Poles?

3. How are day and night accounted for (a) by the geocentric theory and (b) by the heliocentric theory?

4. Why is a degree of latitude, as measured in miles, greater in the polar regions than at the equator?

5. List the pieces of evidence that the earth rotates on a north–south axis. (All should consist of phenomena that cannot be explained by a geocentric stationary earth.)

6. (a) What is the plane of the ecliptic?
   (b) Of what use is it in our study of the solar system?

7. What is the orientation of the axis of the earth (a) to the plane of the ecliptic and (b) to a perpendicular to the plane of the ecliptic?

8. What determines the positions (latitudes) of the Tropics of Cancer and Capricorn?

9. What is meant by the altitude of the sun?

10. How is the altitude of the sun related to the two Tropics?

11. Is the sun ever directly overhead at any place north of the Tropic of Cancer?

12. How many days a year is the sun directly overhead at the equator?

13. On earth, the North Pole is our frame of reference for compass directions. Out in space these directions have no significance, yet we need the terms eastward or westward. How are these terms defined?

14. Suppose you could get the midday sun to vanish by the wave of a magic wand.
    (a) What would the sky look like?
    (b) Do you ever actually see the sky somewhat like this? If so, when?

15. What is the zodiac?

16. What is meant by the apparent eastward drift of the sun?

17. What is 1 astronomical unit?

18. (a) What is a tropical year?
    (b) How does it differ from a sidereal year?

19. What effect does the varying distance of the sun from the earth have on our seasons?

20. What is the *fundamental* reason for colder weather in the middle and higher latitudes in the northern hemisphere in January than in July?

21. What three factors control the seasons?

22. Suppose that the earth took two years to complete one revolution about the sun. Would this change our seasons? Explain.

23. Suppose that the earth's axis did not retain its parallelism but constantly changed so that the axis was always tilted toward the sun in the northern hemisphere. What effect would this have on the seasons (a) in the northern hemisphere and (b) in the southern hemisphere?

24. How do you think the noonday sky would look to an astronaut 1000 mi above the earth? Why? (It wouldn't look blue.)

25. Because of rotation the Empire State Building in New York City is traveling at a speed of about 750 mi/hr. Yet a helicopter with a maximum speed of only 100 mi/hr can hover all day directly above it. Explain.

26. About how fast is a point on the equator traveling because of rotation?

27. (a) Does a degree of latitude represent the same number of miles everywhere on earth? Explain.
    (b) How about a degree of longitude? Explain.

28. It is not possible to design an accurate calendar. Why?

29. Could an accurate calendar be designed if the period of the earth's revolution were exactly 366 days?

30. What effect, if any, does the precession of the equinoxes have on our calendar? Explain.

31. The apparent diameter of the full moon is about the same as the apparent diameter of the sun. However, we know that the actual diameter of the sun is 400 times that of the moon. Why should the apparent diameters be about the same?

32. In what phase must the moon be (a) at the time of a solar eclipse and (b) at the time of a lunar eclipse?

33. What evidence do we have that Venus is a planet rather than a star?

34. Why doesn't the moon rise at the same hour every night?

35. The earth is closest to the sun in January. Why isn't early January the warmest time of the year?

36. The apparent paths of the sun, moon, and the planets across the sky from east to west are approximately the same. Explain why this should be so.

37. Your observation of the moon night after night shows that it apparently moves eastward among the stars. Explain.

38. You observe that the interval between sunrise and sunset and that between sunset and sunrise are equal on February 1. Where must your location on this earth be?

39. Define the term "up" in such a way as to apply to any place here on earth. What would the term "up" mean to an astronaut out in space halfway between the earth and the moon?

40. The apparent diameter of the sun as seen from the earth is not the same throughout the year. Why?

Establishment of the Copernican System

3

From the Greeks to Copernicus

In questions of science the authority of a thousand is not worth the humble reasoning of a single individual.

GALILEO GALILEI

Ptolemy died about A.D. 150, Copernicus in 1543. The interim of about fourteen hundred years was twice that in which Greek science was developed to a high level. During this interim natural science just about vanished from the earth. The Romans made no progress in theoretical science, largely because their viewpoint was clearly a utilitarian one. New ideas never develop when men's minds are ruled by the "What's the use of it?" philosophy, for how can one know the use of an idea in advance of its development? (Thus, friends of Benjamin Franklin wondered why he "fooled" around with electricity. "What's the use of it?" they asked. His answer is said to have been "Of what use is a new-born babe?") Science flourishes best when ideas are advanced for their own sake and not for any possible utilitarian value. The true scientist

45

wants to know, and that is enough justification for his own research.

The barbarian hordes overran western Europe as Rome declined. With the destruction of the Roman Empire, the whole Western World collapsed. There was little else to fill the void. It took centuries for an intellectual world to rise again. Christianity spread, and as it did, it naturally came into contact with Greek science and philosophy and for a time the chief work of the early Christian Fathers lay in combining the two philosophies. Until after the time of St. Augustine (d. A.D. 430) Christian doctrines were fluid, and the alternative ideas could exist peaceably side by side. In time men came to rely more and more on authority. Vague hopes and fears of heaven and hell, the hope of salvation in one and the fear of damnation in the flames of the other, dominated scholars more and more. With their firm belief that the day of judgment and the second coming of Christ were very "near," their efforts naturally went into preparation for them. Small wonder that little interest was shown in secular knowledge for its own sake. "To discuss the nature and position of the earth," said St. Ambrose, "does not help us in the life to come." Secular learning became identified with paganism, and ignorance was exalted as a virtue. Slowly the desire to objectively investigate natural phenomena passed away. Learning had to be crushed before the Dark Ages could be ushered in. The chief use of a knowledge of nature was in illustrating passages from the Scriptures, and almost anything was believed if it accorded with them. The writings of the Greek scientists, Aristotle chief among them, were forgotten.

During the 8th through 11th centuries, the flame of learning was kept burning chiefly by the Arabs. They kept alive the memory of Greek science and made some original contributions of their own, chiefly in chemistry. Arabic became the classical language of learning. Most of the work of the Greeks was translated into Arabic, from which it was later translated into Latin. A revival of learning began in Europe in the 12th century. Slowly the innate curiosity of the human mind began to rebel against the enslavement of medieval theology. Signs of breaking with the medieval habit of mind began to appear. The axioms that "doubt is the road to inquiry," that "by inquiry we perceive the truth," and that "it is necessary to understand in order to believe" grew slowly in the confused jungle that had taken over the once cleared fields of scientific thought. The complete works of Aristotle were rediscovered and translated into Latin between 1200 and 1225. Roger Bacon[1] (b. 1210) stood out from the other philosophers of his time because of his clear understanding that experimental methods alone give any adequate degree of certainty in science.

> Bacon, a learned Franciscan philosopher, was . . . in spirit a man of science and a scientific philosopher, born out of due time and chafing unconsciously against the limitations of his own restricted outlook, no less than against the external obstacles at which he rails so openly and so often . . . for all his comparatively advanced outlook, [he] accepted most of the medieval attitude of mind. No man can do more than advance a little way in front of the ranks of that contemporary army of thought to which, whether he will or no, he belongs.[2]

St. Thomas Aquinas accepted the Ptolemaic system of astronomy as a working hypothesis. His successors, however, welded the whole of Aristotle's science with geocentric theory and Christian theology. The result was a rigid structure in which the parts were so interdependent that to doubt Aristotelian science

---

[1] Not to be confused with Francis Bacon, who lived 350 years later.
[2] W. C. Dampier, *A History of Science,* Macmillan, New York, 1942, pp. 100–102.

was to doubt the Christian faith. Such a structure led naturally to reasoning by authority,[3] and once again progress in inquiry ceased, this time because all of the answers were "known." This setting up of Aristotle as the supreme arbiter of scientific thought caused a 20th-century philosopher, Bertrand Russell, to call Aristotle one of the great misfortunes of the human race—through no fault of his (Aristotle's).

As the revival of learning and the Renaissance progressed, there gradually arose a new concept of man, a man of some confidence in himself, a man of growing curiosity, a man who ceased to devote his whole time to contemplating the life hereafter and who started to live in the present. The search for the knowledge of the past accelerated to a comparatively high tempo, especially in Italy. The spirit of adventure drove men to exploration of the world about them, culminating in the discovery of the Americas by Columbus[4] and the circumnavigation of the earth by Magellan.

Nicolaus Copernicus

Such was the world into which Nicolaus Koppernigk (1473–1543) was born of a Polish father and a German mother. His name was latinized as Copernicus. That this world into which he was born was different from the one

of the thousand years preceding may be seen from a scanning of the names of some of his contemporaries and near-contemporaries: da Vinci, Gutenberg, Michelangelo, Dürer, Erasmus, Columbus, Luther, Henry VIII. It was an exciting world in which he lived, a world that was breaking rapidly from the fetters of the past, a world in which new ideas had some chance of eventually succeeding.

Copernicus studied mathematical science, took a degree in canon law, studied medicine, and found time to study astronomy. He was a devout Churchman and spent most of his time in the service of the Catholic Church.

The Ptolemaic theory of the universe still reigned supreme. Some observations of greater accuracy then before were made during the revival of learning, and these increased the difficulty of fitting the motions of the sun, moon, and planets into the already highly complex system of Ptolemy. We recall that the basic principles of the Ptolemaic system were three: (1) the earth was at rest, (2) the motions of celestial bodies were circular, and (3) these circular motions were uniform. The major problem was to explain the apparent departures from this uniform motion. The Greeks found it necessary to invent epicycles, eccentrics, and equants and to use them in various combinations to account for the vagaries of planetary motions. Later astronomers had no thought of discarding the Ptolemaic theory and starting anew to see if a more satisfactory system could be developed. Instead, they added more complicated assumptions to it so that the 70-odd motions in the time of Ptolemy were increased to 80 or more. The amazing intricacies of the system appalled Copernicus. He found it difficult to believe that an intelligent creator would create such a top-heavy system. By 1450, 19 epicycles[5] were needed for

---

[3]Not to be confused with acceptance of responsible authority. In all fields of knowledge, none more so than in science, acceptance of what has been done previously by competent men is a necessity if further progress is to be made. For a more complete discussion, see p. 170.

[4]The concept of a spherical earth was not original with Columbus. He took it from the rediscovered works of the Greeks. His estimate of the circumference was not from the data of Eratosthenes (Fig. 1-6). Instead he used the figures of another Greek, which gave a much smaller circumference. The result was that he thought he had reached the East Indies when he actually had not sailed half the distance to them. The concept of a flat earth had arisen and spread during the Dark Ages. See Ptolemy's argument for a round earth at the end of Chapter 1.

[5]Various versions of Ptolemy's system existed in the 16th century. They differed from one another by having epicycles of differing sizes, and so on.

Mars alone. More than one devout man jokingly intimated that if he were present at the time of creation he could have made simpler suggestions to the creator. Copernicus saw that the observed phenomena could be more simply explained if he followed Aristarchus in assuming that the sun was at the center of the universe. A corollary would be that the celestial sphere containing the stars was a fixed one; that is, the stars were motionless. The planets revolved about the sun in perfect circles. The moon revolved about an earth rotating on an axis as both revolved about the sun.

Copernicus wrote,

> In the midst of all, the sun reposes, unmoving. Who, indeed, in this most beautiful temple would place the light-giver in any other part than whence it can illumine all other parts? . . . In this orderly arrangement there appears a wonderful symmetry in the universe and a precise relation between the motions and sizes of the orbs which is impossible to attain in any other way.

Despite his desire for simplicity he ultimately had to use more than 30 epicycles and eccentrics—but no equants—because he retained the second and third of the three basic principles mentioned above. The only real advantage that his system had over Ptolemy's system as it stood at the time was the qualitative simplicity of his explanations. His system was no more accurate than Ptolemy's and he had no direct evidence for it, for instance, no observable parallax, no observable phases of Venus. Nevertheless, by making one small change, that of putting the sun at the center instead of the earth, he shattered the whole medieval universe.

Copernicus was well aware that his system would not be readily accepted. For one thing, it was contrary to human experience, for we are not aware of any motion, and we can observe the sun, moon, and planets rise and set. Moreover, it was not only comforting to think of man on an unmoving earth, but it also bolstered his ego to think that he lived at the center of the universe. Copernicus did not seriously attempt to answer these objections directly; he could only hope that the advantages of his system over the rival one would eventually win the battle for him. He knew that the absence of parallax among the fixed stars would have to be explained; his was the same answer as that of Aristarchus—that the stars were many times farther away than even the farthest planets. He could not prove that they were, nor did he think that they were anywhere near as far away as they actually are. He faced the argument that the rotating earth on its axis should burst like a flywheel when driven too fast with the rejoinder, "Why does the defender of the geocentric theory not fear the same fate for his rotating celestial spheres—so much faster because so much larger?"

He also had to bring his system into accord with the religious and philosophical dogmas of the time. He tried to show how much more harmonious and orderly his system seemed than that of Ptolemy, how the observable world was but a symbol of the working of God's mind, and that it was a reverent duty to find symmetry and order amid the apparent chaos of the planets and stars. He felt that the reduction in the number of elements needed in his system (from over 80 to about 34), and the resulting simplification of practical astronomical problems, was a renewed proof of the deity.

He also calculated the relative radii and speeds of the various bodies in his system so that planetary tables could be prepared for use by astronomers and navigators. These tables were as good as, but no better than, those of Ptolemy for predicting future positions of the planets. Both were equally correct within the current error of the time of about $\frac{1}{6}°$ of arc. (Even today the geocentric system is preferred

for calculations in navigation.) From the scientific viewpoint the chief merit of his system
at that time was that it was simpler. Scientists
have learned that there is merit in simplicity
if the observable facts can be equally well
explained by the simpler theory. Even Ptolemy
recognized this principle, as we have already
stated.

Copernicus died in 1543, the year his work
was published. He had dedicated his book to
the Pope. There was little opposition at first,
probably because the churches failed to see
what it would do to their philosophic-religious
beliefs. They disliked the concepts of the stars
being so far away, for that made heaven—
which was supposed to be among the stars—
far, far away, while hell—supposed by most
to be at the center of the earth—was uncomfortably close beneath their feet. The conten-
tion that the Creator had worked from a heliocentric blueprint was not at all convincing to
most Catholic, Protestant, and Jewish religious
leaders, most of whom forbade the heliocentric
theory to be taught in their schools.

The common-sense objections, together
with the conflict of religious and philosophical
dogmas, interwoven with Aristotelian science,
were sufficient to prevent acceptance for a
time, especially in the face of a lack of any
observable parallax. The only sound evidence
that Copernicus could present was based on
logic: his system was simpler and just as much
in accord with the facts as the opposing theory.
This argument was not at all convincing to
people who had not yet developed our modern
way of viewing scientific evidence.

Moreover, an additional scientific objection
was soon presented. It could be shown that
if Venus revolved about the sun it should show
a full set of phases (Fig. 2-12), whereas, according to the geocentric hypothesis, only
crescent phases should be observed. Observations of Venus by the naked eye showed no
evidence of a full phase. There were variations

of apparent brightness, but at the time of
greatest brightness, it was not in the full-phase
position. There was no answer to this problem
at the time. (For the answer, see Fig. 2-13).

Tycho Brahe

Even an unbiased astronomer like Tycho
Brahe (1546–1601) rejected the Copernican
system because he could observe no stellar
parallax. Tycho was a highborn Dane of great
talents, who spent nearly a lifetime making
careful observations of planetary motions,
most of them in the finest observatory of all
Europe. He invented new instruments with
which he made measurements with the naked
eye that were accurate to less than 2 to 4 min
of arc[6] (Fig. 3-1). Compare with the 10 min
of arc probable error prevalent during the
times of Copernicus. Tycho was clearly the
naked-eye observer supreme, an excellent example of a scientist who collects data. He
developed a geocentric theory of his own
which gained favor briefly. His own stated
purpose of his work was to construct better
planetary tables. Despite his high birth and his
very considerable education, he was as full of
superstition and of belief in occult influences
as the rest of the people of his time. Although
he was the greatest of observers, he had little
theorizing ability, and so at the time of his
death his two volumes of data were just that—
two volumes of data.

Johannes Kepler and His Three Laws

Tycho Brahe willed this enormous collection
of data to his assistant, Johannes Kepler
(1571–1630), when he died. Kepler, a German

---

[6] He may have claimed greater accuracy, but the human
eye cannot resolve points closer than 2 min of arc.

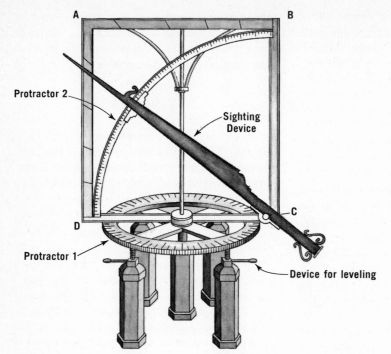

Fig. 3-1. One of Tycho Brahe's Quadrants. They were the most accurate instruments of the time (ca. 1600). The frame *ABCD* can be rotated in a horizontal plane on protractor 1. The sighting device can be rotated vertically on protractor 2.

with a considerable talent for mathematics, knew that he could not improve on the accuracy of Tycho's observations. He therefore used Tycho's data in an effort to bolster the Copernican heliocentric hypothesis, in which he was a devout believer. It is interesting to know why.

To Kepler, a mathematician, the mathematical labyrinth of the Ptolemaic hypothesis was as abhorrent as the simplicity of the Copernican hypothesis was delightful. His motivation was the perfection of the heliocentric theory, but the ultimate reason was not, despite what we have said above, simply a desire for truth. Kepler's mind was a curious mixture of the old and the new. He was convinced that "God created the world in accordance with the principle of perfect numbers, so that the underlying mathematical harmony, the music of the spheres is the real and discoverable cause of the planetary motions." This har-

mony, was, of course, not to be found in the Ptolemaic hypothesis. Kepler, in the beginning, was a symbol-seeking mystic who made his living as an astrologer, but somewhere within him were the makings of a true scientist, for eventually he succeeded in freeing himself to a great extent from the intellectual traditions into which he was born.

Kepler started with the orbit of Mars. His object was to determine its exact path about the sun. His problem was threefold; to find the center of the orbit, to find its distance *relative* to the earth–sun distance, and to find the inclination of the plane of Mars' orbit to the plane of the earth's orbit. After four years of calculation he found that he could not fit Tycho's data into a perfect circle in which Mars moved with uniform speed. The difference was only 8 min of arc (about $\frac{1}{8}°$) but Kepler knew that Tycho's data were far more accurate than that. If he had been a man of less integrity, he could have hidden the difference behind some convenient assumption. This failure of the data to fit this theory distressed him, for he was a devotee of the uniform circular motion concept. Eventually and reluctantly he tried an ellipse with the sun at the center, but without success. Then he put the sun at one focus of the ellipse (Fig. 3-2)—and everything fell into place. He then could formulate the law of the ellipse: *planets move in elliptical paths, with the sun at one focus of the ellipse.*

Gratified though he was, Kepler saw that his second problem was to discover the mathematical laws that describe planetary motions. Tycho's data had shown that the speed of Mars varied within narrow limits. He therefore set out to see if he could discover a law that would relate the speed of a planet at any point in its orbit to its speed at any other point, the evidence for which Kepler was sure must be hidden in Tycho's data. Years of labor went into the effort before he was able to announce the law of equal areas: *during equal time intervals a line from the planet to the sun sweeps out equal areas* (Fig. 3-3). This means that the planet moves faster when nearer the sun, slower when farther away. The two laws together made more accurate astronomical predictions possible.

Still Kepler was not satisfied, because nei-

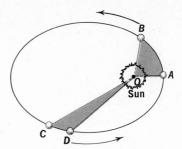

Fig. 3-3. Kepler's Law of Equal Areas. The sun is at one of the foci of the ellipse. The area *AOB* is equal to the area *COD*. A planet moves from *A* to *B* in the same time that it takes to move from *C* to *D*. Thus a planet travels faster from *A* to *B* than from *C* to *D*.

ther law revealed any connection between the radius of the orbit and the speed of one planet and the radius of the orbit and the speed of any other planet. We might ask, "Why should there be?" Kepler believed firmly that there must be an overall pattern in the solar system, that the spacing of the planets was not haphazard, that there must be uniformity in nature to reflect the orderly mind of the Creator. After several more years of work he was able to announce his third law, sometimes called the harmonic law: *the square of the time for one complete revolution of a planet about the sun is proportional to the cube of the mean radius of its orbit,* that is, the cube of its mean distance from the sun. Symbolically, $T^2 \propto r^3$, where the symbol $\propto$ means "proportional to." If we use a proportionality constant, K, to take care of the difference in the units of T and r, we can write

$$T^2 = Kr^3 \qquad [3\text{-}1]$$

Suppose we apply the law to Jupiter, whose observed period is 11.86 of our years. We need to know the value of K, for a unit of time can never equal a unit of distance. We do this by applying the equation to the earth, for which

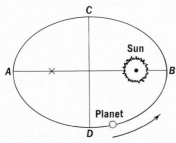

Fig. 3-2. Kepler's Law of the Ellipse. Planets move in elliptical paths with the sun at one focus of the ellipse. The ellipticity is greatly exaggerated here.

we know both T and r. We use the average distance of the earth from the sun (93 million mi), which we will call one astronomical unit (AU). For the earth, r in astronomical units then becomes 1. If we use our year as the time unit, then $T = 1$ also. We have for the earth,

$$T^2 = Kr^3 \quad \text{or} \quad K = \frac{T^2}{r^3} \quad [3\text{-}2]$$

This allows us to solve for K by substituting 1 yr for T, and 1 AU for r.

$$K = \frac{(1 \text{ yr})^2}{(1 \text{ AU})^3}$$

(Note that the *numerical* value of K is 1.) To determine the distance of Jupiter (whose period is 11.86 of our years) from the sun by Kepler's third law, we transpose, thus solving for r^3 in Eq. 3-1 so that

$$r^3 = \frac{T^2}{K} = \frac{(11.86 \text{ yr})^2}{K}$$
$$= \frac{(11.86 \text{ yr})^2}{\dfrac{(1 \text{ yr})^2}{(1 \text{ AU})^3}} \quad [3\text{-}3]$$

Simplifying,

$$r^3 = 11.86^2 \times (1 \text{ AU})^3$$
$$= 140.9 \times (1 \text{ AU})^3$$

hence

$$r = \sqrt[3]{140.7} \times 1 \text{ AU} = 5.2 \text{ AU}$$

Note that yr^2 appears in both the numerator and the denominator and so cancels out.[7]

[7]Note carefully that the units are handled as if they were numerical quantities. Note also that the units in our answer are AU only because we used such units in our determination of K.

It is less cumbersome to omit temporarily the units and use only the numerical value of K (which is 1), but we must remember that omitting units does not do away with them; it simply hides them until we reach the final answer. Thus in Eq. 3-3

$$r^3 = (11.86)^2 = 140.7$$
$$r = \sqrt[3]{140.7} = 5.2 \text{ AU}$$

The average radius of the orbit of Jupiter thus becomes

$$5.2 \times 93 \text{ million mi} = 483.6 \text{ million mi}$$

The actual distance in round numbers (calculated in other ways) is 483 million mi.

The period of Pluto, our outermost planet, discovered in 1930, could be calculated once its distance was measured without waiting the 248.4 years necessary for it to complete one revolution. Conversely, if we wait that long in order to get its period, we can use the period as a check against the distance.

It took Kepler 17 years of hard labor to arrive at these three laws. He was then able to construct tables of planetary motions, tables that remained in use for over a century. Kepler showed himself to have some of the attributes of a true scientist by his attitude toward observations. He made the observations the supreme arbiter of his theory; the theory lived or died according to how well it explained the observations. His overall view, his great overriding purpose, however, was to show that an intelligent Creator would never have made the universe according to that unnecessarily complex device that was called the Ptolemaic theory of the universe.

Kepler's laws helped to convince only those who were already more or less favorably inclined to the Copernican system. They failed completely with the active opponents of the theory. To them it was merely a neat mathematical scheme that permitted calculations of the positions of the planets in their orbits at any particular time. Furthermore, there was still no positive explanation for the lack of observable phases of Venus, nor for the lack of observable parallax. More convincing evidence was needed.

Galileo Galilei

Kepler published his first two laws in 1609 and his third law about ten years later. A friend and avid reader of the works of both Copernicus and Kepler was Galileo Galilei (1564–1642) of Italy. Kepler and Galileo corresponded, keeping each other informed of the latest scientific events in their own parts of Europe. Both were Copernicans living in a world that was still Ptolemaic. Between them they very nearly succeeded in turning it into a Copernican world.

One of Galileo's contributions was to develop a telescope with which he made observations that supported the heliocentric hypothesis. He had heard of the invention of a telescope in Holland. He deduced its principle, made one of his own, and so brought astronomy to the practical test of a telescope. With it the phases of Venus were clearly seen, including the nearly full phase. This was a triumph of the greatest importance for the Copernicans, for in the Ptolemaic system Venus could never get on the far side of the sun so as to show this phase (compare Fig. 2-12 with Fig. 2-13). The fact that Venus has a complete set of phases constitutes the one conclusive proof that it revolves about the sun.

Far greater numbers of stars were visible with the telescope. All still appeared as mere points of light, which bolstered the argument of Copernicus that they were extremely far away. The telescope revealed that Jupiter had four moons revolving about it (Fig. 3-4). (We now know it has twelve.) This came as a shock to the Ptolemaic world, for here were clearly four celestial bodies that revolved about a center other than that of the earth. Furthermore, the celestial bodies were supposed to be perfect spheres, but Galileo could see mountains on the moon, spots on the sun, and bulges

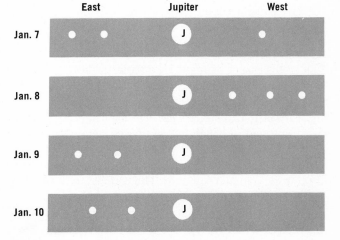

Fig. 3-4. Galileo's Observations of the Moons of Jupiter. The small circles represent the moons of Jupiter and their positions east or west of Jupiter on the dates shown in 1610. The "missing" moon(s) were eclipsed by Jupiter (p. 66). Not drawn to scale.

at the equator of Saturn. These facts annoyed his opponents, for they meant the collapse of the perfect sphere concept.

The battle, however, was not yet won, for the authoritarians refused to be convinced, proving once again that man can believe only what he is ready to believe. Even the concrete evidence meant nothing. Most refused to look through the telescope, for they did not wish to be convinced. The following argument from the Italian astronomer Francesco Sizzi (1611) will serve to illustrate the type of reasoning that Galileo and Kepler had to contend with:

> There are seven windows in the head, two nostrils, two ears, two eyes and a mouth; so in the heavens there are two stars, two un-propitious, two luminaries, and Mercury alone undecided and indifferent. From which and many other similar phenomena of nature such as the seven metals, etc., which it were tedious to enumerate, we gather that the number of planets is necessarily seven. Besides, the Jews and other ancient nations, as well as modern Europeans, have adopted the division of the week into seven days, and have named them from the seven planets: Now if we increase the number of planets, this whole system falls to the ground. . . . Moreover, the satellites are invisible to the naked eye and therefore can have no influence on the earth and therefore would be useless and therefore do not exist.

From 1616, when the Inquisition warned Galileo to cease teaching the Copernican theory as fact (rather than as a hypothesis) because it was contrary to Holy Scripture, until his death in 1642, Galileo's life was a constant warfare waged in behalf of the revised heliocentric theory of Copernicus. We say revised theory, for Kepler had destroyed the concept of uniform circular motion. The extent to which Galileo had advanced beyond either Copernicus or Kepler can be seen in his urging the acceptance of the heliocentric system on its own merits of simplicity and usefulness rather than on how well it satisfied religious views, or reflected the mind of the Creator.

The Final Triumph

Forty-four years after Galileo's death in 1642 (the year of Newton's birth) Newton's *Principia* was published, and with this event the opposition among educated people to the heliocentric theory of the solar system began to crumble. We would like to be able to say that the overwhelming evidence that had developed by 1700 in favor of the theory had convinced even its staunchest opponents. The truth, however, is that in the interim most of these staunch opponents had died, leaving the field largely to those less indoctrinated with the authoritarian attitude and more ready to accept the evidence from observation and experiment. (We must not think that the warfare between authoritarianism and science is yet dead. This warfare, as well as the warfare between ignorance and knowledge, still goes on, but with somewhat diminished intensity. We have only to witness the so-called Monkey Trial in Tennessee in the early 1920's, the banishment of certain textbooks in Germany in the 1930's because of Einstein's Jewish faith, and the passage of laws against the presentation of the theory of evolution in the schools of certain states in 1965 and 1969–70.[8])

Thus, the ultimate success of the heliocentric theory hinged as much on a gradually changing mental climate as on the works of Kepler and Galileo and Newton. The final scientific objection, that of the lack of observed parallax, was removed in 1838 when Bessel observed parallax of a "fixed" star, Proxima Centauri, 2.4×10^{13} mi away.

[8] The U.S. Supreme Court declared such laws unconstitutional in 1970.

Exercises

1. The Ptolemaic system reigned undisputed for at least 1400 years. State four *scientific* reasons for its long reign.
2. What advantage, if any, did the Copernican theory have over that of Ptolemy at the time of its formation?
3. List three scientific objections to the Copernican theory.
4. For what was Tycho Brahe noted?
5. What change did Kepler introduce into the Copernican hypothesis? Why was it necessary?
6. State Kepler's three laws. Which accounted for the varying speed of a planet in its orbit?
7. What were the contributions of Galileo to the heliocentric hypothesis?
8. List the following in proper time sequence: Kepler, Brahe, Galileo, Copernicus.
9. What answer did Copernicus have to the fact that no parallax could be detected among the stars?
10. When was stellar parallax first discovered? Do all stars show it? Explain.
11. A hypothetical planet is 4 AU distant from the sun. What is its period?
12. Do you think that the discovery of an annual parallax of the fixed stars at the time of Copernicus would have clinched his argument in favor of the heliocentric theory?
13. Which is simpler, the system of Copernicus or the system of Kepler? Justify your answer.
14. Why do we accept the Copernican hypothesis as modified by Kepler instead of some other hypothesis?
15. What law explains the fact that the earth is moving fastest about January 7?

The Components of Our Solar System

Our solar system consists of the sun, 9 planets, 32 known satellites, about 1500 to 2000 planetoids (asteroids), myriads of meteors, and several hundred thousand comets. The masses of all the planets and minor bodies taken together equal only about 0.15% of the sun's mass. Almost all these bodies are arranged within a relatively thin, slightly elongated disk that is about $7\frac{1}{2}$ billion mi in diameter. The plane of the ecliptic is parallel to the disk and passes through its center (Fig. 4-1). The orbit of Pluto deviates more than those of the other planets from the plane of the ecliptic. This deviation causes the disk to be thicker than it would be otherwise. The orbits of the comets deviate far more widely than does Pluto's, but these are minor bodies that, despite their great numbers, do not have a total mass anywhere near that of the earth.

Large as the sun and the larger planets may seem to be, almost all the volume of this huge disk is empty. The system is tremendously isolated in space. It takes light traveling at 186,000 mi/sec less than half a day to cross

One of man's most persistent and revealing preoccupations has been his attempt to fashion for himself an adequate conceptual model of the Universe.
GERALD HOLTON

The most incomprehensible thing about the universe is that it is comprehensible.
ALBERT EINSTEIN
(Nobel Prize, Physics, 1921)

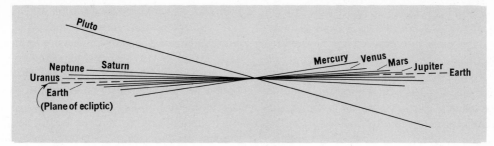

Fig. 4-1. Orbits of Planets Viewed Edgewise. Note that all orbits are nearly in the same plane except that of Pluto. Thus the planets traverse the same relatively narrow band in or near the plane of the ecliptic. This narrow band is the zodiac (Fig. 2-16).

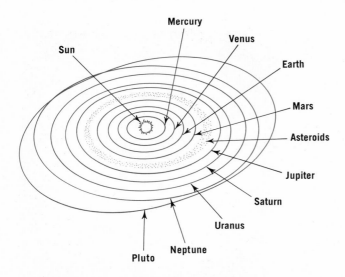

Fig. 4-2. Orbits of the Planets Viewed at an Angle to the Plane of the Ecliptic. The ellipticity of the orbits is exaggerated and the sizes and distances are not in true proportion. Note again how much Pluto's orbit differs from the others.

the disk but over 4 years to reach the nearest body outside the disk, the star Alpha Centauri. A planetary system such as the solar system revolving about this nearest star could not be seen or photographed by any telescope we now have or by any of the light-gathering type that we are likely to ever make, for planets have no light of their own. Moreover, they are probably too small and too close to their "parent" star to be seen at that distance from the earth.

Our solar system is a part of an immensely greater galactic system that we call the Milky Way. Like the planets of our solar system, most of the stars of our galaxy, more than 30 billion of them, are also arranged in a disk. This disk is more than 100,000 light years across (light travels about 6 trillion miles in 1 year) and about 10,000 light years thick. Our solar system disk is far off the center of this galactic disk but is deep enough in it so that if we look out in directions parallel to the "flat" sides of it we see very large numbers of stars,[1] whereas

[1]The light from these myriads of apparently closely spaced stars gives a hazy whitish appearance to this belt, hence the term Milky Way.

if we look in directions at right angles to the plane of the disk, we see comparatively few.

All the planets and most of their 32 satellites revolve about the sun in the same direction (counterclockwise as seen from the celestial North Pole; Fig. 2-1). A few minor satellites are exceptions. Furthermore, all except Venus and Uranus rotate counterclockwise. Planets inside the orbit of the earth exhibit phases because they can get between us and the sun, preventing us from seeing all of the illuminated face of each at all times. Those outside the earth's orbit never exhibit phases because we can always see almost all of the illuminated face.

The Sun

The sun is a star, a rather average star. It is a great sphere of intensely hot glowing gas, 864,000 mi in diameter. Its volume is about $1\frac{1}{3}$ million times that of the earth, but its mass is only $\frac{1}{3}$ million times greater. Its average density is therefore much less than that of the earth, which is what one would expect if all of its matter were in the gaseous state because of an outer temperature of 6000°C (10,000°F). Its interior temperature is estimated to be 14 million °C and its pressure at the center to be over a billion atmospheres. At that temperature probably all compounds are decomposed into atoms; that is, atoms are not combined with one another to form compounds. About 70 of the known elements have been identified; no element not known on earth is present in the sun. Hydrogen and helium are present in the sun in enormous amounts. The conversion of hydrogen to helium is the basic energy-producing reaction in the sun (p. 650). Every second the sun converts over 564 million tons of hydrogen to helium and over 4 million tons of matter into energy. In the process of conversion 560 million tons of hydrogen are

transformed to an equivalent amount of helium, and 4 million tons are converted into energy. This conversion has been going on at least 5 billion years, and is expected to continue at a similar rate for another 40 to 50 billion years; some astronomers would reduce this to 25 to 30 billion years.

The main features that can be observed on the sun are sunspots and prominences. Sunspots range from 500 to 100,000 or even 150,000 mi across (Fig. 4-3). They are huge areas that look black because they are cooler than the areas surrounding them, but they are

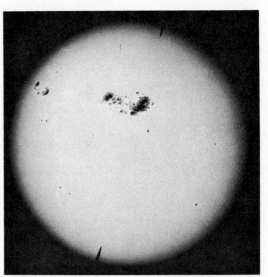

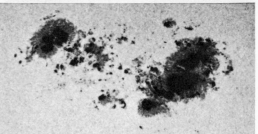

Fig. 4-3. The Sunspot of April 7, 1947. Above: Whole solar disk showing sunspots. Below: An enlargement of the large sunspot group. (Photos from the Hale Observatories.)

still intensely hot. They are temporary features of unknown origin. It is by watching the spots as they move across the sun's face that we know that the sun rotates slowly on an axis. The period of rotation increases as the distance from the equator increases, which is likely only if the surface is entirely gaseous. Prominences are huge streamers of glowing gases rising great distances above the surface (Figs. 4-4 and 4-5). Flares are eruptions of very hot gas of such high velocity that the gas escapes from the sun permanently. Some of it reaches the earth, sometimes causing "magnetic storms" and displays of aurora borealis. Of particular interest at the time of total eclipses is the halo of pearly light around the edges of the darkened sun (Fig. 4-6).

The Planets

Many of the statistical facts about the planets are summarized in Table 4-1. We shall therefore confine our attention here to brief descriptions that cannot conveniently be put in tabular form.

Mercury

Mercury is close to the sun, rising and setting either $1\frac{1}{2}$ hr (maximum) before or $1\frac{1}{2}$ hr (maximum) after it, and so is never above the horizon when the sky is completely dark. This adds to the difficulty of studying its surface details. About $1\frac{1}{2}$ hr after sunset or before sunrise on those evenings or mornings when it is at one

Fig. 4-4. Large Active Prominence, 272,000 mi High. Photographed in the violet light of the calcium K line, June 2, 1946. (Photo from the Hale Observatories.)

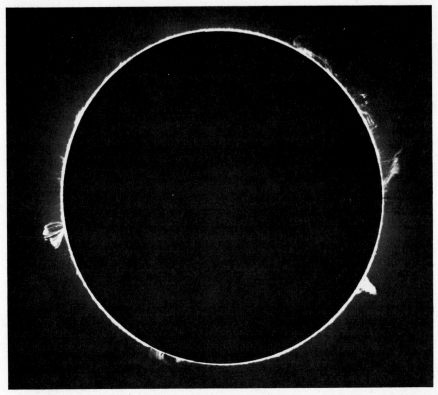

Fig. 4-5. Sun at Time of Near Total Eclipse, December 9, 1929. The whole edge of the sun is seen with several prominences. (Photo from the Hale Observatories.)

of the two maximums is the best time to see it. It is also the smallest of the planets, having a diameter only about 50% greater than the moon but is at least 240 times farther away and hence difficult to see. For these reasons, few people have ever seen it. Even astronomers with their fine telescopes have never been able to get a really good look at it.

Mercury's period of rotation was long thought to be equal to its period of revolution. Radar astronomy in 1965 showed that its period of rotation was about 59 earth days and its period of revolution was 88 days. Since 59 is just about $\frac{2}{3}$ of 88, Mercury rotates three times for every two revolutions about the sun. Its sidereal day is 58.65 earth days and its solar

day is 176 earth days. Thus Mercury's year lasts half a Mercury day. The temperature at the equator reaches 650°F and sinks as low as −300°F during its long night. Mercury has a set of phases as viewed from the earth. It has the highest density of any planet except the earth and is believed to consist of about 30% silicate rocks and 70% metals. Its surface appears to have meteorite pits and ridge-like crater rims. Mercury's orbit is more eccentric than that of any other planet except Pluto.

Mercury has too small a mass to be able to hold an atmosphere by gravitational attraction. It also seems to be at least as mountainous as the moon. As an environment for the development of life, that of Mercury is about as forbidding as anyone would expect to find in the whole solar system.

Venus

Venus as viewed from the earth is the brightest of all the heavenly bodies when at its maximum brilliance, except the sun and the moon. It is only 26 million mi away from us at the closest approach (Fig. 2-12) and would appear many times brighter than it does if we could see the whole of the illuminated face in that position. Actually we can see only a thin crescent when it is of maximum brilliance. Even then Venus is far brighter than any star

(15 times as bright as Sirius, the brightest star) and $2\frac{1}{2}$ times brighter than when in the nearly full phase but on the opposite side of the sun from us and hence much farther away.

The orbit of Venus is about twice as far from the sun as that of Mercury, approximately midway between the orbits of Mercury and the earth. This is not far enough for it ever to be seen for more than about 3 hours before sunrise or after sunset. It is thus either a morning star, when it rises ahead of the sun, or an evening star, when it rises (and therefore sets) later than the sun (Fig. 2-11). It crosses the high part of the sky a little ahead of or a little behind the sun and sometimes is visible if one

Fig. 4-6. Solar Corona at Time of Total Eclipse, June 18, 1918, as Seen from Green River, Wyoming. The corona is the luminous region about the sun that may be seen during a total eclipse. (Photo from the Hale Observatories.)

Table 4-1

| Name | MEAN DISTANCE FROM SUN | | Mean diameter (earth = 1) | Density (water = 1) | Rotation** (earth days) | Revolution about sun (earth days or years) | Surface gravity (earth = 1) | Volume (earth = 1) | Number of satellites | Mass (earth = 1) |
	Astronomical units*	Millions of miles (av)								
Sun	—	—	108 (=864,000 mi)	1.41	25.4 days	—	27.9	1.30×10^6	9 planets 32 satellites	332,700
Mercury	0.39	36	0.38	5.4	59 days	88 days	0.37	0.055	0	0.054
Venus	0.72	67	0.96	5.1	243 days	224.7 days	0.89	0.88	0	0.815
Earth	1.00	93	1.0	5.52	23 hr 56 min	365¼ days	1.0	1.0	1	1.0
Mars	1.52	141	0.53	3.97	24 hr 37 min	1.88 yr	0.38	0.15	2	0.108
Jupiter	5.20	483	11.19	1.334	9 hr 51 min	11.86 yr	2.65	1318	12	317.8
Saturn	9.54	886	9.47	0.684	10 hr 14 min	29.46 yr	1.14	769	10	95.2
Uranus	19.18	1783	3.73	1.60	10 hr 49 min	84.01 yr	0.96	50	5	14.5
Neptune	30.07	2794	3.49	2.25	15 hr	164.79 yr	1.53	42	2	17.2
Pluto	39.44	3670	0.5	4.86	6.39 days	248.4 yr	0.44	0.12	0	0.11
Moon	(Distance from earth: 238,857 mi)		0.2725	3.34	27.32 days	—	0.167	0.02	—	0.0123

* 1 AU = 92,956,000 mi.
**Counterclockwise except Venus and Uranus.

knows where to look. Venus has a full set of phases, but they cannot be seen without a telescope.

Venus is completely blanketed by clouds that extend 35 mi or more above its surface. (On earth the cloud limit is about 10 mi above its surface.) The result is that of a murky twilight or a dense smog. Just what this dense atmosphere consists of is still a puzzle largely because instruments cannot penetrate deep into it. Some experts think that the atmospheric pressure at the surface is about 100 times that on earth, so great that Soviet probes (one in October 1967 and two in May 1969) were reported crushed 15 mi above the surface. The atmosphere contains nitrogen and carbon dioxide, but very little water vapor and no oxygen. The dense clouds cause a "greenhouse effect"; that is, they act as a trap for the sun's energy. Short infrared (heat) waves from the sun easily penetrate the clouds, strike the surface and are reflected back as longer infrared waves that have great difficulty getting back through the clouds. The result is that the temperature rises to 1000°F, a temperature at which lead, tin, and zinc melt and many other substances vaporize.

A space probe by the United States—a 109-day voyage in 1962 to within 21,600 miles of the surface—and radioastronomy have supplied much new information, but nothing about the surface. Venus rotates backward—retrograde;[2] it completes one rotation in 243 earth days and makes one revolution in about 225 days. As a result the sun comes up in the west once every 117 earth days. The prospects for life on Venus are considered to be zero.

Earth

The planet Earth is very nearly a sphere of about 8000 mi diameter (Fig. 2-5) and an equatorial circumference of about 24,900 mi. Its average distance from the sun is 1 AU (p. 29) $\simeq$ 93 million mi $\simeq$ 150 million km. Its average density is about 5.5 g/cm^3 and its mass is about 10^{21} tons. It has been divided into three concentric zones; crust, mantle, and core on the basis of the behavior of earthquake waves that travel through all three zones. The crust ranges from 25 to 50 mi in thickness beneath the great mountain ranges, from 18 to 25 mi elsewhere beneath the continents, and from 2 to 5 mi beneath the ocean basins proper, that is, beyond the continental shelves. It is composed of light rocks with an average density of about 2.9 g/cm^3. The mantle extends from the bottom of the crust downward for about 1800 miles. It is composed of rocks whose average density is considerably greater than those of the crust and which increases with depth because of the enormous pressures (at the center of the core they are about 50 million $lb/in.^2$). The core is believed to consist of two parts, a liquid outer part and a solid inner part. Their composition is probably iron with a few percent of nickel. The density of the core must be high—11 or 12—to give an average of 5.52 g/cm^3 for the earth as a whole.

Earth is surrounded by an atmosphere made up largely of nitrogen and oxygen with small amounts of CO_2 and water vapor. There are very small amounts of some of the rare gases. Without the oxygen, water vapor, and carbon dioxide, life, animal and plant, as we know it would be impossible. The atmosphere serves also to prevent heat from escaping at night.

[2] A recent study (*Science*, Dec. 11, 1970; pp. 1196–1198) indicates a possible cause of both the retrograde rotation of Venus and the extremely high density of its atmosphere. This study offers mathematical evidence that Venus may have captured a moon with a retrograde orbit and that this moon subsequently crashed into Venus. If this moon were sufficiently massive, its retrograde orbital momentum could have changed the original "normal" rotation of Venus (probably a 10 to 20 hr day) to a slight retrograde rotation. Further, the great energy released by this crash "may have provided the trigger for the . . . copious production of an atmosphere through volcanic emissions."

If it did not, the temperature would drop far below zero every night. The lower atmosphere can be divided into two parts, the troposphere, which extends upward about 10 mi at the equator and 5 mi at the poles, and the stratosphere above it to an altitude of about 45 mi. Above the stratosphere is the ionosphere, which extends upward about 200 mi. The concentration of ions (Chapter 18) and free electrons (Chapter 19) makes the ionosphere an electrically conducting layer that acts as a reflecting surface for radio waves. Without it radio transmission would be limited because radio waves travel in straight lines and so do not follow the curvature of the earth.

Mars

From two standpoints Mars is the most interesting of the planets. For one thing, it is the only planet on which man can hope to land and survive for any length of time, if at all, even with the devices that have been invented to aid him. For another, it is the only one on which there is any prospect of life, primitive though it may be—and must be.

It is the nearest planet with an orbit outside that of the earth. Its somewhat ruddy color makes it easy to recognize. The diameter is about twice that of our moon, so Mars is big enough to hold an atmosphere by gravitational force. However, it is unlikely that the density of the atmosphere is much more than half that at the top of Mt. Everest (where man must carry a supply of oxygen in order to live). Furthermore, the oxygen in Mars' atmosphere seems to be only 0.10% of the total (compared to the earth's 20%). The total amount of condensable water vapor present in a column extending upward from Mars' surface to the top of its atmosphere would, if condensed, form a layer about 0.00055 in. thick. This is the only water there is on Mars; thus there can be no oceans, lakes, ponds, or streams of any sort. Mars has about twice as much carbon dioxide in its atmosphere as the earth has.[3]

Any space traveler to Mars would probably find that the so-called polar icecaps, which appear in the Martian winter and disappear in the summer, are not much more than thin layers of frost on the ground. The planet's color is believed to be due to layers of reddish rock particles mantling the surface.

The United States spacecraft Mariner IV, in 1965, took photographs that revealed that the surface of Mars differs widely in different areas. In general, there are three types of terrain—a broad featureless plain 1200 mi across, a cratered region some 300 mi across, and what may be considered a chaotic one in which ridges and hollows predominate. The slopes are gentle for the most part; there are no mountains and no large volcanic fields. Yet there is a difference of 8 mi between the highest and the lowest points; however, the change is very gradual.

Unlike Venus with its dense clouds, Mars has a rarefied atmosphere that allows us to see its surface extremely well, especially when it is closest to us (about 35 million mi). When at its closest, Mars is even brighter than Jupiter. Its average distance from the sun is about 140 million mi, its distance in 1971 being far less than average. Mars, like all other planets with orbits outside that of the earth, has no significant phases, largely because we can see most of the illuminated side all of the time.

The Martian day is very nearly the same length as ours, but the year is twice as long; thus each season takes 6 months. The greater

---

[3] Aside from other considerations, the presence of so much carbon dioxide and so little oxygen may be taken as evidence of the lack of plant life on Mars. Plants use carbon dioxide in photosynthesis and give off oxygen. The earth presumably had a similar atmosphere (aside from water vapor) far back in its history, before plant life developed.

distance from the sun, about 50% greater on the average than the earth's distance, means that Mars is cold compared to the earth. The average temperature is $-45°F$, whereas the average of the earth is about $+59°F$. In its hottest part the temperature on Mars may get as high as 80°F, but it sinks to $-120°F$ at night. The thin atmosphere cannot hold the heat and so it quickly escapes to outer space. Nevertheless, there is a possibility of plant life of the lichen-moss variety in the slightly more humid lower areas. Animal life, as we know it, is out of the question, for there is no reason to believe that there is animal life with a metabolism based on an element other than oxygen and which could originate without water. Life on earth, plant and animal, originated in the oceans. How it could originate on a planet with so little water as Mars would be difficult to imagine. The difficulty is increased by the temperature factor. A maximum temperature of 80°F in the warmest part during the day and a drop to $-120°F$ every night is an enormous change for any form of life to undergo. For life to originate, carbon, nitrogen, oxygen, and hydrogen atoms must have combined in some way. Inasmuch as low temperatures slow the rate of chemical combinations, the probability of life originating on Mars becomes still smaller. Furthermore, Mars must have lost its hydrogen very early in its history because of its small mass. Considering everything, "In looking for life on Mars we could establish for ourselves the reputation of being the greatest Simple Simons of all time."[4]

The so-called canals that have been reported by some observers have never been seen by other equally competent ones. To be seen at all at that distance, they would have had to be more than 20 miles wide. There is not enough water on Mars in all its forms to fill one of

[4]Philip H. Abelson, *Science,* **147,** 1965.

them. Perhaps this is a case of the eye seeing what the mind wants it to see. Mars has two satellites, Phobos and Deimos, both 5 to 20 miles in diameter.

The space probe that took 7 months to come within a few thousands of miles of Mars has so far yielded no information that would contradict any of the essential facts given above. It did reveal that the atmosphere is even less dense than formerly believed and proved by means of photographs that the canals do not exist.

Jupiter

Nearly half a billion miles from the sun is Jupiter, with a volume greater than that of the other planets put together. The equatorial diameter is 88,600 mi, 11 times that of the earth; it is 318 times as massive, and it has 1300 times the volume. There is a marked difference in the average densities of the planets from Jupiter outward, as compared to the densities of the inner planets. The earth, with a density of 5.52 g/cm^3, is the densest planet. Mars has a density of 3.97, but Jupiter drops to 1.334. Aside from atmospheres, the four inner planets (Mercury, Earth, Venus, and Mars) must therefore consist largely of rock. If any part of Jupiter does consist of rock—and this is extremely likely, as its density cannot be accounted for otherwise—the rock probably forms an inner core with a diameter of about 37,000 mi and a density of 6 g/cm^3. Studies seem to indicate that this is the case and that one would have to penetrate 25,000 mi into Jupiter before rock would be encountered.

Of what is this outer 25,000-mi-thick layer surrounding the core composed? The outermost part is the atmosphere, about 8000 mi thick, composed of hydrogen and helium, with ammonia and methane increasing with depth. Beneath this atmosphere is a layer of ice

17,000 mi thick consisting largely of frozen ammonia. Both ammonia (NH_3) and methane (CH_4) contain much hydrogen. Hydrogen, therefore, must have been an original abundant constituent. The force of gravity on Jupiter, unlike that on less massive planets, was so great that the hydrogen did not escape.

Next to the moon and Venus, Jupiter is the brightest object in the night sky except when it is occasionally surpassed by Mars. Jupiter rotates faster than any other planet, its day being about 10 earth hours (9 hr 51 min) long. This rapid rotation has produced a flattening at the poles that is clearly visible from earth. Markings on the several dark bands that encircle the planet, as well as the bands themselves, change their positions from month to month. It is therefore clear to astronomers that what they are observing is a thick, cloudy atmosphere.

Jupiter has twelve satellites, the inner four being as large as, or larger than, our moon. These were the four observed by Galileo. When seen from the earth they pass in front of the planet and they are eclipsed when they pass behind it. The four outermost satellites revolve in a direction that is opposite to Jupiter's rotation.

Saturn

Saturn, second in size and the most distant planet known before 1781, holds the distinction of being the only planet that is less dense on the average than water. It is, however, far more famous because of its three rings. The rings (Fig. 4-7) are formed by billions of small bodies, probably lumps of rock or ice or both. That they are not one solid piece is shown by the faster rate of rotation of the inner part of each ring with respect to the outer part. Their origin is not definitely known. The rings are invisible to the naked eye and so were not discovered before the time of Galileo. The inner ring is about 7000 mi from Saturn's surface and the outer one extends outward another 40,000 mi. The middle ring is the brightest. The rings are not more than 10 mi thick and may be far less than that. The composition of Saturn is similar to that of Jupiter, but there is less ammonia in its atmosphere, more methane, and presumably not much of a rocky core—the low density, 0.684 g/cm^3, would forbid that. The solid part is largely frozen ammonia. Its average temperature is $-155°C$ ($-247°F$). Saturn has ten satellites, one of which was discovered in 1968. One is larger than our moon and has an atmosphere of methane. The outermost satellite revolves backward.

Uranus

Uranus differs from the other planets in its orientation to the plane of its orbit and in its direction of rotation. It rotates clockwise on an axis that is very nearly parallel to its orbital plane. Its five small satellites also revolve clockwise instead of in the more common counterclockwise direction. The density of Uranus is somewhat more than that of Jupiter. Its composition is similar to Jupiter's but with no ammonia in the gaseous state. The ammonia has all been frozen out by the intense cold to form a layer of ice thousands of miles thick. The atmosphere is largely, if not wholly, methane. Its average temperature is $-180°C$ ($-292°F$).

Neptune

Neptune is somewhat smaller than Uranus but has a greater density. Its rotation is normal, but the direction of revolution of one of its two satellites is retrograde. In composition it is about the same as that of Uranus, but it probably has a somewhat larger rocky core, as indicated by considerably greater average

Fig. 4-7. Saturn and Its Rings. Photographed with 100 in. telescope. (Photo from the Hale Observatories.)

density. Neptune was discovered by pure theory (see p. 137).

Pluto

Pluto, discovered in 1930 by pure theory, as Neptune was, is approximately the size of Mars, but little else is known about it. Its period of revolution is about 248 years, so it has traversed less than one eighth of its orbit since its discovery. Its orbit is highly eccentric and inclined more to the plane of the ecliptic (Fig. 4-1) than that of any other planet. It will be closest to us in 1989, at which time it will

be inside the orbit of Neptune by about 35 million mi. It will, however, be 240 million mi away from Neptune at that time, so no collision is possible.

The Moon

The moon is not the largest of the 32 planetary satellites, but it is much the largest in proportion to the size of the planet about which it is revolving. Its diameter is a little over one fourth that of the earth. It is not massive enough for its gravitational force to hold an atmosphere. Its average distance of 240,000 mi, 60 times that of the earth's radius, makes it the nearest of all the celestial bodies to the earth. Its motions have been discussed in Chapter 2 and its phases in Chapter 1.

The lack of an atmosphere is attested to by the fact that none of the effects that can be ascribed to an atmosphere show up during lunar eclipse or when the moon passes between the earth and a star. It seems likely that the moon did have an atmosphere at the time of its "birth." If so, why did it lose it? The reason involves the velocity of escape (see p. 139).

The lack of an atmosphere has extremely important consequences for an astronaut landing on the moon. It means that he not only has to carry his own oxygen supply, but also has to wear a pressurized suit at all times or his blood would literally boil in his veins. There is no atmosphere on the moon to cause friction and vaporize the countless meteors that must be striking it, and if a meteor did no more than puncture the astronaut's pressure suit, it would be fatal to him. Lack of an atmosphere also means that there is no water either on the moon's surface or below it. Thus there are no clouds, and the sun's rays beat down on the surface during its 2-week-long day with an intensity unknown on earth, raising the temperature above that of the boiling point of water. It means that as soon as the sun sets—to begin its 2-week-long night—the temperature plummets to below zero, eventually reaching the neighborhood of −250°F. It also means that there is no atmosphere to filter out most of the deadly ultraviolet rays emanating from the sun. Although protection from some, if not all, of these dangers has been proved possible, life for any length of time on the moon for earthborn visitors would be extremely hazardous. Life native to the moon is, of course, impossible.

A visitor to the moon is treated to a view of outer space that is very unlike that from the earth. The sky in *daylight hours* does not appear blue but black, because there is no atmosphere to scatter the sun's rays; blue is scattered more than the other colors of the spectrum by the atmosphere. Thus, not only the sun, but also the earth, and all the stars and the other planets that are above the horizon are shining out of a perfectly black sky at the same time, with a brilliance that is difficult to imagine. The corona of the sun (Fig. 4-6) would be visible at all times during the 2-week-long day. Next to the sun, the most brilliant object in the sky is the earth, especially after sunset. Its apparent diameter is four times that of the full moon as viewed from the earth. Its oceans and continents look fuzzy as viewed from the moon because of the earth's atmosphere. Clouds are commonly seen floating across its surface.

The first moon landing, made by Apollo 11 on July 20, 1969, proved that the surface of the moon is about as solid as the land areas of the earth. The major features of the moon's surface are the mountain ranges; the vast plains, called seas or *maria;* the craters; and large cracks or fissures, some of which are called rilles.

In the mountain ranges are thousands of high peaks, some reaching an altitude of about 25,000 ft. None of the mountain ranges seems to have the complex folded structure that is characteristic of most of the earth's large mountain ranges (Chapter 32). Some of the mountain ranges may be of volcanic origin, but others are believed to have been formed by the impact of huge meteorites (p. 73) on the surface of the moon. The "impact theory" can account for the origin of the broken rings of mountains that surround many of the maria. This kind of topography is exemplified by the lunar Apennine Mountains and the Sea of Showers (Mare Imbrium), near which the landing from Apollo 15 was made in August 1971. The most probably correct account of the formation of this region is that the impact of an enormous meteorite, about 50 mi in diameter, caused a vast crater where Mare Imbrium now is and the Apennine Mountains were thrown up by the resulting shock waves. Thus the vast plains of the *maria* appear to have been originally impact craters that, at a much later time, were flooded with volcanic lava flows of basaltic composition (Chapter 32).

The craters on the moon's surface number about 30,000 and range from a few feet to over 100 mi across. Many of these craters (Fig. 4-8) were formed by meteoritic impact; certainly the bigger ones were, for volcanic craters

Fig. 4-8. Northern Portion of Moon at Third Quarter. The large crater at bottom left is Copernicus. The broad plain at the center is the Sea of Showers (Mare Imbrium), and the lunar Apennine Mountains are shown in the lower right corner. (Photo from the Hale Observatories.)

here on earth are not nearly so large as some of these moon craters are. Some of the smaller craters are probably volcanic in origin (Fig. 4-9). This hypothesis appears to be confirmed by photographs taken from Apollo 15 during its close orbiting of the moon. Many of the small craters have the shape of conical hills, and the discovery of vent holes (Chapter 32) at their summits indicates a great similarity to the cinder cones of southwestern United States, which are known to be of volcanic origin. The eruptions represented by these lunar cinder cones probably occurred more than 2 billion yr ago. The origin of fissures and rilles is not certain. Some may have been caused by the contraction and cracking

of solidified lava as it cooled, while others may have been formed by the erosional effects of streams of molten lava.

The rock specimens brought back from Tranquility Base by Apollo 11 were found to be basaltic lavas formed at or near the surface or impact breccias (composed of angular fragments "cemented" together) of similar composition. Glass[5] spheres and shards and glass-coated surfaces and pits confirm the tremendous impact energies of meteoritic particles. Surface

[5]A glass in the geologic sense is a noncrystalline rock that cooled very quickly from a once molten state. The molten material may have been a lava, or, as here, a previously formed rock made molten by the heat of impact.

Fig. 4-9. Apollo 14 Lunar Surface Photography, February 1971, Showing Small Craters on the Moon. The crater at the right is about 60 ft from the point where the photograph was taken and is 20 or 30 ft across. The surface here is continuously cratered and covered by grey lunar dust that pervades and covers everything to an unknown depth, but in places appears to be 4 to 6 in. deep. (Description by Astronaut Mitchell. Photo courtesy of NASA.)

abrasion by micrometeorites has been proved. The high titanium content of the basaltic rocks from Tranquility Base may indicate a major difference between lunar and earth rocks, or it may be only a local characteristic. The discovery of a "granite" type rock abnormally high in potassium among the Apollo 12 specimens indicates the probability of considerable variation in their chemistry from place to place.

Lunar rocks have great antiquity. The igneous rocks from Tranquility Base are about 3.4 to 3.6 billion yr old (p. 640). The loose debris—not a true soil because of the absence of chemical weathering (p. 598)—from the same locality is about 4.2 to 4.4 billion yr old, older than any meteorite yet recovered here on earth. It is possible that even older lunar rocks may be found, thus pushing further backward in time the formation of the moon and the solar system.

The records received from the seismometer left by Apollo 12 indicate that the moon has a relatively thick rigid crust perhaps 100 mi thick that transmits "moonquakes" with great efficiency. No records of secondary (transverse) wave records have been received, suggesting that seismic vibrations do not—so far as we know—penetrate the interior of the moon.[6]

The Minor Components

Asteroids

The first asteroid (or planetoid) was discovered the first night of the year 1800 by an astronomer who was searching for a planet that he thought should revolve in an orbit between those of Mars and Jupiter (see the spacing of planets in Fig. 4-2).

This asteroid, too small to be called a planet,

[6]The authors are indebted to Professor Wilbur G. Valentine of Brooklyn College for the summation of the information about the composition of rock specimens from the moon.

was the first of some 1500 to 2000 that have since been discovered. It was the largest, a bit less than 500 mi in diameter. The other known ones range down to masses as small as $\frac{1}{2}$ mi across. Probably none of them has the characteristic oblate spheroidal shape of the true planets. Many thousands probably exist that are too small to be detected with our present instruments. Many of them have highly eccentric orbits. It is possible that some of the meteorites that fall to the earth were asteroids whose orbits eventually brought them too close to the earth. They may be the remains of a planet revolving in an orbit between Mars and Jupiter that was shattered by some unknown catastrophe.

Comets

Comets were once believed to be stars with long hairy tails. Up to the time of Galileo and even later, they were widely regarded as omens of evil and often caused panic among superstitious people. They were thought to be balls of fire flung by an angry Creator to warn the peoples of their wicked ways. Not until the discoveries of Tycho Brahe, Kepler, and Galileo did the peoples' fears of comets begin to be allayed.

What these astronomers did was to establish the fact that comets are members of the solar system just as much as the planets are, although the paths that they describe are usually very different from those of the planets. Most comets pass very close to the sun and then go out to enormous distances, taking scores or even hundreds of years to return. Thus their orbits are generally highly elliptical (Fig. 4-10). A few have relatively small ellipticities, that is, small for a comet. About half move clockwise around the sun, the other half counterclockwise. The inclinations of their orbits to the plane of the ecliptic varies from 0 to 90°. They follow Kepler's laws of planetary motion.

The head or nucleus of a comet consists of

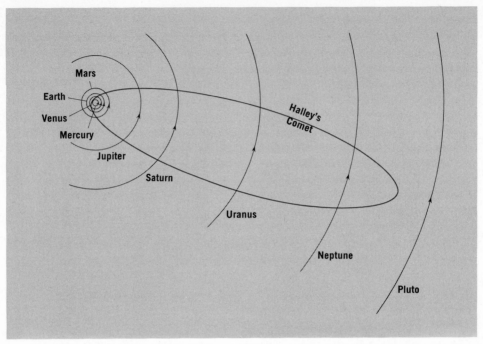

Fig. 4-10. Path of Halley's Comet. Each traverse takes about 75 years.

an immense number of small particles varying in size from specks of "dust" to particles some yards across. According to Whipple, an astronomer at Harvard, the nucleus is a porous mixture of frozen methane, ammonia, and water with pieces of rock and of metals embedded in the ice. It is never composed of one solid mass. Surrounding the nucleus is a foggy mass of gases sometimes hundreds of thousands of miles across. The tail is composed of dust particles and gaseous molecules that trail off behind the nucleus sometimes for hundreds of millions of miles (Fig. 4-11). As the comets approach the sun, the heat vaporizes some of the particles, causing the tails to increase in size. The gases become luminescent under the action of the sun's ultraviolet rays, thus "lighting up" the gaseous parts of the comet. The sunlight exerts a radiation pressure on the gases and the finest dust particles, so that the tail of a comet always swings away from the sun. Thus, when the comet approaches the sun, the tail is behind the head, as all respectable tails should be, but when it is receding from the sun the tail precedes the head.

Meteors and Meteorites

Meteors are the so-called "shooting stars," but they have nothing whatever to do with stars. Most are tiny specks of matter no bigger than a grain of sand or perhaps a pea. Every day many tens of millions encounter the earth's atmosphere. Traveling at a high speed they develop a considerable amount of heat because of friction with the air; they become white hot and are burned up in a second or two. They get hot enough to glow about 60 mi above the earth and are burned up within another 20 mi.

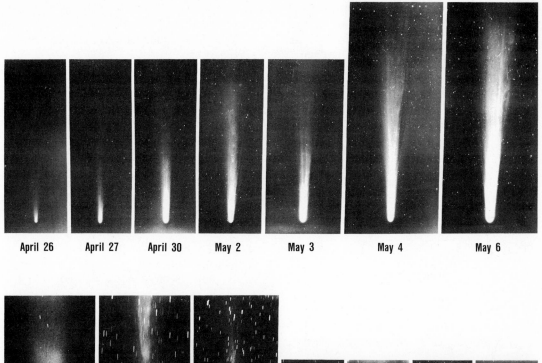

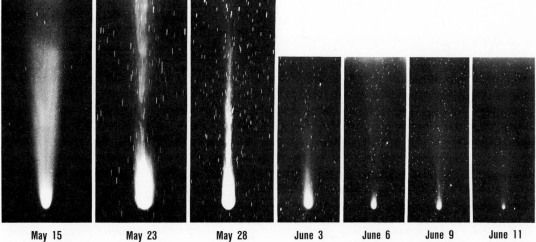

| April 26 | April 27 | April 30 | May 2 | May 3 | May 4 | May 6 |

| May 15 | May 23 | May 28 | June 3 | June 6 | June 9 | June 11 |

Fig. 4-11. Halley's Comet. Fourteen views made during its last appearance in 1910. It will reappear in 1986, reaching its nearest approach on April 29 of that year. (Photos from the Hale Observatories.)

The larger ones fail to burn up completely and strike the earth. They are then called *meteorites*. One of the largest, brought from Greenland, is in the American Museum of Natural History in New York City. It weighs $36\frac{1}{2}$ tons. Still larger ones have struck the earth, causing devastation for miles around. The largest ever known landed in Arizona not more than 5000 years ago. A crater 4200 ft in diameter and 570 ft deep was formed when it exploded as it struck. These larger meteorites are of metallic composition, mostly iron, with several per cent nickel and small amounts of many other metals. Some are made of low-silica igneous rocks. The minerals in them are the same as those formed from molten "lava" here on earth.

There is a close association between most meteors and comets. Many well-known meteoric showers have been caused by the earth's passing through the orbits of broken-up comets. A comet "discards" part of its matter as it revolves about the sun. This debris continues to revolve about the sun in a manner similar to that of Saturn's rings, but it cannot be seen until it encounters the earth's atmosphere and is heated to incandescence.

Exercises

1. Fundamentally, what condition must be met if a planet, or our moon, is to show a complete set of phases to an observer on earth?

2. Why do the superior planets (planets with orbits outside that of the earth) not show phases like those of the inferior planets?

3. From the earth we see the phases of the moon. If you were on the moon, could you observe phases of the earth? Explain why or why not.

4. If we consider the length of a day to be the time between two successive sunrises, about how long is the day on the moon?

5. Compare the following physical constants of the earth with those of the moon: (a) radius, (b) mass, (c) mean density, and (d) escape velocity.

6. Mars, as seen from the earth, varies greatly in brightness. Why?

7. Why do the planets never eclipse one another?

8. Few people have ever seen Mercury. Why?

9. Assuming that Venus is visible on a particular date, where would you expect to see it an hour or two after sunset?

10. When, on that same date, did it rise with respect to the rising of the sun?

11. How was the period of Pluto determined? Why not by some other method?

12. No planet is ever seen in the far northern or the far southern sky. Why?

13. Why is Venus brighter as viewed from the earth at its crescent phase than it is at the nearly full phase?

14. If Venus is brightest as viewed from the earth at the crescent phase, why is the moon not brightest at its crescent phase?

15. What is meant by the velocity of escape?

16. Mars rotates from west to east, yet its satellite, Phobos, rises in the west and sets in the east. Explain.

17. The composition of the atmospheres of the planets is determined from the character of their spectra, which you will learn about in Chapter 20. What gases have been detected in the atmospheres of the other planets? What is the most general and striking difference between these atmospheres and that of the earth?

18. List the advantages that the earth has over any and all of the other planets with respect to the development of life.

19. Why do the so-called shooting stars disappear so quickly?

Mathematics and Mathematical Symbolism

Science without mathematics is impossible, for mathematics is the language of science. Mathematics expresses in a few symbols ideas, concepts, or laws that often require one or more paragraphs to state in words. This simplified representation and economy of thought, combined with the logic inherent in mathematics, is necessary for the comprehension of many natural phenomena. Physical science, first physics and astronomy, and later, chemistry, have long been mathematical, and geology is following in their footsteps, some branches far more rapidly than others. Biology, and even the social sciences, have also learned that some areas in their fields are better investigated by the use of mathematical tools.

Mathematics, however, should not be thought of solely as a tool for the scientist. Hogben, in his book *Mathematics for the Millions,* states that mathematics should be thought of as a language of size, in contrast to ordinary language of sort or kind. At the same time you should not allow the mention of mathematics as a tool of science to convince

Mathematics is thought moving in the sphere of complete abstraction from any particular instance of what it is talking about.
ALFRED NORTH WHITEHEAD
(1925)

you that science must remain an enigma to you. In an elementary course the use of mathematics need not go beyond the use of simple arithmetic and the most elementary concepts of algebra and plane geometry, with perhaps some trigonometry. A clear understanding of ratios and proportions, and the use of the powers of 10 to express very small or very large numbers is absolutely necessary. It is assumed that you learned how to add, subtract, multiply, divide, and use decimals in elementary school. In fact, none of the mathematical techniques used in this text are above those taught in elementary school and the first two years of high school.

Science of Measurement

Measurement has been appropriately called the science of approximation. Shocking though this may seem to you at the moment, it should become clear during the following discussion. Qualitative statements such as "It is cold out today" and "This article is heavy" are of little use in science. Quantitative statements such as "The outside temperature is 30.3°F" and "This jar holds 453.6 g of sodium chloride" are much preferred. We say that they are more precise. But what do we mean by precise? Do we mean they are more exact? And what does exact mean? What does accurate mean?

Consider the temperature measurement. The precision of the reading depends upon a number of things. First, there is the quality of the thermometer itself. Is the tube containing the thread of mercury uniform in diameter? Are the graduations of the scale uniformly spaced? What is the value of the smallest division? We are rarely justified in reading a scale closer than to one tenth of the smallest division. No instrument is perfect, hence all have limitations that govern their use. The scientist is always aware of the limitations of whatever instruments he may use. An inexpensive ruler

is good enough for many measurements, but it is useless for measurements that must be correct to the hundredth or thousandth of an inch. For such measurements instruments with a vernier, or a micrometer caliper, are needed, for the unaided human eye cannot resolve the distances between two such closely spaced marks.

A second factor governing precision is the human factor. This includes not only the quality of our vision, but also the experience, skill, and judgment of the observer. The trained eye is far better than the untrained. Moreover, the physical conditions under which a measurement is made will influence its precision. It is more difficult to measure a moving object than it is a still one, more difficult to read a measuring instrument that cannot be held steady than it is to read a motionless one.

There are other factors, but we have seen enough to convince us that no measurement is exact if by that we mean that there is no possibility of error no matter how many decimal places we wish to use. The scientist recognizes the shortcomings of measurement by always assuming that the last decimal place is subject to question. And yet he is always certain that the next-to-last decimal place is *not* subject to question. For example, suppose a properly trained observer puts a 1 lb mass on a balance that registers grams. Assume also that the smallest division on the balance is 0.1 g. Suppose the observer records a mass of 453.6 g. To the scientist this means that the 6 could be either a 5 or a 7, that the probable error is ±0.1 g. If the smallest division is 0.01 g, so that the observer is certain that the 6 could not be a 5 or a 7, then he records the mass as 453.60. The zero here has significance. Simply adding the zero reduces the probable error from ±0.1 g to ±0.01 g. If we wish greater precision we will have to use a more sensitive balance. Suppose we do so. The observer might now record the mass as 453.592 g. Since the 2 could be a 1 or a 3, the probable error is now ± 0.001 g. Note that we say probable error, not possible error.

Only on a balance of the highest quality and great sensitivity could it be expressed as 453.592427 g—which is the legal definition of a mass of 1 lb in the United States. But even here the scientist recognizes the doubtfulness of the last decimal place. But surely, some one of you might ask, if one made a sufficiently large number of different measurements of or on the same object, would not one of them be exactly right? Possibly so, but which one? How could we ever know that? Thus we are forced to return to our original premise that measurement is the science of approximation, an approximation that comes closer and closer to truth as the expert uses better and better tools and larger and larger numbers of measurements.

Significant Figures

The accuracy of any measurement is given by the number of significant figures. Thus, in the legal definition of a pound there are nine significant figures. This is a degree of accuracy that is uncommon in science. For most purposes we state that a pound weight has a mass of 453.6 g, which has four significant figures. The proper use of significant figures constitutes a kind of rounding off—not a haphazard rounding off, but one done by following certain rules.

Most measurements in science are made with an accuracy that does not extend beyond six significant figures. Consider the equatorial radius of the earth, 3963.34 mi. This is expressed in six significant figures. Rounded off to five significant figures it is 3963.3 mi, to four it is 3963 mi, to three it is 3960 mi, and to one it is 4000 mi. This figure is close enough for most purposes; to use the radius or the diameter to six significant figures, or even to four, involves needless expenditure of time and mental effort. We do the same with the moon.

Its diameter is about 2160 mi. Rounded off to two significant figures it is 2200[1] mi, and to one significant figure it is 2000 mi, about one fourth the diameter of the earth.

How would you express the volume of a box that measures $9.3 \times 4.7 \times 6.5$ in.? Most people think that 284.115 in.^{3} (which is the product of the three numbers) is more accurate than 280 in.^{3} (in.^{3} is read as cubic inches). It is not, however, for it implies an accuracy that is not—assuming the error of each dimension is ± 0.1 in.—warranted by the measurements. We have already learned that the measurements of the box could be as much as $9.4 \times 4.8 \times 6.6$ in. or as small as $9.2 \times 4.6 \times 6.4$ in. Now

$$9.4 \times 4.8 \times 6.6 = 297.792 \text{ in.}^3$$

and

$$9.2 \times 4.6 \times 6.4 = 270.848 \text{ in.}^3$$

Therefore the volume of the box can be between 298 and 271 in.^{3}—anywhere between. If you state it as 284.115 in.^{3}, you are saying that it lies between 284.114 and 284.116 in.^{3}, obviously an untruth. So we may round it off to 280 in.^{3} as a reasonable result. Even then there is doubt about the 8. The figure of 280 is gotten by rounding off only when we make the final calculation. Actually one can—and should—round off at each step in the calculations. The rule when multiplying (or dividing) is never to have more significant figures in your answer than there are in the least accurate measurement. In the case of our box, all measurements are presumed equally accurate. Thus $9.3 \times 4.7 = 43.71$. We round off to $44 \times 6.5 = 284.05$ in.^{3}, which we round off to 284, or 280, depending on our judgment and purpose. Since we have only two significant figures in any of the actual measurements, we want only two in our answer. Therefore the

[1]If the figure being dropped is greater than 5, the preceding figure is rounded upward.

volume of the box would be 280 in.³ as reported by the expert.

Units of Measurement

The process of measurement consists of comparing one item with another that has been selected as a standard. The world of primitive man demanded no accuracy. His first "standards" were those of his own body, for example, his outstretched arms, the length of his forearm, the length of his foot or his hand, and the length and width of his fingers. There were no tribal or community standards, and there was little need for them. The first standards to be developed were those made by the Egyptians and the Babylonians 6000 years ago for the purpose of land measure. These measurements were astronomical in origin and so good that even modern science has not greatly improved on them. The Babylonians revered the numbers 6, 60, 600, and so on. Thus the circumference of a circle is divided into 360 (6 × 60) degrees, the hour into 60 minutes, and the minute into 60 seconds.

In areas other than land measure confusion reigned even as late as the 17th and 18th centuries. In Germany in the 16th century the rod was established as the total length of the left feet of the first 16 men out of a church on a certain Sunday. The yard was defined by Henry I of England as the distance from the tip of his nose to the end of his thumb when his arm was outstretched. The poppyseed became a means of precise linear measure in the 1700's. In France nearly every city and province had its own system of weights and measures. As time passed, means of communication and transportation improved and there was an increasing need for neighboring communities to use the same system, that is, a need for standardization.

Length. In 1790 the decimal metric system was imposed by law in France; it was to go

into effect 3 years later. In this system the meter was defined as 1 ten-millionth the distance from the pole to the equator. Seven years were spent in measuring that part of a meridian that runs between Barcelona in Spain to Dunkirk in France. On the basis of these measurements a standard meter (see Table 5-1) was established as the distance between two microscopic hairlines on a platinum–iridium bar. This bar was placed in a carefully guarded vault in Sèvres, a suburb of Paris. In time the

Table 5-1

Units of length (metric system)

10 millimeters (mm) = 1 centimeter

100 centimeters (cm) = 1 meter (39.37 in.)

Note: 1 in. = 2.54 cm; 1 ft = approx. 30 cm; 1 mm = approx. 0.04 in.; 1 cm = approx. 0.4 in.

1000 meters (m) = 1 kilometer (0.62 mi)

Note: To convert miles to kilometers, multiply by 1.61.

Units of volume (metric system)

1 cm³ = 1 milliliter (ml)

1000 cm³ = 1 liter

Note: 1 liter is slightly more than 1 quart (1.06 qt)

Units of mass (metric system)

1 gram (g) = very nearly the mass of 1 cm³ (1 ml) of water at 4°C; the difference is in the sixth decimal place

1000 g = 1 kilogram (2.20 lb)

Note: 1 ton = 909 kg; 1 long ton = 1000 kg

Other units based on the metric system

1 micron (μ)	= 1 millionth (10^{-6}) meter
	1 thousandth (10^{-3}) millimeter
1 millimicron (mμ)	= 1 millionth (10^{-6}) millimeter
1 Ångström (Å)	= 10^{-8} cm, the order of magnitude of the diameter of an atom

length of half a meridian (distance from pole to equator) was found to be 22,288.3 m (meters) longer than the 10 million m originally assigned to it. The error did not matter, because we knew the length of the standard in the vault.

Mass. The metric system introduced a new unit of mass[2] called the gram. It was originally defined as the mass of 1 cm^3 (cubic centimeter) of water at the temperature of its greatest density (about 4°C), but it is now defined as $\frac{1}{1000}$ of the mass of the standard kilogram. A standard mass of 1000 g (1000 cm^3 of water at 4°C) was fashioned of platinum–iridium alloy. This is the standard kilogram; it is kept in the vault along with the standard meter.

The great advantage of the metric system is that it is a decimal system. The metric system is used in all countries of the world except the English-speaking countries. Japan officially adopted it in 1966. Britain adopted it in part in 1970, and the United States, as of 1971, had a commission studying the problems involved. International accord has recently been reached for the use of the wavelength of the orange line in the spectrum (see p. 352) of the element krypton-86 as the standard of linear measurement. This new standard is reproducible by any country; it eliminates the need to keep bars of platinum–iridium metals called standard meters in carefully guarded vaults. It will eliminate the necessity of periodically sending these standard meters to a suburb of Paris for careful checking with the master bar that is kept there.

In the United States, as an alternative, the common units have been defined in terms of the metric units. We have already stated that the pound is equal to 453.592427 g. In 1933 the American Standards Association (now the American National Standards Institute) de-

fined the inch as exactly 2.54 cm. For more than 20 years opposition from civil engineers, mapmakers, and the U.S. Coast and Geodetic Survey prevented legalization of this inch. Finally, the inch was legally defined as exactly 2.54 cm in 1959.

Time. The basic unit of time is the day. The length of a day is not arbitrary; it is the time between two successive crossings of the same meridian by the sun (p. 38). This time has been divided into 24 hours, equal to 86,400 seconds. It is possible, but not practical, to divide the day into 10 equal parts, each 2.4 times the length of one of our present hours as the start of a decimal system for time. Further subdivision does not yield a unit of time that is very close to one of our present seconds in length. A change to a decimal system for measuring time would cause untold confusion among all the civilized peoples of the world, for they all use the same standard of time. The problem is made much more difficult than that of a change to a metric system of weights and measures because time plays a much more intimate role in our daily lives than do weights and measures. Most of us go through many a day without much concern for distances or masses, particularly for distances or masses of a fair degree of accuracy. Time, however, is never far from our minds except when we are asleep. We get up in the morning, go to work, eat our meals, and go to bed all with reference to the clock. Planes, trains, buses, all run on a time schedule. TV and radio programs and all other recreational events are geared to a more or less precise time schedule, often to the second. We take it for granted that there is a time schedule for almost everything.

We have not yet defined *time*. The word merely stands for our ability to perceive events one after the other. Man's concept of time is directly due to his ability to perceive motion. The human mind seems to take a sequence of events and string them together like beads

---

[2]Commonly called the standard of weight. For the difference between mass and weight, see p. 134.

in a necklace, to create a sense of time. However, there is a limit to the smallest unit of time that the mind can detect. A movie film consists of a large number of still pictures that the mind interprets as moving pictures when they are normally projected on to a screen. Thus our sense of time is full of possibilities for illusions.

Time zones first came to be standardized by the railroads. Before Nov. 18, 1883, each town or community kept its own time—usually called suntime—independent of most other towns. Then the railroads were built across the country. Synchronization of time among them became a necessity if people were to make connections from one train to another. Time was soon standardized the world over, and the system works wonderfully well for most of us. But as we travel faster and faster, confusion begins to mount up. The person who travels by jet plane can have breakfast twice in the same day, once in New York and once in San Francisco. An astronaut orbiting the earth may see the sun set several times the same day. Scientific needs required that time measurement be split finer and finer. Instruments are needed to time the frequencies assigned to radio and television stations; a frequency of 1600 kilocycles means 1.6 million vibrations per second. A vibrating crystal is used for such precise measurements. As of 1971 the rate of vibration of a crystal of the metal cesium governed the most precise clock known. Such a crystal, placed in an electric field, vibrates very nearly 9,192,631,700 times per second. The modern definition of a second is therefore the time it takes such a cesium crystal in such an electric field to vibrate that many times.

Having defined the three basic units for distance, mass, and time, we can derive the units for all other physical quantities from them. Thus we express velocities in centimeters per second (cm/sec), accelerations in centime-

ters per second per second (cm/sec²), and density in grams per cubic centimeter (g/cm³). This system is referred to as the *cgs* system of units. Physicists commonly use a metric system with larger units, called the *mks* (meter, kilogram, second) system. One or the other of these systems is used almost exclusively in scientific investigation. In this textbook we shall occasionally lapse into the foot, pound, second (English) system in those situations where it will profit the student to relate the units to his everyday experience.

Units in Calculations

Every quantity in science consists of two parts, a number and the name of the unit. Many students have the bad habit of reporting only the number. To state the volume of a box as 290 is meaningless. In solving equations the units themselves are treated in exactly the same way as algebraic quantities; that is, they are multiplied, divided, squared, and so on. Any algebraic statement in quantitative determinations must be consistent with respect to the units. For example, consider a cube of brass, 3 cm × 4 cm × 5 cm. Its volume is given by

$$3 \times 4 \times 5 \times cm \times cm \times cm = 60 \text{ cm}^3$$

Suppose that its mass is 504 g. Density = mass/volume. Hence

$$\frac{504 \text{ g}}{60 \text{ cm}^3} = 8.4 \text{ g/cm}^3$$

is the density of the brass cube.

Consider another example, that of momentum, mv. If m is in grams and v is in centimeters per second, then mv is expressed in gram-centimeters per second. In solving a problem, units may sometimes cancel, as do numbers, but you can never just drop them and then forget about them.

Ratios, Proportions, and Proportionality Constants

Ratios imply comparisons. In its simplest terms a ratio is one number divided by another. The ratio of 8 to 16 is $\frac{8}{16}$. It is also $\frac{4}{8}$, $\frac{2}{4}$, and $\frac{1}{2}$. It tells us that 8 is half as large as 16.

Direct Proportions

Any proportion simply states the equality of two ratios. Thus $\frac{8}{16} = \frac{4}{8}$. Simple proportions of any kind deal with pairs of variable quantities in which the magnitude of one depends upon that of the other. Another way of stating this is to say that one variable quantity is proportional to another if the ratio (quotient) of their corresponding values is constant. Thus, in a circle, circumference/radius = constant, regardless of the size of the circle. If we double or triple either the circumference or the radius, we double or triple the other. This is a *direct* proportion, for the quantities vary directly with each other; that is, if one quantity is increased, the other increases proportionately. In buying commodities we often encounter direct proportions: For example, if pencils cost 5 cents each, the total money to be paid for pencils depends on the number of pencils bought; that is $x = Ky$, where x is the total money, y the number of pencils, and K a proportionality constant that is the price per pencil.

Inverse Proportions

In some cases of proportionality, one quantity decreases as the other increases. Thus the time it takes to travel a given distance decreases as the average velocity increases. Dou-

ble the average velocity and we halve the time. This inverse relationship is expressed by writing one of the quantities as a reciprocal.[3] Thus we may write $v \propto 1/t$, or, if a constant is used, $v = K/t$. The symbol $\propto$ means "proportional to."

Proportionality Constants

By means of proportionality constants we may change any proportionality into an equation. In doing so we replace the proportionality sign by an equals sign and write in the symbol K to represent a fixed number. This number does not change as long as the conditions giving rise to the proportionality do not change.

In science and mathematics we encounter two kinds of proportionality constants: those that do not depend upon the units used and those that do. An example of the first is that of our circle, in which $c/r = K$ (where c is the circumference and r the radius). Here the value of K is 2π, *under any circumstances whatever,* as long as the units in which c and r are expressed are the same. If c/r is not equal to 2π, then the figure in question is not a circle.

The units used in an equation determine the value of the second kind of constant. Commonly we choose our units so that the value is one.

Consider Kepler's third law (p. 51), $T^2 = Kr^3$. We cannot write $T^2 = r^3$, for time is certainly not equal to distance. The K has to take care of the difference in the units. It can do this only if we define our unit of time in terms of our unit of distance, or vice versa. Thus, if we take as our time unit the time that it takes the earth to complete one revolution

---

[3] A reciprocal of any quantity is 1 divided by that quantity. Thus, the reciprocal of 2 is $\frac{1}{2}$, that of x is $\frac{1}{x}$, and so on.

about the sun—that is, the year—and take as our distance unit the average distance between the earth and the sun, 1 AU, we can write

$$(1 \text{ yr})^2 = K \times (1 \text{ AU})^3$$

Solving for K,

$$K = \frac{(1 \text{ yr})^2}{(1 \text{ AU})^3} = \frac{1^2}{1^3} = 1$$

(Strictly speaking the answer should read 1 yr^2/AU^3, for the units do not cancel. We commonly omit them for convenience only.) We can now use the equation $T^2 = Kr^3$ for all other planets, provided we use the same units. Since $K = 1$, we can now write $T^2 = r^3$. The K is still present in the equation, but because it is 1, it does not change the equation, and we can omit mention of it, even though we cannot forget that it is there. You will encounter many other equations in which K becomes 1 because of the way the units are defined.

A few constants determined by experiment seem to hold under all conditions, and so are called universal constants. An example is the one in Newton's law of universal gravitation (pp. 130, 134).

Other Proportionalities

Important proportionalities concern the areas of squares and circles. The area (A) of a square is proportional not to the length (d) of one side, but to the square of one side; that is, $A = Kd^2$. Let one side have a length of 1 (cm, in., ft, and so on). $A = K \times 1^2 = 1$ cm^2, in.^{2}, ft^2, and so on. Now let us increase the length by a factor of 2; that is, let us double the length of one side, making $d = 2$. Then $A = K \times 2^2 = 4$ cm^2, in.^{2}, ft^2, and so on. If d is increased by a factor of 3, $A = K \times 3^2 = 9$ cm^2, in.^{2}, ft^2. The same is true of the area of a circle as given by $A = Kr^2$, where $K = \pi$ and r is the radius of the circle.

More important to us are the inverse-square relationships, for we shall encounter them at least four times. Consider yourself reading at a distance d from a light source. You now double the distance so that $d = 2$ and find that the brightness has decreased by considerably more than a factor of 2 (Fig. 5-1). A light meter

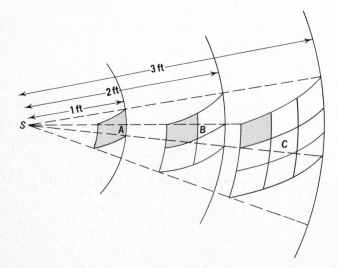

Fig. 5-1. Inverse Square Relationship. Square A is 1 ft from the light source, S, square B is 2 ft away, and square C is 3 ft away. The area of B is then four times the area of A, and the area of C is nine times the area of A. A certain amount of light falls on A. If A is now removed, the same amount of light falls on B, where it is spread over four times the area. The light intensity has been reduced to one quarter by doubling the distance from the source. In the same way, at C, triple the distance, the light intensity is reduced to one ninth.

would show that it had decreased by a factor of 4 (the square of 2); that is, it has decreased to $\frac{1}{4}$ of the original amount. The same light meter would show that if you increased the distance to $3d$, the brightness (B) of the light would be only $\frac{1}{9}$ that when $d = 1$. Thus $B \propto 1/d^2$, and $B = K/d^2$. The reason for this is shown in Fig. 5-1. This general principle holds for all inverse-square laws.

Graphs

A common and extremely useful way of showing proportionalities is by graphs. Every student should be able to read and interpret simple graphs, for we encounter them in every walk of life. Graphs are in one sense pictures. They allow considerable information to be taken in at a glance, they help us to under-

stand what we are talking about, they help us to detect errors in experimental data, and so forth. A variety of graphs are illustrated in Figs. 5-2 through 5-6. Their captions explain them.

Graphs are easiest to plot on graph paper on which a horizontal axis and a vertical axis are drawn. The intersection of the axes is called the *origin*. Values of quantities plotted parallel to the vertical axis are called *ordinates*, those plotted parallel to the horizontal axis are called *abscissae*. The ordinate and the abscissa of a point are called its *coordinates*.

Every graph must have a scale for both the ordinates and the abscissae; the scales are arbitrary within limits. They should be such that the arithmetic involves division or multiplication of simple numbers only, and they should be of a size to fit on the page, yet large enough to plot and to read with the precision

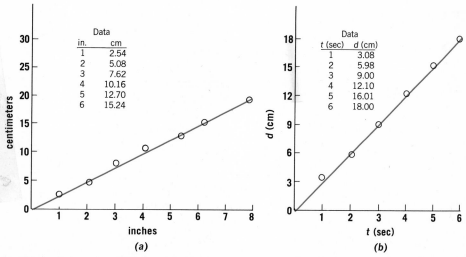

Fig. 5-2. Direct Proportionality Graphs in Which Two Quantities Increase at Same Rate. (*a*) Here, if we double the number of inches, we double the number of centimeters. Algebraically, inches = K centimeters, where K is the number of centimeters in 1 inch. If either the relative scale or the proportionality constant were changed, the slope of the curve would change. The requirements for a direct proportion are that its graph must be a straight line and that it must pass through the origin. (*b*) Distance is plotted against time in motion at uniform velocity.

given by the data. Experience only will teach you how to choose satisfactory scales.

In making a graph the ordinates and the abscissae of the quantities are plotted and marked by a fine point. This point is then neatly circled for ease of finding. A smooth fine line is then drawn so that the plotted points will be as symmetrically arranged on either side of the line as possible. If our data are perfect, the line will pass through all the points. Since errors are present in all experimental work, some of our measurements will be a little too big, some a little too small. Thus, our graph averages out these errors.

Once the graph is drawn we can proceed to obtain information from it—which is why

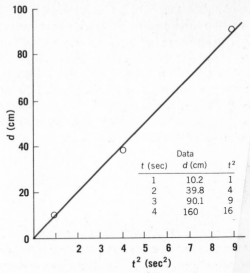

Fig. 5-4. A Graph in Which One Quantity Increases as the Square of the Other (as in uniformly accelerated motion). Note that here the graph is a straight line—which proves that distance is directly proportional to the square of the time in uniformly accelerated motion (compare Fig. 5-3).

we drew it in the first place. A graph in which centimeters have been plotted against inches can be used to convert inches to centimeters or centimeters to inches quickly and easily (Fig. 5-2a). The shape of the curve (all lines on graphs are called *curves* whatever their shape) tells us something about the way the two quantities vary. Direct-proportion graphs are straight lines passing through the origin (Fig. 5-2a and b). A moment's thought should show you why this is so. The slope of the curve will depend upon the relative lengths of the scales used in plotting the points.

If one quantity increases at a faster *rate* than the other, as in uniformly accelerated motion, the curve cannot be a straight line because we no longer have a direct proportion. Our graph is a curved line that passes through the origin, as in Fig. 5-3. Note that this is a graph in which distance is plotted against time, not against time squared. If we plot d against t^2 (Fig. 5-4),

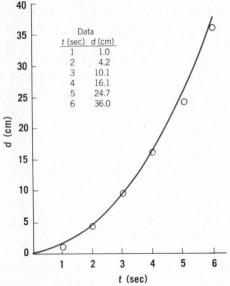

Fig. 5-3. A Graph in Which Two Quantities Increase at Different Rates (as in uniformly accelerated motion). Here distance is plotted against time. Note that increase in distance during the third second is greater than it is during the second second, and this in turn is greater than during the first second. The curve of such a graph cannot be a straight line. The graph shows that distance is *not directly* proportional to time in uniformly accelerated motion.

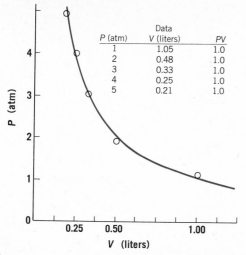

Data		
P (atm)	V (liters)	PV
1	1.05	1.0
2	0.48	1.0
3	0.33	1.0
4	0.25	1.0
5	0.21	1.0

Fig. 5-5. Inverse Proportionality Graph. The curve of an inverse proportionality does not pass through the origin, for it is concave upward. Here the pressure of a *given mass* of a gas confined within a receptacle is shown to be inversely proportional to its volume (size of the receptacle). In other words, $P \propto 1/V$ or $PV = K$.

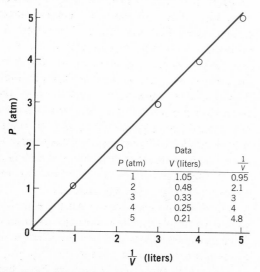

Data		
P (atm)	V (liters)	$\frac{1}{V}$
1	1.05	0.95
2	0.48	2.1
3	0.33	3
4	0.25	4
5	0.21	4.8

Fig. 5-6. An inverse proportionality is turned into a direct proportion if we plot one quantity against the reciprocal of the other. Its graph is therefore a straight line. Here P is plotted against $1/V$.

we get a straight line through the origin, for here, in uniform accelerated motion, the distance is directly proportional to the square of the time.

Graphs that represent inverse proportions cannot pass through the origin, for the value of one of the quantities is greatest when the other is least. Such a graph will be a curve that looks like the one shown in Fig. 5-5. Here we plot the pressure of a gas against its volume at constant temperature (see p. 197). Since neither zero volume nor zero pressure is possible, the curve never touches either axis. If we plot one of these quantities against the reciprocal (p. 81) of the other, we turn the inverse proportion into a direct one whose curve starts at the origin. This happens because the proportionality, $P \propto 1/V$, means either that P is inversely proportional to V, or that P is directly proportional to $1/V$ (Fig. 5-6).

Variety among graphs is tremendous. The ones shown are those with which you should be familiar in this course. You should study them until you understand why the curves are shaped as they are.

Vectors and Scalars

All quantities that we will be confronted with in science may be said to be either vectors or scalars. *Scalars* are quantities that are completely described by magnitude only. Mass, volume, speed, and time are examples. *Vectors* are quantities that need not only magnitude but also direction in space in order to be completely described. Examples are displacement, velocity, acceleration, force, and momentum. In general discussions the vector nature of these quantities is often overlooked, but in many specific situations, it cannot be. The usual arithmetical rules for addition and subtraction do not apply to vectors. Vectors are represented by arrows whose lengths are proportional to the magnitudes, and which point in the appropriate direction. Obviously the length of the arrow must be drawn to scale. Once this is done for one vector, all other vectors in the same problem must be drawn to the same scale.

Addition and Subtraction of Vectors

Vectors may be added or subtracted if certain rules are followed. One must first decide which directions are plus, which minus. Commonly to the right and/or up is considered plus, to the left and/or down minus. Obviously two vectors that have the same length and direction are equal anywhere in space. Not so obvious and vital to the use of vectors is the rule that a vector can be moved anywhere in space without changing its value as long as it is kept parallel to its original position. Vectors that have the same direction may be added simply by placing the tail of one to the head of another.

Thus

$$\overrightarrow{\text{2 units}} + \overrightarrow{\text{3 units}} = \overrightarrow{\text{5 units}}$$

If they are to be subtracted (algebraically added),

$$\overrightarrow{\text{5 units}} + \overleftarrow{\text{2 units}} = \overrightarrow{\text{3 units}}$$

Two or more vectors may have different directions as well as different magnitudes. Remembering that vectors can be moved about freely as long as we do not change their directions, we can see that if the tail of one is put at the head of another not parallel to it, they will be at an angle to each other. Obtaining their vector sum, called the *resultant,* will be more complicated.

The use of vectors may be understood from the following: A plane flies 50 mi east and 50 mi north. What is its displacement; that is, what is its new position? Obviously this cannot

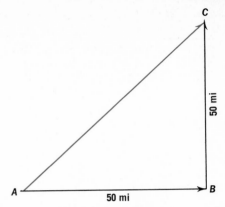

Fig. 5-7. Vector Diagram. This diagram shows displacement of a plane that has flown 50 mi east and 50 mi north from a starting point, *A*. The direction of the displacement *AC* can be measured by a protractor and the distance can be measured on a scale.

be given in miles only; direction must be included. We have two vectors given us, both of the same magnitude. First we choose a convenient scale, say 1 in. = 25 mi, and draw an arrow 2 in. long with its head pointing either east or north, say east. Then we draw another arrow the same length pointing north with its tail at the head of the first vector (Fig. 5-7). These two vectors have been added by placing the tail of one at the head of the other. Then we connect the tail of the first arrow to the head of the second and put a head on this end. It now points northeast (north 45° east in this case). This arrow points in the direction of the displacement, and if we measure the length of this arrow we would find it to be about 2.8 in. long ($= \sqrt{8}$), since in a right triangle $a^2 + b^2 = c^2$. Thus, the new position of the plane, that is, its displacement, is about 2.8 in. × 25 mi/in. = 70 mi N 45° E from its initial position.

We call this third vector the *resultant,* because flight along this line for a distance of a bit over 70 mi would produce the same result (displacement in this case) as a flight of 50 mi east and then 50 mi north. We have added two vectors to produce a resultant. We can, of course, add (or subtract) as many vectors as we wish. Suppose the plane was delivering passengers and mail at a number of places on a scheduled route. Suppose that it flew first 50 mi east, then 50 mi north, followed by 100 mi N 45° E, then 100 mi west, and then 50 mi south. How far is the plane from its starting point S and in what direction? For the solution see Fig. 5-8.

Resolution of Vectors

We have already determined the resultant of two displacements at right angles to each other. Frequently we may wish to do the reverse, that is, to determine the two vectors, at right angles to each other, that would produce the same result as a given vector if the two acted simultaneously. For example, in Fig. 5-9, an object is moved from A to B. This object can be moved along a straight line from A to B either by a force of a certain magnitude acting along AB, or it can be moved along AB by a combination of two forces acting at right

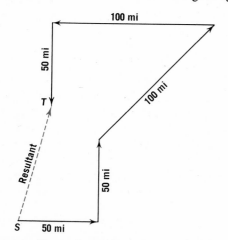

Fig. 5-8. Vector Solution of the Airplane Flight Problem. All true directions are measured in the horizontal plane of the earth's surface and from a line running from the observer to the North Pole. Thus the angle gives the direction in degrees east of north.

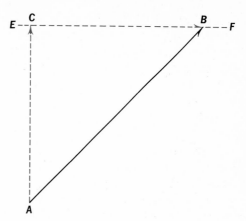

Fig. 5-9. Resolution of a Vector into Two Components Acting at Right Angles to Each Other. See text for explanation.

angles to each other simultaneously. The displacement vector AB is first drawn. Then a line is drawn through either A or B in any desired direction except that it may not be perpendicular to AB. Let us draw it through B, giving us EF. A perpendicular is dropped from A to a point C on EF. The lines AC and CB are at right angles to one another and their lengths represent the magnitudes of the two displacements. There is an infinite number of pairs of forces such as AC and BC that will add up to the single vector AB because an infinite number of lines can be drawn through A or B.

This process is called the *resolution of a single vector into two components operating at right angles to each other*. Since the triangle formed by the three vectors is a right triangle, the sum of the squares of the two right-angled components is equal to the square of the displacement vector AB.

Scientific Notation

In many areas of science the use of very large or very small numbers is essential. These areas vary from the distances of stars and galaxies to the mass of an atom or an electron. The distance to some stars is of the order of

1,000,000,000,000,000 mi or even thousands of times that. The number of atoms in a gram atomic weight of any element is somewhat greater than 600,000,000,000,000,000,000,000, and the mass of a hydrogen atom is 0.00000000000000000000000166 g. To multiply or divide such a number is an exceedingly cumbersome process; to state it in words is almost impossible. Hence these numbers are reduced by scientists to a standard form, a form with usually just one number in front of the decimal point, and multiplied by some power of 10. Consider the number 50,000. If the significant figure here is only the 5, the zeros merely indicate where the decimal point is. In the standard form it is written 5×10^4. If one of the zeros is significant, we write 5.0×10^4. The exponent indicates the number of places the decimal point should be moved to the right. Thus 51,400 is 5.14×10^4 in the standard form; 1,000,000 becomes 1×10^6, or simply 10^6. The number of atoms in a gram atomic weight of any element is 6×10^{23}.

Very small fractions are always converted to decimals and written with a negative power of 10. Thus 0.003 may be written 3×10^{-3}, 0.00001 simply as 10^{-5}. The exponent indicates the number of places the decimal point should be moved to the left; for example, the mass of a hydrogen atom is 1.66×10^{-24} g. With a few minutes of practice you should be able to write any number in the standard form, that is, in scientific notation.

Multiplication in the Standard Form

Multiply the significant figures and add the exponents. Thus 9.3×10^7 multiplied by 5.1×10^9 is

$$9.3 \times 5.1 \times 10^{16} = 47 \times 10^{16}$$
$$= 4.7 \times 10^{17}$$

Note that to compensate for moving the decimal point one place to the left (equivalent to

dividing by 10) we had to multiply 10^{16} by 10.

Let us try another example. Let us multiply 6.02×10^{-4} by 7.5×10^{-8}. This gives us

$$6.02 \times 7.5 \times 10^{-12} = 45 \times 10^{-12}$$
$$= 4.5 \times 10^{-11}$$

Suppose we wish to multiply 3×10^{10} by 5×10^{-5}. The only possible source of trouble here is with our exponents. The algebraic sum of 10 and -5 is 5. So our answer is 15×10^5, or 1.5×10^6. Note that we multiplied a number greater than 1 by a number less than 1. The product must therefore be less than the larger number.

Division in the Standard Form

Divide the significant figures and subtract the exponents. For examples let us use the same numbers we used in multiplying.

$$\frac{5.1 \times 10^9}{9.3 \times 10^7} = 0.55 \times 10^2 = 5.5 \times 10^1 = 55$$

$$\frac{7.5 \times 10^{-8}}{6.02 \times 10^{-4}} = 1.2 \times 10^{-4}$$

$$\frac{3 \times 10^{10}}{5 \times 10^{-5}} = 0.6 \times 10^{15} = 6.0 \times 10^{14}$$

Suppose we wish to find the kinetic energy of a nitrogen molecule at room temperature and want our answer in joules (pronounced jowls). The equation is $KE = \frac{1}{2}mv^2$. The mass of the nitrogen molecule is 0.00000000000000000000000465 g and its average velocity is about 52,000 cm/sec. Hence,

$$KE = \frac{4.65 \times 10^{-24} \times (5.2 \times 10^4)^2}{2 \times 10^7}$$

$$= \frac{4.65 \times 5.2 \times 5.2 \times 10^{-24} \times 10^4 \times 10^4}{2 \times 10^7}$$

$$= 63 \times 10^{-23} \text{ joule} = 6.3 \times 10^{-22} \text{ joule}$$

Check this out yourself.

Exercises

1. The dimensions of a block of wood are 1.2 in. $\times$ 2.2 in. $\times$ 1.6 in. What volume of the block should be reported?
2. Your grades on quizzes during the term are 82, 61, 75, 72, and 77%. What is your average grade?
3. Did you have proper respect for significant figures in your answers to exercises 1 and 2?
4. What is the metric system of measurement? What are its advantages over the English system?
5. How many centimeters are there in (a) 1 in., (b) 1 meter, and (c) 1 kilometer?
6. The cgs system is a decimal system. This fact is brought out in the following two problems:
   (a) What is the sum of 2.05 m, 2 km, 34 cm, and 23 mm?
   (b) What is the sum of 176 g, 112 g, and 5.13 kg?
7. (a) Approximately how many grams are there in a pound?
   (b) How many grams in a kilogram?
   (c) How many pounds are there in a kilogram?
   (d) Express your weight in kilograms.
8. Express the following in centimeters: (a) 1 ft, (b) 1 yd, (c) 1 mi, and (d) 1 km.
9. (a) How many centimeters are there in a meter?
   (b) How many millimeters in a meter?
   (c) How many meters in a kilometer?
10. (a) Which is the greater distance, 100 yd or 100 m?
    (b) By how many feet?
11. Estimate the distances between the points A, B, and C below *directly* in centimeters. (Do *not* first estimate in inches and then convert to centimeters.) Making a direct estimate involves having a mental picture of how long a centimeter is. Record your answers in the spaces provided.

Now measure them with a ruler to see how nearly right you are.

12. Write the following, using the powers of 10:
    (a) 500   (b) 2000
    (c) 32,000   (d) 758,400
    (e) 0.03   (f) 0.007
    (g) 0.00092   (h) 0.000000016
13. Multiply the following:
    (a) 3×10^{10} by 6×10^5
    (b) 3×10^{10} by 6×10^{-5}
    (c) 3×10^{-10} by 6×10^5
    (d) 3×10^{-10} by 6×10^{-5}
    (e) 3×10^{10} by 1.5
14. Square the following:
    (a) 10^5 (b) 10^{13}
    (c) 10^{-5} (d) 10^{-10}
    (e) 3×10^7 (f) 7×10^{-6}
15. Cube the following:
    (a) 10^2 (b) 10^7
    (c) 10^{-2} (d) 10^{-6}
    (e) 2×10^5 (f) 4×10^{-3}
16. Divide the following:
    (a) 3×10^{10} by 6×10^5
    (b) 3×10^{10} by 6×10^{-5}
    (c) 3×10^{-10} by 6×10^5
    (d) 3×10^{-10} by 6×10^{-5}
    (e) 3×10^{10} by 1.5
17. The mass of a hydrogen atom is about 1.66×10^{-24} g. How many atoms are present in 1 g of hydrogen? Use powers of 10.
18. The radius of the earth is about 4000 mi. Express this distance in centimeters, assuming 5000 ft/mi and 30 cm/ft. Do the *whole* calculation by powers of 10.
19. The distance to the nearest star is 25 trillion mi. Express this distance in centimeters, using the same assumptions as above.
20. Using the symbols given, show that there is either a direct or an inverse propor-

tionality or both in each of the following by writing the proper equation. (Use K as the proportionality constant.)

(a) Monthly milk bill (B) versus the number (N) of quarts delivered.

(b) The weekly income of an hourly wage earner (I) versus the number of hours worked (H).

(c) The time required (t) to fly from New York to Chicago versus the average speed (s) of the plane.

(d) The rent of an antomobile or bus per person (R) versus the number of persons in the group (P).

(e) The number of slices of bread (S) cut from a loaf of bread of a certain size (L).

21. The speed of light is about 186,400 mi/sec. Express this speed in centimeters per second using the powers of 10.

22. A boat whose speed is 6 mi/hr in still water is traveling downstream where the current is flowing 2 mi/hr. Show the boat's velocity by a vector diagram. Do the same for it traveling upstream.

23. A boat is steered due east across a large river at a speed of 4 mi/hr but is carried north by a strong current flowing 3 mi/hr. Draw a vector diagram to show the boat's velocity.

24. A delivery truck makes a number of stops where the blocks are each 0.2 mi long in any direction. From his first stop he goes six blocks east, then three north, four east, five north, and finally seven west. Show by a vector diagram how far he is from his first stop.

25. An airplane whose normal speed in still air is 300 mi/hr must travel due west. What course must the pilot set if there is a 50 mi/hr wind from the north? Solve by vectors.

26. What is the meaning of the word *error* in the science of measurement? Does it mean "wrong" or "mistaken"?

27. What is the meaning of the word *exact* in the science of measurement?

PART II

Force, Motion, and Mechanical Energy

Galileo's Study of Motion

Nothing is more familiar to us than motion. We see it everywhere, from the apparent motions of the sun, moon, stars, and planets to the real motions of clouds drifting across the sky, and the raindrops and snowflakes that sometimes fall from them. We see it as the winds rustle the leaves, as the streams flow toward the sea, as the waves lap gently on the shore or pound it with savage fury. We see it in all of man's activities, in the transportation not only of ourselves to and from our work or play, but in the supplying of our daily needs of every sort. We ourselves, or some part of us, are in constant motion from even before birth to the time we die. So used to motion of many kinds are we that if we rise at dawn on a still summer morning, we look out upon a world that seems unnatural because of the lack of motion, and we are often moved to comment on it. Not only is motion a characteristic of much of our macroscopic and microscopic worlds, but it is even more a characteristic of the submicroscopic world of atoms and molecules. It may truly be said that there

> Nothing in Nature is more ancient than motion, and the volumes that the philosophers have compiled about it are neither few nor small; yet have I discovered that there are many things of interest about it, that have hitherto been unperceived.
> GALILEO GALILEI
> (1636)

is not a single completely motionless atom or molecule in the whole universe. Yet man for thousands of years believed that rest was the natural state of matter. Let us inquire into the reasons for this belief.

Primitive man had long been concerned with the problems of motion, chiefly because he needed more efficient means of transportation for his goods as well as himself. This concern with transportation led to the early invention of sails, the wheel, and the horse collar.[1] Yet a true insight into the fundamental concepts of force and motion was long delayed. Looking backward, we can see why—these concepts are extremely subtle, so much so that it might well be said that the average intelligent and educated person is intuitively an Aristotelian unless he has had special instruction. So subtle and contrary to common sense are many of the aspects of ordinary motions, and so great is the tendency for us to therefore draw the wrong conclusions concerning them, that one of the foremost contemporary historians was moved to say,

> Of all the intellectual hurdles which the human mind has been faced with and has overcome in the last fifteen hundred years the one which seems to me to have been the most amazing in character and the most stupendous in the scope of its consequences is the one relating to the problem of motion.

The choice between the heliocentric and the geocentric theories could not be made with finality much before 1620. There were no dynamic principles to help, no clear understanding of force and motion. What force, or forces, kept the planets moving? What kept them in their elliptical paths? The latter question was easily answered by the followers of

Ptolemy. Planets were embedded in crystal spheres or domes that held them in their courses. To turn these great transparent but solid domes Aristotle postulated a supernatural Prime Mover. Much later, after comets from far out beyond the sun were seen to cut paths through the supposedly hard crystal spheres, the planets had to be viewed as floating in empty space. Without the domes it was extremely difficult to see how they could follow exactly the same paths revolution after revolution about the earth. The early Christian followers of the Ptolemaic system supposed the planets to be composed of light fluffy materials carried along in their orbits by angels. The earth, however, was obviously made of heavy materials which would require force to move—all the more reason for believing it motionless. Copernicus and his followers had no answer to this problem of a moving earth except to point out that the moving system of stars in the Ptolemaic system presented an even greater problem because they were so much farther away.

Many realized, the philosopher René Descartes among them, that a new start in science as a whole, a new manner of attack upon the unknown, was needed. A scientific revolution was being called for, even though no one knew what kind of a revolution was needed. The first to use a new manner of attack upon the unknown openly, consistently, and effectively was Galileo (1564–1642). Hence, more than anyone else, he deserves to be called the father of modern science. To be sure, Kepler had showed a tinge of modernity by his acceptance of the explanation of observable facts as the criterion of the worth of a theory, but he did not progress far beyond this. Kepler could not divorce his science from medieval mysticism. We feel far more at home with Galileo, for with him the last vestiges of mysticism disappeared. Galileo clearly formulated his

---

[1]These have been called the three most significant inventions of all time because each released man from great drudgery, giving him more time to use his slowly developing mind.

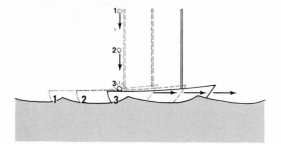

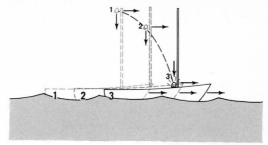

Fig. 6-1. Aristotle's Solution to the Problem of Falling Bodies. The boat is moving forward at a uniform velocity. The stone, dropped from the top of the mast, is falling down (moving vertically), but has no horizontal component of motion; that is, it does not partake of the boat's motion. Thus the stone's path is assumed to be a vertical line, and the stone hits the deck considerably back of the mast.

Fig. 6-2. Galileo's Solution to the Problem of Falling Bodies. The boat is moving uniformly and the stone is falling, as in Fig. 6-1, but the stone partakes of the boat's horizontal motion, and its path therefore is along the curved line. It lands on the boat's deck alongside the mast because its path *relative to the mast* is parallel to the mast. Compare with Fig. 6-1; which version is correct?

problems, a necessary first step toward their solution. He was able to correct a fallacious view of motion because he was able to restate the problem in very different terms (Figs. 6-1 and 6-2). It is, therefore, to him that we turn (after first considering the fallacious view) in our efforts to understand the causes of motion, not only among the celestial bodies, but also here on earth.

Aristotle's Concept of Free Fall

Aristotle appears to have been the first one to attempt to give rational explanations to the phenomena of freely falling bodies. Before considering these concepts we must clearly understand that the scientific concepts, not only of Aristotle but of all the early Greeks, were intimately tied into a comprehensive philosophical-religious system whose main function was to interpret nature and its processes in terms that could be understood.

To the Greeks it was the system that was most important. In any conflict between its

postulates and observation or experiment, usually the latter was ignored; observable facts did not have to be strictly in accord with the postulates. In other words, they gave philosophic "truth" precedence over scientific "truth." Contrast this attitude with the modern concept that all scientific theorizing must proceed from observed facts, and that if other pertinent observable facts are not in accord with the theory, then the theory must be altered or abandoned. That part of Aristotle's philosophic-religious system which concerns the motion of bodies had its origins in his concept of matter, to which we will turn our attention briefly.

Early man lived at the mercy of uncontrolled nature, and his first attempts to control it were by magic. The Greeks were the first to make any large-scale attempt to understand and interpret nature rather than to control it. If man could understand nature, he would feel more at home in this world, for, generally, what we understand we no longer fear. The first step in this direction concerned the constitution of matter, for its behavior would depend mostly upon its composition (and also upon its structure). Therefore, we need to understand Aristotle's concept of matter in order to understand his views on its "natural" motion.[2]

Aristotle had accepted the Pythagorean concept of four basic elements, earth, water, fire, and air. In an attempt to explain why solids and liquids free to move always fell toward the earth, whereas fire and air seemed to rise, Aristotle conceived that each of these four elements had a natural home. That of earth and water is the earth itself; that of air is obviously above the earth, as was also that of fire, for does not one see the flames leaping upward? All of the various kinds of matter consisted of combinations of these four elements. Each kind took on the characteristics of the particular element or elements that it had in greatest abundance. Thus, when fire was added to water (that is, when the water was heated), the water turned to vapor and escaped upward because it now had one of the characteristics of fire. When the vapor "lost the fire," when it cooled and condensed, it became water again and returned to earth (its natural home) as rain. Thus, the concept of what Aristotle called natural motion was intimately related to matter itself.

Also related to Aristotle's concepts of both motion and matter was that of the division of the universe into two major parts, the sublunar and the supralunar. The latter was that part of the universe *outside* the orbit of the moon. Here everything was perfect and changeless. All celestial bodies were perfect spheres and moved in perfect circles with uniform speed. No force was required to keep the bodies moving. This type of motion he called perfect motion. The sublunar part of the universe lay *within* the orbit of the moon and had terrestrial characteristics. It was a region of change, of

clouds, storms, lightning, varying weather, and meteors. It was a region where bodies, unless supported, fell to earth with velocities that changed, becoming faster as the bodies neared the earth. Here also was another kind of motion, horizontal motion,[3] such as that involved in throwing a ball. A force was obviously needed to produce this motion. Thus Aristotle was led to believe that in the sublunar world a force was needed to make a body move at all. This force was needed to overcome the resistance of the medium through which the body was moving. Of two bodies of equal mass, size, and shape, one freely falling in water and the other in air, the latter will fall faster, for air offers less resistance than water. The greater the amount of matter in a body, that is, the greater its mass, the faster the fall[4] because of a greater "eagerness" of the heavier body to reach its natural home. Experiments would have shown that if two compact dense bodies of the same size but of very different masses fell from the same height in the same medium, they fell practically side by side. There is no evidence that Aristotle performed this experiment.[5] It is doubtful that he would have changed his mind even if he had done so for reasons already stated.

Aristotle's theory of natural motion was used by him to explain why a vacuum could not exist. If the thinner the medium (consider the fall through air and water mentioned above) the faster the fall, then in an infinitely thin medium such as a vacuum, the "maximum" rate of fall must be infinitely high. If this speed

---

[2] By natural motion of solid bodies, Aristotle meant the motion of bodies falling freely toward the earth; that is, he meant free fall.

[3] Aristotle called horizontal motion, and all motions here on earth other than free fall, *violent motion*.

[4] If air is the medium, and one of the bodies is a light one, such as a feather, and air resistance is taken into account, the heavy body will fall the faster.

[5] Aristotle preached the checking of concepts by observation or experiment insofar as it was possible, but he commonly failed to follow his teaching. An example is the report that he once said that women had more teeth than men.

is infinitely high, a body will fall through an infinitely great distance in an infinitely short time. This means that the body will be at the top, the middle, and the bottom of its fall at the same instance of time. This, of course, is absurd, and so a vacuum cannot exist. This view of Aristotle's gave rise to the expression "Nature abhors a vacuum." One may still hear it used today.

Description of Linear Motion

Any effort to understand how objects fall freely will involve the use of certain concepts necessary to any quantitative treatment of the subject of motion, namely, distance, time, velocity, and acceleration. We will therefore pause to make sure our understanding of them is sufficient.

There are various kinds of motion, but for the present we will concern ourselves only with linear motion, that is, motion in a straight line. Later, when we need it, we will introduce circular motion. In this textbook we will be concerned with two kinds of linear motion, (1) uniform motion, by which we mean motion with a constant velocity, and (2) uniformly accelerated motion, of which free fall is a classic example. We will always carefully state the type with which we are dealing.

The concepts of distance and time are so familiar that they need no explanation, except for the units in which they are stated. We will at times use the centimeter, gram, second (cgs) system of units, and at other times the foot, pound, second (English) system. Thus, distances will be either in centimeters (or in rare cases, meters) or in feet. Masses or weights will be either in grams (occasionally in kilograms) or in pounds. Distances, masses, and weights are easily measurable if they are appreciably large; Galileo had no difficulty with them. The accurate measurement of time is far more difficult, as we have seen; but modern electri-

cal timing devices can measure intervals of time that are small fractions of a second.

Consider the concepts of distance, time, and speed. It takes us only a moment to deduce the relationships between them. Thus,

$$\text{speed} = \frac{\text{distance traveled}}{\text{time elapsed}}$$

In symbolic form,

$$v = \frac{d}{t} \qquad [6\text{-}1]$$

To use it we need some units to make the equation meaningful. For example, a car travels 400 mi in 8 hr. It has a speed of

$$v = \frac{400 \text{ miles}}{8 \text{ hr}} = 50 \text{ mi/hr} \qquad [6\text{-}2]$$

If the speed were constant, v is the same at all times, so that we can write $d = vt$, or $v = d/t$, or $t = d/v$. Given two of the three quantities, the third is easily calculated by substituting the known quantities in the proper equation. For example, suppose a car travels 400 mi at a constant speed of 50 mi/hr. How long did it take?

$$t = \frac{d}{v} = \frac{400 \text{ mi}}{50 \text{ mi/hr}} = 8 \text{ hr} \qquad [6\text{-}3]$$

Note the manner in which the units are handled; the miles cancel out, they are not just dropped. Units are multiplied or divided just as numerical quantities are. In the example above, miles are divided by mi/hr as

$$\text{mi} \div \frac{\text{mi}}{\text{hr}} = \text{mi} \times \frac{\text{hr}}{\text{mi}} = \text{hr}$$

Note that in Eq. 6-2 we divided miles by hours, and that this fact is shown in the answer. Again, if a car traveled at a constant speed of 50 mi/hr for 8 hr, how far would it have gone?

$$d = vt = 50\frac{\text{mi}}{\text{hr}} \times 8 \text{ hr} = 400 \text{ mi} \quad [6\text{-}4]$$

Note that the hours cancel out, leaving miles as the only unit in our answer.

Another often useful method of writing such equations as the above is as follows:

$$\Delta d = v \times \Delta t \quad \text{(at constant speed)} \quad [6\text{-}5]$$

where Δ is the Greek letter delta, which here means "change of" or "change in." Thus $\Delta d = v \times \Delta t$ means change in distance (or position) $= v \times$ change in time. This Δ notation will be used many times in the following pages.

Velocity vs. Speed in Uniform Motion

You may have noted in the past few pages that we have sometimes used the term *speed* and sometimes the term *velocity*. These terms are synonymous to the average person, but never to the scientist. The scientist uses the term *speed,* as you do, to mean *the time rate of motion,* but to him *velocity* means speed *in a given direction.* To say that a body is moving with uniform velocity means that it is moving in a straight line with unchanging speed. In such motion the distance traveled is *directly proportional to the time.*

Uniformly Accelerated Motion

The above concept of velocity does not apply when we are dealing with uniformly accelerated motion. Although our experience with "pick-up" in automobiles has given us an intuitive understanding of acceleration, it is not enough for our purposes here. Galileo seems to have been the first to have a clear concept of it. Acceleration is not simply a change in velocity but is a rate of change in velocity. Defined precisely, it is change in velocity per unit time. What makes the concept a bit difficult is that it is a rate of change of a rate of motion; since there are two rates, there must be two time units to express them.

Putting this definition of acceleration in equation form, we have

$$\frac{\text{change in velocity (or speed)}}{\text{time taken for the change}} = \text{acceleration}$$

or

$$\text{acceleration} = \frac{\text{change in velocity}}{\text{change in time}} \quad [6\text{-}6]$$

In symbols

$$a = \frac{\Delta v}{\Delta t} \quad [6\text{-}7]$$

For example, suppose we start a car moving from rest, so that it accelerates from 0 to 30 mi/hr in 5 sec. What is its acceleration?

$$a = \frac{\Delta v}{\Delta t} = \frac{30 \text{ mi/hr}}{5 \text{ sec}} = \frac{6 \text{ mi/hr}}{\text{sec}}$$

Thus the car's speed was increased 6 mi/hr for each second that we are accelerating it.

Here the two units, hour and second, are different. Ideally they should be the same, for we are much more likely to stay out of trouble in solving problems if they are. Thus in the above problem we convert 6 mi/hr to 8.8 ft/sec.[6] Our acceleration is then

$$8.8 \frac{\text{ft/sec}}{\text{sec}} \quad \text{(also written 8.8 ft/sec}^2\text{)}$$

(read as "8.8 feet per second per second").

[6]You will find it useful to remember that a velocity of 60 mi/hr is identical with 88 ft/sec. Therefore 30 mi/hr is 44 ft/sec and 6 mi/hr is 8.8 ft/sec. The mathematics of the change from mi/hr to ft/sec is a good exercise in how to handle units in calculations:

$$6 \text{ mi/hr} = \frac{6 \text{ mi} \times 5280 \text{ ft/mi}}{1 \text{ hr} \times 3600 \text{ sec/hr}} = \frac{5280 \text{ ft}}{600 \text{ sec}} = 8.8 \text{ ft/sec}$$

Note carefully the cancellation of units.

At times it is desirable to write Eq. 6-6 in another form,

$$a = \frac{v_f - v_i}{t} \qquad [6\text{-}8]$$

where v_f and v_i are the final and initial velocities, respectively. If the body starts from rest, as in the case of the car, $v_i = 0$. Using this equation we can easily solve for v_f. Multiplying both sides by t and reversing the equation gives

$$v_f - v_i = at$$

Adding v_i to both sides,

$$v_f = v_i + at \qquad [6\text{-}9]$$

Since $v_i = 0$, then

$$v_f = at \qquad [6\text{-}10]$$

Average Speed

Average speed is defined as the total distance divided by the total time; that is

$$\bar{v} = \frac{d}{t}$$

($\bar{v}$ means average velocity). For uniform motion, speed and average speed are the same. For nonuniform motion, they are distinctly different. Suppose you drive 10 mi along city streets to visit a friend, slowing down and speeding up according to traffic conditions, or even stopping at red lights. To speak of your speed on such a trip is meaningless, but your average speed is obviously d/t, the distance divided by the time. Your average speed in the above example is a statistical speed, just as statistical as it is to say that the average number of children in an American family is $2\frac{1}{2}$. It is, however, a useful concept in everyday life.

Average Velocity in Uniformly Accelerated Motion

In uniformly accelerated motion, average velocity is a more difficult concept. Consider a car starting from rest and accelerating uniformly for 10 sec, at which instant its velocity is 60 mi/hr. Its acceleration is given by

$$a = \frac{\Delta v}{\Delta t} = \frac{60 \text{ mi/hr}}{10 \text{ sec}} = \frac{6 \text{ mi/hr}}{\text{sec}}$$

At the end of 5 sec, its velocity is

$$5 \text{ sec} \times \frac{6 \text{ mi/hr}}{\text{sec}} = 30 \text{ mi/hr}$$

This is precisely half the final velocity.

For any *uniformly* changing quantity, it can be shown that the average value of the quantity is one half the sum of the initial and final values. Thus for uniformly accelerated motion, where $\bar{v}$ is the average velocity:

$$\bar{v} = \tfrac{1}{2}(v_f + v_i) \qquad [6\text{-}11]$$

and if the object starts from rest, so that $v_i = 0$, then

$$\bar{v} = \tfrac{1}{2}v_f \qquad \text{or} \qquad \bar{v} = \frac{v}{2} \qquad [6\text{-}12]$$

Galileo, the Father of Modern Science

Galileo (1564–1642) is important and interesting to us in the study of force and motion for several reasons. For one thing, he not only had to criticize, alter, and eventually destroy faulty theories and replace them with better ones, but he also had to destroy a whole intellectual world and replace it with another. He had to evolve a new concept of science that was completely independent of the philosophical and religious dogmas of the time. Like Copernicus with respect to the relative motions of the earth, sun, stars, and planets, Galileo had to replace a common-sense approach to motion by one that is "uncommon-sensical." Here we have two cases one by Copernicus, the other by Galileo, out of many in which things are not as they seem to be, two cases in which we cannot believe the conclusions of our own senses.

Galileo may truly be called the father of modern science, for he was the first to use modern experimental methods throughout his work. If Galileo could return to earth today, he probably would, after a period of study, feel right at home in many fields of science. Kepler, on the other hand, despite his new attitude toward observed facts and his successful attempt to formulate physical laws in mathematical form, would probably find it far more difficult, even impossible, to make the transition, for he had far too much of medieval mysticism bred into him.

Galileo first studied medicine at the University of Pisa, but soon changed to the physical sciences and mathematics. At the age of 26 he was appointed to the University Chair of Mathematics. His unusual mental qualities, his independence of spirit and his intellectual integrity, alloyed with a testy temper, a gift for ridicule, and no semblance of patience or tact, were soon displayed in his refusal to accept the reasoning by authority in scientific matters (see p. 47) that had pervaded all institutions of learning in Western Europe for over three hundred years.

Despite his almost constant warfare with scientific authoritarianism, Galileo managed to escape arrest and trial for heresy until the last few years of his life. At no time was he forced to discontinue his experiments. His quarrel with the Jews and with the Christian churches, Protestant and Catholic, was over his insistence on teaching the Kepler version of the Copernican hypothesis as fact rather than as a hypothesis. Eventually he was forced to recant.

He spent the last few years of his life under "house arrest."

Galileo's Concept of Free Fall

The legend of Galileo testing the Aristotelian view that the rate at which an object falls is proportional to its weight, by dropping large and small balls made of metal and wood from the Leaning Tower of Pisa, is an old and repeatedly told one. If he did so, neither he nor any of his contemporaries recorded it.

All bodies are slowed down by air resistance, the lighter ones more than the heavier ones. In a *long* fall the speed of any body reaches a maximum and then becomes constant. Heavy objects fall farther before reaching this speed than do light objects of the same density. The followers of Aristotle in the Middle Ages used the above facts to "quote" Aristotle as saying that bodies fall with speeds proportional to their weights. Thus Aristotle is supposed to have said that a 1 lb ball, dropped from a height, should be only halfway down at the instant a 2 lb ball, dropped from the same height at the same instant, strikes the ground. This is easily disproved by experiment, for the two strike the ground almost at the same instant. We attribute the slight difference to the greater effect of air resistance on the smaller ball. Today we can demonstrate that in a near vacuum a feather and a lead ball will drop together. If one is medieval-minded, one can deny that the experiment proves anything by insisting that the experimenter has bewitched either the two balls or the eye of the observer, so that the balls appear to fall together. This is what some of Galileo's colleagues said with respect to his experiments. Some also refused to look through his telescope, claiming that they would be bewitched into seeing what Galileo wanted them to see.

We must not suppose that Galileo was the originator of all the ideas that are associated with his name. No large intellectual enterprise ever starts from nothing; there are always previous investigators who contribute an isolated bit here and another there. What every great innovator does is take these bits, check them, add his own to them, and shape them all into a consistent whole. James R. Newman put it aptly when he said, "Great ideas emerge from the common cauldron of intellectual activity, and are rarely cooked up in private kettles from original recipes." It was Galileo's point of view that was original.

True scientist that he was, Galileo was not content merely to prove that light and heavy bodies fell at the same rate if air resistance was neglected. He set out to investigate how they fell. He wanted to know the relationships between the distance fallen, the speed, and the time. It is an easily tested fact that an object falling through a distance of 20 ft has a greater final velocity than one falling through a distance of 2 ft. You could test the truth of this statement by jumping first from a chair to the floor and then from a second-story window.[7]

Galileo reasoned that the rate of increase in velocity should be uniform, for he could visualize nothing that would change it in an irregular manner. If he were right, a freely falling body should have uniformly accelerated motion. Galileo also reasoned that the velocity of such a body, which obviously was neither constant nor proportional to its weight, had to be proportional to either the time of fall or to the distance fallen. If he had had the proper apparatus, he could easily have performed an experiment to find out. Even today we cannot measure the velocity directly without the aid of electricity in timing.

Before performing an experiment, Galileo

[7]The force of your impact with the floor compared to that with the ground would be a measure of the velocity (assuming the floor and the ground to be equally "hard").

made certain mathematical calculations involving distance, time, velocity, and acceleration, quantities that we discussed on pp. 97–99. We have seen that

$$a = \frac{v_f - v_i}{t}$$

or

$$a = \frac{v_f}{t} \quad \text{if } v_i = 0$$

Solving for v_f, we have, as in Eq. 6-10,

$$v_f = at \quad \text{if } v_i = 0$$

The average velocity, $\bar{v}$, would be $\bar{v} = d/t$, where d is the distance traveled in time t. Solving for d,

$$d = \bar{v}t \qquad [6\text{-}13]$$

But the average velocity for a body uniformly accelerated from an initial velocity of zero to the final velocity, v_f, is, as shown in Eq. 6-12,

$$\bar{v} = \tfrac{1}{2}v$$

Combining Eqs. 6-10, 6-12, and 6-13 gives

$$d = \bar{v}t = \tfrac{1}{2}vt = \frac{at \times t}{2} = \tfrac{1}{2}at^2 \qquad [6\text{-}14]$$

The above mathematical reasoning told him that distance should be proportional to the time squared, but we must remember that nature is not bound to follow the reasoning of man. Mathematics cannot manufacture scientific facts, though it may help us to discover them. Failure to realize this truism is a mistake that the early Greeks made; it was one of the reasons they performed so few experiments and sometimes ignored observational data. Moreover, their methods were still followed by Galileo's opponents some 2000 years later.

Galileo's Free Fall Experiments

Note that Galileo eliminated velocity from his final equation [6-14] so that he had three unknowns, d, t, and a, to determine. By measuring two of them he could calculate the third. Distance was easy, but time was extremely difficult, for he lacked a good timing device. Consider that the time of fall from the ceiling to the floor of your classroom is less than one second, and we can appreciate his difficulty. Moreover, the clocks of his time had only hour hands. He tried using his pulse but found it unsatisfactory. A more successful device was a vessel of water from which the water was allowed to escape through a tiny jet that he could open or close with his finger. He could then weigh on a balance the water that escaped during short time intervals. This balance was the most accurate instrument he possessed, even though crude by modern standards. Still the time rate of free fall was too rapid to measure directly with an accuracy sufficient to prove or disprove his mathematical reasoning.

Galileo resorted again to reasoning and invention. His invention was a pendulum "clock." His reasoning resulted in his conviction, reached after extensive experimentation with inclined planes,[8] that a ball rolling downhill is really "falling" downhill. In other words, a ball rolls downhill for the same reason that it would fall vertically if free to do so. By adjusting the tilt of this inclined plane to a low angle so that the velocity of the ball was small, he found that he could measure the time of "fall" quite accurately with his pendulum "clock."

[8] For his inclined planes he used long straight strips of lumber in which he cut narrow grooves down the full length. Since he lacked modern tools to make a smooth groove, he eliminated its irregularities by lining it with parchment paper.

He found that the ball rolled four times as far in two swings of the pendulum as in one, and nine times as far in three, and so on. This was in accord with his mathematical reasoning. He varied the steepness of the inclined plane; the ball rolled faster and faster as the steepness increased, but in every case the distance rolled was proportional to the square of the time. As the angle of tilt was increased until it was near the vertical, he found that the speed of the ball became too great to measure the time accurately. Again he had to resort to reasoning, somewhat as follows: "If, finally, I increase the steepness until the plank is vertical, the ball would hardly touch the plank at all, but rather would fall freely alongside of it. I shall then have a freely falling body, and the distance should still be proportional to the square of the time." Modern experiments prove that he was right. Put formally, Galileo's law of free fall states that a *uniformly accelerated body, starting from the rest, traverses a distance proportional to the square of the time of travel.* Mathematically stated it is $d \propto t^2$. Using a proportionality constant it is

$$d = Kt^2 \qquad [6\text{-}15]$$

Since free fall is a typical case of uniformly accelerated motion, this equation applies to all uniformly accelerated motion.

You are probably wondering about that K in the law. Since it is a constant that does not change as d and t are varied, it will have a definite value as long as the conditions under which the experiment is performed do not change. When Galileo changed the angle of the inclined plane, he changed one of the conditions of the experiment. Therefore, the value of K changed with each new angle. Yet intuitively we may feel that there should be some order in this change, that K cannot change randomly. We feel the need to know what K really is.

Let us look at his mathematical calculations

again (p. 101). If they are correct, then $d = \frac{1}{2}at^2$. If his experimental data are correct, then $d = Kt^2$. So $Kt^2 = \frac{1}{2}at^2$. Canceling the quantities that appear on both sides gives $K = \frac{1}{2}a$. Galileo found that a increased as he increased the tilt of his inclined plane (the ball reached the bottom in a shorter time). Thus the numerical value of K changes whenever one of the fundamental conditions of the experiment changes, but whatever that value is, it is always $\frac{1}{2}a$.

A Modern Experiment to Test Galileo's Hypothesis

Let a straight aluminum bar about 15 or 16 ft long be mounted on edge so that one end is 8 or 10 in. above the other. The upper edge has a smooth groove cut in it so that a steel ball can roll down the bar freely. An electrical device (electromagnet) holds the ball at the high end of the bar (Fig. 6-3). When a switch is pulled, the ball starts rolling and another electrical device starts clicking off the seconds.

Our equation [6-13] predicts that if the ball rolls 10 cm the first second, it will have rolled 40 cm at the end of 2 sec, 90 cm at the end of 3 sec, and so on. We therefore measure off and mark on the bar these distances: 10 cm, 40 cm, 90 cm, 160 cm—all from the starting

point. We now carefully adjust the angle of inclination so that the ball will actually roll 10 cm the first second. Next we start the ball rolling to see if it is at the 40, 90, and 160 cm marks at the end of 2, 3, and 4 sec, respectively. We find that it is, and so observation checks with theory. If we put our data and the information gained from it in the form of a table, we will understand it better. Remember that Galileo's hypothesis says that $d = Kt^2$. Dividing both sides by t^2, K must equal d/t^2. If K is also equal to $\frac{1}{2}a$, then

$$\frac{1}{2}a = \frac{d}{t^2} \quad \text{and} \quad a = \frac{2d}{t^2} \quad [6\text{-}16]$$

We will check our experimental data (Table 6-1) to see if this is so.

The first two columns in Table 6-1 constitute the data obtained in our experiment.[9] From these data we can gain all of the information

[9] The d column is too perfect to be true—and it isn't true! Experimental errors of many kinds (see Chapter 5) cause variations from ideal results and variations between successive trials of any experiment. Numerous trials of this experiment result in considerable variation, as should be expected. The more carefully the measurements are made, the smaller the range of variations becomes. The numbers given in Table 6-1 are fairly close to the averages of careful measurements and have been rounded off only to make the calculations simple and to emphasize the basic mathematical relationships involved without confusing the issue with too much arithmetic.

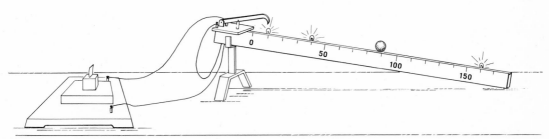

Fig. 6-3. A Modern Apparatus to Test Galileo's Hypothesis. The timing device emits a very brief electric current once every second. This electric current activates the mechanism that releases the ball and also flashes a set of movable small lamps and makes an audible click once every second. The position of each lamp is adjusted so that at the moment a click is heard, one lamp is obscured by the ball. Thus the total distance traversed by the ball at the end of each second can be measured.

Table 6-1

EXPERIMENTAL DATA*		To SHOW THAT $d = Kt^2$ (OR $d/t^2 = K$)		To IDENTIFY K WITH $\frac{1}{2}a$			
t (sec)	d (cm) (cumulative)	t^2	$d/t^2 = K$ (cm/sec^2)	Distance covered during each successive second (cm)	Increase** in v during each second (cm/sec)	a (cm/sec^2)	$K = \frac{1}{2}a$ each (cm/sec^2)
1	10	1	10	10 (10 − 0)	20	20	10
2	40	4	10	30 (40 − 10)	20 (30 − 10)	20	10
3	90	9	10	50 (90 − 40)	20 (50 − 30)	20	10
4	160	16	10	70 (160 − 90)	20 (70 − 50)	20	10
5	250	25	10	90 (250 − 160)	20 (90 − 70)	20	10
6	360	36	10	110 (360 − 250)	20 (110 − 90)	20	10

*Reread footnote 9 on p. 103.
**This is the increase necessary to account for the increased distance covered during each second. Do not confuse the *increase* in velocity with the velocity.

in the other columns. Make certain that you see how this is done. The value of K will hold for all values of t as long as we do not change the value of a by changing the tilt of the bar. The steeper the tilt, the greater the value of a.

Let us continue increasing the tilt. As we do so, we will find that we have increased our experimental difficulties because of the increased acceleration of the ball—our eyes are not good enough to mark the position of the ball at the end of the first second, let alone the second or third. We saw how Galileo had to give up and resort to reasoning. Modern electrical devices enable us easily to overcome Galileo's difficulty. With such a device we can measure the value of a when the bar is *vertical*. Actually, we dispense with the grooved bar since we are now measuring free fall. The value of a in free fall, commonly called the acceleration due to gravity, and hence assigned the special letter g, is very nearly 980 cm/sec^2 at sea level. This is slightly more than 32 ft/sec^2. These two figures should be memorized.[10] More important, you should know how

---

[10] Memorizing it as 1000 cm/sec^2 is easier; the error is about 2%.

to use them, just as you should know how to use the equations $d = \bar{v}t$, $v = at$, $d = \frac{1}{2}at^2$.

Another equation that is useful in calculating the velocity when we know only a and d is $v^2 = 2ad$. It is derived as follows:

$$t = \frac{v}{a}$$

Substituting this value of t in $d = \frac{1}{2}at^2$, we have

$$d = \frac{1}{2}a \times \frac{v^2}{a^2}$$

Solving for v^2

$$v^2 = 2ad \qquad [6\text{-}16]$$

Merely memorizing these equations is not learning science. You can learn to use them only by solving a number of problems in which they are essential. For this purpose, solve the exercises at the end of the chapter.

Although Galileo did not have the concept of force that we have today, he reasoned that in the case of a body thrown vertically upward, the cause of the slowing down on the upward journey should be the same as that which speeded it up on the downward journey. We now know that both of these effects are due to the downward-acting force of gravity on the ball. The same law ($d = \frac{1}{2}at^2$) applies; the slowing down is just as much a time rate of change in velocity as is the acceleration while the body is on its downward journey. The slowing down is called deceleration or negative acceleration.

Aristotle's Views on Horizontal Motion

Aristotle was less successful in his attempts to arrive at plausible conclusions regarding horizontal motion, which he called forced or violent motion, in contrast to free fall, which he called natural motion. He believed that a continually acting cause (which we now call a force) was necessary to keep a body moving horizontally at a uniform velocity. Inherent in this belief is the concept that rest is the natural state for terrestrial bodies. This is a common-sense view, for (as everyone has observed) if you leave a moving body alone it will come to a stop. All experiments that man could perform from Aristotle's day to 1957[11] led to the same view, even though from Newton's time on—if not from Galileo's—physicists have believed that if there were no air resistance, bodies in orbital motion about the earth would continue in motion forever.

The Aristotelians had to postulate a continuous force to act on a ball thrown by a pitcher

to a catcher if the ball was to continue moving after leaving the pitcher's hand. They thought the eddies of air that developed behind the ball as it moved onward supplied this force for a brief time. This view was a great stumbling block for 2000 years in the effort to arrive at a true concept of horizontal motion.

Galileo's Views on Horizontal Motion

Galileo contributed a wholly new point of view. Instead of continuing to try to answer the Aristotelian question concerning the cause of continued forced motion,[12] Galileo asked the more fruitful question, "What would make it stop?" He could devise no experiment (nor can we today) to test the Aristotelian question, but found it easy to test his more fruitful question.

Almost too obvious to be noticed is the observation that objects at rest stay at rest unless disturbed. Equally obvious is the necessity of a force to put them in motion. Galileo's experiments attempted to compare the effort to put in motion a body that is at rest with the effort needed to stop it. These he found to be nearly equal. What he did was to let a ball roll down one inclined plane and up another (Fig. 6-4a, b, c). No matter what weight ball he used, no matter whether the two planes were inclined at the same or at different angles, the ball would always roll to a height that was a little less than the height at which it started. He found that the smoother the planes and the rounder and smoother the ball, the less this difference in heights was. He reasoned that if the planes and the ball were infinitely smooth,

---

[11] The year the first artificial satellite was put in orbit around the earth by the Russians. It continued to move around the earth for some months—even though there was no force acting on it to propel it forward. There was a force acting on it to change its direction, that of gravity. Many artificial satellites have been put into orbit since 1957, and men have landed on the moon and returned to earth. None of these events has made any basic contribution to the science of motion as known by Newton 300 years ago. A more complete discussion follows in the next chapter.

[12] The reader must bear in mind the difference between Aristotle's natural motion and forced (violent) motion here on earth. Free fall was natural motion and needed no force to keep a body in motion. All other motion was forced motion.

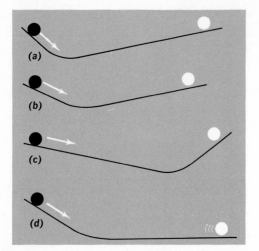

Fig. 6-4. Galileo's Experiment on Horizontal Motion. (*a–c*) Neglecting friction, a ball rolling down any incline to the bottom and up another will rise to the height from which it started but no farther. (*d*) Galileo generalized that if the plane were horizontal and infinitely smooth, the ball should roll on forever.

there would be no friction and the difference in heights would become zero. His conclusion was that the downward-acting force that caused the ball to roll down the incline also acted on the ball as it rolled up the opposite incline, causing it to slow down until it stopped. This force is, of course, gravity.

In another experiment he used a single inclined plane with long level boards as an extended horizontal plane (Fig. 6-4*d*). Given the same initial force, a ball rolling on a rough plane did not roll so far as on a smoother one. The smoother the plane and the rounder the ball, the farther the ball rolled. Galileo came to the conclusion that if a perfectly round and perfectly smooth ball were rolled along a perfectly smooth horizontal endless plane there would be nothing to stop the ball (assuming no air resistance), and so it would roll on forever. Here we find Galileo using a method that has been fruitfully used by scientists ever since. He idealized the situation by creating

an ideal world in which there was no friction to stop the ball, in order to understand better how the ball really rolled.

We know now that it is friction between the ball and the surface, and between the ball and the air, that stops the rolling. By stating that uniform motion is just as natural as is rest for bodies here on earth, Galileo gave these terrestrial bodies an attribute heretofore reserved for celestial bodies. Note also that Galileo here once more invoked *the method of the limiting case,* a method in which he first reasoned from motion on an inclined plane to motion in the vertical path of free fall, and then from a rough horizontal plane to a perfectly smooth frictionless one. On Galileo's ideal smooth horizontal plane no negative acceleration was discernible; that is, the ball showed no appreciable slowing down—its velocity appeared to be uniform.

The conclusion that in the absence of a net force, whether of friction or otherwise, a body will remain in unchanging motion or else at rest, was first given precise form in 1644 (two years after Galileo's death) by Descartes:

> We may remark that any velocity once imparted to a moving body will be rigidly maintained as long as there are no causes of acceleration or retardation, a condition that is found only on horizontal planes where the force of friction has also been minimized; for in case of planes that slope upwards there is already present a cause of retardation; from this it follows that motion along a smooth horizontal plane is perpetual.

Projectile Motion

Watch the path of a long high fly ball hit by a baseball batter on a windless day, or of a football on the kickoff, or of a thrown ball. If you are a careful observer, you will be struck by the near symmetry of its path. The second half of the path appears to be the same shape

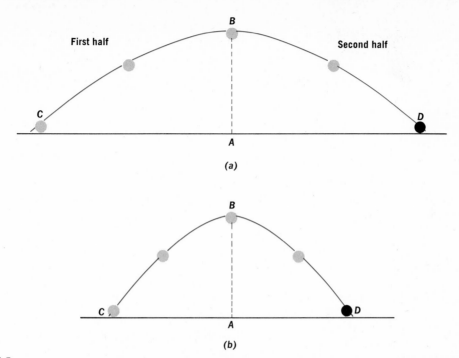

First half

Second half

(a)

(b)

Fig. 6-5. Independence of Horizontal and Vertical Motions. Paths of balls fired from an old-fashioned cannon, or of baseballs batted on a windless day. Note the symmetry of the paths. If the height *AB* is the same, the time the ball takes to move from *C* to *D* is the same regardless of the distance *CD*. (Air resistance is neglected.)

as the first half, except in reverse (Fig. 6-5). The path of a cannon ball (a projectile) is similar, especially that of a slow-moving old-fashioned one. To Galileo the problem was simply that of a horizontal motion combined with a completely independent downward motion (free fall).

To an inquiring mind, this symmetry of the path might suggest that the upward and the downward paths are traversed in equal times. This seems reasonable enough, and it can be checked by experiment.

There is, however, far more to projectile motion than this (Figs. 6-6 and 6-7). Consider the path of a bullet fired *horizontally* from a modern high-powered rifle, say one with a muzzle velocity of 3000 ft/sec. Assume that the ground surface is level and that the barrel

of the gun is 4 ft above the ground when you fire, and that you are out in the wide open spaces. Where and when will the bullet hit the ground? What will its path be like? When will the bullet start to fall to the ground? Suppose that, at the exact instant the bullet left the barrel of your gun, your friend dropped an identical bullet from the same height to the ground. Would it strike the ground before, at the same time, or later than the bullet fired from the gun?

All the ancients up to Galileo would have failed these questions just as dismally as you probably will. Galileo worked out problems such as these when he solved the closely related problem of projectile motion. He did this by recognizing two facts: that the path of a projectile was a combination of vertical and

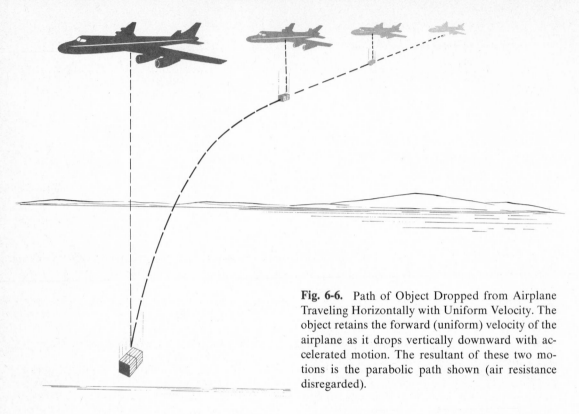

Fig. 6-6. Path of Object Dropped from Airplane Traveling Horizontally with Uniform Velocity. The object retains the forward (uniform) velocity of the airplane as it drops vertically downward with accelerated motion. The resultant of these two motions is the parabolic path shown (air resistance disregarded).

horizontal motion and *that these two motions are completely independent of each other*.[13] This means that, in Fig. 6-5, the vertical motion indicated by *AB* is governed by the law of free fall and that the horizontal motion indicated by *CD* will, if we neglect air resistance, go on forever *if* there is nothing to stop it. There is, of course, something to stop it—the earth—for every body thrown into the air at any angle whatever is acted on by a force, that of gravity, which starts to act to bring the body to earth *the instant that it leaves the propelling instrument*.[14] You should now go back and try to

answer the questions concerning the firing of the rifle bullet.

The concept that bodies in motion will remain in motion forever if there is nothing to stop them is incorporated in the law of inertia (later known as Newton's first law of motion). This law and the law of uniformly accelerated motion (of which the law of free fall is a special case) are Galileo's two great contributions to the understanding of the problem of motion. In the hands of Newton their inherent potentialities led, as Galileo himself predicted, "to wonderful new knowledge." Of equally great importance was Galileo's emphasis on clear, well-formulated problems capable of being analyzed mathematically and checked carefully by experiment. He defined the physical properties of motion so precisely that they could be used in mathematical operations. He established the necessary conditions for the

[13] One should not read into this statement the concept that projectiles have separate vertical and horizontal motions. In our analysis of motion we split the real motion into two parts to understand it better. The rules for doing this are discussed under vectors in Chapter 5.

[14] This means that no unsupported object can ever move horizontally through the air, for the instant it leaves the hand (or the gun barrel) it starts to drop with an acceleration of 32 ft/sec^2.

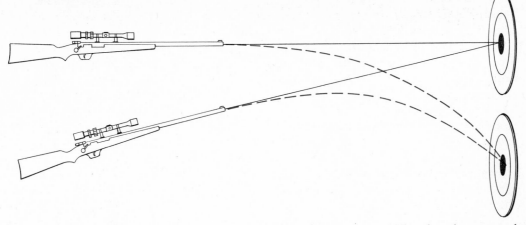

Fig. 6-7. To hit the bull's eye the rifle must be aimed at a point somewhat higher than the target unless the proper adjustment has been made in the sights to take care of the fall of the bullet. How much higher or how much adjustment depends on two things, the muzzle velocity of the bullet and the distance from the target. It is impossible to make any unsupported object follow a horizontal path for even one second.

great growth of science that took place in the 17th century, a century justifiably called the century of genius.

Exercises

1. Every equation has its limiting conditions; that is, no equation is valid under all conditions in experimental science. Which of the equations below are valid for uniformly accelerated motion?

$$d = \bar{v}t$$
$$d = \tfrac{1}{2}at^2$$
$$v^2 = 2ad$$
$$v = at$$
$$a = \frac{v_f - v_i}{t}$$
$$\bar{v} = \frac{v_f + v_i}{2}$$
$$d = Kt^2$$

2. You should not so much memorize the above equations as understand them. Memorizing science is not learning science.

What two equations (above) are different forms of the same equation?

3. If $v_i = 0$, what do $\bar{v}$ and a, respectively, become?

4. Why may Galileo be considered the father of modern science?

5. How did Aristotle explain free fall?

6. Why did Galileo use inclined planes in his experiments on free fall rather than let objects drop from high places?

7. How did Galileo progress from the steepest inclined plane that he could use to completely free fall?

8. A car starting from rest is uniformly accelerated to 60 mi/hr in 12 sec. What equations do you use to determine (a) its acceleration and (b) the distance it traveled in those 12 sec? (c) What was its velocity at the end of 5 sec?

9. In the equation $d = \tfrac{1}{2}at^2$, what is the value of K in general? What is its numerical value in free fall?

10. Before Galileo came to his final conclusion regarding either free fall or horizontal motion, he was forced to indulge in some

thought experiments. What were these thought experiments, and why were they necessary?

11. Why are two time units, such as in 15 (cm/sec)/sec or 5 (mi/hr)/sec, necessary in any quantitative statement about acceleration?

12. A car travels 40 mi at 40 mi/hr and 40 mi at 60 mi/hr. Calculate its average speed for the 80 mi. Show how you arrived at your result. (The answer is *not* 50 mi/hr.)

13. A ball is dropped from the top of a building. It takes 8 sec to reach the ground.
    (a) How high is the building?
    (b) What, neglecting air resistance, will the velocity of the ball be the instant before it touches the ground?

14. You wish to measure the depth of a deep well but have no line long enough. You drop a stone and time it until you hear it strike the water. If the time is 5 sec, how deep is the well? (Neglect the time for sound to travel back to you.)

15. A ball is thrown vertically upward with an initial velocity of 128 ft/sec. Neglect air resistance.
    (a) What will be its velocity after 1 sec?
    (b) How long will it take to rise to its highest point?
    (c) How high will it rise?
    (d) How long will it take to return to the thrower's hand?
    (e) What will be the velocity of the ball as it returns to the thrower's hand?

16. You are in an elevator at the 50th floor of the Empire State Building when some-thing goes wrong with the mechanism. The elevator drops with an acceleration of 32 ft/sec^2. On the way down you accidentally let go of a package you have been carrying. Will the package drop to the floor, rise to the top of the elevator, or remain stationary relative to you? Explain.

17. An object is given both an initial horizontal velocity and a vertical velocity. What effect will these two velocities have upon each other, if any?

18. From an airplane flying at an elevation of 5000 ft and with a velocity of 300 mi/hr a package weighing 50 lb is dropped. After the package is dropped, the plane continues to fly in the same straight line at the same elevation and the same speed. Where will the plane be when the package strikes the ground with respect to the spot where the package lands? Neglect air resistance.

19. Memorize $g = 980$ cm/sec^2 = 9.8 m/sec^2 = 32 ft/sec^2. What is g?

20. What "kind" of velocity does the speedometer on a car record?

21. Galileo once said that in order to test Aristotle's statement that two objects of different weights would fall at "rates" proportional to their weights, it would be necessary to drop the objects from a station of substantial height and then to drop them from a station at twice that height. For what reasons might Galileo have suggested this experiment from two such stations rather than from a single station?

The Laws of Motion and Gravitation

It was fortunate that Isaac Newton was born in the year Galileo died rather than in the year Galileo was born, because it is unlikely that Newton would ever have published anything if he had encountered the same sort of opposition that Galileo had to contend with. He was a shy introspective man, who disliked intensely the controversy on which Galileo thrived.

No one must think that Newton's great creation can be overthrown by Relativity or any other theory. His clear and wide ideas will forever retain their significance as the foundation on which our modern conceptions of physics have been built.
ALBERT EINSTEIN

The Changing Mental Climate of the Seventeenth Century

In the 50 years that followed Galileo's death there occurred a striking change in the mental climate of the time. Experimental science became a respectable tool, used by men like Boyle, Huygens, Pascal, Torricelli, von Guericke, Halley, Roemer, Hooke, Descartes, and others. The new attitude of these men led to an impressive array of discoveries, theories, and inventions, an array responsible for the

17th century being called the century of genius.

This is not to say that the religious opposition and its strong reliance on tradition had died. It had, however, become less intense; men were less intolerant, and more willing to attempt to reconcile traditional views with a Copernican universe. This change came about, not by any change of heart among Galileo's opponents, but by their deaths. A new generation, born, reared, and educated in a world of quickening cultural, political, economic, and scientific changes, was less ready to condemn for heresy. Medieval mysticism and medieval habits of thought still lingered on, even among the scientists themselves, for every man is a prisoner to some extent of the mental climate of his time. Astrology was still almost universally accepted; even Newton investigated it seriously. Newton, however, would not pretend to explanations that could never be tested.

We must not look back with scorn on the beliefs of the literate people of the 17th century, for we have only to look around us today to see that many literate people, including hosts of college graduates, still accept one or more of those mystic beliefs. We might almost say that most people would rather accept a supernatural explanation than a natural one for an unfamiliar phenomenon. To many, the fact that a satisfactory natural explanation is not at hand at the moment is evidence enough that the cause is a supernatural one.

One other consideration differentiated the scientific world of Newton from that of Galileo. This was the emergence of scientific societies, which made it possible for scientists to meet to discuss, debate, and cooperate (or quarrel) and to publish scientific journals in which their discoveries and their theories were made public. These journals also played a leading part in making science international, for, previously, scientists could inform others of their discoveries only by writing long, time-consuming letters.

Sir Isaac Newton a Biographical Sketch

Isaac Newton (1642–1727), son of an English farmer, has been called the greatest genius that ever lived; certainly there are few who could contest him for that honor. If he had died at the age of 26, his name would still have gone down through the ages as one of the greatest scientists of all time, for he had already formulated his laws of motion, invented both differential and integral calculus, laid the groundwork for his famous law of gravitation, and made fundamental discoveries in optics. He had also done extensive work in astronomy, chemistry, and logic. Throughout his lifetime he spent fully as much, if not more, time on theology and biblical research as he did on scientific research. When he was about 40, after much urging, he published the results of his researches in the *Principia,* said by many to be the greatest book in science ever written.

Newton's genius was recognized in his own lifetime. As a reward for his scientific contributions he was made Director of the Mint in 1699 and was knighted in 1703. In addition, he served in Parliament and was president of the Royal Society from 1703 until his death in 1727. He was buried in Westminster Abbey.

Newton's First Law of Motion—The Law of Inertia

As we already know, Newton's first law of motion was not original with him. He took it over almost verbatim from Galileo. Newton's contributions to the law were that he defined inertia and that he generalized beyond all experience when he stated: *Every body continues in a state of rest, or of motion at constant speed in a straight line, unless disturbed by a force acting on it.* The first proposition is as apparent to us as it was to Galileo and Newton. So certain are we that a body at rest will remain so unless disturbed that if we see movement without noticeable cause, we feel impelled to investigate.

The second proposition in this first law is far more subtle, even difficult, for some to believe. It means that *the velocity of a moving body does not change unless a force acts on it.* In still other words, *a force is not needed to keep a body in motion.* This seems contrary to experience. Neither Galileo nor Newton could prove it. However, Newton realized that it is a common phenomenon in the solar system. Although gravity is a force acting on the planets, their satellites, the sun, and the other components of the solar system, it does not keep them in motion but it does change their paths from straight lines to elliptical orbits. Galileo reasoned the law out from one of his inclined-plane experiments (Fig. 6-4*d*). He concluded that if he kept the inclined plane on the left at a constant angle as he reduced the angle of the plane on the right, the ball would roll farther and farther before it reached the height from which it started. If the plane on the right were horizontal, the ball could never rise to its original height. Therefore, he reasoned that it should go on forever. Note that he "reasoned away" friction and air resistance. This was one of Galileo's "thought" experiments. We can never isolate our experiments here on earth from friction and air resistance, so this second proposition seems contrary to experience.

It may be possible in the future to test the law of inertia by means of space probes in outer space far beyond the gravitational influences of the solar system or any atmospheric resistance or frictional forces. Such interstellar probes should, according to the first law, travel in straight lines only. However, at present such observations are beyond the abilities of our detecting instruments.

To fix firmly the meaning of this first law let us consider the following: Suppose that you had filled a cart with groceries at a supermarket and were taking it to the checkout station. Let us assume that there is no friction, either by the wheels on the axles or by the wheels on the level floor. The cart with its load weighs 50 lb and you are pushing it at a constant velocity of 100 ft/min. What force must you exert on it as long as it moves in a straight line at this constant speed? The answer is, "None." You needed to exert a force to start it from rest. You will also need to exert a force if you want to change its direction or to change its speed or to stop it, but you need no force to keep it moving at constant velocity—*if there is no friction.*

But there are no frictionless carts, so you do have to exert a force even if you push it in a straight line at constant speed. How much force? Just enough to counterbalance the opposing frictional force. The net force, sometimes called the resultant force, is then zero. The net or resultant force is defined as the *vector sum* (Chapter 5) of all the forces acting on the cart. If the frictional force is 10 lb, then you need to exert a force of 10 lb to keep it moving at constant velocity. If you exert a greater force than this, the cart will accelerate. We say again, an object with zero *resultant* force acting on it stays either at rest or moves with constant velocity. Such an object is said to be in *equilibrium.* It will show no change of speed or direction. Equilibrium refers to a *single* object only. Newton's second law will give us a clearer insight as to how this comes about.

Concepts of Force, Mass, and Inertia

We have been talking somewhat glibly about force, mass, and inertia without defining them precisely. Intuitively we know what a *force* is. We might simply call it a push or a pull. More formally, it is anything that tends to accelerate a body either positively or negatively, that is, anything that tends to slow down or speed up the motion or change the direction of motion of a body. The acceleration is always in the direction of the force, for force is, as we have already intimated, a vector quantity. If the resultant force is in the direction of motion, the body will be speeded up; if it is opposite to the motion, it will be slowed down, and if the force is at right angles to the motion, the body will be continuously deflected from a straight line (see discussion of circular motion).

Mass is another term with which we all feel some familiarity, even though our ideas about it may be somewhat vague. Most of us think of mass as quantity of matter, and many confuse it with weight. Matter is anything that requires a force to accelerate it. Thus we identify electrons as particles of matter because they require a force to accelerate them. Newton stated that a fundamental property of all matter is its ability to resist any change in its state of motion; that is, it resists acceleration. This resistance to a change in its state of motion is called *inertia*. Anything that has inertia has mass. In fact, the mass of a body may be measured by the amount of inertia it possesses. We might refer to the mass determined in this way as the inertial mass. This inertial mass may be determined by measuring the force needed to give a body a certain acceleration (which can also be measured). Ordinarily we determine the mass of a body simply by weighing it (for a fuller discussion see p. 134).

Newton's Second Law of Motion

Experiment shows that if we double the force, F, on the same body, its acceleration, a, will be twice as great; if we triple the force, the acceleration will be tripled, and so on. In other words, for a given mass, $F \propto a$. Experiment also shows that if we double the mass, m, we will have to double the force to get the

same acceleration. This means that $F \propto m$. It follows that if we double the mass but keep the force as before, we will get only half the acceleration. Thus, the acceleration is inversely proportional to the mass if F remains constant, that is, $a \propto 1/m$.

Newton combined these proportionalities to formulate his second law: *A force is required to accelerate a body; the magnitude of this force is directly proportional to the mass of the body, and to the acceleration produced.* Mathematically,

$$F \propto ma \qquad \text{or} \qquad F = Kma \qquad [7\text{-}1]$$

Since we will define force in the same system of units (p. 80) in which we expressed m and a, the value of K in Eq. 7-1 is 1, and so may be omitted as a convenience. Hence, we write

$$F = ma$$

Other forms of this proportionality are

$$a = \frac{F}{m} \qquad \text{and} \qquad m = \frac{F}{a}$$

The second of these forms shows us how to calculate the inertial mass if we know F and a.

This law tells us that if a is 0, F is also 0, and so no force is required to keep a body moving at constant velocity if there is no friction. This is what we were saying in our discussion of the first law, which is therefore a special case of the second law. The second law reiterates in a mathematical form our statement in the first law that if there is no friction, no counteracting force, a moving body will continue moving at constant velocity forever.

We need to clarify the concept of friction. Friction is a force that commonly arises at the contact between two objects, and always opposes the relative motion of objects. Galileo maintained that friction between two bodies in contact was always present because perfectly smooth surfaces were impossible to make. Newton's approach was somewhat different. Since experience shows us that here on earth all moving bodies slow down and stop, there must be a force acting on them, for only a force can produce an acceleration. It follows that friction is a force, for it slows down moving bodies here on earth. It also follows that if the frictional force is 0, there will be no slowing down unless some other force is exerted.

The Concept of Momentum

Newton did not express his second law in terms of mass and acceleration but in terms of time rate of change of momentum. By motion Newton meant quantity of motion, which is what we call *momentum* today. Mathematically it is *mv* (mass times velocity). Thus a 2 ton car has twice the momentum of a 1 ton car moving at the same speed, or it has the same momentum as a 1 ton car moving at twice the speed. Today we try to answer, in terms of momentum, the old pre-Galilean question, "What keeps a body in motion after the impelling force has been removed?" Consider an ice hockey puck sliding over the ice. We say that the puck has been given a quantity of motion that is gradually dissipated by friction as motion is imparted to the atoms or molecules of the ice at the contact of the puck and the ice.

The identity of $F = ma$ and $F = $ rate of change of momentum is shown as follows:

$$F = ma$$

and

$$a = \frac{v_f - v_i}{t}$$

Hence

$$F = m\left(\frac{v_f - v_i}{t}\right)$$

Therefore

$$F = \frac{mv_f - mv_i}{t} \qquad \text{[7-2]}$$

Units of Force

To make quantitative determinations by use of the second law, we need a unit of force. For example, how much force is necessary to give a mass of 1 g an acceleration of 1 cm/sec^2?

$$F = ma$$
$$= 1 \text{ g} \times 1 \frac{\text{cm}}{\text{sec}^2}$$
$$= 1 \frac{\text{g-cm}}{\text{sec}^2}$$

The unit g-cm/sec^2 is an inconvenient unit to write and is therefore given a shorter name, the *dyne*. Thus 1 dyne is the force that can impart an acceleration of one cm/sec^2 to a mass of 1 g. The dyne is a very small unit, about the size of the force imparted by a mosquito alighting on your forehead.

An important special case is illustrated by this question: How much force is necessary to give a mass of 1 g the acceleration of gravity, 980 cm/sec^2?

$$F = ma = mg$$
$$= 1 \text{ g} \times 980 \frac{\text{cm}}{\text{sec}^2}$$
$$= 980 \frac{\text{g-cm}}{\text{sec}^2}$$
$$= 980 \text{ dynes}$$

This is the force that the gravitational attraction of the earth exerts on a 1 g mass and is called the *weight* of a 1 g mass; that is, a 1 g mass (at the surface of the earth) has a weight of 980 dynes. However, in common laboratory usage, 980 dynes weight is usually called a 1 g *weight* as distinguished from 1 g *mass*. On some other planet the acceleration of gravity would be different; therefore, the force the planet exerts on a 1 g mass (by the second law) would be different and the weight of this 1 g mass would be different (not 980 dynes).

A larger unit is commonly used by physicists. It is that force which will impart an acceleration of 1 m/sec^2 to a mass of 1 kg. It is called the newton (for obvious reasons). It is equal to 100,000 dynes. To give a mass of 50 kg an acceleration[1] of 9.8 m/sec^2, the force necessary is

$$F = ma \ (= mg)$$
$$= 50 \text{ kg} \times 9.8 \ \frac{\text{m}}{\text{sec}^2}$$
$$= 490 \ \frac{\text{kg-m}}{\text{sec}^2} = 490 \text{ newtons}$$

Did You Ever See a Force?

Physiologically it is quite possible to detect a force applied to one's own body. But how do you know when a force is being applied to some other object? A force cannot be seen (like matter), nor can it be measured *directly* (like length). The only evidence we have for the existence of a force—and only an unbalanced force at that—is a change in the state of motion of an object. For example, suppose a small piece of iron is standing on a table. We strike it with a hammer; it moves. We bring a magnet near it; again it moves. In each case, we say a force has been exerted on the iron. But we have not seen the force; we have only seen a change in a state of motion. From this point of view a force has no concrete existence; it is a "construct" that we find useful in explaining quantitative aspects of motion. Then are forces "real"? Such a question has little

value in science. The concept of *force* is useful and therefore we use it, for it leads to a better understanding of natural phenomena.

Newton's Third Law of Motion—The Law of Action and Reaction

Simple as the statements of the first two laws seem, we have learned that they have hidden subtleties in them, subtleties that must be grasped if the laws are to be understood. The third law is still more subtle. It was these subtleties that escaped the ancients and that make force and motion so difficult to understand. Galileo took the first few steps toward understanding and Newton went the rest of the way.

To paraphrase Newton's original statement of the third law: "The mutual actions of *two* objects on each other are always equal but opposite in direction." More commonly we say: *To every action there is an equal and opposite reaction. The action is always on one body, the reaction always on another.* Another way of expressing the third law is, "If one object exerts a force on a second object, then the second object exerts an equal and opposite force on the first." This third law means that there is no such thing as a single force; forces always go in pairs and act along the same straight line, but in opposite directions and on two different bodies. Neither force is the cause of the other; rather each is the cause of the other. They appear exactly simultaneously and disappear the same way.

Applications of the Third Law

Consider the earth in its orbit about the sun. If there were no forces operating on either, both would travel in straight lines (Newton's first law). The fact that they do not is evidence

---

[1] The acceleration due to gravity (*g*), expressed in meters per second per second, is 9.8 m/sec^2.

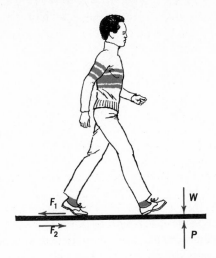

Fig. 7-1. Forces Acting on Man Walking at Constant Velocity. If all motion were truly horizontal, the W–P pair could be eliminated from consideration. It is the F_1–F_2 pair that produces the motion.

that forces are operating on them. The sun exerts a force on the earth by virtue of its gravitational attraction and the earth exerts an equal and opposite force on the sun. *Note carefully that these forces operate on different bodies.* $F = MA$ for the sun, and $F = ma$ for the earth. It follows that $MA = ma$. However, M is so vastly greater than m that the value of A is insignificant compared to that of a. The result is that the earth is being constantly accelerated toward the sun (p. 131) and so travels in a nearly circular path.

Let us now take the case of a man walking on a level stretch of ground (Fig. 7-1). To walk he must push against the earth with his feet (force F_1).[2] The earth also pushes against his feet with an equal and opposite force (force F_2). The man is accelerated forward because of an unbalanced force on him; the earth is also accelerated in the opposite direction, but

[2] If you do not see that this is so, imagine yourself trying to walk on perfectly smooth ice, where your feet cannot push against the ice nor the ice against your feet.

by a negligible amount because the reaction is on such a large mass. If you can imagine a man walking on an earth that has the same mass as the man, you should be able to see that such an earth would be accelerated backward while he is accelerated forward at the same rate.

As another example, let us assume that you are holding a book up in the air as shown in Fig. 7-2. What are the forces acting on the book? There is a downward force, W, due to the pull of the earth on the book. Another is the upward push, F_1, of your hand on the book. These two forces are equal and opposite if you hold the book still, but *they are not action and reaction forces.* For one thing they both operate on the same body, the book, whereas action and reaction forces never act on the same body. The reaction force to W is the upward pull, P, of the book on the earth, whereas the reaction force to F_1 is the downward force, F_2, of the book on your hand. In other words, Newton's third law says that $W = P$ and $F_1 = F_2$. It says nothing whatever about the relationship of W to either F_1 or F_2. If you hold the book still, then $W = F_1$; but if you raise the book, you are accelerating it (momentarily, at least), and F_1 becomes greater than W, but F_1 still remains equal and

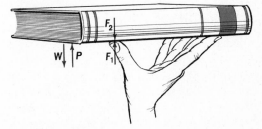

Fig. 7-2. Forces Acting on Book Held on Hand. There are two sets of reaction forces, W–P, and F_1–F_2. Note carefully the origin of the two forces in each action-reaction pair. If the book is at rest, the two pairs of forces are equal. If the book is being accelerated either upward or downward, they are not equal.

opposite to F_2. The resultant force, $F_1 - W$, accelerates the book upward; that is,

$$F_1 - W = ma$$

If the book is lowered, then F_1 becomes less than W (momentarily, at least). The resultant force, $W - F_1$, accelerates the body downward; that is,

$$W - F_1 = ma$$

But, as always, $F_1 = F_2$. Throughout all of these changes the action-reaction pairs of forces remain equal and opposite.

Consider one more everyday example, a woman pushing a shopping cart at constant velocity in a supermarket (Fig. 7-3). There are at least three important pairs of forces here, F_1-F_2, F_3-F_4, and F_5-F_6 (we will ignore the gravitational forces):

F_1 = force exerted by woman against cart
F_2 = reaction force exerted by cart against woman
F_3 = force exerted by feet of woman against floor

F_4 = reaction force exerted by floor against feet of woman
F_5 = force of friction of wheels against floor
F_6 = reaction force of floor against wheels

The last two pairs of forces, F_3-F_4 and F_5-F_6, arise because of friction. The resultant force on the cart is zero and the cart continues at constant velocity. Then why must the woman continue to exert a force on the cart? There is one force acting to stop the cart: the frictional force F_6. If the woman's force F_1 is equal to F_6 then the cart is in equilibrium and it continues to move with uniform motion. Suppose the woman spies a bargain down the aisle and wants to accelerate the *cart,* then what change must she make in the force relationships on the *cart?*

Why do we perform involved analyses such as these? Are Newton's laws really necessary? It is quite true that you could go through life without knowing anything about them; after all, people have been doing just that for many millenia. First, let us consider an "impractical" noneconomic reason that is, in our opinion, the most important one of all. An understanding of these principles and this method

Fig. 7-3. Pushing Shopping Cart at Constant Velocity. Three pairs of action-reaction forces are involved. Although each member of any one pair is equal but opposite to the other member of the pair, the various pairs are not necessarily equal to each other (see text).

Fig. 7-4. Newton's Proposed Jet-Propelled Steam Engine. A fire built under the boiler partly filled with water created large quantities of steam, which, on being ejected at high speed to the rear, drove the cart forward. Thus the principle of jet or rocket propulsion was known to Newton. (Courtesy The Bettmann Archive.)

of analysis gives one a different view of the operation of simple, everyday phenomena, a view that should be more satisfying than just accepting the surface appearances of these phenomena without any inquiry into possible basic relationships. From a practical standpoint, these principles are necessary for the design of almost all our modern structures and probably all modern machinery. They also are necessary for investigations of the motions of planets, stars, galaxies, and subatomic particles. They are one of the most important bases of science.

We may illustrate the usefulness of such analyses by additional examples of the application of Newton's third law. What propels a propeller-type airplane forward, on the ground or in the air?[3] What propels a jet plane or a rocket? In the first, the propeller throws great quantities of air to the rear (action) and is itself "thrown" forward (reaction). In a jet plane or a rocket, great quantities of hot gases are ejected (pushed) to the rear (action) and the plane or rocket is pushed forward (reaction) (Fig. 7-4).

The propeller of an outboard motor or those

[3]What provides the lift is another problem.

of a great ocean liner push water to the rear and so they are propelled forward. If you attempt to take what looks like an easy jump from a rowboat or canoe to the shore or a dock without taking into account Newton's third law, you may be in for a ducking. Many more examples could be cited, for Newton's laws are applicable to the whole field of linear motion.

Linear Momentum and Its Conservation

We have already seen (p. 115) how Newton used rate of change in momentum to derive his second law. Our previous discussion of the concept dealt only with its relationship to that law. Restated in terms of momentum, the second law becomes: *The net force acting on a body is equal to its change in momentum per unit of time.* We have already learned that when a net force acts on a body, that body is accelerated. Since Newton defined momentum as *mv* (mass times instantaneous velocity), it is seen that the momentum of a body being accelerated is changing (since the velocity is changing). A given net force, acting on a body, A, for a given time, will produce a certain change in its momentum. This same force acting for the same time on a body, B, of twice the mass will give B only half the acceleration of A (for $F \propto ma$). Yet the same change of momentum results. Similarly, the same change in momentum results if the same force acts for the same time on a body, C, of half the mass of A. Our conclusion is that *a given net force will produce the same change in momentum in a given time regardless of the mass of the body.*

Perhaps the role of time in the change of momentum is not clear. Suppose that a number of you are in an automobile driving down a road at 60 mi/hr. The car and each of you have a certain momentum. If the car slows down and stops, there is a certain change in momentum. The change in mv is the same regardless of the time involved in stopping. But all of you know that if the driver has to slam on the brakes (which are excellent) the effect

on you will be very different than if he slowed down gradually. Look at the equation,

$$F = \frac{mv_2 - mv_1}{t}$$

listed on p. 115 as one form of Newton's second law. This equation could be written

$$F(t_2 - t_1) = mv_2 - mv_1$$

where $t_2 - t_1$ is the time the force operates. Applied to our automobile it is the time interval between the first application of the brakes and the final stopping of the car. Since for a given situation $mv_2 - mv_1$ is constant, it should be apparent that the bigger $t_2 - t_1$ is, the smaller F will be. Thus F will be small if one slows down gradually, large if one has to slam on the brakes, or hit a truck, to stop.

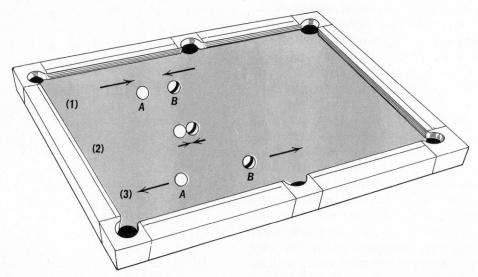

Fig. 7-5. Head-on Collision of Billiard Balls. Since the masses of the two balls are equal in (1), $(+mv_A) + (-mv_B) = 0$ if the velocities are the same. At the instant of impact (2) the velocity of each is 0, so that the same relationship holds. If the collision is perfectly elastic, after collision $(-mv_A) + (mv_B) = 0$ also. Note that $+mv$ indicates motion to the right, $-mv$ to the left. Thus, the total momentum of the system remains constant throughout if there is no loss of velocity due to friction.

It is advisable to have some part of the car other than the passenger compartment designed to collapse comparatively slowly. Commonly the trunk and the engine compartments are so constructed. This will increase $t_2 - t_1$ and thus decrease F. Of course, F is also exerted on the occupants, and, unless there is some physical restraint on them, F will throw them against the walls or windows of the car or even out of the doors. This effect is prevented by seat belts, which apply a reactive F against such comparatively safe parts of the body as the chest and abdomen and prevent contact of head and limbs with the passenger compartment walls.

There are various ways of stating the law of conservation of momentum. It states in effect that *no operation of forces between the bodies in a system can change the momentum of the system as a whole.* Two balls colliding may have very different velocities before and after the collision but their resultant momentum is the same. It makes no difference whether the collision is head-on, or one is struck from behind as the other overtakes it, or one is at rest when struck by the other, just so long as the only net forces acting are mutual interaction forces of the bodies within the system.

This returns us to the third law. When two billiard balls, A and B (Fig. 7-5), collide, the forces between them are equal and opposite. Since the time the forces act is the same for both balls, both must undergo the same change in momentum but in opposite directions. Thus, the change in mv of A equals the change in mv of B. It matters not what the masses are, or what the original or final velocities are. If the mass of B were twice that of A, its instantaneous velocity would be half that of A. For two balls with equal masses rolling toward each other with the same speed (Fig. 7-5), the momentum of A before impact is $+mv_A$ and that of B is $-mv_B$ where $(+)$ means to the

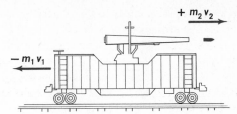

Fig. 7-6. Conservation of Momentum (Linear) Illustrated by Shell Fired from Cannon Mounted on Railway Car. Neglecting friction, the mv of the gun and car to the left equals the mv of the shell to the right; that is, $(-m_1v_1) + (+m_2v_2) = 0$. If m_1 and m_2 are known and the velocity given to the car, v_2, is measured, the muzzle velocity of the shell can be calculated.

right and $(-)$ to the left. At any time the total momentum of the balls is $(+mv_A) + (-mv_B) = 0$. The force on each ball and the time of their mutual interaction are the same, but the forces are oppositely directed.[4] Therefore the resultant force is zero, and there is no change in momentum. After impact the balls have reversed their directions, so the momentum of each has the opposite sign from that before impact. The total momentum after impact is given by $-mv_A + mv_B$.

Another way of saying this is that if the external resultant forces are zero, momentum is conserved. If we compare this statement with Newton's third law, we find that it is simply another way of stating that forces occurring in pairs are equal and opposite. All of the phenomena explained by action and reaction can be equally well explained by the law of conservation of linear momentum. Thus, in a jet plane or rocket, the momentum of the gases ejected from the rear is equal to the momentum given to the plane in the opposite direction.

In all our examples illustrating action and reaction, there is none that proves that the ac-

[4] Friction with the table is external force, that is, outside the system.

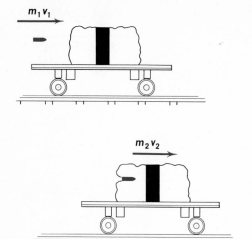

Fig. 7-7. The velocity of a bullet at any distance may be determined by firing it into a bale of cotton on a nearly frictionless cart and measuring the velocity given to the cart. The *mv* of the bullet before impact must be equal to the *mv* of the cart and the bullet after impact.

tion and the reaction are equal. The only way that they can be proved equal is by measuring the changes in the momenta of the bodies on which action and reaction take place (Figs. 7-6 and 7-7). These changes can be measured in most cases, though not in all. For instance, we cannot measure the momentum given the earth when we start to run, but we can measure the corresponding momentum given a movable platform mounted on nearly frictionless wheels and floor as we run on the platform. We therefore feel that momentum is conserved wherever action and reaction take place.

Uniform Circular Motion

Before we leave the all-important subject of force and motion, we must investigate briefly motion in a circle with uniform speed if we wish to understand the motions of the planets and satellites of our solar system. The essential difference between linear and circular motion

is that the direction of the motion in the latter is constantly changing, whereas in the former it is constant. This difference is important, because, as we have already learned, (1) a body in motion will continue in motion in a straight line forever if no forces act on it, and (2) it takes a net force to change the direction of a moving body.

Is an object in uniform circular motion being accelerated? Yes, the term *acceleration* applies to any change in motion whether it be in speed or direction or both. Since an object moving in a circle is continuously changing direction, it is continuously being accelerated and therefore is subject to a continuously acting unbalanced force. We shall show that this acceleration and the force that causes it are both directed toward the center of the circle.

The force needed to maintain uniform circular motion turns out to be mv^2/r; that is, $a = v^2/r$ in the equation $F = ma$. There are various ways of deriving this ratio for a, one of which is given in the next section. The mathematically inclined will have little trouble in following the geometry. All, however, should master the material on forces in uniform circular motion, if they are to understand the orbiting of artificial satellites and spaceships.

Determination of Acceleration in Uniform Circular Motion

Consider a stone of mass m being whirled in a horizontal circle of radius r with a constant speed of v cm/sec (Fig. 7-8). A little experimentation will show that as we vary r the minimum speed necessary to keep the stone moving in the circle will vary also. It will also show that the force necessary to maintain circular motion varies as either r or v is varied.

At the instant the stone is at A (Fig. 7-9), the velocity is given by the vector v_{old}. When the stone is at a point farther on in its orbit, say at B, it has a new velocity vector, v_{new}. Where there is a change in velocity, there is

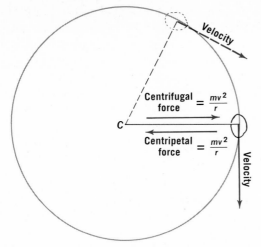

Fig. 7-8. Forces in Circular Motion. A stone at the end of a string is whirled in a horizontal circle (to negate the effects of gravity) at a constant speed by a hand at C. The speed of the stone along its circular path is constant, but its direction and therefore its velocity change. The inward-pointing arrow (centripetal force) represents the action force exerted on the stone by the hand. The outward-pointing arrow (centrifugal force) represents the reaction force exerted on the hand by the stone. The stone is accelerated toward the center of the circle by the centripetal force. Note that only one force (centripetal) acts on the stone.

an acceleration. Our problem is to determine the magnitude and direction of the acceleration.

Acceleration is defined as

$$a = \frac{v_{\text{new}} - v_{\text{old}}}{t_A - t_B} = \frac{\Delta v}{\Delta t} \qquad [7\text{-}3]$$

The symbol Δ (delta) means "change in." Thus Eq. 7-3 reads "The acceleration is the change in velocity divided by the change in time." The Δ is merely an abbreviation and does not indicate a multiplication. Here Δt (delta t) is the change in time in going from A along the arc of the circle to B. This acceleration can be calculated in terms of v and r only, and to do it we resort to geometry.

Let us draw the chord $\overline{AB}$ (we place a bar over $\overline{AB}$ to distinguish it from the arc $\widehat{AB}$). If A is only an infinitesimally small distance from B, then the difference in length between $\overline{AB}$ and $\widehat{AB}$ is likewise infinitesimal.[5] Then, for all practical purposes, $\overline{AB} = \widehat{AB}$, and isosceles triangle $\overline{ABC}$ = circular sector $\widehat{ABC}$.

Consider the two shaded triangles, one with sides r_1, r_2, and $\overline{AB}$, and the other v_{old}, v_{new}, and Δv. Both are obviously isosceles triangles ($r_1 = r_2$ and $v_{\text{old}} = v_{\text{new}}$) and the apex angles C and O are equal.[6] Therefore the two triangles are similar, so that the lengths of their corresponding sides are in the same proportion. Thus,

$$\frac{\Delta v}{v} = \frac{\overline{AB}}{r}$$

[5] This geometrical analysis is not as precise as that got by use of the calculus, but the result is exactly the same.
[6] In Fig. 7-9 v_{old} is perpendicular to r_1 and v_{new} is perpendicular to r_2; hence the corresponding angles formed by their intersections are equal.

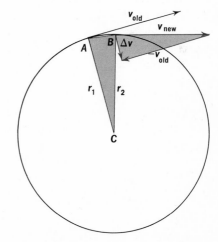

Fig. 7-9. Derivation of $a = v^2/r$. Since $\Delta v = v_{\text{new}} - v_{\text{old}}$, a vectorial subtraction has been performed. The direction of v_{old} has been reversed (vector subtraction) and it has been drawn parallel to itself, tail to head of v_{new}. The resultant vector is Δv. It can be seen that as the time interval between A and B becomes smaller, Δv would point more toward the center C.

Solving for Δv,

$$\Delta v = \frac{v \times \overline{AB}}{r}$$

Dividing both sides by Δt,

$$\frac{\Delta v}{\Delta t} = \frac{\frac{v \times \overline{AB}}{r}}{\Delta t} = \frac{v}{r} \times \frac{\overline{AB}}{\Delta t} \qquad [7\text{-}4]$$

Now since $\widehat{AB}/\Delta t$ is the speed of the stone along $\widehat{AB}$, and $\widehat{AB} = \overline{AB}$, then $\overline{AB}/\Delta t = v$. Substituting v for $\overline{AB}/\Delta t$ in Eq. 7-4, we have

$$\frac{\Delta v}{\Delta t} = \frac{v}{r} \times v = \frac{v^2}{r}$$

Since $\Delta v/\Delta t$ is the acceleration (Eq. 7-3), we have

$$a = \frac{(\text{speed around orbit})^2}{\text{radius of orbit}} = \frac{v^2}{r} \qquad [7\text{-}5]$$

Forces in Uniform Circular Motion

Since we will encounter the equation $a = v^2/r$ several times in this book, the student should be well acquainted with it and its meaning. It is the acceleration that a body has if it is moving with speed v in a circular orbit of radius r. Substituting v^2/r for a in $F = ma$, we have

$$F = \frac{mv^2}{r}$$

which is the force that must be applied to make a body of mass m move in a circle. Since the acceleration of the body is acting along a line directed toward the center of the circle,[7] it

[7] We can also see that this is so from our geometric analysis (Fig. 7-9). As B gets closer and closer to A, the angle between v_{old} and v_{new} gets smaller and smaller and Δv becomes nearly perpendicular to v. If the angle is infinitely small, we may say that to all intents and purposes, Δv is perpendicular to v. Since v is tangent to the circle at all times, the vector Δv must be directed toward the center, for a perpendicular to a tangent of a circle at the point of tangency must pass through the center.

follows that the force acting on it is also directed toward the center. Note that here a body has an acceleration that is directed toward a center, and yet the body neither goes any faster nor gets any closer to the center.

This inwardly directed force, F, is called *centripetal* (center-seeking) *force*. In the case of our stone revolving on the end of a string

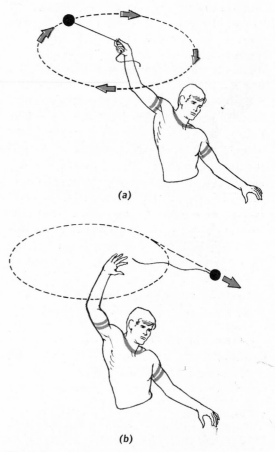

(a)

(b)

Fig. 7-10. An Inward-Directed Centripetal Force Acts upon Every Object That Moves in a Curved Path. (*a*) The string provides centripetal force. (*b*) If the centripetal force is removed, the object continues along a straight line tangent to the original circular path.

(Fig. 7-8) in a horizontal[8] circle, the inward force is provided by the string acting on the stone. If the only force acting on the stone when it is moving in its orbit at uniform speed is the centripetal force, "What," you may ask, "keeps it moving?" The answer is, "Nothing." You should not forget that it does not take a force to keep it moving, but only to start it moving, to change its speed, or to change its direction.

Thus, the only force needed to give a body uniform circular motion is one to push it in toward the center, if it has no other force operating on it. Cut or release the string and the centripetal force instantly disappears; the stone travels (neglecting gravity) in a straight line tangent to the circle at the point where it was when the string was cut (Fig. 7-10). The stone is merely "obeying" Newton's first law. Because of the stone's inertia, a force must be applied to it to change its direction. This is the centripetal force. The instant that centripetal force attempts to change the direction of the body's motion, a counterforce springs into being which resists that change of direction. This is the force of the stone on the string; it is the reaction force in Newton's third law. In uniform circular motion this force is properly called *centrifugal force*.[9] It is the force that the moving object (the stone) exerts on whatever is holding it in its path (the string); it is the force you feel operating on your hand via the string. If we treat the string as a mere transmitter of force, then the centripetal force is the inward force that your hand exerts on the stone via the string, and the centrifugal

force is the outward force exerted on your hand by the stone via the string. (Pay attention to the words *on* and *by*.) Note carefully that, like all action-reaction forces, centripetal and centrifugal forces are equal and opposite, and never operate on the same body. *There is no outward force exerted on the stone;* that is, no centrifugal force is exerted on the stone, and so centrifugal force plays no part in keeping the stone moving in a circle. Every moving body tends to move according to Newton's first law. To make such a body move in a circle a force is needed—centripetal force.

In Fig. 7-8 note the relative directions of the centripetal force, centrifugal force, and velocity vectors. If the diagram represented a car wheel turning clockwise rapidly in a mud hole, the mud would be "thrown" in a direction parallel to a velocity vector, not parallel to a centrifugal force vector. Actually the mud is not thrown when it leaves the wheel; it is merely continuing to move in the same direction it was moving at the instant before it left the wheel.

The fact that centrifugal force does not tend to push a body outward can easily be understood if we consider the revolution of the earth about the sun. No force is needed to keep the earth moving; one is needed to change its direction. This centripetal force is the gravitational attraction of the sun for the earth; it acts *on* the earth. But the earth also has an attraction for the sun. This is the centrifugal force; it acts *on* the sun, and tends to pull the sun closer to the earth. Again we say that there is no centrifugal force acting on the earth.

Angular Momentum and Its Conservation

Linear momentum is, as we have learned, a quantity of motion expressed by mv, a quantity that for any given body remains constant as long as v is constant. Since v is a vector, it cannot remain constant if its direction

---

[8] We will confine our attention to a circle in a horizontal plane because the force supplied by the hand may be kept constant without the force of gravity complicating the situation.

[9] There is frequent confusion in the literature on the use of the term *centrifugal force,* confusion with the so-called *centrifugal d'Alembert force.* The latter is a fictitious quasigravitational force used most commonly by engineers who wish to reduce problems in dynamics to problems in statics. Because of this fictitious force, some writers state that there is no real centrifugal force.

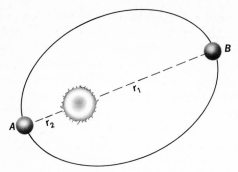

Fig. 7-11. Conservation of Angular Momentum. The earth in its orbit moves faster at A than at B, enough faster to compensate for the difference between r_1 and r_2. Thus, $mv_1r_1 = mv_2r_2$. The earth's angular momentum is therefore constant.

is constantly changing, as in the case of a body in uniform circular motion. Such a body has angular momentum as well as linear momentum.

For a revolving or rotating object we can make the general statement that *angular momentum = mvr*, where m is the mass of the object, v is its speed, and r may be loosely defined as the distance of the mass from the

center of revolution or rotation. Thus we can see that for an object of mass m, if we wish to increase its speed of revolution v (without applying an external force), we must decrease r, and vice versa. We will not attempt any rigorous mathematical derivation of the formula *mvr* here because such a derivation is complicated by distribution of mass throughout the body in relation to various distances from the axis of revolution or rotation. It will be sufficient to remember that the law of conservation of angular momentum states that *for any revolving or rotating system, if no external force is applied, the product of m × v × r will remain constant*. If the mass of the system is fixed, then any change in v or r must produce an inverse change in r or v, as can be seen in the following two examples.

The earth and all the other planets have orbits that deviate to some degree from perfect circles. Because of this ellipticity the earth is about 3 million mi closer to the sun in January than it is in July (Fig. 7-11). In January r therefore decreases. If the quantity *mvr* is to remain constant, v must increase enough to

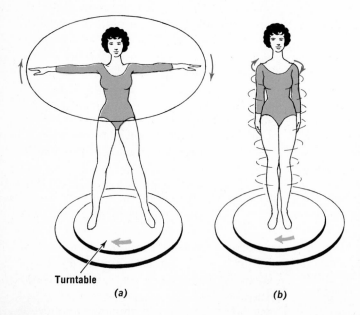

Turntable

(a)   (b)

Fig. 7-12. Conservation of Angular Momentum. (*a*) The girl is spinning with her feet apart and her arms outstretched while standing on a nearly frictionless turntable. (*b*) She has moved her feet close together and pulled her arms close in to her body, thus reducing her average distance from a vertical imaginary axis passing through her body. The result is that she automatically spins faster, for her *mvr* in the first situation will equal her *mvr* in the second. Since m is constant for both, v must increase if r is decreased. Thus, angular momentum (*mvr*) is conserved.

compensate. Similarly, in July, r is at a maximum and so v must be at a minimum. Thus, the earth travels faster in January than it does in July, as Kepler's second law states. Newton arrived at the concept of the conservation of angular momentum by way of Kepler's second law (Chapter 3).

Another example is that of a girl on a nearly frictionless turntable (Fig. 7-12) or a figure skater who begins to pirouette with outstretched arms. After gaining as much rotational motion as she can in this way, she shifts all her weight to one skate and draws her arms very close to her body in order to reduce r. Without any further effort on her part she starts to spin faster as she lowers her arms, reaching her fastest speed when her arms are against her body. To slow down she simply increases r by raising her arms. Neglecting friction with the ice, angular momentum has been conserved.

The Universal Law of Gravitation

Historical Note

Once Galileo's law of inertia (better known as Newton's first law) had been formulated and the concepts of force and mass clearly defined by Newton, it was obvious that some force must be operating on the planets and their moons to keep them in their elliptical orbits. The old belief that terrestrial laws could not be expected to apply to celestial bodies was being replaced, chiefly under the influence of Newton, by a belief that some natural laws had universal application. Galileo was probably aware of some such force; certainly a belief in the nonapplicability of terrestrial laws to celestial bodies would have left him scornful.

It is also certain, without looking at the record, that Newton formulated his first two laws of motion before he did his work on gravitation. Once laws are formulated and verified they are available for use in the study of other phenomena. Newton immediately applied the laws of motion to the astronomical problem of planetary orbits. He was especially equipped to do this, for he was a mathematical genius. While still an undergraduate at Cambridge he was doing original work in mathematics, work that shortly was to result in his discovery of the binomial theorem and the invention of the calculus. His work in the latter field was spurred by his need for certain mathematical proofs in parts of his gravitational theory.

The concept of gravity was not original with Newton. It had been used with respect to falling bodies[10] even before the time of Galileo. Members of the newly formed Royal Society of London were discussing it before Newton published his theory. They were trying to discover the force the sun exerted on planets to cause them to move according to Kepler's laws. Huygens had published his version of centripetal acceleration ($a = v^2/r$) and others were trying to apply it to the elliptical orbits of planets. They had managed to prove that an inverse-square law would account for circular orbits when it was combined with Kepler's third law, but they failed with elliptical orbits.

One of them, Halley (of Halley's comet fame), appealed to Newton for help, and found that Newton had solved the problem many years before,[11] using his own derivation of $a = v^2/r$. He had found that a force whose

---

[10] You should realize that to say that a body falls because of gravity is in no sense an explanation.

[11] This failure to publish or otherwise make known the results of his work was characteristic of Newton. His personality was the exact opposite of Galileo's. He was a shy, retiring man with no liking for controversy, even with respect to his own work. If it had not been for the urgings of some of his fellow scientists, particularly Halley, he might never have written his *Principia Mathematica*, which is very probably the greatest single book on science ever published.

magnitude was inversely proportional to the distance between a celestial body and another revolving about it would require the revolving body to obey all three of Kepler's laws. These laws had been begging for an explanation for generations; there was as yet no "reason" for the regularities described by them.

A Problem: Why Do Planets Move in Orbits Described by Kepler's Laws?

It was evident from the mechanics[12] of Newton that the planets were simply moving according to the same laws of motion applicable to all moving bodies here on earth. It will be highly instructive to give a plausible account of the reasoning used in applying these laws. (We do not, however, imply that our account is either correct in minor details or set forth in the order followed by Newton.)

As we have already stated in other words, Newton knew that a net force was acting continuously on the planets; otherwise they would all be moving in straight lines. In his speculations on the nature and the magnitude of this force, it has been said that he was led to the possibility of gravity as a cause by the fall of an apple from a tree while he was sitting in its shade. He knew that gravity operated everywhere here on earth, from the highest mountain peak to the deepest well, and even at the bottom of the ocean. If an apple released from the tree falls to the earth's surface, would not an apple released from a tree on the moon fall to the moon's surface? If an apple were released one mile, two miles, ten miles above the earth's surface, would it not also fall back to the earth because of gravity? If gravity extended that far, perhaps it extended as far as the moon, perhaps as far as the farthest planet, perhaps to infinity. Perhaps the planets were held in their orbits by the gravitational force of the sun. This was Newton's great in-

[12] Mechanics is the science of motion.

spiration, that the force causing an apple to fall from a tree to the ground was the same force holding the moon in its orbit. If such is the case, then perhaps the moon is a falling body, falling with an acceleration directed toward the center of the earth. As the moon is moving in an approximately circular path, the laws of uniform circular motion should apply. Its acceleration should therefore be subject to calculation from the equation $a = v^2/r$, as follows:

$$v = \frac{d}{t} = \frac{\text{length of orbit}}{\text{time for one revolution}} = \frac{2\pi r}{t}$$

Squaring both sides,

$$v^2 = \frac{2^2\pi^2 r^2}{t^2} \qquad [7\text{-}6]$$

Dividing both sides by r,

$$\frac{v^2}{r} = \frac{4\pi^2 r}{t^2} \qquad [7\text{-}7]$$

Hence

$$a = \frac{4\pi^2 r}{t^2} \qquad [7\text{-}8]$$

Since we want our answer in our usual cgs units, r must be reduced to centimeters and t to seconds. Therefore,

$$a = \frac{4\pi^2 r}{t^2}$$

$$= \frac{4 \times (3.14)^2 \times 240{,}000 \text{ mi} \times 5280\frac{\text{ft}}{\text{mi}} \times 30\frac{\text{cm}}{\text{ft}}}{\left(27.3 \text{ days} \times 24\frac{\text{hr}}{\text{day}} \times 3600\frac{\text{sec}}{\text{hr}}\right)^2}$$

When the arithmetic is performed, we get

$$a = 0.264 \text{ cm/sec}^2 \qquad [7\text{-}9]$$

This acceleration is far smaller than the value of g on the earth's surface (980 cm/sec^2).

To a man of Newton's ability the much smaller value of a would suggest that the acceleration due to gravity (hence the force causing it) is dependent in part on the distance between the two bodies involved. If so, how should this distance be measured—from surface to surface or from center to center? Newton used the latter distance but, being unable to show why, put aside his whole work on gravitation for some years and spent his time doing work on optics. Eventually he was able to show by means of his newly invented calculus that a solid sphere attracting another sphere by inverse-square-law forces attracts as if its mass were all at the center.

To a man of Newton's genius the inverse-square-law relationship between the force of gravity and the distance between the two bodies involved presented no real problem as long as he used circular orbits as a first approximation. With the aid of his calculus he was able to derive a more precise result. He was able to prove that a body traveling in a path other than a circle, and continuously acted on by a force varying inversely with the square of the distance from a central point, must travel in an ellipse. The mathematics involved are beyond us; we will be content with an approximation by use of circular orbits. For our purposes the error is insignificant, less than that introduced by other approximations such as the distance from the center of the earth to the center of the moon, the radius and mass of the moon, the radius of the earth, and so forth. The method is as follows:

From Newton's second law we have $F = ma$. From the laws of uniform circular motion we get $a = v^2/r$, so that the second law becomes $F = mv^2/r$. It follows that $F \propto m$, and $F \propto v^2/r$. From Eq. 7-7 we have

$$\frac{v^2}{r} = \frac{4\pi^2 r}{t^2}$$

Since $4\pi^2$ is a constant, we can omit it and write the remainder as a proportionality:[13]

$$\frac{v^2}{r} \propto \frac{r}{t^2}$$

Since $F \propto v^2/r$, $F \propto r/t^2$ also. From Kepler's third law, $t^2 \propto r^3$. Therefore,

$$F \propto \frac{r}{r^3} \propto \frac{1}{r^2} \qquad [7\text{-}10]$$

or

$$F = K\frac{1}{r^2} \qquad [7\text{-}11]$$

This equation told Newton that the gravitational force between the moon and the earth should be inversely proportional to the square of the radius of the moon's orbit, that is, to the square of its distance from the center of the earth. If the earth and the moon were twice as far apart, the force would be one fourth as much; if they were half as far apart the force would be four times as much, and so on.

The next problem was the role that the masses of the earth and the moon played in determining the force. Newton's second law, $F = ma$, demanded that m be as important as a in measuring or calculating any net force here on earth. We measure the force of gravity every time we weigh anything. All of us learn quite early in life that weight depends upon the amount of matter in a body, that two similar bags of potatoes weigh about twice as much as one bag. We can therefore readily accept the premise that the weight of a mass increases with an increase in the mass of a body. And if the force increases with the mass of one body, would it not increase with the mass of the other? Newton's third law says that it does. If so, $F \propto m$ and $F \propto M$, where m and M are the masses of the two bodies (Fig. 7-13).

[13] Note that this is the reverse of changing a proportionality into an equation by adding a proportionality constant.

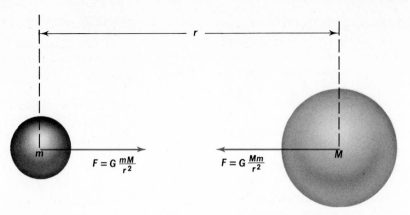

Fig. 7-13. Mutual Gravitational Attraction Between Two Bodies. The attraction of the earth, M, for the moon, m, is equal in magnitude to the attraction of the moon for the earth. This follows from Newton's third law. Thus the E's in the two equations are equal but oppositely directed. G is the universal gravitational constant.

Combining these proportionalities we have $F \propto Mm$. Combining this new proportionality with the one expressed in Eq. 7-10, we have $F \propto Mm/r^2$. Writing it as an equation,

$$F = G\frac{Mm}{r^2} \qquad [7\text{-}12]$$

where G is a constant called the *universal gravitational constant*. It should never be confused with g.[14]

In words, Eq. 7-12 states that the force of gravitation between the earth and the moon is proportional to the product of their masses and inversely proportional to the square of the radius of the orbit of the moon. Newton used the moon in its orbit about the earth in his calculations because it is much the nearest of the celestial bodies and because he knew its average distance and its period with satisfactory degrees of accuracy.

[14] The value of g, the acceleration due to gravity, may vary from place to place even here on earth. The value of G is postulated to be the same everywhere in the universe.

Newton was not yet quite ready to call Eq. 7-12 his universal law of gravitation. From the standpoint of mathematical reasoning the equation was sound, but as we have observed before, nature is not bound to follow the reasoning of man. The equation may at this point be said to be a hypothesis in mathematical form. It had to be tested in various ways before it could be converted into a law. The first test was against the observation of the moon. We have already calculated what the acceleration of the moon would be if it were accelerated in circular motion. For our data we used the observed period, and its measured distance. We found a to be 0.264 cm/sec². Now if Eq. 7-12 is to hold, F must also be equal to ma; that is, it must satisfy Newton's second law, a law that has been derived by experiment. Therefore

$$F = G\frac{Mm}{r^2} = ma \qquad [7\text{-}13]$$

in which M and m are the masses of the earth and the moon, respectively, r is the distance between them, and a is the gravitational acceleration of the moon toward the earth. Solving for a,

$$a = G\frac{M}{r^2} \qquad [7\text{-}14]$$

Note that m cancels out. Now, r is 240,000 mi. Substituting this quantity for r,

$$a = G\frac{M}{(240,000)^2} \qquad [7\text{-}15]$$

Newton could not solve this equation directly because he knew neither G nor M. However, Eqs. 7-13 and 7-14 should also hold if we substitute a stone on the earth's surface at a distance of 4000 mi from the earth's center for the moon in its orbit. Using g as the acceleration of the stone,

$$g = G\frac{M}{r^2} = G\frac{M}{(4000)^2} \qquad [7\text{-}16]$$

We have learned that a ratio is simply a fraction formed by dividing one number by another. We can therefore obtain the ratio of a to g by dividing Eq. 7-15 by Eq. 7-16. Note that we get rid of the G's and the M's, for they cancel out.

$$\frac{a}{g} = \frac{\dfrac{GM}{(240,000)^2}}{\dfrac{GM}{(4000)^2}} = \frac{(4000)^2}{(240,000)^2} = \frac{1}{3600}$$

Solving for a,

$$a = \frac{1}{3600}g \qquad [7\text{-}17]$$

Thus Eq. 7-17 tells us that the acceleration of the moon toward the earth should be $\frac{1}{3600}$ of

the value of g. Therefore,

$$a = \frac{980 \text{ cm/sec}^2}{3600} = 0.272 \text{ cm/sec}^2 \quad [7\text{-}18]$$

Note that what has been done here is to test the validity of the inverse-square law (Eq. 7-11), for the two masses from Eq. 7-12 were eliminated (m by solving Eq. 7-13, and M by solving for a/g in deriving Eq. 7-17) before we achieved our final result. This test simply shows that the acceleration of a stone (or the moon) due to gravitational attraction of the earth, at a distance of 60 times that of the earth's radius, should be $\frac{1}{3600}$ that of a stone here on the earth's surface—the stone is only *one* earth's radius away. We found that $\frac{1}{3600}$ of 980 cm/sec^2 is 0.272 cm/sec^2, very near that calculated from the observed values of the moon's distance, velocity, and period (p. 128). The result of 0.264 cm/sec^2 from the observed values is closer than we have any right to hope for, considering the round figures we used for both the radius of the orbit of the moon and the earth's radius.

The result of 0.272 cm/sec^2 means that the moon is falling toward the earth with an acceleration of 0.272 cm/sec^2. We speak of it as an acceleration because the moon is constantly changing its direction as it falls. Translated into miles, it means that the moon "falls" about 6300 mi in one day, and it has been doing that for some billions of years without ever getting any closer to the earth. How can this be? What do we mean when we speak of the moon as a "falling" body? Newton's first law states that if no force were acting on the moon it would follow a straight-line path (Fig. 7-14). But there is a force, the gravitational attraction of the earth, acting as a true centripetal force to cause the moon to deviate continuously from such a path. The "falling" of the moon is simply its deflection away from this straight-

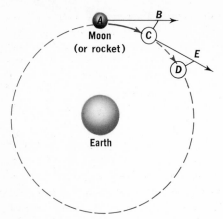

Fig. 7-14. The Moon as a Falling Body. If there were no force of gravitation, the moon would move along the line AB in time t. Instead it moves to C in time t; AC may be viewed as the resultant of $AB + BC$. In other words, the moon has "fallen" a distance equal to BC in moving from A to C. Similarly, it has fallen a distance equivalent to DE in moving from C to D, and so on.

line path. In other words, the moon has to "fall" 6300 mi a day toward the earth to keep from getting farther and farther away from the earth. A careful study of Fig. 7-14 should make this clear if it is not so already. To summarize, the kind of force that holds the moon in its orbit was proved identical with that which causes objects to have weight and to fall freely here on the earth's surface. Thus, it is the force of gravity that holds the solar system together.

In order not to break the continuity of our account, we have omitted certain details. There were a number of possible variables that had to be considered, variables that had either to be eliminated or to be determined and a method developed to control them. Some of them were temperature, density, shape, volume, composition, and speed. Would they make a difference? As we will see, they did not; only mass and distance need be considered.

The gravitational hypothesis of Newton could then be taken out of the hypothetical

category and stated as a law insofar as the solar system was concerned. But did it apply to the whole universe? Newton believed it did, and he boldly stated that *every particle in the universe attracts every other particle with a force that is directly proportional to the product of their masses, and inversely proportional to the square of the distance between them.* This is what we now call Newton's universal law of gravitation. Its mathematical expression is

$$F = G \frac{Mm}{r^2} \qquad [7\text{-}13]$$

Another Problem: Why Is the Acceleration of Gravity Here on Earth Constant?

It is a remarkable experimental fact that all objects at any given point on or near the surface of the earth experience the same gravitational acceleration, g (neglecting the effects of air resistance). That is, a 1 kg iron block will fall to the earth with the same acceleration as a 2 kg iron block. How can we explain this? One would think that since the force of attraction between the earth and the 2 kg block is twice that of the 1 kg block, it should fall twice as fast. But a kilogram is a measure of mass. A 2 kg block has twice the mass of a 1 kg block. Mass is a measure of inertia and inertia is resistance to change in motion, that is, resistance to force. Thus not only does the 2 kg block have twice as much gravitational attraction (weight) toward the earth as the 1 kg block but it also has twice the inertial resistance against this force. The result is that both objects fall to earth with the same acceleration.

Experimental Proof of the Law of Gravitation by Cavendish

A little over 100 years after Newton published his *Principia*—which included his derivation of the law of gravitation—Henry

Cavendish of England actually succeeded in directly measuring the force of gravitation by experiment in the laboratory.

The principle is extremely simple but the execution extremely difficult, for the forces involved are incredibly small. This is the reason that Newton did not try the experiment himself. Newton had made guesses of the value of G but succeeded only in arriving at the conclusion that no experiment that he could perform with the equipment available could give it to him. Other scientists tried to use the deflection of a pendulum by a mountain mass but succeeded only in getting very rough estimates.

As shown in Fig. 7-15, Cavendish used two small lead balls and two large ones. The small ones were attached to a light metal rod, which in turn was supported by a very thin wire. This apparatus was at rest and enclosed in a glass

case (not shown) so that air currents would not disturb it. The large balls (M) were then brought near in such a manner that the attractions of the heavy balls for the small ones would tend to twist the bar containing the small ones in the same direction. Since the amount of twisting is very small, a special device was needed to measure it. This device consisted of a tiny mirror attached to the twisting wire, a thin beam of light directed at the mirror, and a scale in the path of the reflected beam. By noting the positions of the reflected beam both before and after the large balls were brought into position, the amount of twisting could be determined. The farther the scale from the mirror, the greater the magnification of the twisting. Knowing by experiment the amount of force it took to twist the wire, the masses of both sets of balls, and the distances between their centers, the forces of attraction could be calculated.

Fig. 7-15. Cavendish "Weighs" the Earth. Two small balls suspended by a light bar and wire are at rest in a closed glass cage (not shown). The two large heavy balls are brought near the small balls in such a manner that both tend to turn the bar in the same direction. As the bar turns, the wire twists and the mirror turns. A very small movement of the mirror can cause a considerable movement of the reflected beam of light on the scale. See text for more details.

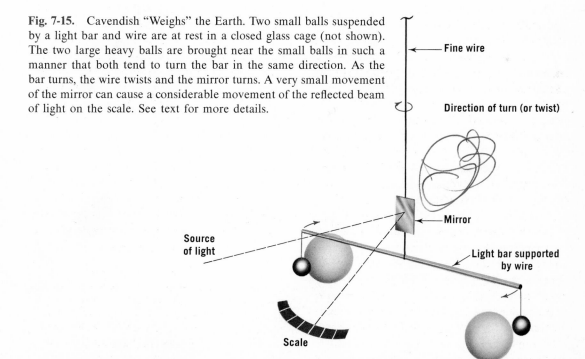

The best modern value for G, the universal gravitational constant, is 6.673×10^{-8} dyne-cm²/g² for all substances. This means that if two 1 g masses are placed so that their centers are 1 cm apart, they will attract each other with a force of about two thirds of a ten-millionth of a dyne. Many experiments have been performed since Newton's time to see if gravitational attractions are influenced by any conceivable factor—composition of material, shielding, temperature, crystal form, and so on—but so far none has been found. The constant is regarded as a truly universal one.

Consequences of Gravitation

Weight vs. Mass

The most obvious consequence of gravitation is that objects here on earth have weight. When we weigh something we are literally measuring the force of gravitation between that body and the earth. If you weigh 120 lb we say that the earth attracts you with that force. The attraction is mutual, however, and so we say also that you attract the earth with a force of 120 lb. Newton's third law demands that this be so, just as much as does the law of gravitation itself. Since the force of gravitation varies with the distance from the center of the earth, it varies both with latitude and with altitude. Therefore, you should weigh a bit less at the equator than at the poles, and a bit less on the top of a mountain than at sea level. This will be evident if you weigh yourself on a spring scale (Fig. 7-16a). If you weigh yourself on a balance scale, you are simply comparing the pull of the earth on you with the pull of the earth on a known mass. Since both you and the weights are attracted equally, a balance scale will give the same reading anywhere.

We see now the difference between mass and

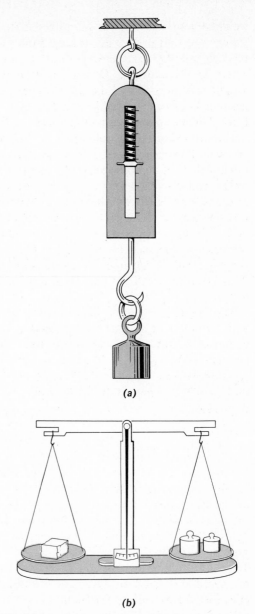

Fig. 7-16. Spring Scale (a) and Balance Scale (b). Objects weighed on the balance scale give the same reading anywhere because they are simply balanced against another set of weights of the same mass. In the spring scale the reading is directly dependent on the pull of gravity. Hence the reading will vary as the value of g varies.

weight. If mass is defined as quantity of matter, we can see that it does not change from one place to another but remains constant anywhere in the universe. On the other hand, weight is a measure of the gravitational attraction between two bodies; that is, it is a force. On the moon you would weigh in the neighborhood of 20 lb if you weigh 120 lb here on earth. Far out in space outside the gravitational field [15] of any celestial body, you would weigh nothing, but your mass would be the same as here on earth. However, as long as we stay here on the earth's surface, weight is both a measure of the mass of a body and of the earth's attraction for that mass. But this is not to say that weight and mass are the same thing (see exercise 26c at the end of this chapter).

The differences in the force of gravitation with latitude and altitude are reflected in the values of g. This acceleration varies from 983 cm/sec^2 at the poles to 978 cm/sec^2 at the equator. At New York it is 980.27 cm/sec^2. On the top of Mt. Everest it should be slightly less than 980.

Shape of Earth

From his law of gravitation and the laws of rotational motion, Newton calculated that an earth rotating on an axis should bulge at the equator and be flattened at the poles. He figured that an equatorial radius about 14 mi greater than the polar radius should suffice. Ten years after his death such a bulge was first measured. The modern figure for the difference in the two radii is 13.35 mi.

Why, we may ask, should Newton have deduced a spheroidal shape for the earth? Why should it not be shaped like a cube, or a cylinder, or a football, or a doughnut? This same

[15]Actually there is no such place, but you could be so far away that the force is too small to be measured.

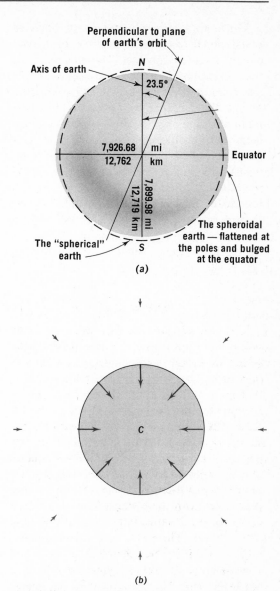

Fig. 7-17. The Spheroidal Earth. (*a*) The equatorial diameter is about 26 mi greater than the polar diameter (N–S). (*b*) The inward pull of gravity on all points on the surface tends to make the earth spherical. Away from the earth's surface the force becomes less in accordance with the inverse-square law. A perfectly smooth-surfaced earth would be possible only if the density varied *uniformly* from the center outward everywhere.

question applies equally well to all celestial bodies. Aside from comets and asteroids, whose masses are too small for gravity to be significant, all celestial bodies are spherical or, if rotating rapidly, spheroidal. Since all matter is subject to gravitation, it follows that no matter what the origin of any of these celestial bodies was, whether by contraction and condensation from a once-gaseous state or from a "dust" cloud or other mass of solid particles, the resulting shape would be the same. The pressure of the particles, as great size was attained, would prevent any one part of the celestial body from projecting much farther out from the center than any other part (Fig. 7-17).

Consider the earth, for example. As we go downward into it, the pressures quickly become enormous. At depths of 12 to 15 mi below sea level they are so great that even solid rock will flow in response to them. At these depths the pressures are equalized everywhere if the distance beneath sea level is the same. Thus, the rocks beneath the ocean basins exert the same pressure at the 12 to 15 mi depth below sea level as do the rocks beneath a high mountain range at the same depth below sea level. We may therefore conclude that the rocks beneath these ranges have less mass per unit volume (that is, less density) than do the rocks beneath the ocean basins.

Precession of Equinoxes

Newton was also able to explain the precession of the equinoxes, unexplained since the time of Hipparchus. The sun's attraction for the earth's equatorial bulge is slightly greater than for the rest of the earth, thus tending to pull the earth's equatorial region into the plane of the ecliptic. Because the earth is rotating, this pull is translated into a slow motion of the axis, which describes a cone about a perpendicular to the plane of the ecliptic (Fig. 2-24).

The Tides

Newton also used his theory to explain the tides, another phenomenon that had been begging for an explanation ever since man began his quest for understanding. The tides correlated with the motion of the moon, but even Galileo could see no relationship.[16] The moon does not revolve about the earth's center but about a center of gravity common to both the moon and the earth 1000 mi below the surface of the earth. The sun in turn revolves about a center of gravity common to the sun-earth-moon system, a center very close to the center of the sun because of its enormously greater mass. Thus, we say the system is heliocentric. The pull of the earth on the moon and of the moon on the earth provides just enough mv^2/r to keep the earth (and the moon) moving around the common center of gravity once a month. Imagine the earth covered with a universal ocean and no continents to complicate matters. The part nearest the moon is pulled with a greater force than average and so the water rises in a hump to form one tide (Fig. 7-18). The side farthest away is pulled less than average, less than enough to keep it moving with the rest of the earth in its motion about the common center of gravity. Therefore it lags behind, fails to "make the curve," so to speak, and so forms another hump opposite the first one. As the earth spins, its surface travels around, while the humps are held almost in one place by the moon and the sun. Thus, the two humps move like a wave as the oceans spin beneath them. High tide is not beneath the moon but lags behind by about six hours, owing to friction and inertia. The sun also produces tides, smaller than those of the moon, in the same manner. Twice a month the tides of the sun and the moon

---

[16] Actually Galileo gave a wrong explanation for the tides. The inability of some thinkers to accept his explanation played a role in their refusal to accept the heliocentric hypothesis.

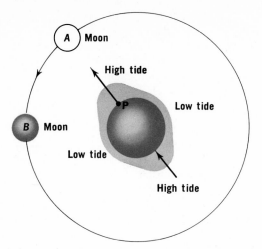

Fig. 7-18. The Tides. Tides are due to differences in the gravitational attraction between the moon and the various parts of the earth at any one instant. The side nearest the moon experiences an extra large pull as compared with the earth's center which is 4000 miles farther away, so that the ocean waters are pulled up on that side. The side opposite the moon experiences an extra low pull so that the water flows away to produce another high tide there. The piling up of the water to form the two high tides causes the water to flow away from the areas in between, producing the low tides as shown. Because of inertia, tidal friction, coastal configurations, and rotational effects, the tides are delayed by several hours so that they are highest when the moon is at *B* rather than when it is at *A*.

coincide, giving us the high spring tides, and twice a month they are out of step, giving us the low neap tides.

Discoveries of Neptune and Pluto

Perhaps the greatest success, certainly the most astonishing to the layman, was the predicted existence and the final discovery of the planet Neptune in 1846. Eight major members of the solar system—sun, moon, Mercury, Venus, Earth, Mars, Jupiter, and Saturn—had been known for some thousands of years. To these Galileo had added the four moons of Jupiter. Uranus had been discovered in 1781 by William Herschel while searching the sky with his homemade telescope. He began computation of its orbit by use of Kepler's laws and the law of gravitation. Its period—84 years—was too long to observe in one lifetime. But, by 1830, it was apparent that the calculated orbit and the observed orbit did not quite match. Some of the deviations, called perturbations, could be explained by the attractions of Jupiter and Saturn. There still remained one of the order of $\frac{1}{100}$ of a degree that was unexplained. Some astronomers suggested that perhaps the law of gravitation was not really universal in its application; others suggested that perhaps some as yet undiscovered planet was perturbing Uranus. An undergraduate at Cambridge University, John C. Adams, began to map the orbit of this as yet undiscovered planet by plotting mathematically the positions it would need in order to cause the observed perturbations of Uranus. When he thought he had this planet located he wrote to the astronomers of the Royal Observatory at Greenwich, asking them to turn their powerful telescope to a particular spot in the heavens at a specified hour. Because he was an unknown they paid him no heed.

Meanwhile a young Frenchman, Leverrier, was doing exactly the same thing independently in France. In 1846 he sent his calculations to the astronomer in charge of the Berlin Observatory. This man looked and found the planet at almost the predicted spot. When the news was flashed to London, the Royal Astronomer confirmed the discovery, finding the new planet within two degrees of the position predicted by Adams. It was a magnificent triumph for the law of gravitation. Pluto was discovered in 1930 in much the same way, that is, from perturbations in the orbit of Neptune.

Spaceships and Artificial Satellites

Newton stated that any projectile is potentially an earth satellite. Suppose we fired one at high speed horizontally. If there were no force of gravity, it would get farther and farther away from the earth as the earth's surface curved away from it. Because of gravity it falls in a curved path toward the earth. If fired fast enough it would follow a curved path having the same curvature as the earth (Figs. 7-19 and 7-20) so that, like the moon, it would be constantly falling toward the earth without ever getting any closer. Orbit 5 in Fig. 7-19 is impractical; air friction will cause the satellite to burn up or slow down and fall to earth. Assuming that orbits 6 and 7 are beyond the

atmosphere, such altitudes are reached by firing the satellite vertically. The necessary horizontal component of motion is given in part by the rotation of the earth (of which the satellite partakes, by Newton's first law), and the remainder is supplied by auxiliary steering rockets fired at the desired altitude. The relationship between horizontal velocity and altitude is determined from Kepler's third law: $T^2 \propto r^3$. Many artificial satellites have been put into orbit and men have landed on the moon and returned to earth, but none of this has made any contribution to the science of motion not already known to Newton (Fig. 7-21).

For a projectile to escape[17] from the earth's gravity, the vertical component of its motion

[17] Theoretically the gravitational field of the earth extends to infinity, but there is a distance at which it becomes immeasurably small by any practical means.

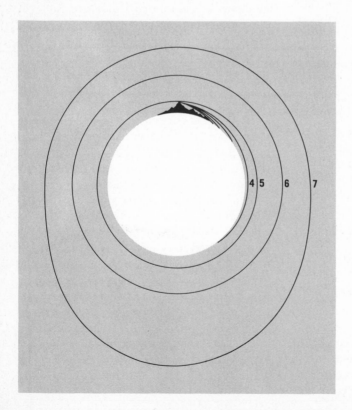

Fig. 7-19. Paths of Projectiles, Rockets, Satellites with Velocities Less Than the Escape Velocity. A slightly modified drawing from Newton's *System of the World* showing the paths that a projectile would follow if fired from a gun on a mountain top at velocities less than the escape velocity of approximately 25,000 mi/hr. The drawing shows Newton knew that a body would go into orbit about the earth if its speed were great enough. The first four paths were made by projectiles with too low a speed.

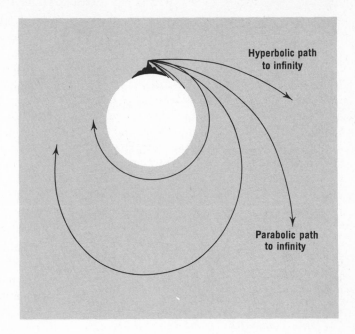

Fig. 7-20. Paths of Projectiles, Rockets, Satellites with Velocities Greater Than the Escape Velocity. Another of Newton's drawings showed various projectile paths. Those for projectiles fired at velocities greater than the escape velocity are either parabolic or hyperbolic. The hyperbola requires a higher speed than the parabola. In either case the projectile will never return to earth. The principles of present-day rocketry were laid down by Newton 300 years ago.

(escape velocity) must be more than 25,000 mi/hr (7 mi/sec). For the moon with only about $\frac{1}{6}$ the earth's gravitational force, escape velocity is a little less than 5000 mi/hr. The low escape velocity from the moon accounts for the lack of atmosphere there. Air molecules have average velocities (see p. 215) of more than 5000 mi/hr at the high midday temperatures on the moon. At the earth's distance from the sun, the required escape velocity from the sun's gravitational attraction is more than 100,000 mi/hr (28 mi/sec).

Neither artificial satellites nor rockets to the moon, Venus, or Mars would be any surprise to Newton. He worked out the principles on which they could operate nearly 300 years ago. We have the technology to make them; Newton did not.

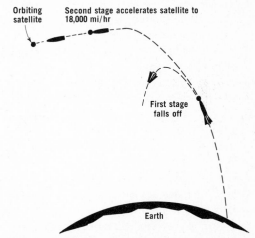

Fig. 7-21. Putting a Satellite into Orbit. The first stage lifts the entire space vehicle above the atmosphere. The second stage orients the satellite and gives it sufficient orbital velocity to put it into a stable orbit.

Exercises

1. Two identical cars each travel 100 mi over the same road in the same total time. One travels at a uniform speed; the other speeds up and slows down over and over again, stopping several times. The latter car will use appreciably more gasoline. Explain why in terms of Newton's laws.

2. Define (a) a force, (b) a dyne, and (c) a newton.

3. A net force of 40 newtons is applied to a cart having a mass of 20 kg. What acceleration is imparted to the cart?

4. (a) Why is more force needed to start a heavy cart moving than to keep it moving at a uniform velocity?
   (b) What law is involved?

5. A weight is attached to a string that is strong enough to lift the weight if one uses a slow steady pull, but weak enough to break if a sudden rapid pull is exerted.
   (a) Explain why the string does not break in the first case but does in the second.
   (b) What law is involved?

6. A toy steam engine that really runs is placed on a track that is shaped like a bicycle wheel and is free to turn on an axle. The wheel is mounted in a horizontal position. The engine is started. Describe the motions of the system and explain in terms of one or more of the laws of motion.

7. A shotgun (or any other gun) "kicks" when it is fired. Explain why.

8. A car is traveling along a straight level road at a uniform speed. State specifically the forces that must be overcome by the energy in the gasoline used. In other words, for what purposes is gasoline used?

9. Suppose this car is traveling at the same uniform speed around a circular track. Would you use more or less gasoline or the same amount? Justify your answer in terms of one or more of Newton's laws.

10. Newton's second law states that if a net force is applied to a body the body will be accelerated. Yet you can push a cart along a sidewalk at a constant velocity while exerting a steady force of, say, 40 newtons on it. Explain.

11. Use Newton's laws of motion to show that epicyclic motion of the planets, as assumed by the followers of Ptolemy (Fig. 1-9), is not possible.

12. It is frequently said that when a car turns a sharp corner rapidly, the passengers are "thrown" toward the outside of the curve by centrifugal force. This explanation is fallacious. Show why, and give the correct explanation.

13. What force does it take to give a 1 g mass an acceleration of 980 cm/sec^2?

14. Would the acceleration of a falling body on the moon's surface be greater or less than that on earth? Why?

15. The gravitational force between the earth and the moon at the average distance between them may be expressed as F. For the following changes in mass or distance or both, will the value of F remain constant, increase to $2F$, $3F$, $4F$, and so on, or be reduced to $\frac{1}{4}F$, $\frac{1}{3}F$, $\frac{1}{2}F$, $\frac{1}{9}F$, and so on? It is understood that the factors not mentioned remain unchanged.
   (a) The moon's mass is doubled.
   (b) The earth's mass is doubled.
   (c) Both the mass of the earth and that of the moon are doubled.
   (d) The earth's mass is doubled and that of the moon is tripled.
   (e) The distance between the centers of the two is doubled.
   (f) The distance between the centers of the two is halved.
   (g) The distance between the centers of the two is tripled.
   (h) Both masses are doubled and the distance is halved.

(i) The mass of the moon is doubled and the distance is halved.

(j) Both masses are halved and the distance is doubled.

16. The moon is being constantly accelerated toward the earth but never gets any closer. Explain.

17. Because of the earth's rotation, objects on the surface of the earth are, in general, subjected to a force directed inward toward the center that is called *centripetal force*. Is this force equal everywhere on the surface of the earth? Explain.

18. Learn the difference between weighing on a spring scale and weighing on a balance.

(a) Does each measure the pull of gravity directly? Explain.

(b) If you were buying gold high in the Sierra Nevada Mountains and selling it at sea level, which scale would be more advantageous for you at each weighing?

19. Consider yourself out in space all by yourself 4000 mi from the surface of the earth. If you could weigh yourself on a spring scale, how much would you weigh if you weighed 120 lb at the earth's surface?

20. How much would a man weigh on the moon if he weighed 150 lb on earth? (*Note:* This, and similar problems, are best solved in two parts. On the moon you will be closer to the center of gravity because the moon's radius is only about $\frac{1}{4}$ that of the earth. First solve for this condition, assuming that the mass of the moon is equal to that of the earth. You will, of course, get a figure that is far higher than your weight on earth. Next, correct for the mass of the moon. Its mass is only about $\frac{1}{80}$ that of the earth. Now solve the problem.)

21. The planet Sassafrune has a mass 16 times that of the earth and a radius 4 times that of the earth. How much would a man who weighs 150 lb on earth weigh on Sassafrune? What would his mass be on Sassafrune?

22. The radius of Jupiter is 11 times that of the earth and its mass is about 317 times that of the earth. Its escape velocity is nearly 135,000 mi/hr.

(a) How much would you weigh on Jupiter?

(b) Suppose you landed on Jupiter in a spaceship. What difficulties would arise because of this weight?

(c) What difficulty would your spaceship have in getting away from Jupiter? Be explicit.

23. Distinguish between mass and weight by defining the two terms.

24. List as many consequences of the law of gravitation as you can.

25. An astronaut in orbit disposes of a bag of garbage by pushing it through a specially designed exit. What is the immediate fate of the bag?

26. Assume an astronaut who weighs 180 lb on earth to be orbiting the earth at a uniform speed in an approximately circular orbit that lies 4000 mi above the earth's *surface,* and so is beyond the effective reach of the earth's atmosphere. Explain the following:

(a) What force keeps him moving?

(b) What force keeps him in his orbit?

(c) He experiences a sense of weightlessness. Is he actually weightless?

(d) He steps outside of his capsule, so that he is completely free of it. He is careful not to push against the capsule. Explain what would happen to him.

(e) Suppose he gave himself a push away from the capsule. What would happen to him? Explain.

(f) What would happen to his capsule if its speed were increased? (It would obviously go faster, but what else?)

27. Newspapers reported that the space probes to the moon, Venus, and Mars had at one stage of their flights passed beyond the earth's gravity. Were these meaningful statements? Explain. What were they trying to say?

28. What part is played in the orbiting of an artificial satellite by (a) centripetal force and (b) centrifugal force? Explain.

29. Suppose that an artificial satellite is placed in orbit at a distance that is half that of the moon's distance. How would its period of revolution around the earth compare with that of the moon?

30. Suppose that scientists wish to place an artificial satellite in orbit at an average distance of 10,000 mi from the earth.

  (a) Would they do this by a trial-and-error method or would they use some law as a guide? If the latter, what law?

  (b) What quantity would they have to calculate?

The Concepts of Work and Energy

The terms *work* and *energy* are closely associated with each other, even in the minds of people who never heard of them as scientific concepts. Both words are part of our ordinary language and of our everyday experiences. Everyone realizes that energy is something that enables us to do things, whether at play or at work.

If you think briefly about how we get energy, you soon realize that it is something we pay for, directly or indirectly, as bills for electricity, gas, fuel oil, or coal for our homes, gasoline for our cars, or even as food for us. If we count food as a fuel, we may almost say that energy is what we pay for when we buy fuel of one sort or another. True, the energy of the sun is free, and so is the energy of running water, and of the wind, but we usually have to pay for the machinery that enables us to use it.

Almost all of the energy we use has its source in the sun. Whether our energy comes from our food, from running water, from the wind, or directly from the sun to dry our clothes and heat our bodies, it is recent sun-

One machine can do the work of fifty ordinary men. No machine can do the work of one extraordinary man.
ELBERT HUBBARD

143

shine that we are drawing on; if it comes from fuel oil or gasoline or natural gas or coal, it is ancient sunshine that has been stored in the earth. Only when we use nuclear energy do we employ a source other than that of the sun.

It is clear, then, that energy is what we need to get work done. In short, we say that *energy is the capacity to do work*. Intuitively, we realize that application of twice the energy results in twice the amount of work done.

The Concept of Work

At first the concept of work seems clear enough—until we ask, "What is work?" Serious thought shows that we must make a distinction between the colloquial and the scientific concept, for in everyday life we make a distinction between work and play that has nothing whatever to do with the amount of energy used. You may say of a friend, "He is out playing tennis, while I am sitting here quietly, hard at work reading my physical science textbook." If you study long enough, you will learn that you have misstated the facts, for your friend is doing a considerable amount of work while he is "playing," whereas you, sitting at your desk "working," are actually doing little or no work at all. The need to clarify the concept of work becomes clear.

It will probably be more meaningful to plunge ahead and define the modern scientific concept of work, and then proceed to its derivation from the mechanics of Newton and Galileo, than it is to reverse the presentation. From this point on we will refer to work only in the scientific sense. Work, *W*, is done on a body when a force acting on the body moves it through a given distance; that is, work is *force multiplied by the distance the object moves while the force acts:*

$$W = F \times d \qquad [8\text{-}1]$$

always with the understanding that only that part of the force which operates along, or parallel to, the direction of motion is to be used in the equation.[1] Thus, if we lift a 10 lb weight from the floor to the top of a table 3 ft high, we do a certain number of units of work. We now see why your friend, the tennis player, does work while he is "playing," for he is applying a force to his racket as he swings it through the distance necessary to hit the ball. We also see why you are not doing any work while you are studying. Aside from the fact that a force is not operating through any distance, we cannot quantitatively measure mental work.

The scientific definition of work causes us to change some other aspects of our everyday concept of work. For example, you may get very tired holding a heavy parcel, but you are doing no work that can be measured, using Eq. 8-1. True, you are applying a force sufficient to overcome the gravitational force of attraction for the parcel, but this force is not operating through any distance. If you drop the parcel to the floor, work is done (but not by you), for a force (gravitational force) is operating through a distance. You will note that the usefulness of the work has nothing to do with our definition. Even if you carry the heavy parcel as you walk home along a level sidewalk, the work you do cannot be calculated simply by multiplying the weight of the parcel by the distance. This is because the force you are exerting on the parcel is directed vertically upward (against the force of gravitation) whereas the parcel is moving

[1] The concepts of force, energy, work, and power should not be confused. We do not need to use energy to exert a force, for a clamp can maintain a force indefinitely without any energy source. Consequently, no work is done, nor is any power involved. Power, *P*, is the time rate of doing work. Thus, *P = Fd/t*. Greater power does not necessarily mean more work done, but it always means that a given amount of work is done in less time or more work is done in the same amount of time.

horizontally[2] along with you. If you were to carry the parcel up a stairway, you would be doing work, for you would then be exerting a force against that of gravity through a distance equal to the vertical height of the stairway.[3]

Relationship of Work and Energy to Mechanics

The concept of work, and therefore of energy, can be obtained by an analysis of Newton's mechanics, but we will make no attempt to follow the long and difficult road that later scientists pursued while clarifying these concepts. We may gain some insight, however, by reviewing the mechanical concepts that we have studied so far.

We started with three directly measurable quantities, (1) distance, (2) time, and (3) mass. These are quantities whose meanings are intuitively clear to us. From these three concepts we derived those of (4) average speed—distance divided by time, (5) velocity—speed in a given direction, (6) acceleration—velocity divided by the time to achieve that velocity, (7) force—mass times the acceleration, and (8) momentum—mass times the velocity.

Thus, we started with three simple directly measurable quantities and from them we derived five concepts of higher and higher levels of abstraction. We are now in the process of adding two more concepts of a still higher level

of abstraction, those of work—force times distance—and energy. Note that no new quantities have been introduced. The new concepts arise from a new relationship between quantities with which we are already familiar. We have not given any mathematical expression for energy simply because we can determine how much energy a body or system of bodies has only by determining how much work the expenditure of that quantity of energy can do. If you say that you are full of energy today, we can measure the amount you have only by putting you to work and measuring the amount you do. We therefore measure this energy either in terms of how much force you can exert on a body through a given distance, or of how great a distance you can move an object by exerting a definite force. When work is done on a body, some change in its energy content or energy level occurs. If we can calculate the work, we can calculate the energy. We even use the same units for expressing both. The student should therefore not be confused by the seeming interchangeableness of the two concepts in the following pages.

Units of Work and Energy

Since work is defined as force times distance (measured in the direction the force is operating), the units used arise naturally. In the cgs system, force is expressed in dynes and distance in centimeters. The fundamental unit of work is therefore the dyne-centimeter. A special name for it is the erg, which may be formally defined as *the work done by a force of 1 dyne acting through a distance of 1 cm.* This is an extremely small unit, about equivalent to the work done in lifting a mosquito 1 cm. Therefore, a larger unit, the joule (pronounced "jowl," although "jool" is common in the United States), is more commonly used. It is equal to 10^7 ergs. It is also equal to

---

[2] It is not strictly correct to say that you therefore do no work, for the parcel adds to the friction between your shoes and the ground, and there is a slight air resistance to be overcome. Also, the muscles of your body quiver; some muscular energy is turned into heat energy.

[3] If this restriction of the meaning of work to force times distance through which the force operates (the distance always being measured in the direction of the force) seems arbitrary, we agree that it is. The necessity for it is that we cannot otherwise develop the concepts associated with work without contradictions.

1 newton times 1 m. The foot-pound (ft-lb) is the common unit in the English system of units. It equals the work done when a force of 1 lb weight acts through a distance of 1 ft.

It is here in our calculations of work and energy, more than anywhere else, that we must not misinterpret the terms *weight* and *mass*. The *weight* of a body is a force that represents the pull of the earth on that body. Its *mass* represents the inertia of the body and is the property that determines how big a force is required to produce a given acceleration. Weight is always proportional to mass. There are many systems of units and thus much confusion. For example, in the cgs system, since $F = ma$, a force of 1 dyne will give a mass of 1 g an acceleration of 1 cm/sec^2. But the weight of a 1 g mass is sometimes called a gram or a gram force. Since $w = mg$, a gram force is g dynes; that is, a 1 g force is 980 dynes, and this quantity must be used in this equation. When F is in dynes, m is in grams and a in centimeters per second per second. Do not confuse w (weight) with W (work).

Mechanical Energy

Mechanical energy is used to do work (1) against the inertia of a body, (2) against gravity, (3) against friction, or (4) against any combination of them.[4] Respectively, this work increases (1) the speed of a body, (2) the height of a body, (3) the temperature of a body, or (4) any combination of them. Thus, the work done on the body produces some change in the energy of the body. In (1) the energy of motion (kinetic energy) is increased, in (2) the energy due to position (potential energy) is

increased, and in (3) the heat energy (thermal energy) of the body is increased. In all cases, the magnitude of the energy change is equal to the work done. Two kinds of mechanical energy are recognized, potential and kinetic. They are commonly abbreviated as PE and KE, respectively.

The Concept of Potential Energy

If we lift a 10,000 g mass vertically from the floor to the top of a table 100 cm high, we do an amount of work equal to $F \times d = 98$ joules.[5] We can say that we have accomplished that much work by expending 98 joules of energy. In a sense we have transferred this energy to the mass, for it now can do work by falling back to its original position. In doing so, it can, by use of a rope and pulley, raise another 10 kg mass an equal distance, or a 5 kg mass twice the distance, and so on, if we disregard frictional losses. The only difference between the mass on the floor and the mass on the table is its position. This increased energy due to increase of height above the floor is called *potential energy*. If we raised the mass twice as far, its potential energy would be twice as great. If the mass were twice as much, and the distance it was raised remained the same, its potential energy would again be twice as great. Thus, the potential energy of any body is directly proportional to both the mass and the distance through which it is raised. This type of potential energy is sometimes called *gravitational potential energy* because it is a consequence of the earth's gravitational attraction for the mass, and in this chapter we will confine our discussion to this type. As we shall see later, there are others.

In our example we have calculated the potential energy by using the floor as a level of reference. In doing so we have assumed that

---

[4] There are other possibilities. Some common examples are stretching, compressing, or twisting a spring; stretching a rubber band; compressing a gas.

[5] For this calculation see Eqs. 8-2 and 8-3.

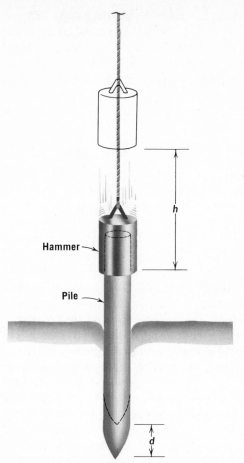

Fig. 8-1. Piledriver. The work done by the hammer on the pile depends on the mass of the hammer, m, and the distance, d, that the pile is driven into the ground which is also the distance required to bring the hammer to a stop. Since the hammer is changing its velocity, there is an acceleration, which we will designate as a. The force exerted by the hammer on the pile is therefore ma and the work done by the hammer on the pile is mad. Using the symbol W for work and the subscript "down" to indicate the falling hammer, we may write $W_{down} = mad$. To lift the hammer the distance h, work must be done against the weight of the hammer. This weight is mg, and therefore the work done is mgh. With the subscript "up" to indicate the raising of the hammer, this is written $W_{up} = mgh$. From the definition of acceleration $v^2 = 2ad$ (p. 104). Then $ad = v^2/2$, and since $W_{down} = mad$, then $W_{down} = mv^2/2$. Similarly $v^2 = 2gh$, so $gh = v^2/2$, and since $W_{up} = mgh$, then $W_{up} = mv^2/2$. Thus the KE at the instant of impact equals the PE at the raised position. The striking hammer imparts KE to the pile. The distance d that the pile is driven into the ground is less than h because the total mass of hammer and pile is greater than the mass of the hammer alone (see conservation of momentum, p. 120). By the time the motion of the pile has stopped, all of the KE imparted to it has been transformed into heat.

the potential energy is 0 when the mass is on the floor. It is possible to use the surface of the earth at whatever place we happen to be, or the surface of the earth at sea level even if we are not there, as our level of reference. This, however, is cumbersome at best, and impossible at worst, so we use whatever level is convenient. This practice is easily justified because it is only differences in potential energy that we need to know. Thus, in the case of our 10,000 g mass, we are concerned only with the difference in potential energy between the floor and the table. That difference will be unaffected by whatever potential energy the mass has while on the floor.

The Concept of Kinetic Energy

If our 10 kg mass is dropped from the table to the floor, it will lose its potential energy, but in doing so it will gain a totally different kind of energy. This is the energy due to its motion, called *kinetic energy*. The energy of a falling mass is used for useful work in a pile driver, a machine in which a heavy weight (the hammer) is allowed to fall onto a pile[6] to drive it into the ground (Fig. 8-1). The engine is used to hoist the hammer to the desired height,

[6] A pile is a long large stake, or pointed timber, driven into the earth for the purpose of supporting the foundations of buildings or other structures in wet or yielding ground that is itself too weak to support such structures.

giving it potential energy. In falling, the hammer loses its potential energy, but not all at once, for when it has fallen halfway it still has half. At the instant before the hammer strikes the pile, the potential energy is zero, and the kinetic energy is at a maximum. Calculation of the kinetic energy at this point shows that it is exactly equal to the potential energy at the maximum height of the hammer, if we overlook the small loss due to friction. On the way up and on the way down, the energy is part kinetic and part potential.

Mathematical Expressions for Potential and Kinetic Energy

The formulas for both potential and kinetic energy can be derived from the mechanics of Newton and Galileo. That for potential energy is as follows:

$$PE = W = F \times d \qquad [8\text{-}2]$$
$$\text{where} \quad F = ma$$

but for a freely falling mass, a is designated by g, so,

$$F = mg$$

If we let h represent the height of the raised mass, then $h = d$, and Eq. 8-2 becomes

$$PE = W = mgh \qquad [8\text{-}3]$$

Thus, for our 10,000 g mass raised to a height of 100 cm, the potential energy is given by

$$PE = 10,000 \text{ g} \times 980 \text{ cm/sec}^2 \times 100 \text{ cm}$$
$$= 98 \times 10^7 \text{ ergs or 98 joules}$$

The derivation of the formula for kinetic energy is as follows:

$$KE = W = F \times d$$
$$\text{where} \quad F = mg$$

According to Galileo's law of acceleration,

$$d = \tfrac{1}{2}at^2$$

For a freely falling body, then,

$$d = \tfrac{1}{2}gt^2$$

Substituting these values for F and d,

$$KE = W = mg \times \tfrac{1}{2}gt^2 = \tfrac{1}{2}m \times g^2t^2 \quad [8\text{-}4]$$

But $$v = gt$$

so $$v^2 = g^2t^2$$

Substituting v^2 for g^2t^2 in Eq. 8-4,

$$KE = W = \tfrac{1}{2}m \times v^2 = \tfrac{1}{2}mv^2 \quad [8\text{-}5]$$

Thus, the kinetic energy of our 10,000 g mass an instant before the end of a fall of 100 cm is 10,000 g times half the square of the velocity. The velocity is given by the equation $v^2 = 2gd$ (p. 104).

$$2gd = 2 \times 980 \text{ cm/sec}^2 \times 100 \text{ cm}$$
$$= 196,000 \text{ cm}^2/\text{sec}^2$$

Hence

$$\tfrac{1}{2}mv^2 = \frac{10,000 \text{ g} \times 196,000 \text{ cm}^2/\text{sec}^2}{2}$$
$$= 1 \times 10^4 \times 98 \times 10^3$$
$$= 98 \times 10^7 \text{ g-cm}^2/\text{sec}^2$$
$$= 98 \times 10^7 \text{ ergs} = 98 \text{ joules}$$

Note that the potential energy is equal to the kinetic energy. Since this is true, mgh at B (Fig. 8-2) must be equal to $\tfrac{1}{2}mv^2$ at A (Fig. 8-2). In other words, $KE = mgh$, and we should be able to derive $\tfrac{1}{2}mv^2$ from this equation. This we can easily do, but we will not belabor the point here. Thus, in Fig. 8-2, $PE_{top} = KE_{bottom}$ if there are no frictional losses, or $PE + KE = $ constant. If there are frictional losses, $PE + KE + \text{heat} = $ constant.

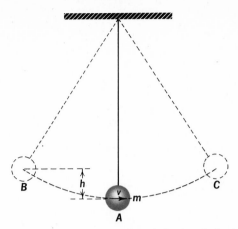

Fig. 8-2. Energy Changes in Frictionless Swinging Pendulum. At A, the lowest point of the pendulum's swing, all energy is kinetic: at B and C, the high points of its swing, all energy is potential. Thus $mgh = \frac{1}{2}mv^2$, where v is the velocity at point A. Since m and g are constant, the total energy depends upon the value of h. How does h govern v?

The latter equation is written in accord with the law of conservation of energy insofar as it can be applied to mechanical energy. We will learn more of this law later after we have studied heat. We will then find that the law applies to all forms of energy. Still later we will have to combine this law with the law of conservation of mass to give us the more accurate law of conservation of mass and energy.

Potential and kinetic energy are collectively known as *mechanical energy*. Other forms of energy, all of which we will study later, are heat energy, electrical energy, magnetic energy, chemical energy, radiant (electromagnetic) energy, and nuclear energy. At various places in this course we will also learn more about the transformation of one type of energy into other types.

Machines

Machines are devices that change either the magnitude of the force required to do work or the direction of the forces so that it is more conveniently applied. Some simple machines are the inclined plane, the lever, the pulley, the wheel and axle, the wedge, the screw and nut, the jack, the propeller, and the pump. No matter how complicated a machine may look, it is essentially a combination of simple machines. Throughout human history machines have been the means of shifting backbreaking physical labor from the shoulders of man to those of animals like horses and oxen, to steam and gasoline engines, and to electric motors.

Despite the enormous advantages of machines, one cannot get more work out of a machine than is put into it. Suppose you wish to raise a 100 kg mass. If you were strong enough to lift it 1 m, you would do a certain number of joules of work. It is much too heavy for you, so you use a lever instead (Fig. 8-3). The lever enables you to use a smaller force operating through a greater distance, but $f \times D$ will be equal to $F \times d$. The longer the lever (measured outward from the fulcrum), the less the force needed.

Actually you get less work out of a machine than the theoretical value because there is always some friction involved. The work against friction[7] is not recoverable as is the work against gravity or the work to overcome inertia. This loss decreases the efficiency of a machine. Efficiency is defined as the ratio of

[7]When two surfaces in contact move over each other, there is always some resistance to the motion. This resistance gives rise to the force that we call *friction*. It always opposes the motion. Friction at the start is always greater than after motion has begun. The smoother the two surfaces, the less the friction, provided they are not so smooth that they stick together. Rolling friction is less than sliding friction; hence the advantages of the wheel over a sled, and the advantage of roller bearings between a wheel and its axle. A lubricant reduces friction by changing the contact between two solids to that of two liquid films. Man is forced to expend enormous amounts of energy to overcome friction, but he could not do without it. Belts cling to pulleys because of friction and so drive machinery. Brakes on cars operate because of friction. Screws and nails hold objects together by means of friction. Without friction we could not walk.

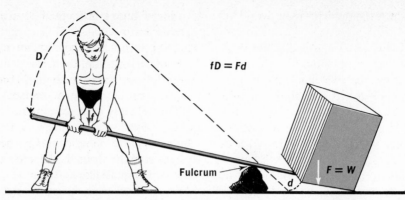

Fig. 8-3. A Simple Lever. By pressing down on the lever, the man raises the weight. The ease with which he can do this for any given weight depends on how much bigger the distance D is than the distance d. F represents the downward force exerted by the weight due to gravity, and f the force the man must exert to raise the weight distance d. Since the work done is equal to the force exerted multiplied by the distance through which the force operates, $F \times d = f \times D$. Thus the man, by exerting a lesser force through a greater distance, can move a body that exerts a far greater downward force. Note that D and d are essentially vertical distances.

the work done by the machine to the work done on the machine:

$$\text{efficiency} = \frac{\text{work done}}{\text{energy supplied}}$$
$$= \frac{\text{output of energy}}{\text{input of energy}}$$

It is always less than 100%.

Perpetual Motion and the Law of Conservation of Mechanical Energy

For centuries man has been trying to make the energy output-input ratio greater than 100%—to find *perpetual motion*. This is not a very good term, for it is misleading. It leads people to think of the problem as simply one in which all that is necessary is to eliminate friction. Nature has done this with our solar system, in which all of the planets keep moving without the addition of any new energy. But even nature would fail if we succeeded in taking energy out of the system, for if we continued to do so long enough the planets would move closer to the sun, gradually spiraling into it.

The essential problem of any perpetual-motion device is to make the output greater than the input, so that the output from the device would provide the input and leave something over to do useful work. If successful, the machine would be a creator of energy without cost, thus solving all of the energy problems of the world. Thousands of devices have been tried, but all have failed to deliver a continuous supply of energy without using additional fuel themselves. Professional scientists state that perpetual motion is impossible. This statement cannot be proved mathematically. In large part it is based on a summary of a very great number of experimental tests, and in smaller part it is a *statement of faith* in the law of conservation of energy as applied outside the submicroscopic world of the atom.

The belief is bolstered in still another way. If we believe perpetual motion is impossible—that is, if we believe machines cannot create energy—we might ask if they could destroy some. Only by carefully balancing the energy books in every energy transformation, taking particular pains to account for all frictional (heat) losses, have scientists come to a belief in the law of conservation of energy in the macroscopic world. If energy is always conserved—that is, if energy cannot be destroyed—it seems unlikely that energy can be created. A belief in perpetual motion and a belief in the conservation of energy in the macroscopic world are inconsistent with each other.

Exercises

1. Distinguish among work, force, and power.
2. Define work mathematically.
3. Give two examples of the conversion of kinetic energy into work.
4. State the equations for KE and PE.
5. Why is a level of reference necessary for potential energy?
6. Define (a) an erg and (b) a joule.
7. Distinguish between work and energy.
8. Where is the kinetic energy of a swinging pendulum (a) greatest and (b) least? Where is the potential energy (c) greatest and (d) least?
9. What is the kinetic energy of a 2 g mass moving with a speed of (a) 1 cm/sec, (b) 2 cm/sec, (c) 3 cm/sec, (d) 4 cm/sec? (e) By what factor does the KE increase if m is constant?
10. If we neglect the small amount of friction involved, how much work do you do in "pushing" a well-oiled cart with ball-bearing wheels and weighing 20 kg across a level floor a distance of 20 m at constant velocity?
11. A huge rock falls from the top of a vertical cliff to the ground below.
    (a) What happens to its kinetic energy when it strikes the ground?
    (b) When is its kinetic energy at a maximum?
    (c) Will its kinetic energy be half the maximum when the rock is halfway down? Explain.
12. A mass m slides down a frictionless inclined plane 10 ft long from a height of 6 ft above the ground. What is the difference in work done in this situation from that done by the same mass falling freely through a distance of 6 ft?
13. We have learned that the earth in its path about the sun travels faster when it is closer to the sun than when it is farther away. Its kinetic energy must therefore be greater when it is traveling faster. Yet the total mechanical energy, KE + PE, must be constant.
    (a) In terms of velocity, when is the earth's potential energy least and when is it greatest?
    (b) How can you explain the earth's potential energy in this situation? (*Hint:* The earth, like the moon, is a "falling" body.)
14. What happens to the kinetic energy of a car when it stops?
15. What is a machine? Name some simple machines.
16. Why do scientists not believe that perpetual-motion machines are possible?
17. Is the motion of the earth around the sun an example of perpetual motion? Explain.
18. When energy is transformed from one type into another, we commonly say that some energy has been "lost." What do we mean by that?
19. May one type of energy be completely

transformed into another type? Explain.

20. A simple machine, such as, a lever, enables you to do work that you could not do otherwise. Is this a violation of the law of conservation of energy? Explain.

21. Make a list of all of the types or sources of energy that you can think of. Which, if any, are not traceable to solar energy?

22. What increases in our standard of living have not resulted from an increase of our energy resources?

23. A 2 kg mass is moving at a constant speed of 5 m/sec. What are (a) its kinetic energy and (b) its momentum?

Waves and Wave Motions

Chapter 9

Waves as Transmitters of Energy

Anyone who has been in a boat floating idly on ocean waters well out from shore, where the waves roll in unimpeded from as far out as the eye can see, is aware that water waves are carriers of energy. These waves are set in motion by the wind, and they continue to move long after the wind has died down. The kinetic energy of the wind did work upon the water, and the waves thus created do work on your boat, causing it to bob up and down as they pass. Your boat shows no inclination to move shoreward with the wave. Pour a bottle of red ink into the wave, and you discover the reason; the water itself is not moving toward shore. The ink shows a strong tendency to stay near the place where it entered the water. Yet something is obviously being transported shoreward, for your eyes do not deceive you. Further analysis will show that there is no transport of matter of any kind, that instead

An ocean traveler has even more vividly the impression that the ocean is made of waves than that it is made of water.
A. S. EDDINGTON

153

it is a state of motion—and energy—that is being transported, energy given the wave by the wind.

That energy is transmitted shoreward is proved by what the waves do when they reach shallow water and break. Even casual observation reveals that a new situation has arisen, for now the water of the breaking wave rushes up on shore, moving sand and gravel as it does so or crashing against a cliff if one is there. Not only is there a transport of energy, but from the moment of breaking there is a transport of matter shoreward—of water, of sand and gravel, or even boulders "on stern and rockbound coasts." Note how different this transport of energy is from that which caused the boat merely to bob up and down.

This transport of energy by the breaking wave is in principle no different from that of the familiar mechanical methods. The latter include transmission by gears (in your automobile), and belts (as in a washing machine or the fan belt of your car), or chains (as in a bicycle), or a falling weight (as in a pile driver). The transference of electrical energy by means of wires and of heat energy by means of conduction is also mechanical in nature, though less obviously so. But none of these resembles a method in which energy is transferred without anything of a material nature moving from the center of disturbance to the receiver. We may now define a *wave* as a state of disturbance that is propagated from one point to another at a definite velocity.

A center of disturbance may be visualized by the tossing of a stone into a pond. We see a wave spread out in all directions, forming a circular wave front. Suppose a number of leaves scattered over the surface of the pond. As the wave reaches each leaf, it bobs up and down, but shows no inclination to travel with the wave. We conclude that the energy given to the leaf which causes it to bob up and down is transmitted by the surface wave but that no water molecules are transferred from the center of the disturbance to any of the leaves. Only energy is transmitted from water molecules to water molecules all along the path of the wave.

For a succession of waves to be generated a succession of disturbances must occur. This is best accomplished by a vibrating source.

Classification of Waves

We can divide waves into two groups: those that need a physical medium for their transmission and those that do not. The former are *mechanical;* the latter are *electromagnetic* waves such as light and heat waves, radio and television waves, and X rays and gamma rays (see Chapter 20).

The necessity of a physical medium for the water waves and rope waves (Fig. 9-1) is clear, for we can see the energy advance as the wave moves over the water surface or along the rope. That we need a medium for the sound waves emitted by a violin can be proved by substituting an electric bell for the musical instrument and placing it in an airtight jar from which the air is being evacuated. As the air is pumped out, the ringing of the bell becomes fainter and fainter, until it can scarcely be heard at all. We conclude that sound waves cannot be transmitted through a vacuum. It follows that the medium transmitting the sound is air, also a physical medium. Further investigation reveals that sound waves are also transmitted by liquids and solids in the same way as they are transmitted by air. Sound waves travel faster in solids, slowest in air, and not at all in a vacuum.

But this does not mean that energy cannot be transmitted through a vacuum. We know that the sun and stars transmit light and heat energy vast distances across space that is far emptier than any vacuum we can produce on

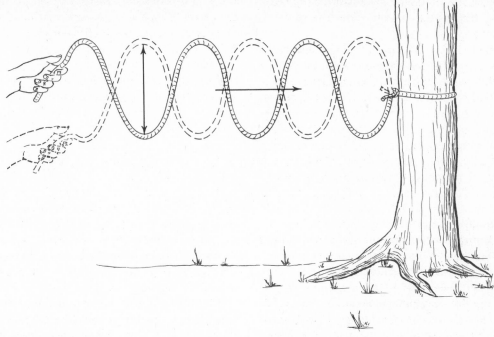

Fig. 9-1. Wave in a Rope. An up and down motion (vibration) of the hand generates the wave. The wave travels from the hand to the tree but the rope does not. Instead it moves up and down in a direction at right angles to the direction of wave travel. This wave is therefore a transverse wave.

earth. If we accept wave motion as the method of transmission, then we must accept the fact that no medium is necessary for this type of wave transmission. Laboratory experiments show that light can travel through a vacuum and that it does so faster than through air.

A second classification is based upon the direction of vibration with respect to the direction the wave is traveling. One group is called *longitudinal* because the direction of vibration of the particles of the transmitting medium is back and forth parallel to the direction the wave is traveling (Fig. 9-2). All longitudinal waves are mechanical and can travel in any medium. Sound is the only familiar example. When sound is traveling through air, air molecules are set vibrating by the source in an ordered back and forth motion

that is superimposed upon the normal random motion of air molecules (p. 204).

A second group is called *transverse* because the direction of vibration of the particles of the transmitting medium is across (transverse to) the direction of travel. Transverse waves may be mechanical or electromagnetic. Examples of mechanical transverse waves are the waves in a rope (Fig. 9-1) and one of the two kinds of earthquake waves (p. 551). Electromagnetic waves (light, radio, X rays, and so on) of all sorts behave like transverse waves. Water waves are combinations of longitudinal and transverse waves. Transverse mechanical waves travel only through solids; they cannot travel through liquids or gases because the transverse motion requires that each moving particle drag adjacent particles with it. To do

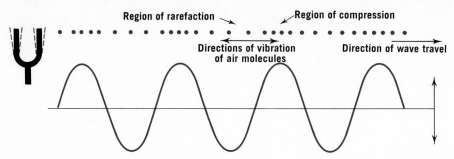

Fig. 9-2. Representation of Longitudinal Wave. A sound wave is emitted by a tuning fork. Regions of compression of the particles composing the medium alternate with regions of rarefaction as these regions (not the particles) are propagated through the medium. Such a wave may be represented graphically as a series of crests and troughs. (See caption to Fig. 9-3.)

so the particles must be bound together—which they are not in a liquid or a gas. Longitudinal motion requires only that each particle exert a push on the particle ahead or the particle behind—as easily done in a gas or liquid as in a solid. Electromagnetic waves (light, and so on) can travel through gases, liquids, and solids, but they do not make use of these media in doing so; that is, they do not cause the particles of the media to vibrate transversely to their paths. Mysteriously enough they travel best through a vacuum.

Frequency, Wavelength, and Velocity of Waves

The most fundamental properties of periodic waves are frequency (f), wavelength (λ), and velocity (v). Frequency is the number of vibrations per second, commonly stated in cycles per second (or simply cycles). The frequency is determined by the source and so is constant unless a change is made at or in the source. Wavelength is the distance between two successive crests or two successive troughs or, more generally, between any corresponding points on two successive waves (Fig. 9-3). Wave velocity is the speed with which the crests (or troughs—pronounced "troffs") appear to travel. Since frequency, f, is the

number of wavelengths passing a given point per unit time, the velocity of the wave is given by multiplying the frequency by the wavelength. Thus $v = f\lambda$. The period of a wave is sometimes important. It is defined as the time interval during which the source emits a single wave. The frequency is related to the period by the formula $f = 1/\text{period}$. Thus the period is the reciprocal of the frequency.

The velocity of any wave depends upon the nature of the medium through which it travels—if there is a medium. For example, sound waves travel in air at about 1100 ft/sec, in water at about 5000 ft/sec, and in ice at about 10,500 ft/sec. The speed of sound in cast iron is about 15,000 ft/sec, and in rubber it is only about 100 ft/sec.

For electromagnetic waves the situation is quite different. Light travels through a diamond only about half as fast as it does through air. It travels fastest through a vacuum, where its speed is nearly 3×10^{10} cm/sec (about 186,000 mi/sec). All electromagnetic waves, regardless of their frequency or wavelength, travel at this speed in a vacuum. Therefore, the greater the frequency, the smaller the wavelength.

The frequency of a wave governs one other property of sound and light waves. In the case of sound it is called *pitch*. The higher the

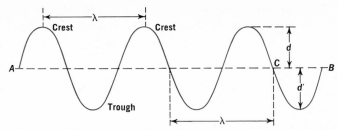

Fig. 9-3. Conventional Representation of Waves. The diagram resembles a water wave but is used for all types of waves, even for light waves, which cannot be visualized under any circumstances. Since all waves originate from a vibrating source, a wave motion traveling the path *AB* may be considered to consist of a vibration from crest to trough and back again, and so on, thus producing a visualizable form. The diagram is actually a graph whose curve shows the displacement at any instant along the path of the wave. λ = wavelength, d and d' = amplitude. Frequency, f, is the number of wavelengths passing a given point, C, per unit time. The velocity, v, is given by $f\lambda$.

frequency, the higher the pitch. The human ear can detect frequencies that range from about 20 cycles/sec to about 20,000 cycles/sec. Our ears react best to frequencies of about 2000 cycles/sec. To detect the very low frequencies, the energy of the waves must be enormously greater (a million times or more) than when in the optimum range of the human ear. As a person grows older, the ability to detect the higher frequencies diminishes greatly. Certain animals, for example, dogs and bats, can hear frequencies higher than can man. For purposes of convenience we refer to all such vibrations as sound waves whether they are within the range of the human ear or not. In the case of light the corresponding property governed by the frequency is *color*. Since this phenomenon can more adequately be dealt with under the subjects of refraction and dispersion, we will omit it here.

Amplitude vs. Energy Carried by a Wave

If, in Fig. 9-3, the line *AB* is considered the level surface of the water before the stone is dropped, then the distance d represents the maximum displacement of the water above *AB* when the wave passes by. This distance is called the *amplitude* of the wave. It is half the distance between the top of a crest and the bottom of a trough.

A moment's reflection will show that the amplitude is a measure of the energy carried by the wave. A large stone will obviously create a bigger disturbance than a small one, and so the wave will be larger, will have a bigger amplitude, and will carry more energy. In sound waves greater amplitude means greater loudness; in light waves it means greater brightness. However, amplitude is not the only factor controlling loudness, if by loudness we mean the ease by which the sound may be heard by the human ear. The other factor is *pitch*. A high-pitched whistle can be heard above lower-pitched sounds carrying much greater energy—which is why most whistles are high-pitched.

The energy of a wave decreases as it travels outward from the vibrating source, varying inversely as the square of the distance from it. Consider a point source of light or sound in which the waves are propagated outward in all directions. Their wave fronts (Fig. 9-4) will be spherical, and since the surface of a

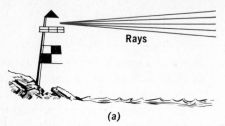
(a)

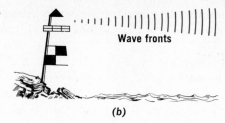
(b)

Fig. 9-4. Rays vs. Wave Fronts in Light. (*a*) Rays. (*b*) A series of expanding wave fronts. Note that the rays are at right angles to tangents to any wave front if the medium of transmission is uniform. Each wave front is a portion of a spherical surface. The ray specifies the direction of transmission of energy.

sphere increases as the square of its radius, the inverse-square law applies. Doubling the distance to the source thus results in the energy being distributed over four times the area (see Fig. 5-1). It should be noted that the amplitude decreases with increasing distance from the source, but that frequency and wavelength are not diminished as long as the medium is homogeneous. Thus, the frequency and the wavelength of the light from a star a million light years distant remain unchanged during the whole of its million-year journey through space. (*Note:* Other aspects of light as a wave motion are discussed in Chapter 20.)

Doppler Effect

If a source of sound waves is approaching the observer, the frequency, as detected by the ear of the observer, is increased and the pitch rises; if the source is receding from the observer, the frequency, as detected by the observer, is decreased and the pitch is lowered. Thus, if you were standing near a railroad track as the fast express approached, blowing its whistle, the pitch of the whistle would rise until the engine reached you, then as it receded in the distance the pitch would decline, yet the

Fig. 9-5. The Doppler Effect with Respect to Sound. (*a*) The train is standing still; both boys hear the same pitch because the pitch of any whistle is constant. (*b*) The train advances toward *A*; thus its velocity seems to add to that of the sound waves from the whistle. This increases the number of waves reaching *A* per unit time; that is, it increases the frequency and so raises the pitch. At *B* the velocity of the train seems to subtract from that of the sound waves, thus decreasing the frequency and the pitch.

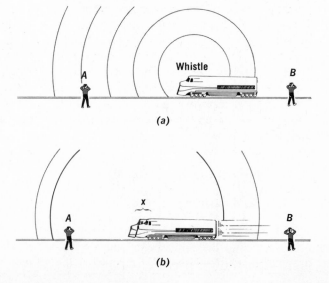

frequency of the sound waves actually emitted by the whistle would be constant all of the time (Fig. 9-5).

This apparent change in frequency due to relative motion of the source and observer is the Doppler effect. As far as the source is concerned, the change is only apparent; as far as the observer is concerned, there is an actual change in the frequency.

The Doppler effect applies to light waves equally well. Changing of frequency by motion of the source of light toward or away from the observer causes a change in color. The Doppler effect is used to tell whether a particular star is moving toward us or away from us.

Diffraction of Mechanical Waves

The ability of a wave to spread out around the edges of an obstacle in its path is called *diffraction*. Since the wave is a carrier of energy, then energy must be carried around the edges of the obstacle (Fig. 9-6). In order for a disturbance to be transmitted from one point to another, it must have an effect on all neighboring points. Thus if you press a finger against some stretched surface, say a drumhead, you depress not only the area in contact with your finger but all the neighboring regions too.

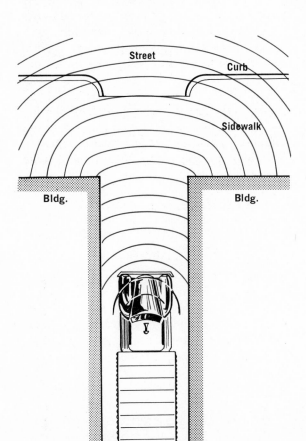

Fig. 9-6. Diffraction of Sound. A truck coming out of an alley sounds its horn before crossing the sidewalk to enter the street. The sound waves are diffracted—that is, bent around the corners. Thus pedestrians beyond the corners hear the sound of the horn and are warned by it.

Consider a breakwater built out across the entrance to a harbor to reduce the force of the waves coming in. There is an opening in the middle, a gap through which boats may pass in and out. A succession of waves from the open sea approaches the gap, and the ends of each successively crash against the breakwater while a portion of the middle of each passes through the gap and continues on into the harbor. As they do so we may see the waves spreading out to some extent behind the harbor side of the breakwater—the waves are being diffracted (bent) as they spread out around the end of the breakwater (Fig. 9-7). The precise behavior of the waves as they spread will depend upon the ratio of the wavelength (not the length of the wave) to the width of the opening. If the opening is large

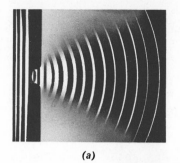

(a)

(b)

Fig. 9-8. Diffraction of Waves: Relationship Between Width of Opening and Wavelength. (*a*) The width of the opening is greater than the wavelength and the diffraction effect is relatively small. (*b*) The width of the opening is substantially less than the wavelength. The diffraction effect is much greater; that is, the waves have spread out much farther on each side of the opening. Note that this illustration is adapted from photographs of small waves in a glass-bottomed model of a breakwater. The apparent changes in wavelength do not occur; they are only photographic effects.

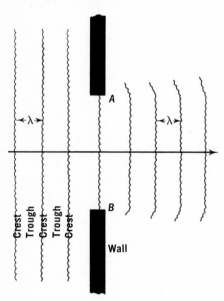

Fig. 9-7. Diffraction of Water Waves. A wall (breakwater) across a harbor entrance has a gap, *AB*, in it that is considerably wider than the wavelength, λ, is long. There is little bending (diffraction) of the waves as they pass the ends of the wall under these conditions.

(wide) relative to the wavelength—many times as large—the waves in the harbor will not bend much around the end of the breakwater, and so will be only slightly longer than the width of the breakwater opening; the amount of diffraction is small. If the opening is small relative to the wavelength, the waves will spread out considerably more to each side beyond the opening (Fig. 9-8).

Similarly, in music the longer wavelengths (or those of lower frequency) bend around the corners more easily than the shorter, so that in the adjoining room, there is a tendency for the lower notes (longer wavelengths) to be accentuated, the higher ones (shorter wavelengths) subdued. Proper placing of the speakers that reproduce the high notes is more critical than for those that reproduce the low notes. (For diffraction of light and other electromagnetic waves, see Chapter 20.)

Interference of Mechanical Waves

That two sound waves may be added together to produce a single wave of greater amplitude is not at all surprising to any of us, but that two sound waves may also be combined, though somewhat differently, to produce virtual silence[1] may seem unlikely to some of us. All that is necessary to produce silence is to have two identical sound waves reaching a receiver completely out of phase. Two waves of the same frequency from the same source and traveling paths of somewhat different lengths will, on reaching the same receiver, be exactly in phase if crests and troughs of each are exactly in step—that is, if crest meets crest and trough meets trough— and exactly out of phase if they are exactly out of step—that is, if crest meets trough and trough meets crest (Fig. 9-9).

Suppose we consider wave crests as representing upward displacements, and troughs as downward displacements. If two waves of the same wavelength (or frequency) and amplitude arrive at the same receiver exactly out of step, the resultant of the two displacements is zero; that is, one displacement cancels the other. If they are exactly in step; that is, in

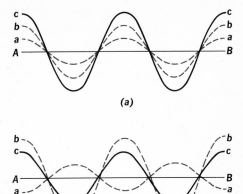

Fig. 9-9.   Interference of Waves Traveling the Same Path. (*a*) Two waves, *a* and *b*, with different amplitudes are in phase. They therefore completely reinforce one another, producing a result like that of single wave, *c*, with an amplitude equal to the sum of the amplitudes of *a* and *b*. (*b*) Here the two waves are exactly out of phase. The final result is like that of a single wave, *c*, with an amplitude equal to the difference between the amplitudes *a* and *b*.

phase, they reinforce each other, causing increased loudness in sound. If the two waves are neither completely in phase nor completely out of phase, there will be partial cancellation or partial reinforcement. The combined phenomena of cancellation and reinforcement constitute *interference*. Cancellation may be called *destructive interference*. Reinforcement may be called *constructive interference*. For interference of light see Chapter 20, where we will learn that diffraction and interference are closely related, that they are really different aspects of the same thing.

Standing Waves

Progressive waves are ones in which the disturbance travels continually outward from

---

[1]Complete silence by such combination is highly unlikely because of reflections.

the source. Waves in a long rope are progressive waves. When they are reflected upon themselves, interference results and standing waves are formed. A standing wave is unlike a progressive wave because it does not seem to advance. Actually two trains of waves continually travel to and fro in the rope. Study Fig. 9-1 carefully. The two wave trains, traveling in opposite directions, are exactly out of phase at the nodes; destructive interference occurs. At the loops constructive interference occurs.

Standing waves can be produced in any kind of wave motion by causing interference in this manner. Since interference is common to all types of waves, this phenomenon comprises a crucial test for wave motion; that is, the production of any sort of interference pattern is evidence of wave motion.

Exercises

1. What are mechanical waves?
2. What determines the energy of a wave?
3. What finally happens to the energy of sound waves in open air?
4. What are the relationships among the frequency, the wavelength, and the velocity of a periodic wave?
5. Differentiate between longitudinal and transverse waves. Give an example of each.
6. Differentiate between mechanical and electromagnetic waves.
7. Mechanical waves travel fastest in what medium?
8. What type of wave motion is a water wave in the open ocean?
9. What is the relationship, if any, between (a) loudness and pitch, and (b) pitch and frequency?

Facts, Concepts, Laws, Theories, and Hypotheses

Chapter **10**

We have delayed defining or discussing the terms in the title of this chapter until a number of them had been presented to you in enough detail to form a background for the present discussion. To have made this chapter the first in this book would, in the opinion of the author, have been largely a waste of time, somewhat like trying to understand the culture of a primitive people without having any background of information about them. Until one has had experience with scientific laws, theories, or hypotheses, and has had the opportunity to discover, think about, and describe a number of them—and until one has some knowledge of the mental climate of the time in which a theory, law, or hypothesis was developed—it is difficult to approach, much less reach, a true understanding of them.

This is not to imply that all a student has to do to obtain this understanding is to read this chapter. Only a start will be made at this time, a start that will not be completed even when this course is ended. It is hoped, how-

The study of nature that is a part of man's intellectual life is a delight to all scientists. In their hands, science is not just a business of collecting facts or stating laws or directing experiments. It is above all an *art* of sensing the best choice of view or the most fruitful line of understanding of nature.
ERIC M. ROGERS
Physics for the Inquiring Mind
(1960)

163

ever, that in the end the student will have gotten rid of many mistaken notions about these terms, and that he will be able to distinguish between a law and a theory. It is also hoped that if he is somewhat disdainful of theories, as so many people are, and is prone to laud the practical over the theoretical, that he will come to the realization that man's success in his upward struggle from caveman to modern civilized man is almost wholly due to the curiosity of a relatively few individuals and their penchant for formulating theories. Some peoples, even today, have never lifted themselves above primitive levels because they lack not only sufficient curiosity to seek natural explanations, but their minds are so dominated by the supernatural, by witch doctors, medicine men and the like, that they are quite content to leave the mysteries of nature to their gods. Without theories the search for the laws of nature is mere fumbling in the dark.

Theories

A scientific theory is an explanation of some natural phenomenon. In general, theories contain (or consist of) well-developed ideas that provide ways of interrelating many different phenomena. This is not a complete definition, nor is one possible. The term *theory* is very widely misused, sometimes by people who know, or profess to know, considerable science. It is often used as a synonym for an educated guess. Sometimes a tentative answer to almost any problem, no matter how trivial, is referred to as a theory. This is the common use of the word in newspapers and magazines, on TV, and in everyday conversation. In the minds of some, a theory is something that has not been proved. Often the word *theory* is used to refer to an hypothesis or is used improperly in place of the word *speculation*. If we had to make a

two- or three-word definition, we would call theories *conceptual schemes:* "conceptual schemes that have developed as a result of experimentation and observation and are fruitful of further experimentation and observation." Conant says that the emphasis should be on the word *fruitful*.[1]

Fruitful means that the conceptual scheme should suggest the making of new observations, new experiments, new explanations for inadequate old ones, or explanations for phenomena that have long gone without them. A good conceptual scheme will

> . . . penetrate beyond the immediate and visible to the unseen, and thereby . . . place the visible into a new, larger context. For like a distant floating iceberg whose bulk is largely hidden under the sea, only the smallest part of reality impresses itself upon us directly. To help us grasp the whole picture is the supreme function of a theory. On a simple level, a theory helps us to interpret the unknown in terms of the known. It is a conceptual scheme which we invent or postulate in order to explain to ourselves, and to others, observed phenomena and the relationships between them, thereby bringing together into one structure the concepts, laws, principles, hypotheses, and observations from often widely different fields. These functions may equally well be claimed by the hypothesis. In truth, we need not lay down a precise dividing line, but might regard theory and hypothesis as differing in degree of generality only. Therefore, at one extreme we might find the *limited working hypothesis* by which we guide our way through a specific experiment, placing at the other end of the spectrum the *general theory,* which guides the design and interpretation of all experiments in that field of study.[2]

[1] James B. Conant, *Science and Common Sense*, Yale University Press, New Haven, 1951, p. 25.
[2] Gerald Holton, *Concepts and Theories in Physical Science*, Addison-Wesley, Reading, Mass., 1952, p. 138.

We have emphasized that a theory should be fruitful. Such a theory should correlate many separate, and perhaps seemingly unrelated, facts into a logical, easily grasped structure of thought. A fruitful theory should spark the imagination to see if paths that have heretofore been considered entirely unconnected may not connect up with the new paths. A good theory should make it possible to predict specific new observable phenomena, and it may offer a solution to some practical problems. The heliocentric theory, for example, helped to determine the exact lengths of the year and of the lunar month.

Let us consider Newton's theory of gravitation, one of the most fruitful of all theories, in the light of these functions of a theory. Once the mathematics involved had been worked out, not only was an understanding of what kept the planets in their orbits possible, but it also became possible to map the orbits of undiscovered planets, to explain the tides and the precession of the equinoxes, to determine the masses of the earth, the planets, and the sun and to calculate their densities, to predict the shape of the earth and give a reason for it, to understand the variations of the value of g in different parts of the earth, to plot the paths of artificial satellites, and even to understand why the high mountains are able to stand so far above the floors of the ocean basins.

A theory that is not fruitful is a "bad" theory because it does not lead to further knowledge. For example, the theory that the earth was specially created as is is a "bad" theory, not because it is not true, but because it does not lead one on toward a better understanding of nature. Such a theory is barren, for it gives a final explanation to all things, that they are as they are because they were created that way. A believer in such a theory has no incentive to investigate nature except to describe it, for he already has all of the answers as to why things are as they are.

Difficult for the layman to understand is that the scientists' criterion for a "good" theory does not depend upon whether it is true or not. He measures it only by its consequences—". . . consequences in terms of other ideas and other experiments. Thus conceived, science is not a quest for certainty; it is rather a quest which is successful only to the degree that it is continuous."[3] If the viewpoint that the validity of a theory depends only upon its ability to suggest new experiments, which in turn generate new ideas, and so on, seems like a form of madness, we will have to let it seem so. For to seek to justify this attitude of the scientist would take far more pages than we have available here. Suffice it to say that some theories that have been completely discarded were "good" theories at one time. They became "bad" theories when they not only failed to suggest new experiments or to account for new facts but actually became stumbling blocks to the development of new ideas, and hence to the acquisition of new knowledge. Eric M. Rogers of Princeton says that one needs to develop an educated taste for good theories just as one does for good cooking; in a sense, scientific theory is a form of intellectual cookery.

From what has been said, one should infer that the scientist does not expect any theory to go down through the ages unchanged. Theories are always subject to change (by scientists themselves and not by others) as new facts and observations accumulate. Even Newton's theory of gravitation underwent a refining modification as a result of Einstein's general theory of relativity, which predicted an extra motion for the planet Mercury. This extra motion, involving a slewing around of the long axis

[3] Conant, *op. cit.*

of the elliptical orbit by 0.00119° per century, had already been observed but not explained before Einstein. This refinement does not invalidate Newton's theory nor make Einstein's theory better than Newton's. Actually Einstein's theory still has some doubts and problems, but such doubts and problems about theories in general do not irritate scientists. They keep them in mind with hopes that the future will be more interesting to them because of the unsolved problems. No scientist expects that the day will ever arrive when he has all the answers. He is convinced that new knowledge begets new facts and new experiments, which in turn beget new knowledge, and so on ad infinitum.

Hypotheses

Considerable confusion exists between the terms *theory* and *hypothesis*. In general, we might say that a hypothesis is a single provisional conjecture regarding the causes or relations of certain phenomena offered without proof, whereas a theory offers considerable evidence as proof. Frequently a hypothesis is intended to guide an experiment that is in the process of being devised. It is thus seen that a hypothesis is much more limited in scope than a theory, and that what many people refer to as a theory is really a hypothesis.

Uncertainty in Science— The Role of Probability

We have already seen that measurement is the science of approximation (p. 76). Another way of saying this is that there is some uncertainty in every measurement. This fact has been discussed in detail in connection with significant figures (p. 77). Each measuring

device, including your eye, has limitations on its accuracy. Every regularity in nature, be it summarized in a law, principle, or theory, is discovered through observations or is based on individual observations that have some uncertainty attached to them. Therefore, every scientific statement involves some uncertainty. In other words, nothing is absolutely certain in science. This should not dismay you, for there are a great many degrees of preciseness, some bordering on perfection even if not absolutely reaching it.

The role of probability in respect to the truth or falsity of scientific theories is pertinent here. The competent scientist never speaks of "proving" a theory but only of obtaining a sufficient degree of confidence in it. He may speak of a theory as being acceptable or unacceptable, adequate or inadequate, valid or invalid, but never of its being true or false. For one thing, what is truth in the context used here? Is truth absolute? Certainly it is not in the scientific sense. We have already learned that we cannot always believe our senses—the sun does not really rise and set, the color-blind person does not see the same colors as the rest of us, Venus does not emit light of its own even though we may see it as the second brightest object in the night sky. In science, there is no such thing as absolute certainty; there is at best only a high degree of probability. This lack of absolute certainty often places the scientist at a disadvantage in a dispute with the nonscientist. In the widespread dispute over the fluoridation of water, qualified scientists were asked, "Are you absolutely certain that fluoridation of water will not injure the health of anyone drinking it?" Since there can never be any truthful "yes" answer but only a high degree of probability that it will not, the antifluoridationist thinks he has the better of the argument.

This sort of thing, to the student and the

layman, is frustrating. It is far easier to talk about principles, laws, hypotheses, or theories, as if they were true or false. Yet science cannot be correctly learned without taking into account its uncertainties, its limitations, and its incompleteness. But you should not misunderstand; none of this gives anyone a license to let his mind roam fancy free.

Judging the degree of probability of something being "certain" is something that only the properly qualified should attempt. The probability that there is life on Mars above that of the primitive plant life stage is so extremely low that no properly informed person thinks that there is. On the other hand, the probability that there is intelligent life on some unknown planet revolving about some unknown star far beyond our solar system is extremely high, so high that every properly informed person believes that there is. The difference between these two cases is that there is only one Mars about which we have a large number of facts; whereas in the other case, there are billions of billions and billions of stars, millions of which have a high degree of probability of having solar systems of their own but about which we have no facts at all. The law of chance enters here. The mathematician and the scientist find it impossible to believe that there is only one solar system (ours) in so vast a universe.

Because there is no such thing as certainty in theories, no competent scientist sets out to "prove" a theory, but rather seeks to disprove it. If he does not, he knows that someone else will. It is more correct to say that he gathers not only all of the pertinent facts that tend to support a theory but also all those that might tend to contradict it. For, to quote Einstein, "no number of observations or experiments will ever prove my theory to be true, but it will take only one observation, one experiment, to prove it false." Facts are the su-

preme arbiters of theories. More than one beautiful theory has fallen because of its failure to explain one ugly fact.

Facts

It is extremely difficult to state what a fact is. Since most physical scientists believe they are dealing with a real external world, they start with sense impressions as their facts of nature. In general, the facts of the physical scientist are the measurements he makes, measurements that can be checked and agreed upon by different independent observers. If an experiment reveals unexpected and perhaps startling results, the important question asked of the experimenter is, "Are your results repeatable?" Thus, science is in a sense self-correcting, for the scientist trusts only those "facts" that are the same in different laboratories, for different observers, and on different days of the week. Every scientist knows that sooner or later someone is sure to check and repeat his experiments, his observations, and his calculations and so will most likely uncover any errors and self-deceptions. In one sense facts are more important than theories, for, as previously stated, facts are the supreme arbiters of theories.

Scientific Laws

Scientific laws, sometimes called principles, are generalizations that describe the behavior of matter under a specific set of conditions. The work of the physical scientist is based on the premise that there is order in the universe, and that this order can be expressed mathematically, that nature works according to mathematical laws, and the observations of the scientist are best explained when the mathematical law relating the observations is found. From the time of Kepler and Galileo mathematical methods have provided the best means for understanding nature. To see this we have only to recall $T^2 = Kr^3$, $d = \frac{1}{2}gt^2$, $F = ma$, and $F = GMm/r^2$.

Essential to the understanding of scientific laws is a recognition of their limitations. Thus, $d = \frac{1}{2}gt^2$ only in the absence of air resistance. We will learn that Boyle's law does not hold at either very high pressures or very low temperatures. Some laws are universal, or very nearly so. Such a one is Newton's law of gravitation. Another is Einstein's mass/energy law, $E = mc^2$. Nevertheless, the most certain truth about scientific laws is that sooner or later some situation will arise in which they are found to be inaccurate or too limited. To the scientist this is no longer surprising, for matter is not compelled to obey physical laws. Unlike political laws there is never compulsion; yet the scientist expects matter to behave according to the laws, first, because the laws are an expression of the previous behavior of matter under specified conditions, and, second, because he believes that nature is orderly, not capricious. If the scientist finds that a law does not apply beyond certain limits, it does not mean that he is disappointed or that the law is a failure. Instead he tries to find out why, for beyond the limits of a law may lie new and exciting knowledge.

The Role of Speculative Ideas

Some phases of scientific thinking fail to fit precisely into any part of the general picture so far presented. One of these is the role of speculative ideas. Such ideas are the product of the imagination. They may be extremely useful if we bear in mind their status; how useful will depend largely upon the background of information and the level-headedness of the man begetting them. In general, we may say that only the well-informed have the right to speculate seriously on any subject. An example is space travel, now that it is more than just around the corner. It has become common for writers and radio or television commentators to comment confidently on these matters even though they know nothing about interplanetary distances or conditions on other planets. Many fields of knowledge today are in the speculative stage; in the hands of experts, promising speculative ideas may be sorted out and, possibly, some means devised for investigating them further.

The So-called Scientific Method

There are few things about science that are more widely misunderstood by the nonscientist than those concerning the method or methods of science. In general, scientists are in agreement that there is no such thing as a scientific method. Few would agree that there are even a number of methods, unless you let that number equal the number of scientists. This is not to say that the methods of different scientists do not have some things in common. They do so, very definitely, but the term *method* implies proceeding step by step and this is rarely done, except by those who are tabulating facts.

The so-called scientific method makes little allowance for the "happy accident"—more commonly known as the role of chance. The initial observations leading to the invention of the battery, the discovery of X rays, the vulcanization of rubber, the discovery of radioactivity, and many other things, were made more or less by chance. Chance, however, favors the prepared mind, the mind ready to seize upon an unexpected observation and turn it to advantage. To one man the fogging of photographic plates kept in a room where a cathode-ray tube was operating meant (eventually) the discovery of a new kind of radiation; to another it merely meant that such a room was a poor place to keep undeveloped photographic plates. (See pp. 320–21.)

To some scientists their solutions came "in a sudden flash of insight" but only after they had been completely immersed in their problems for some time. To most, if chance or inspiration enters at all, it is greatly overshadowed by hard work. In any case, once a discovery is made, the good scientist subjects it to all conceivable tests, trying to ruin it, so to speak, for he knows that if he does not do so before publication, someone else will afterward.

Someone has said that the scientific method consists simply of observing and experimenting. This is woefully insufficient for it leaves out the most important ingredients of all, those of planning and pondering, doing and pondering, and just pondering. For you do not learn simply by doing, as some educators would have us believe. You learn by thinking about what you are doing while you are doing it. The planning is important, for a scientist does not just search; he searches for something. Otherwise he might pass by the critical observation without recognizing it.

Scientific Explanation

Scientific explanations cannot be divorced from definitions of scientific terms. The definitions of many of them constitute complete, or nearly complete, explanations. An example is that of *inertia,* which may be defined as the property possessed by all bodies of matter that causes them to resist changes in their state (or states) of motion.

Definitions may be classified as either operational or conceptual. With definitions to help

us it is possible to sort things out, separating those that fit the definition from those that do not. The operational definition is a better one for this purpose than the conceptual, for it is the one that lists the properties from which you can decide whether certain things belong to one group or another. As an example, suppose you are given a number of colorless water solutions and asked to separate those that are acidic from those that are not. First you need to know what an acid is; that is, you need the definition of an acid. Let us define an acid as a substance that, when dissolved in water, tastes sour, turns blue litmus red, conducts electricity, and reacts with zinc to release hydrogen gas. This is an operational definition, for it lists the criteria by which you make your division of the solutions into acids and nonacids.

Now let us define an acid as a substance that can donate protons to certain other substances. This is a conceptual definition. You could not use it to classify the above solutions, and so it is not operational. Yet it has a deeper significance than the operational one. By means of it you can give an explanation of *why* an acid has some of its properties.

Physical scientists like to make their concepts clear by operational definitions, for by doing so they eliminate the likelihood of misunderstanding by other scientists. P. W. Bridgman, a Nobel Prize winner for physics, has said that the true meaning of a term is to be found by observing what a man does with it rather than by what he says about it. It is apparent from the definitions of his terms that the physical scientist limits his admissible experiences to quantitative concepts. He believes that the observable phenomena of nature can be described in terms of postulates or axioms that are mathematical, and that when he finds mathematical expressions to relate them, the observations are explained. An example is the law of free fall, mathematically expressed as $d = \frac{1}{2}gt^2$. Aside from the convenience of expressing the law in mathematical form, the possibility of any misunderstanding of its meaning is eliminated.

The critic of science is not likely to be satisfied with a mathematical explanation of a scientific law. He may maintain that it does not explain anything. He wants to know the ultimate reason why bodies fall in accordance with the law of free fall. Any attempt to answer brings up the subject of gravity, and perhaps the law of gravitation. What is gravity? Why do all bodies possess such a force of attraction? And so on. Any attempt to go beyond the mathematical expressions for the above two laws ultimately and inevitably leads us into a discussion of final causes where we quickly find ourselves out of the field of science and into the fields of philosophy and religion where one can argue interminably over the meaning of terms. To help us we need to consider, what is a scientific explanation? In general, to explain means to reduce the unfamiliar to the familiar. It means to establish a relationship between what is to be explained and whatever relevant preconceptions we already have. There are no final answers, and the scientist, at least while he is doing scientific work, does not waste his time trying to find them.

These remarks are not intended to downgrade conceptual definitions. Conceptualization and abstraction are indispensable to the fruitful development of scientific knowledge, but they must be firmly supported by the two pillars of observation and experience.[4]

Science vs. Nonscience

The various definitions of science and how it differs from other human endeavors would

fill a moderate-sized book. James B. Conant says that "Science is an interconnected series of concepts and conceptual schemes that have developed as a result of experimentation and observation and are fruitful of further experimentation and observation."[5] Einstein stated that, "The object of all sciences is to coordinate our experiences and to bring them into a logical system." Niels Bohr made a similar statement when he said that, "The task of science is both to extend the range of our experience and to reduce it to order."

Both Einstein's and Bohr's "definitions" are much broader and far less specific than Conant's. Note the emphasis that Conant puts upon conceptual schemes. These schemes, theories if you like, form the flesh and blood of any science. Without them, all we would have is a bunch of dry bones. In a course such as this book is intended for, the study of science is, to a great degree, the study of the development of conceptual schemes.

One important difference between science and nonscience is that in the course of time there has accumulated a set of basic concepts, conceptual schemes, and physical laws that have been endorsed by scientists of every country. Thus, Kepler's laws, Galileo's law of free fall, and Newton's laws of motion and gravitation are acceptable wherever scientists work. This can scarcely be said of other human endeavors.

Science, more than most fields of study, is cumulative. By this we mean that in large part one man builds on the work that his predecessors have done; that is, he begins where the others have left off. To do this he may repeat some of the work they have done, but essentially his aim is to advance the knowledge of the subject beyond that of those who went before him. Newton said that if he had seen farther than others it was because he had the

[4] Much of this chapter has been abstracted from G. Holton and P. H. D. Roller, *Foundations of Modern Physical Science,* Addison-Wesley, 1958, Chap. 13.

[5] Conant, *op. cit.*

shoulders of giants to stand on. At the same time, the scientist has no hesitation, if he thinks fit, in altering these predecessors' theories or laws, or even their facts and, more frequently, the interpretations placed upon them. Note how different it is in the fields of literature, art, and music. Newcomers in these fields do not begin where others left off, nor would they think of ever trying to improve their works by changing words, adding brush strokes, or changing notes of masters like Shakespeare, Leonardo da Vinci, or Beethoven.

Science is just as much a creative endeavor as are the arts, and the motivation is much the same. Some scientists have been just as willing to "starve in a garret" as any writer, artist, or composer, provided only that they could continue their work.

Henri Poincaré, the great French mathematician, supported this view when he said,

> The scientist does not study nature because it is useful; he studies it because he delights in it, and he delights in it because it is beautiful. If nature were not beautiful, it would not be worth knowing, and if nature were not worth knowing, life would not be worth living. Of course, I do not speak of that beauty which strikes the senses, the beauty of quality and appearances; not that I undervalue such beauty, far from it, but it has nothing to do with science; I mean that profounder beauty which comes from the harmonious order of the parts and which a pure intelligence can grasp. This it is which gives body, a structure so to speak, to the iridescent appearances which flatter our senses, and without this support the beauty of these fugitive dreams would be only imperfect, because it would be vague and always fleeting. On the contrary, intellectual beauty is sufficient unto itself, and it is for its sake, more perhaps than for the future good of humanity, that the scientist devotes himself to long and difficult labor.[6]

[6]Jules Henri Poincaré, *Foundations of Science*, Science Press, New York, 1929.

Practical Science vs. Fundamental or Pure Science

Many people are prone to laud the practical scientist, like the late Thomas Edison, for example, while tending to scoff at the theoretical scientist. The practical scientist is trying to invent something that will be of some practical use, and this everyone can understand and appreciate. Far more difficult for the layman to appreciate is the work of a pure scientist on some problem that can result in nothing apparently useful at the time. Furthermore, he is amazed that the scientist considers usefulness as unimportant. The layman fails to realize that little progress in science can be made if usefulness is the sole criterion.

At the time of discovery one can rarely predict where that discovery will find its uses. Because of Michael Faraday and Joseph Henry, both experimenters in the search for fundamental truth, Thomas Edison, the practical scientist, was able to invent the electric light bulb. Without the work of pure scientists, both theoretical and experimental, practical scientists would have nothing to invent.

There are many examples of man's inability to evaluate the full significance of a discovery at the time it is made. Consider, for instance, the rather casual discovery of radioactivity in the 1890's. Out of it has come a tool for extremely effective research into the structure of the atom, the treatment of certain diseases, a method for estimating the minimum age of the earth, and innumerable other uses in biology, geology, astronomy, metallurgy, archeology, and other fields. But let it not be thought that the pure scientist seeks to justify his work by citing such uses. To him—and to you—it should need no such justification, for knowledge for its own sake is sufficient an answer. Or, as Michelson answered when asked why he spent so much time measuring the velocity of light, "Because it's so much fun."

Exercises

1. Distinguish between a theory and a law.
2. Criticize the statement: When a theory is proved, it becomes a law.
3. What is meant by a fruitful theory?
4. What is the essential difference between a theory and a hypothesis?
5. You have learned that measurement is the "science of approximation." What would be your estimate of the probability of any measurement of length being exactly right no matter how many decimal places are used?
6. In what way did the Greek attitude toward theories differ from our own?
7. Criticize the following statement as an explanation: A body falls to earth because of gravity.
8. (a) What is an operational definition?
   (b) Transform the statement made in exercise 7 into an operational definition of free fall.
9. What is the essential difference between the pure scientist and the so-called practical scientist?
10. It has been said that a scientific question is one that can be answered by the methods known to science. Criticize the question, "Why is there matter in the first place?" in terms of that statement.
11. One who uses accurate language does not speak of the "truth" or "falsity" of a scientific theory. What words does he use? Explain.
12. Consider the following: Every particle in the universe attracts every other particle in the universe with a force that is proportional to the product of their masses and inversely proportional to the square of the distance between them.
    (a) Does the above sentence include Newton's theory of gravitation, or Newton's law of gravitation, or does it include both the theory and the law?
    (b) If both the theory and the law, can you break it down into two statements, one being the theory, the other the law? If you can, do so and justify your decision.

PART III

Molecules, Atoms, and Heat Energy

Heat, Temperature, and the Law of Conservation of Energy

It is hardly necessary to add, that anything which any insulated body, or system of bodies, can continue to furnish without limitation, cannot possibly be a material substance.

COUNT RUMFORD

We have already stated that heat is associated with the transformation of potential energy into kinetic energy. We have implied that heat is a form of energy that can be produced by friction. How can friction produce heat? That it does can be attested by a vast number of examples. If a nail that has been firmly driven into solid wood is pulled quickly, it will feel uncomfortably warm. Try to force a dull power-saw blade to cut rapidly through hard wood, and it will get so hot that it smokes as it chars the wood. Even rubbing your hands together rapidly warms them. All are examples of heat produced by resistance to motion, that is, by friction. We all know that heat is produced in other ways. The most familiar is by combustion. Also, if we quickly compress a gas it gets hot. The rays of the sun, coming 93 million miles mostly through empty space, likewise give us heat.

Clearly, any definition of heat must account for these very different methods of producing it. Equally clearly, such a definition cannot be a simple one. Heat is commonly defined as a form of energy—which it is. But this is no more a meaningful definition of heat than saying

175

that "an automobile is a vehicle used in transportation" is a meaningful definition of an automobile. Newton, more than 250 years ago, made a reasoned guess that "heat consists in a minute vibratory motion of particles of bodies." His guess was right, but he did not follow it up with adequate arguments and demonstrations. Note carefully that he did not say that this motion produced heat. That would be difficult to accept. To understand Newton's statement we need to know more about heat and the associated concept of temperature. We need to know something about the particles of matter and their vibratory motions, and we can learn this best by studying particles in the gaseous state. Eventually the knowledge that comes from several streams of scientific inquiry will be joined together and explained by one great integrating theory, in particular, the great kinetic molecular theory of matter.

Heat vs. Temperature

Laymen use the word *heat* in many situations in which scientists use the word *temperature*—for example, "blood heat" and "in the heat of the day." Essentially, heat is that which makes things hotter, that which causes a body to undergo a rise in temperature. Temperature shows how hot a thing is, how full of heat it is. In general, heat refers to quantity, as, "How much heat does a body have?" Temperature refers to intensity; it is the degree of hotness measured on some definite scale. A short piece of thin wire heated to redness is intensely hot; that is, it has a high temperature even though it has a small quantity of heat—it will melt very little ice. A barrel of lukewarm water has a relatively low temperature but a lot of heat—it will melt considerable ice. Thus the heat a body has depends both on its temperature and on the kind and amount of matter in it.

Thermometers

We use the terms *hot* and *cold* and the intermediate terms *warm* or *lukewarm* to express temperatures without the use of instruments. Our standard of comparison is our own body temperature, and we all know that it is an extremely unreliable standard. Consider an air-conditioned butcher shop. On a warm summer day you find that the shop feels cool, even uncomfortably cool. The butcher, coming out of his big cold storage room where he has been working for some time, will find it pleasantly warm. Galileo recognized the need for a reliable standard and so he invented a thermometer. The concept of the intensity of heat is derived from our sense perceptions, but it is the thermometer that enables us to measure it.

All types of thermometers make use of some physical property that varies with the temperature. Galileo's first thermometer is shown in Fig. 11-1a. The level, L, of the water rose and fell with changes in temperature. This thermometer worked quite well as long as the pressure of the atmosphere remained constant. If the atmospheric pressure changed significantly, the level, L, would rise (if the pressure increased), or fall (if the pressure decreased), even though the temperature remained constant. How could this drawback be overcome? In time it was recognized that whereas the volume of a gas enclosed by a liquid, as this one was, changed with the air pressure, the volume of a liquid remained practically constant at any reasonable pressure. Therefore, Galileo's thermometer was turned upside down (Fig. 11-2a), and the bulb filled with a liquid, water at first. Water, like all liquids, expands as the temperature rises; thus, the liquid level rises with the temperature, and is a measure of it. However, water not only freezes at a moderately low temperature but it contracts on cooling until near the freezing point and then expands. Mercury, the only

(a)

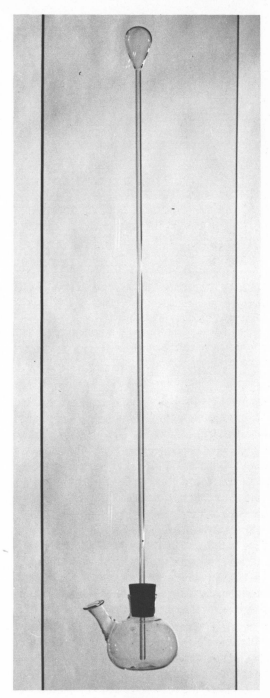

Fig. 11-1. Galileo's Thermometer. (*a*) As the temperature changed, the air in the bulb expanded or contracted in volume, so the level, *L*, of the water in the tube rose or fell. Unfortunately, this level may change because of a change in air pressure without any change in temperature. (*b*) A model of Galileo's thermometer. (Courtesy of The Smithsonian Institution.)

(b)

metal that is liquid at room temperature, was found to expand and contract uniformly; it does not wet glass; and it has a much lower freezing point ($-102°F$) than water. It is opaque, it is easily obtained pure and it does not evaporate readily at ordinary temperatures. It is therefore commonly used in thermometers, barometers, and certain other measuring instruments.

Fahrenheit (ca. 1715) constructed a mercury-in-glass thermometer, in which the zero point was the coldest temperature that he could get with an ice–water–salt mixture. The level of the mercury in the tube when it was at the temperature of the human body was marked 96°. The intervening space was divided into 96 parts and the same spacing carried above the 96° mark and below the 0° mark. On this scale the freezing point of water

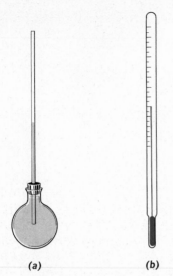

(a)   **(b)**

Fig. 11-2. By turning Galileo's thermometer upside down, a thermometer was made that was not affected by changes in air pressure. Water was used at first (*a*), mercury (*b*) later. The upper end of each tube is sealed, and the inside of each tube is a good vacuum.

came out about 32° and the boiling point about 212° (Fig. 11-3*a*). Later, to make these two points come out exactly at 32° and 212°, the size of the divisions was altered slightly, so that the temperature of the human body now is 98.6°F. When the English-speaking countries adopt the cgs (and mks) system of units, the Fahrenheit scale will probably go the way of the English system of units.

Some 20 years after Fahrenheit's invention, Celsius, a Swedish astronomer, devised a decimal scale on which the freezing point of water is 0° and its boiling point is 100° (Fig. 11-3*b*). This decimal scale is used in all scientific work. For many years it was called centigrade, but now, by international agreement, Celsius is the official name for this scale. A room temperature of 68°F corresponds to 20°C, and the temperature of the human body is 37°C.

Still later, the Kelvin (or absolute) scale was

devised in which the coldest possible temperature was marked 0°. The divisions on the scale are exactly the same as those on the Celsius thermometer. It should be realized that the zero marks on both the Celsius and Fahrenheit thermometers have no *absolute* significance at all; these scales are purely relative, and so we

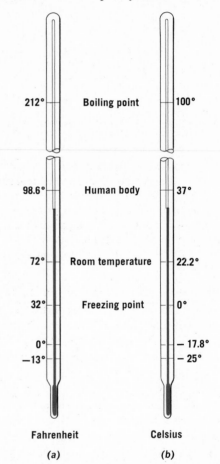

Fahrenheit   **Celsius**

(a)   **(b)**

Fig. 11-3. Fahrenheit and Celsius Thermometers. Note that 0°F is colder than 0°C and that 180 1° graduations on the Fahrenheit scale equal 100 1° graduations on the Celsius scale. In other words, $1°C = \frac{180}{100}$ or $\frac{9}{5}°F$. Conversion equations are

$$t°F = \frac{9}{5}t°C + 32°$$
$$t°C = \frac{5}{9}(t°C - 32°)$$

have no right to think of water at 100° on either scale as being twice as hot as water at 50° on either scale.[1] Neither should we assume that a temperature rise of 10° on one part of the scale is exactly equal to that of 10° on some other part of the scale. From the standpoint of accuracy at any reasonable temperature, the gas thermometers are the best. It matters little, if at all, what common gases are used, for all gas thermometers use the pressure change of a fixed volume of an enclosed sample of the gas. Boyle's law (p. 196) assures us this is equivalent to measuring the temperature by the expansion of a sample of the gas.

It is common knowledge that most materials expand as the temperature rises and contract as it drops.[2] To allow for expansion in warm weather, the girders beneath the roadway of a long steel bridge are placed so that they do not quite meet at the middle, concrete roadways have small gaps at intervals filled with a tarlike substance, and the ends of steel rails of the subway or other railroad tracks do not quite touch the adjoining ones.

Not so familiar is the fact that different substances have this property to different degrees. Brass expands nearly twice as much as iron does per unit length per degree rise in temperature. Thus, a brass strip welded to an iron strip will bend one way as the temperature rises and the other as the temperature falls.

[1] On the Kelvin, or absolute, scale 0° does have absolute significance, but we will postpone discussion of it until we have learned more about heat and the kinetic theory of gases.
[2] The exceptional behavior of water should be noted here. Like other substances, water contracts in volume until the temperature is about 4°C. It then begins to expand and continues to do so down to 0°C. At this temperature water freezes. The resulting ice has a larger volume (lower density) because of its crystal structure. Thus ice floats in water. It is this property that often causes containers of water to break when the water freezes. The expansive force in a closed container full of water is sufficient to crack the cylinder head of an automobile engine.

Many thermostats are as simple as that, for as they bend one way or the other, electrical contact is made or broken. In general, liquids expand more than solids do per unit volume per degree rise in temperature. Gases will expand still more.[3]

Heat Transfer

The transfer of heat from a source to other regions is what makes life possible on this earth. Transfer is accomplished (1) by radiation, as from the sun or a hot stove or fire; (2) by convection, as in the heating of buildings (Fig. 11-4) or the transfer of heat by the wind; and (3) by conduction, as in the transfer of heat through a piece of metal when one end of it is placed in a flame (Fig. 11-5). In convec-

[3] We must not confuse the property that allows a gas to fill all available space regardless of the temperature with that which is associated with temperature changes and changes in volume under constant pressure—for which see Charles' law (Chapter 12).

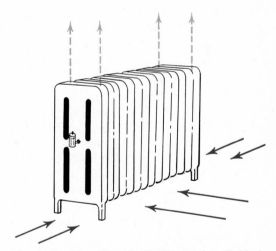

Fig. 11-4. Heat Transfer by Convection. Cold air moves in below the radiator, is heated, expands, becomes less dense, and so rises and spreads through the room to heat it. The radiator also radiates some heat into the atmosphere.

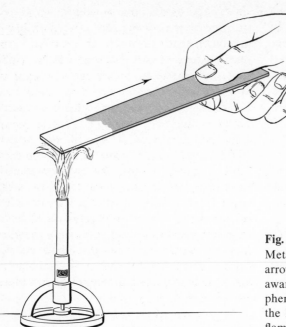

Fig. 11-5. Heat Transfer by Conduction Through a Metal Bar. Heat is *conducted* in the direction of the arrow, a fact that the person holding the bar is soon aware of. Heat is also radiated through the atmosphere. This radiated heat can be detected by holding the hand a few inches from either the bar or the flame.

tion, air that is heated expands, becomes less dense, and rises, allowing colder air to move in to be warmed by the source. *If left to itself, the natural transfer of heat is always from a warmer region to a colder one.* There are no exceptions to this rule. Nor can such transfer by one method or another ever be prevented. We can insulate a body to prevent some of the heat from escaping (or from entering), as in a thermos bottle, but we can never prevent it entirely. We will have more to say about heat transfer later.

Heat Units

We have used the phrases "intensity of heat" and "quantity of heat," but we have not yet defined either heat or temperature. We measure the intensity of heat in degrees—Celsius, Fahrenheit, or Kelvin. Quantity of heat is measured in calories. A *calorie* (cal) is the heat needed to warm up one gram of water one degree Celsius. Until recently, this "small" calorie was always used except in dietary matters. For convenience in dealing with larger quantities, there is the kilocalorie (kcal), equal to 1000 small calories. Its use is increasing with the gradually wider-spreading use of the kilogram. The word Calorie, spelled with a capital C, means a kilocalorie. In dietary matters calorie means 1000 small calories, equal to a kilocalorie, whether spelled Calorie or calorie.

Specific Heat

It was about 1750 that Joseph Black made the clear distinction between intensity and quantity of heat and defined what we now call specific heat. He had noted that the quantity of heat absorbed per unit mass varied with the substance. Whereas it takes 1 cal to raise the temperature of 1 g of water $1°C$, it takes only 0.11 cal to raise the temperature of 1 g of iron $1°C$.

To describe this observation *we define specific heat as the number of calories that will raise (or lower) the temperature of 1 g of the substance by 1°C.* Thus, by this definition, the specific heat of water is 1.0 cal/g/°C whereas that of iron is 0.11. Some other specific heats (at about 20°C) are aluminum, 0.22; copper, 0.09; silver, 0.06; lead, 0.03; magnesium, 0.25; soil and rocks, about 0.20.

Note that the specific heat of water is much larger than that of any of the other substances. This means that 1 kg of water[4] contains as much heat as 4 kg of magnesium if they are both at the same temperature. If we mix 100 g of water at 20°C with 100 g of water at 40°C, the resulting mixture will have a temperature of 30°C. If, however, we add magnesium at 40°C to the 100 g of water at 20°C, it will take 400 g of it to raise the water temperature to 30°C.

In any heat transfer from one body to another, the heat lost by one is equal to the heat gained by the other. In the process of transfer the rise in temperature of one body and the decline in temperature of the other depend on two factors (assuming no loss outside the system): (1) the relative masses of the two bodies and (2) their specific heats.

Problems in heat transfer can be solved by application of the following equations:

heat loss from one body = mass
    × specific heat × change in temperature

heat gained by the other body = mass
    × specific heat × change in temperature

States of Matter

We are all familiar with the fact that water can exist in three different states or phases, solid (ice), liquid, and gaseous (vapor). All substances[5] that do not decompose on being heated may also exist in these same three phases under certain conditions. Many kinds of matter, including water, can also exist in all three phases side by side if the conditions are right.[6] At normal atmospheric pressures the most important condition is the temperature. At temperatures significantly above 100°C only the vapor phase of water can exist for any length of time, and at temperatures far below the freezing point only the solid phase is of any significance. The state in which matter exists is therefore largely a function of temperature. Oddly enough, water is the only naturally occurring abundant liquid on the surface of the earth,[7] and it is significantly absent in any important amount on any other planet in the solar system.

Any attempt, therefore, to classify matter as solid, liquid, or gaseous is certain to run into difficulties. We think of bromine and mercury as the only two elements that exist in the liquid state at room temperature and pressure, but if we leave bromine liquid in an open dish, it quickly changes to the vapor state by evaporation. So will water, only not so quickly. Even ice will "evaporate" without melting by a process that is more properly called *sublimation.*

Gases and liquids are both fluids because both take the shape of their containers under all circumstances, whereas solids do not. Gases differ from liquids in that they completely fill their containers no matter how small the amount present. This means that they can expand indefinitely. It also means that gases

---

[4] The statement is restricted to water in the liquid state because ice and steam both have different specific heats. Water also possesses heat of fusion—80 cal/g—in addition to the heat due to temperature above absolute zero.

[5] Helium is the only exception at ordinary pressures.

[6] This statement does *not* imply that the three phases will be in equilibrium with one another.

[7] Petroleum, a mixture of liquids, gases, and solids in mutual solution with one another, exists at relatively shallow depths (up to 3 or 4 mi) in the earth's crust. Molten rock exists in a few places at greater depth, but brought to the surface it quickly solidifies.

are easily compressed into smaller volumes. Thus, 1 g of oxygen will fill any size vessel you put it in. Put 1 g of another gas in the same closed vessel with the oxygen, and it will shortly fill the whole vessel also. The two gases have spontaneously mixed thoroughly with each other. Or if someone opens a bottle of ammonia on the far side of the room, you will soon know it. This process is called *diffusion*. Liquids, however, maintain a fixed volume. True solids maintain not only a fixed volume but a fixed shape. A few substances, for example, pitch, sealing wax, and shoemaker's wax, appear to be so hard and brittle that they will shatter like glass when a sheet of any one of them is dropped. But if thick lumps of these same substances are allowed to stand in containers at room temperature they will gradually spread out to take the shape of the container. Such substances are classed as highly viscous liquids. The ability of liquids and solids to maintain fixed volumes under ordinary conditions means that they are very nearly incompressible except at unusually high pressures.

Changes of State

Latent Heat of Fusion

Consider a vessel of crushed ice cubes well below the freezing (or melting) point[8] and at normal atmospheric pressure. We add heat to it as we watch a Celsius thermometer immersed in it. We note that the temperature rises until it reads 0°C. At once the ice begins to melt, and we have a mixture of ice and water. If we keep the mixture well stirred, we find that the thermometer continues to read 0°C even though we continue supplying heat

at the same rate. This added heat that does not make the mixture any hotter is called the *latent*[9] *heat of fusion*. For ice it is 80 cal/g (or 80 kcal/kg). When the ice is all melted, the temperature of what is now all water at once begins to rise again. Conversely, when water is cooled to the freezing point (0°C), its temperature remains at 0°C as the ice forms even though heat continues to be removed. Not until 80 cal/g has been removed from the well-stirred mixture will the water be turned completely into ice and the temperature begin to drop again.[10]

Latent Heat of Vaporization

A similar phenomenon is observed when liquids are boiled. In an open system they cannot be heated above the boiling point no matter how much heat is applied or how rapidly. Heat is absorbed in changing water to steam without raising the temperature; this heat is called the *latent heat of vaporization*. For water it amounts to 540 cal/g at atmospheric pressure. In condensing back to water, the steam gives up a like amount of heat. Therefore, 1 g of steam at 100°C has 540 cal more heat than 1 g of water at the same temperature. This is what makes burns from steam worse than those from water at the same temperature.

We have given the main facts about latent heats of fusion and vaporization. However, we might very well ask where the heat is "hidden." We can say that it is stored in the water (heat

---

[8] Ice cubes taken from a good freezer are considerably below 0°C. Observe that there is no film of meltwater on them.

[9] Meaning hidden or dormant.

[10] Under certain conditions water may be cooled a few degrees below the freezing point (supercooled) without freezing. But when it does start to freeze, it freezes so quickly that heat is liberated faster than it can escape. Thus, the water actually becomes warmer as it freezes, the temperature rising to the normal freezing point. The heat of fusion that water absorbs during the melting process is given off during the freezing process. This is also 80 cal/g at atmospheric pressure.

of fusion) and in the steam (heat of vaporization) as potential energy. The student should realize that to say this is merely a matter of convenience of statement; it is in no way an explanation. The kinetic molecular theory (Chapter 13) will give us a better explanation, but the electronic theory of chemical bonding (Chapter 25) will give us a still better one.

Caloric Theory of Heat

Most of the facts that we have noted in the preceding pages were known in a qualitative way, if not in a quantitative one, by the middle of the 18th century. There was as yet no suspicion that heat was a form of energy. This should not be surprising, for the general concepts of work and energy had not yet been clarified when Newton died in 1729. The belief that all matter consisted of four elements—earth, air, fire, and water—was not yet entirely dead. It was therefore easy to consider it possible for heat to be a form of matter.

It was Joseph Black, a Scotsman, who made clear the distinction between heat and temperature and who defined specific heat. During the course of his investigations into these phenomena he developed the caloric theory of heat to explain them. Its chief assumptions were essentially as follows:

1. Caloric is an invisible self-repulsive weightless substance that is attracted by the corpuscles of all matter, forming a kind of shell about them. The thickness of the shell determines the temperature.
2. Different substances have different capacities for holding caloric. For any one substance the gaseous phase can hold the most caloric and the solid phase the least.
3. As more and more caloric is added, the corpuscles are forced farther and farther apart as the amount of self-repulsion increases.

4. Stresses reduce the ability of substances to hold caloric. (Yet friction, obviously a kind of stress, increased the temperature.)

The theory could explain most of the observed facts. By 1780 it was firmly entrenched. Among its staunch supporters were many of the renowned men of science of the times. Yet by 1850 it had been largely discredited by Joule and Helmholtz, who showed it to be about as wrong as it is possible for a theory to be. In large part it was slow in being rejected because its only rival was so slow in developing; you cannot replace something with nothing.

There were a number of objections; we shall content ourselves with citing three. The first is not an objection if you can "swallow" the existence of a weightless substance—that is, a substance without mass—crowding the corpuscles of matter apart as the temperature was increased. The second is that of an apparent contradiction. If adding caloric to a substance causes it to get hotter, how could "squeezing it out," as in friction, also cause a rise in temperature? The third was the lack of a relationship between the specific heats and the melting points.[11]

Cannon-Boring Experiments of Count Rumford

During the late 1700's and early 1800's more and more scientists were suggesting that heat was a form of motion (equivalent to saying that it was a form of energy), but none produced any evidence until a traitor to the American Revolution, born Benjamin Thompson, gained everlasting fame as Count Rumford by presenting a paper to the Royal Society of London in 1798. Rumford was one of the

---

[11] Lead, gold, and platinum have specific heats of 0.0306, 0.0312, and 0.0324, respectively, but their melting points are 327, 1063, and 1773°C.

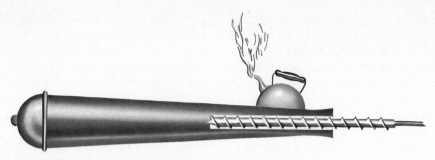

Fig. 11-6. Rumford's Cannon-Boring Experiment. Rumford used horses as his source of energy. The heat developed by friction boiled the water in a receptacle placed on the cannon.

most colorful men who ever lived. He led a life of unswerving honesty in science and unconscionable duplicity in politics. George III hated him but used him; the Elector of Bavaria ennobled him and made him his prime minister; Napoleon considered him one of the great minds of the day. He was unsurpassed in arrogance; he had few peers in science.[12]

While Rumford was Minister of War in Bavaria, he became interested in the boring of cannon made of brass (Fig. 11-6). A horse in a treadmill furnished the force to turn the boring instrument. Rumford discovered that the duller the instrument, the greater the amount of heat produced—that heat was something that could be manufactured in unlimited amounts at the expense of mechanical energy. Ultimately he concluded that "heat is nothing but a vibratory motion taking place among the particles of a body"—a conclusion reached by Newton 100 years earlier.

However, like Newton, Rumford was unable to devise a good working theory of heat as a form of motion. He failed to answer the question "Does the same amount of heat always arise from the expenditure of the same amount of mechanical energy?" In other words, proof that heat was a form of energy was still lacking. In part, the delay in obtaining such proof was due to a very human characteristic, the un-

willingness of people to give up a long-held belief if it explains many of the observed facts. A new idea in science, as in other fields of endeavor, often supplants an older one only by the dying of the defenders of the older belief, leaving the world to the upholders of the new one.[13] The caloric theory is probably the finest example we have of a scientific theory being able to explain most of the facts while being completely false. No matter how beautifully a theory explains most of the facts, it can fatally flounder by its failure to explain one recalcitrant fact.

Work of Joule: The Mechanical Equivalent of Heat

It was left for an English physicist, James P. Joule, son of an English brewer and an amateur scientist, to do the quantitative work necessary to establish the fact that heat is a form of energy. In doing this he not only established that Rumford was right, but he also established the law of conservation of

---

[12] Mitchell Wilson, "Count Rumford," *Scientific American,* Vol. 203, No. 4, p. 158, October 1960.

[13] One should not reach the conclusion that this reluctance to discard the old for the new is necessarily bad. A certain skepticism toward a new idea is a healthy attitude. In science it forces the advocates of the new to obtain all the evidence they can, to develop their theories carefully, and to subject them to further experiment. If the evidence is overwhelmingly in favor of the new, only a few die-hards will stick to the old.

energy and laid much of the groundwork for the kinetic theory of gases. Joule devoted his life to proving his conviction that heat is a form of energy. Much of his most important work in this field was done between 1840 and 1850.

One of the things that Joule did was to heat water by churning it with a paddle wheel driven by falling weights. His problem was to compare the amount of mechanical energy used to do the stirring with the amount of heat produced. Great difficulties are always encountered in performing experiments on heat. The experimenter must not only do all that he can to prevent the escape of heat insofar as that is possible, but he must also measure or make a reliable estimate of the amount of heat that cannot be prevented from escaping. The devices that Joule used were many and varied; the most famous was the one used in his paddle wheel experiment (Fig. 11-7) in which potential energy could easily be measured. His thermometers were graduated to $\frac{1}{200}$ of a degree Fahrenheit, for the rise in temper-

ature was always uncomfortably small. He repeated his experiments many times, one of them 34 times. He also used liquids other than water, including mercury and whale oil.

First Law of Thermodynamics: Law of Conservation of Mechanical Energy

Ultimately Joule was able to announce that the expenditure of a certain number of units of work always gave rise to a certain number of calories of heat. This ratio is called the *mechanical equivalent of heat*. Here we shall express it in mks units rather than in the English system that Joule used, and we shall use the more precise modern figure.

$$J = 4.185 \text{ joules/cal or } 4185 \text{ joules/kcal}$$

where J is the mechanical equivalent of heat. It is, of course, a constant. By means of it we

Fig. 11-7. Joule's Paddle Wheel Experiment. Weights could be shifted from the hook on one side to that on the other to turn the paddles in the tank. The potential energy of the weights when elevated could be calculated, and the rise in temperature of the known mass of water measured.

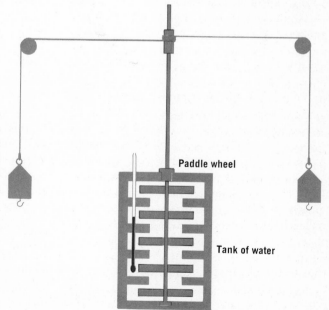

Paddle wheel

Tank of water

can equate joules to calories and vice versa. This means that for every 4.185 joules of mechanical energy expended, 1 cal of heat is produced regardless of the mechanism involved. It follows that heat must be a form of energy. Our equation expresses mathematically the first law of thermodynamics: *Heat and mechanical energy are interchangeable at a fixed rate of exchange.* This is also known as the law of conservation of mechanical energy.

The Law of Conservation of Energy

Joule made many other ingenious experiments and developed incredible skill in performing them. His work was a miracle of careful experimenting made with outstanding instruments, chiefly of his own design. With them he not only converted mechanical energy into heat and vice versa, but he also converted chemical energy to heat, chemical energy to heat and then to electrical energy, and electrical energy to chemical energy and then to heat. In all these experiments he checked and cross-checked his measurements. The energy books were balanced and the case finally proved: *Energy, though interconvertible, is indestructible.* It may be the only indestructible thing in the universe. In the myriads of experiments that have been performed since Joule first started his work, in the enormously varied operations and processes of modern industry, and even in the complexities of biological processes, the energy books have always been found to balance. No matter how small an amount of energy with which we start, no matter in what form or in what disguise, if we keep track so that none of it slips away unnoticed between our fingers, we will always wind up with the same amount in one form

or another. There resulted the broadening of the law of conservation of mechanical energy to include all forms of energy, so it is now known as the principle or (law) of conservation of energy. By use of it engineers can accurately calculate the energy obtainable from a machine. This fact has spelled death to the age-old dream of perpetual motion.

This age-old dream had engaged some of the greatest intellects in earlier centuries, for it was plausible and challenging until the law of conservation of energy was firmly established and made known to our technological and scientific world. "Crackpots" continued the search well into the present century for they, like most human beings, wanted to get something for nothing.

In the years just preceding, during, and just following World War II, it was shown that tiny amounts of some kinds of mass could be turned into energy (see Chapter 37). (Einstein had predicted as much back in 1905.) This discovery in no way makes invalid anything that we have said. It merely means that to include the processes of conversion of matter into energy, processes that are limited to those going on in the stars, in atomic bombs, and in substances subject to radioactive decay, we need to combine the great laws of conservation of mass (Chapter 14) and energy into one: *The total mass and energy in the universe is constant.*

The law of conservation of energy was one of the great concepts of the 19th century, probably the greatest, for it helped to integrate all the other great concepts that developed during that tremendous scientific century. Modified as we have shown, it states that the only thing that is taking place in this world of matter is a transformation of matter into energy and of energy from one form to another. The scientist believes this law applies not only here on earth, not only in the motions of the solar system, but also to all of the stars of our galaxy, the Milky Way, and to all of those other millions of galaxies whose distances are far beyond our imaginations. We can never test this statement, of course; our belief must therefore rest on reasoned faith. It is not so much faith in the validity of the principle of conservation of energy as it is in the principle of uniformity of nature and her laws, the faith of every scientist that order and regularity exist in the universe.

Exercises

1. What property of mercury makes it particularly useful in glass thermometers?
2. (a) In what way is water different from any other common substance with respect to its behavior on being cooled to the freezing point?
   (b) Is this a desirable characteristic or not? Explain.
3. Explain the three methods by which heat is transferred.
4. Define a kilocalorie (but not in terms of calories).
5. (a) What is the latent heat of fusion?
   (b) How many calories per gram of water are involved?
6. (a) What is the latent heat of vaporization?
   (b) How many calories per gram of water are involved?
7. How much more heat is required to vaporize 500 g of water than to melt 500 g of ice?
8. Which has more heat, 100 g of steam at 100°C or 100 g of water at 100°C? How much more?
9. Define specific heat.
10. The specific heat of metal X is 0.2. If you put 100 g of it at a temperature of 100°C in 100 g of water at 25°C, what is the resulting temperature of the water?
11. In colonial America it was a common practice to put tubs of water in root cellars during the cold months to prevent the root vegetables and the fruit from freezing. Explain.
12. If you find exercise 11 difficult, consider the fact that as a pond freezes the air close to and in contact with the water is slightly warmer than that in contact with the land surrounding the pond. Explain.
13. What are some of the difficulties encountered in any attempt to classify matter as gaseous, liquid, or solid?
14. Does a block of ice contain heat? Justify your answer.
15. What is the essential difference between the Celsius and the Kelvin temperature scales?
16. Calculate the heat required to transform 500 g of ice (a little over a pound) at −10°C to steam at 100°C. The specific heat of ice is about 0.5. (*Note:* This must be done in steps.)
17. Using Fig. 11-3, determine room temperature, blood temperature, and 0°F on the Celsius scale.
18. Why is a piece of ice at 32°F more effective in cooling a drink than the same quantity of water at 32°F?
19. The high specific heat of water is an aid to living organisms. Explain.
20. If 10,000 cal of heat is added to a quantity of water at 25°C, the new temperature is 60°C. What quantity of water is involved?
21. Why did so many prominent scientists in the last half of the 18th and first half of the 19th centuries believe in the caloric theory of heat?
22. Who was Benjamin Thompson and for what (in science) is he particularly remembered?
23. What were the essential points in Count

Rumford's cannon-boring experiments that were detrimental to the caloric theory of heat?

24. Why could Rumford not make his cannon-boring experiment quantitative?

25. State Rumford's final conclusion.

26. What did Joule do that Rumford did not that made him successful in overthrowing the caloric theory?

27. Describe and state the significance of Joule's most famous experiment.

28. What is the proof that heat is a form of energy?

29. Specifically, what is heat according to Joule? (To say that it is a form of energy is entirely inadequate as an answer.)

30. What is meant by the mechanical equivalent of heat? What is J?

31. Did the caloric theory recognize heat as a form of energy?

The Gaseous State of Matter

As previously stated, there is no such thing as heat apart from matter. In fact, it is the quantity of heat associated with a definite amount of matter that determines the state of that matter—gas, liquid, or solid. The theory that heat itself was an all-pervading kind of matter called caloric was doomed by the work of Count Rumford and dealt the final deathblow by Joule, but scientists were not happy about discarding the caloric theory until a more acceptable theory was developed. In general, a poor theory is better than no theory, just as a poor guide is at times better than no guide when one is investigating uncharted territory. More knowledge of matter was necessary, and this knowledge could be obtained through a study of gases and their behavior despite the fact that our senses give us little direct information about gases.

Gases are much better understood by scientists than are liquids and solids because they have many important simple properties in common. Specifically, gases fill any confined space offered to them and hence are easily compressed, whereas liquids and solids are not.

> The things that any science discovers are beyond the reach of direct observation. We cannot see energy, nor the attraction of gravitation, nor the flying molecules of gases, . . . , nor the forests of the carbonaceous era, nor the explosions in nerve cells. It is only the premises of science, not its conclusions, which are directly observed.
> C. S. PIERCE
> (1898)

Each discrete particle of gas acts almost independently of all the other molecules around it except at unusually high pressures. It does so because individual particles are separated from one another by relatively enormous distances as compared with the particles of liquids and solids. These distances allow one gas to diffuse through another with little difficulty. Gases also diffuse through porous solids. They exert a pressure on every surface with which they are in contact. When a gas is confined, the relations between pressure, volume, and temperature are governed by simple laws. How can all of these relatively simple properties be explained?

We need to construct a theory of gases, a kind of mechanical model,[1] that we can use to explain all these observations, including the general gas laws—a theory that will enable us to make new predictions, as any successful theory must do. In our attempt to construct such a theory we will begin by studying the pressure-volume relationships, for they are simple and easily measurable by instruments. This study will eventually introduce us to Robert Boyle and the law that bears his name.

Pressure

Pressure (in a gas, liquid, or solid) *is defined as force per unit area.* This means that the average pressure on any plane surface is equal to the total force on that surface, *acting in a direction perpendicular to that surface,* divided by the area of the surface. Thus

$$P = \frac{F}{A} \qquad [12\text{-}1]$$

[1] By a model we do not mean a much reduced replica of an object, but a system of concepts, of ideas, and such that allows us to "think describe" the things that we wish to investigate.

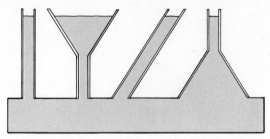

Fig. 12-1. Pressure in a Liquid. A number of tubes of various sizes and shapes are all parts of the same open receptacle. The water rises to the same level in all of them. This means that the pressure at any point in any of them depends only on the depth below the surface and not on the width or shape.

where P is the pressure, F the force, and A the area. Note carefully that *pressure* is not just another word for force. The pressure acting on a body should never be confused with the total force acting on it. Although we will be concerned exclusively with pressure in gases, it may be instructive to compare such pressure with that in liquids (since both are fluids). Gases and liquids are both called fluids because they flow, as contrasted with solids, which, of course, retain their shape except under extreme pressure.

In gases and liquids the pressure at any one point is the same in all directions, up, down, or sideways. In both, any change in the pressure at any one point is accompanied by a change in pressure at every other point if the liquid or confined gas is at rest, that is, if it is not flowing. (This statement is known as Pascal's principle.) In any one *liquid* the magnitude of the pressure (due to the liquid only) at any point depends solely on the distance that point is below the surface (Fig. 12-1).

Thus at the top of a liquid-filled container the pressure due to the weight of the liquid is zero. The pressure at the bottom is measurably greater because of the weight of the liquid. Strictly speaking, this is also true of gases. However, for common gases confined in ordinary size containers the difference in pressure between top and bottom is almost immeasurable (because of the very small weight of the gas) and is usually disregarded. If the gas or liquid is packaged under external pressure in a sealed container, this external pressure will be found throughout the fluid and will be in addition to any pressure due to weight, as in tanks of compressed or lique-fied gases for portable heat sources. Where the quantity of gas is very large, as in the earth's atmosphere, the gravitational forces cause a significant difference in density, hence in pres-sure, of the gas at the top and the bottom of the system.

Concept of Air Pressure

The concept of gases exerting pressure is one of the things most people take for granted in this age of automobile tires, gas stoves and furnaces, balloons, and so forth. Likewise, we take the weight of gases for granted, although the average student would undoubtedly be surprised to learn that the air in an average classroom weighs several hundred pounds. Yet it was not clear until about the time of Galileo's death (and Newton's birth) that air had weight, and the modern concept of gas pressure was not advanced for another two centuries. Balances sensitive enough to weigh small quantities of air had not yet been in-vented in Galileo's time.

It had been known since the 16th century that water would rise in a vertical pipe with one end submerged if air were extracted from the other end (Fig. 12-2). Aristotle would have explained this phenomenon by stating that the water rises when an attempt is made to create a vacuum by the extraction of the air because nature abhors a vacuum (see his vacuum

Fig. 12-2. Principle of Suction Pump. By sucking on it the boy removes air from the straw. Pressure of the outside air on the surface of the liquid in the glass then causes the liquid to rise in the straw. If the straw were 34 ft long and the boy could suck all of the air out of it, he could still obtain the liquid, but not if it were longer. Why not?

argument on p. 96). A workman had told Galileo that a suction pump[2] attached to such a pipe would work only if the pipe were less than 34 ft long; that is, if all the air were sucked out of a vertical pipe longer than 34 ft, the water would still not rise higher than 34 ft (Fig. 12-3).

Galileo wondered why nature's abhorrence of a vacuum stopped at 34 ft. He therefore

[2] A suction pump removes air from a pipe that extends down below the surface of the water in a well. This removal makes the air pressure in the pipe less than that on the surface of the water in the well. The water then rises in the pipe because of the pressure difference. This rising eliminates the pressure difference (see Fig. 12-3).

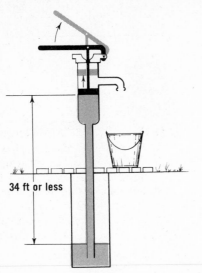

34 ft or less

Fig. 12-3. The Suction Pump. At sea level, water can be raised to a maximum height of only about 34 ft because it depends on atmospheric pressure to push the water up the pipe from the well to the pump. As the piston is raised, the pressure inside the pump cylinder is reduced below the outside atmospheric pressure and the well water is pushed up into it. If the pipe is longer than 34 ft, the atmospheric pressure is not great enough to push the water all the way up the pipe. (Details and valves have been omitted.)

suggested that the rise of the water in the pipe was due to the air pushing down on the surface of the water in the well rather than to a "pulling up" of the water inside the pipe. Before the pump sucked air out of the pipe, this push was balanced by the air in the pipe pushing down with an *equal force per unit area.* Sucking the air out of the pipe eliminated this force, so that the water rose until the downward force exerted by the weight of the water in the pipe equaled the downward push of the air on the surface of the water outside the pipe. Thus, the pressure of the air in pounds per square inch should be equal to the weight of a column of water about 34 ft long and

1 in.^{2} in cross section, that is, 14.7 lb/in.^{2}.

However, a column of water that high is extremely difficult to work with. Torricelli, a student of Galileo's, knowing that mercury was about 13.6 times as dense as water, took a 48 in. glass tube sealed at one end, filled it level with mercury, and inverted it into a dish of mercury without allowing any air to enter the tube (Fig. 12-4). The level of the mercury in the tube fell until the distance between it and the surface of the mercury in the open dish was about 30 in. He then had a nearly perfect vacuum[3] above the mercury in the tube. The weight of this 30 in. of mercury was equal to the weight of a column of water of equal cross section and 34 ft high. If we add a scale to the mercury column so that we can read its changing level as air pressure changes, we have the modern barometer.

Torricelli's Experiment

Torricelli thought that if the mercury were held up in the tube by the weight of the atmosphere, then the weight should decrease as one climbed a mountain. His reasoning was that we live on the earth's surface at the bottom of a "sea of air," just as many organisms live on the ocean floor at the bottom of a sea of water. As we have already seen, Pascal had shown that the pressure in the water became less and less as its depth decreased. Going to the top of a mountain should therefore decrease the depth of the sea of air and the pressure should drop. This should constitute evidence in favor of the air-pressure theory. The experiment was performed, and the theory confirmed, under the direction of Pascal. He was thoughtful enough to have a man watch the level of the mercury in a second barometer

[3] Few of Torricelli's fellow scientists would concede that there was a vacuum above the mercury. They preferred to follow Aristotle.

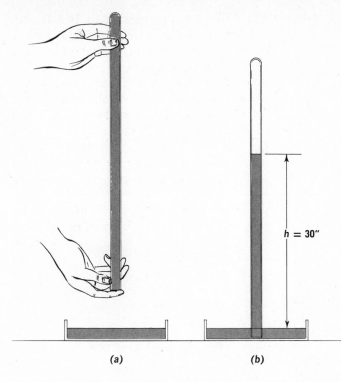

Fig. 12-4. A simple mercury barometer can be made by filling a glass tube (about 36 in. long and closed at one end) with mercury, then inverting it into a dish of mercury while holding a finger over the open end. When the finger is withdrawn, the level of the mercury will drop to about 30 in. (at sea level).

$h = 30''$

(a)   (b)

at the foot of the mountain while the first was being carried to the top.[4] Still, the evidence was not very convincing to many.

This experiment is often listed as providing direct evidence that air had weight.[5] This is not true. It did provide direct evidence that air exerted a pressure on surfaces with which it was in contact. That air had weight could be inferred, however, unless one believed it to be a weightless material substance that could exert pressure.

The cause of this pressure was assumed by Torricelli and many of his colleagues to be the

weight of the air. There seemed to be no alternative at the time; the kinetic theory of gases was far in the future. Many modern physics books and other physical science books still follow Torricelli's explanation, even though it can easily be shown by a variety of experiments to be incorrect. For example, suppose we enclose a quantity of air (or any gas or mixture of gases) in a sealed vessel with a pressure gauge attached, and apply heat. Suppose the pressure at room temperature is normal. Now let us heat this vessel of gas. As the temperature rises, the pressure rises. If we heat it until the temperature is 300°C, we will find that the pressure is a bit more than twice normal, even though the weight of the air supposedly causing this pressure hasn't changed a bit. How, then, can weight of the air be the cause of air pressure? We can also

[4] This made the experiment what we today call a controlled experiment. It eliminated the possibility that the change in air pressure as one ascended the mountain might be due to an atmospheric change that would also produce a similar change at the foot of the mountain.

[5] We have defined weight as a force (force of gravity) directed toward the center of the earth.

pack the sealed vessel with its pressure gauge in ice, or better still in dry ice (frozen carbon dioxide). The gauge will show a much decreased pressure. Yet the weight of the air responsible for the pressure remains the same.

It should be noted that the analogy between the sea of air and the sea of water is far from perfect. The pressure in water increases rapidly with depth with almost no change in the density of the water. In fact the pressure would increase almost as rapidly if there were no change in the density of the water with depth. The pressure in air decreases rapidly with decrease in density. The numerical magnitude of the pressure of the atmosphere in pounds per square inch (14.7 lb/in.^{2} at sea level) is exactly equal to the weight of a column of air 1 in. square in cross section, extending from the earth's surface to the top of the far reaches of the atmosphere, but this is not the same as saying that the pressure of the atmosphere is *directly* due to, or is *directly* caused by, the weight of the air.[6] The more direct cause of air pressure is discussed in Chapter 13.

Boyle's Experiments with His Vacuum Pump

The acceptance of the Galilean view that air exerted a pressure had to be postponed a

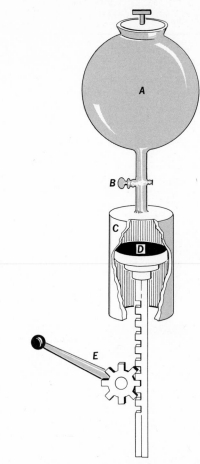

Fig. 12-5. Boyle's Vacuum Pump. *A,* airtight receptacle from which air is to be evacuated. *B,* stopcock, which is open while piston (*D*) is descending in the cylinder (*C*), and closed at the end of the downstroke of the piston. When the piston is raised (by the device at *E*), the air in *C* is expelled to the outside through a valve not shown. The stopcock (*B*) is opened as the piston again descends, allowing air from *A* to enter *C* again.

---

[6]Nothing that we have said so far should be taken to mean that the weight of air (gravitational attraction of the earth for air molecules) has nothing to do with its pressure. It is gravitational attraction that permits the earth to have an atmosphere in the first place. If the force of gravity were reduced to that of the moon, the earth would soon lose its air by diffusion into space, just as has happened to the moon (if it ever had an atmosphere). It is this gravitational attraction that is responsible for the decreased density, hence the decreased pressure, at high altitudes. But this is *not* to say that air pressure is *directly* caused by its weight. It does say that we cannot have air pressure in an open system without gravitational attraction to prevent the atmosphere from diffusing into outer space. In a closed system, say in a gastight container at a pressure of 14.7 lb/in.^{2} and constant temperature, in an environment completely free from gravitational forces, the air pressure would be only slightly less than in our normal environment. Lack of space forbids further discussion of this subject.

few years until Robert Boyle invented a new type of pump (Fig. 12-5) that allowed him to remove air directly from a sealed container. Boyle (1627–1691) was a teenager when Galileo died and when Newton was born. He was the precocious son of a wealthy Irish earl; he gave his life and much of his considerable wealth to scientific research and writing. His wealth enabled him to set up the finest laboratory in Europe.

His pump allowed him to make experiments that would otherwise have been impossible. This is a fine example of research of a particular type having to await technological improvements. Otto von Guericke had invented the first type of vacuum pump a few years before, and had performed his famous experiment with the Magdeburg hemispheres (Fig. 12-6). Boyle's crucial experiment[7] consisted of enclosing one of Torricelli's barometers (Fig.

[7] Boyle performed many experiments. Among them was the demonstration that a coin and a feather fall together in a near vacuum. In another he showed that a bell ringing in a vacuum cannot be heard. More important were those that led to the relations between pressure and volume at a constant temperature.

Fig. 12-6. Magdeburg Hemispheres. *Above:* The edges of two large hollow copper hemispheres, *A* and *B*, were smoothly polished until they fitted together nicely. Otto von Guericke (1654) then pumped the air out with his newly invented vacuum pump. Fifteen horses hitched to each could not then pull them apart until air was readmitted. (From an old engraving. Courtesy The Bettman Archive.) *Below:* The pressure of the atmosphere holds the Magdeburg hemispheres together (left); the total force against the flat plate (right) is equal to the atmospheric pressure (minus any remaining inside pressure) times the surface area covering the open end of the hemisphere.

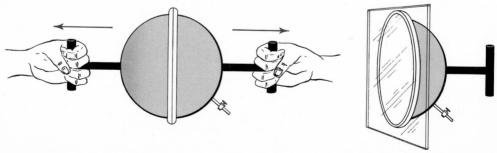

12-4) in a gastight apparatus (Fig. 12-7) and pumping air out. As he pumped more and more air out, the level of the mercury dropped in the tube, thus proving that it was air pressure that held the mercury up in the tube. Note carefully that the *weight* of the air played no part in this experiment, for the total weight of the air in the gastight apparatus need not have been more than 5 or 6 g, depending on the size of the jar.

It should be noted that the height at which

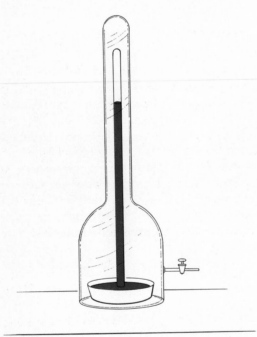

Fig. 12-7. Mercury Barometer in a Gastight Bell Jar. The air pressure inside the jar and out is the same so that the barometer reads the same as it would outside the bell jar. Note that the weight of the atmosphere above but outside the bell jar can have no effect on supporting the column of mercury. If a vacuum pump is attached to the stopcock and most of the few ounces of air inside the bell jar removed, the mercury level in the tube drops nearly to the level of that in the dish, proving that the mercury is forced up in the tube by the pressure of the atmosphere.

the mercury stands in a barometer has nothing to do with the size or shape of the tube (Fig. 12-1). Since mercury is a liquid it obeys a law that states that the pressure at any point in a liquid (due to the liquid) depends only on the *vertical* distance between that point and its upper surface. This distance may be measured in inches, centimeters, or millimeters, and the pressure is usually expressed in these units instead of in pounds per square inch or grams per square centimeter, and so on. Thus we say that the pressure of the atmosphere is 30 in. or 76 cm or 760 mm at a particular place and at a particular time.[8] The actual pressure varies with the altitude above sea level, the temperature, and other physical conditions. The above figures represent average atmospheric pressure at sea level and are the pressure we mean when we speak of a pressure of 1 atmosphere (atm).

Boyle's Law

The fact that decreasing the volume of a given amount of gas causes the pressure to rise can be tested by squeezing a sealed toy balloon. If we reduce the volume sufficiently by squeezing, the balloon will burst. We need more complicated apparatus to demonstrate the quantitative relationship (see Fig. 12-9). Boyle used a tube of glass bent into the shape of a J (Fig. 12-8) with the short end graduated and sealed. The tube was carefully made so that the graduated part was as nearly uniform as the techniques of the time would allow. A small quantity of air was trapped in the short end by mercury as shown in the figure. When the mercury stood at the same level in both parts of the tube, the air pressure in the trapped end equaled the outside air pressure. Adding more mercury to the longer tube in-

[8]The new International Unit of pressure is the torr. It is not affected by variations in gravitational acceleration, as is the weight of a millimeter of mercury.

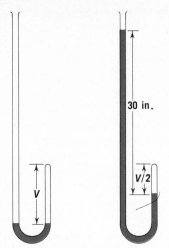

30 in.

V/2

V

Fig. 12-8. Boyle's J Tube. When the mercury was at the same level in both arms of the tube, the air pressure in the enclosed end of the tube was equal to that outside. Let the volume of the air trapped in the closed end be V and the pressure be P. Boyle now added mercury to the other arm until the volume of the trapped air was $V/2$. The difference in the new levels of mercury was then about 30 in. The pressure on this air was now $2P$. How much more mercury would he have to add to reduce the volume to $V/4$? What would the pressure on it then be?

creased the pressure on the trapped air, and raised the level of the mercury in the longer part. When the volume of air was half the original, the difference in the heights of the mercury in the two parts of the tube was about 30 in. (760 mm). We have already seen that this is a pressure of 1 atm. Since Boyle started out with 1 atm of pressure and added another, the pressure on the trapped air has been doubled, whereas the volume has been halved. To reduce this new volume to half again, he would have had to add about 60 in. more of mercury (2 atm), and so on (Table 12-1). How much more mercury would be needed to reduce the volume, V, to $V/8$?

Thus, we see that there is an inverse proportion between the pressure and the volume.

Table 12-1

Volume (in.^{3})	Pressure (atm)	Pressure (mm Hg)
48	1	760
24	2	1520
12	4	3040
6	8	6080

Mathematically,

$$P \propto \frac{1}{V} \quad \text{or} \quad P = \frac{K}{V} \qquad [12\text{-}2]$$

Transposing,

$$PV = K \qquad [12\text{-}3]$$

This is now known as Boyle's law (Fig. 12-9). The value of the constant, K, depends only upon the quantity (mass, not volume) of the gas and the units used. Boyle was careful to keep the temperature of the gas constant. In words, Boyle's law states that *the volume of a fixed mass of gas varies inversely with the pressure if the temperature is constant.* Experiment shows that the PV relations begin to break down as the pressure becomes high (see Chapter 13).

We can write the equation in another form,

$$P_1 V_1 = P_2 V_2 \qquad [12\text{-}4]$$

where P_1 and V_1 represent one pressure and volume of a given amount of gas, and P_2 and V_2 represent its pressure and volume after expansion or compression of the same gas without change of temperature. For example, suppose 22.4 liters of a gas at 1 atm pressure is compressed to a final volume of 5.6 liters. What is its new pressure? Substituting in Eq. 12-4:

$$1 \times 22.4 = 5.6 \times P_2$$
$$P_2 = \frac{22.4}{5.6} = 4 \text{ atm}$$

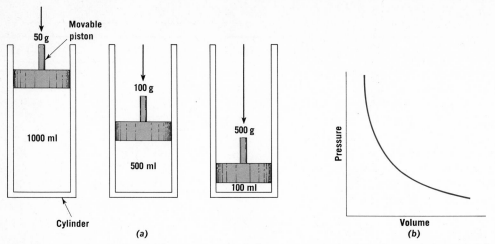

Fig. 12-9. Boyle's Law. (*a*) The temperature is kept constant. As the pressure is increased from 50 to 100 g/cm^2, the volume is decreased from 1000 to 500 ml; that is, doubling the pressure halves the volume. Increasing the pressure by a factor of 10 (from 50 to 500 g/cm^2) reduces the volume by a factor of 10 (from 1000 to 100 ml). Thus pressure is inversely proportional to volume, $P \propto 1/V$. (*b*) Graphic representation of Boyle's law. At constant temperature, the pressure of a gas is inversely proportional to its volume.

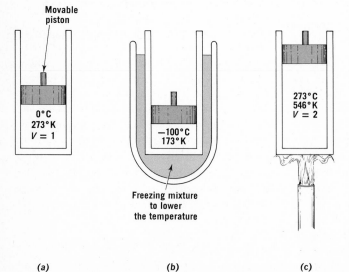

Fig. 12-10. Charles' Law. Let $V = 1$, $P = 1$, and $t = 0\,°C$ (or $273\,°K$) in (*a*). In (*b*) the temperature is reduced by immersing the cylinder in a cold liquid (for example, liquid nitrogen). When the temperature is $-100\,°C$ ($173\,°K$), the volume is reduced to $^{173}/_{273}$ of its original volume if P remains constant. In (*c*) the temperature has been raised to $273\,°C$ ($546\,°K$); that is, the absolute temperature has been doubled, thus doubling the original volume whereas the pressure remains constant. Thus the volume is directly proportional to the absolute temperature at constant P.

Charles' Law

Boyle knew that the pressure of a gas varied with the temperature if the volume was kept constant, but he did not investigate the problem. For one thing, adequate thermometers had not yet been invented. Later experimenters encountered the same problem. About 100 years after Boyle's death, Jacques Charles of France proved that the pressure of all gases changes by the same amount per degree change in temperature if the volume is kept constant, and if the temperature and pressure are such that the gas is not near the liquefying point. Also, the volume changes by the same amount per degree change in temperature if the pressure is kept constant (Fig. 12-10).

Let us examine this last sentence by means of a combination of experiment and reasoning. Experiment has shown that if we start with a gas at 0°C and cool it to 1° below zero (−1°C), with the pressure remaining constant, its volume will decrease by $\frac{1}{273}$ of its original volume. With certain limitations, depending on the actual gas used, a reduction of temperature to −10°C will reduce the volume by $\frac{10}{273}$ of the original volume. Then at −100°C the volume should be reduced by $\frac{100}{273}$ and at −273°C the volume should be reduced by $\frac{273}{273}$; in other words, at 273° below zero Celsius the volume of a gas should be zero (Fig. 12-11). Now this is contrary to common sense, and it turns out to be contrary to experiment also. It is ridiculous to expect that cooling a gas to −273°C would make it dwindle away to nothing and disappear. Experimentally, too, we find that although we can produce temperatures very close to −273°C (within a small fraction of a degree), we have never actually reached this temperature. Furthermore, the conditions of the experiment state that we are cooling a *gas*, and it has been

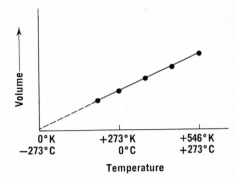

Fig. 12-11. Graphic Representation of Absolute Zero via Charles' Law. *V* for a definite weight of a gas is plotted against temperature. Extension of the graph downward to the left gives us the lowest theoretical temperature possible.

found that *all* gases liquefy before −273°C is reached.

What use, then, is this temperature if we cannot reach it? As suggested by Fig. 12-11, −273°C represents an absolute lower limit on temperature, a natural zero point, and therefore could be called absolute zero. It is, in fact, zero degrees on the Kelvin or absolute scale.

The capital letter *T* from now on in this book will always refer to temperature measured on the absolute scale. The capital letter K following a temperature reading indicates the Kelvin temperature scale, just as F and C indicate Fahrenheit and Celsius scales, respectively.

We may now state Charles' law, as follows: *The volume of a definite quantity of confined gas varies directly with its absolute temperature if the pressure is kept constant.* Mathematically,

$$V \propto T \quad \text{or} \quad V = KT \quad \text{[12-5]}$$

Transposing

$$\frac{V}{T} = K \quad \text{[12-6]}$$

The value of *K* here is dependent upon the quantity (mass, not volume) of gas and the units used. Note, however, that the value of K here is different from the K in Boyle's law because the units are different. Here the units are those of V and T, whereas in Boyle's law the units are those of P and V.

As in the case of Boyle's law, it follows that

$$\frac{V_1}{T_1} = \frac{V_2}{T_2} \quad \text{or} \quad V_1 T_2 = V_2 T_1 \quad [12\text{-}7]$$

Ideal (General) Gas Law

We now have two gas laws, Boyle's law, in which the volume is inversely proportional to the pressure, and Charles' law in which the volume is directly proportional to the absolute temperature. We can combine them into a single law, called the ideal (or general) gas law.[9] Thus,

$$V \propto \frac{1}{P} \quad \text{and} \quad V \propto T$$

Hence

$$V \propto \frac{T}{P} \quad \text{or} \quad V = \frac{KT}{P} \quad [12\text{-}8]$$

Transposing

$$PV = KT \quad\quad\quad [12\text{-}9]$$

The constant K is a number whose magnitude depends upon the mass of the sample of gas and upon the units chosen for P, V, and T. Obviously, it is not the same K that was used in either Boyle's or Charles' laws.

We prefer to refer to this general law as the *ideal* gas law to help us remember that gases do not obey the law precisely. The deviations

[9] A well-known law of proportionality states that (at constant T) if V is proportional to $1/P$, and V is proportional to T (at constant P), then V will be proportional to the product of $1/P$ and T.

are negligible if the pressures are low and the temperatures high, that is, if the gas is not near its liquefaction temperature and pressure. The causes of these deviations will be discussed in Chapter 13.

Despite the deviations, the ideal gas law has helped in the organization of our knowledge about gases. However, we still have no overall theory that will explain all of our observations. For example, what is the mechanism by which gases exert pressure? Why does the ideal gas law hold at some temperatures and pressures but not at others? A theory seems called for, but not quite yet. For, curiously enough, the development of our knowledge of the constitution of matter, as may be inferred from the preceding questions, was intimately associated with the development of our knowledge of heat.

Exercises

1. Consider the three equations $PV = K$, $V/T = K$, and $PV = KT$. Are the K's the same or are they different? Explain.
2. Distinguish between the force acting on a body and the pressure exerted on it.
3. Describe and state the significance of von Guericke's Magdeburg hemispheres experiment.
4. Suppose that your classroom measures 50 by 30 by 12 ft. If the density of air is 0.08 lb/ft^3, how much does the air in the room weigh?
5. In the experiment to check Torricelli's air-pressure theory, Pascal had a man keep constant watch on a barometer at the foot of the mountain. Why was this necessary?
6. Why is mercury used in a barometer? Would some other liquid, such as water, not do equally well?
7. State Boyle's law. What are its limitations?
8. Show that the accompanying data con-

cerning the pressure and volume of a gas demonstrate Boyle's law (a) without drawing a graph and (b) by drawing a graph.

P (cm Hg)	V (cm³)
76	283
150	140.3
40	537.5
210	102.4
30	707.1

9. A cubic inch of mercury weighs 0.491 lb. What is the weight of the mercury in a barometer with a cross section of 1 in.² and a height of 30 in.? How does this compare with normal atmospheric pressure?

10. In Fig. 12-11 we plotted temperature against PV to obtain absolute zero. We can also plot temperature against V (at constant P) and reach the same result. Do so.

11. If $PV = K$ at constant T, then changes in the product PV can be used to construct a temperature scale. Take a sample of gas and measure its volume and pressure at the temperatures of melting ice and boiling water. A device that makes this sort of measurement is called a gas thermometer. Such an instrument is not graduated to read temperature directly. Instead V and P are read and the product PV determined from a graph. Other kinds of thermom-

eters may agree with one another at 0° and at 100° but not in between, because their scales depend upon the properties of particular substances. Disagreement among gas thermometers, no matter what gas is used, is insignificant. Why?

12. State Charles' law. What are its limitations?

13. If 32 g of oxygen occupies 22.4 liters at 0°C and 760 mm pressure, what volume will it occupy at 100°C at the same pressure? [10]

14. Under what conditions may matter absorb heat without increasing its temperature?

15. What conclusions can you reach about the nature of a gas *solely* from the laws of Boyle and Charles?

16. Increase or decrease the density of a fixed volume of a gas, keeping the temperature constant, and you increase or decrease the pressure. Why should this be so?

17. The pressure of a certain volume, V, of a gas is increased by compression by a factor of 3, the temperature remaining unchanged.
    (a) What is the new volume?
    (b) It is possible to increase the pressure by a factor of three without changing the volume. How do you do it? (Give a quantitative answer.)

[10] To solve problems involving changes in V due to changes in both T and P, solve for new V due to change in T; then use the new V to solve for change in P.

Heat, Temperature, and the Kinetic Theory of Gases

Chapter 13

Continuity of Matter

Only two possibilities exist with respect to the fundamental nature of matter; it is either continuous or discontinuous. If it is continuous, it is theoretically possible to subdivide matter endlessly, without ever reaching a particle too small to be divided again. If discontinuous, subdividing would eventually end with some fundamental discrete[1] particle. Democritus (ca. 400 B.C.) advanced this latter view, and gave us the word *atom* as the name of that particle. Aristotle rejected this view, and his great influence caused it to be forgotten for 2000 years. The atomistic concept was revived in the 16th century but was not developed until the beginning of the 19th century, when Dalton advanced his atomic theory. Others before him—Boyle, Newton, and the great French chemist Lavoisier—believed in the atomicity

[1] Meaning separate or discontinuous; composed of distinct parts.

[Science is] an essentially artistic enterprise, stimulated largely by curiosity, served largely by disciplined imagination, and based largely on faith in the reasonableness, order and beauty of the universe of which man is a part.
WARREN WEAVER

of matter, but none of them defined the properties of the atoms.

We how have sufficient background concerning the nature of heat, temperature, energy, and the behavior of gases to formulate a theory that will explain and integrate most of the phenomena noted in Chapters 11 and 12. We could go on citing more experiments and thus accumulate more evidence, but such a procedure would be unnecessarily tedious, for it would tax our memories to remember all of the evidence, and increase the difficulty of keeping track of the interrelationships. We will proceed to the development of a theory and will begin, as usual, by listing its chief assumptions and by citing a few of the more obvious observations we may have mentioned previously but not discussed. We remind you that there is nothing dubious about a scientific explanation just because it is called a theory.

Assumptions of the Kinetic Molecular Theory of Ideal Gases

1. Gases consist of tiny discrete particles called molecules.
2. Gas molecules are in constant *random* motion.
3. Gas molecules are, on the average, far apart relative to their size, so they exert no forces on each other except at the instant of collision.
4. Gas molecules collide with one another and with the walls of their container without loss of kinetic energy; that is, all collisions are perfectly elastic.

We must remember that assumptions are not simply the products of man's imagination, but are really clues obtained through observations and experiments. Perhaps it is better to say that they are *inferences,* reasonable ones in all cases if proper attention is paid to the obser-

vations and experiments; they cannot be classified as facts because they have not been "proved" beyond all doubt. In the kinetic molecular theory all but the last assumption are readily seen to be reasonable inferences derived from observation and experiment.

We cannot observe a lone molecule directly, even with a high-powered optical microscope. We can, under certain circumstances, observe the behavior of masses of molecules. This is most difficult to do in the solid state, somewhat less difficult in the liquid state, and relatively easy when molecules are in the gaseous state. This is true despite the fact that our senses give us much *direct* information about liquids and solids and relatively little about gases. Yet, it is through a study of gases that we have learned what liquids and solids are really like. In large part this is because each molecule of gas acts almost independently of all the other molecules around it, and also in part because gases exert pressure, occupy volume, and undergo behavior changes as the temperature changes, all of which can be measured by instruments. We can even make some direct observations on gases if they are colored, as are bromine and chlorine, or if they possess characteristic odors or tastes, as does ammonia. For these reasons we began our investigation into the fundamental nature of matter by a study of gases rather than of liquids or solids.

Justification of the Assumptions

We will adopt the discrete-particle concept here—leaving the development of the atomic theory until later—but we will omit the distinction between atoms and molecules at this time and call all such discrete particles molecules if they can exist independently *when that matter is in the gaseous state.* In almost all cases this use will be consistent with modern meaning. On occasion we will carry over the same general concept of the word to liquids and solids in order to prevent confusion—which certainly would result otherwise. Later on we will give a more rigorous definition of a molecule. The reality of molecules in constant random motion is illustrated by observation of Brownian movement (Fig. 13-6). Our first assumption seems well justified.

Break a small vial of bromine (brown in color) in the bottom of a glass cylinder and it can be seen to diffuse throughout the whole cylinder in a matter of minutes (Fig. 13-1). If we evacuate the cylinder first, the diffusion is almost instantaneous. We are also all aware of the fact that gases can leak through the tiniest of openings, as in automobile tires; we already know that gases expand without limit to fill their containers no matter what the size or shape. The above observations merely con-

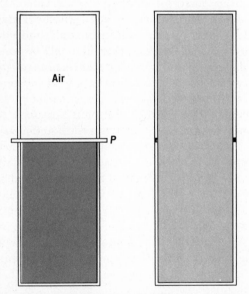

Fig. 13-1. Diffusion of One Gas Through Another. Bromine, a reddish brown gas, fills the lower half of the container on the left. After the dividing plate, *P,* is removed, the bromine quickly diffuses through the air in the upper part to form a uniform mixture of bromine and air. If the space above the dividing plate were a vacuum, diffusion would be almost instantaneous on removal of the plate.

firm this knowledge, and so justify our second assumption. By *random motion* we mean that just as many molecules move in one direction as in any other. Random motion is often called translational motion. Belief in random motion is justified only when dealing with enormous numbers of molecules.

When molecules of gases are violently aroused, as in hurricanes, tornadoes, or explosions of all kinds, there is little that can withstand the forces they collectively exert. It is not this type of motion, however, that we are discussing. The random motion that we refer to is that of gas particles seemingly at rest, as are the molecules of air in this room. We should realize, though, that even in those masses of air that move in one direction (as in steady winds), sometimes at high speeds, these same random motions are still taking place. The directional motions of molecules in winds are superimposed upon the far more rapid random motions. We may be very conscious of the directional motions but wholly unconscious of the random motions because the latter impinge upon us from every direction; the vector sum of their forces is zero, or close to it.

We also know that gases are easily compressible, so that we can walk through air, pushing the molecules aside without effort. Moreover, steam at 100°C and a pressure of 1 atm occupies 1700 times the volume of the same number of molecules of water. Steam molecules must be much farther apart than water molecules. That gas molecules diffuse so rapidly suggests that they exert no appreciable forces on one another except at the instant of collision. Thus our third assumption also seems justified.

We have already seen that gases exert a pressure on every surface with which they are in contact. Assumption 2 gives us a logical explanation, for we should expect that rapidly moving molecules would exert a force on the walls of the container as they bump into them.

If the impacts were frequent enough and made by an enormous number of molecules per unit area, a continuous force would result. Using the laws of mechanics we should be able to calculate the value of this force. Since the number of molecules per cubic inch, even in a rarefied gas, is enormous, the number of collisions with the walls and with one another is fantastically high. Furthermore, these collisions should all be perfectly elastic; that is, there should be no loss of energy during the collisions. If this were not so, the molecules of the gas would gradually slow down, losing their kinetic energy, and finally settle to form a layer on the bottom of the container. That they do not do this is obvious, so we conclude that all collisions are elastic. Since the molecules rebound elastically, there is no friction and so none of the kinetic energy of the molecules is converted into heat during these collisions with either the walls or one another.

What we have said is only statistically true—that is, it is true only when we consider very large numbers of molecules—for in every collision one molecule will gain some kinetic energy and the other will lose the same amount so the total kinetic energy of the whole mass remains the same if the initial conditions (temperature, pressure, mass, volume) are kept constant. This follows from the law of conservation of energy. A conclusion from this assumption is that the molecules remain eternally in motion. Our fourth assumption seems justified.

By means of these four assumptions all the readily observable phenomena with respect to gases seem perfectly reasonable. The same is true for Boyle's law, for if gas pressure is due to the impact of enormous numbers of molecules upon the walls of the container or other surfaces, then compressing these molecules into half the space should cause twice as many impacts per unit time and so double the pressure. However, the relationship between P and V on the one hand and T on the other is not

at all evident from our assumptions. Perhaps a mechanical model will help. It was Lord Kelvin who said, "If I can make a mechanical model then I can understand; if I cannot make one, I do not understand." But first of all we will review the history of the development of the kinetic theory.

The First Theory of Gases

The first to devise a theory of gases was Daniel Bernoulli, a member of one of the most illustrious families in the annals of science. He began his career a few years before the death of Newton, and advanced his theory in 1738, over 100 years before Joule put the finishing touches to the concept of heat as a form of energy. He explained gas pressure as due to the impact on the walls of a container. By mathematical analysis he deduced Boyle's law—which Boyle had established by experiment some 80 years earlier. Bernoulli believed that heat was "an internal motion of the particles." This conclusion was a logical outcome of his theory of gas pressure, for if heat is a form of motion, then heat must be associated with gas particles that are in motion; gas particles had to be in motion if they were to exert pressure upward as well as downward. His views were too advanced for his time, and so his theory fell by the wayside, not because of any contrary evidence but simply for want of attention. This is a common happenstance for those in any field whose ideas are too far in advance of the mental climate of their times.

Derivation of the Dynamical Theory of Heat

The present kinetic molecular theory arose from two investigations, one into the nature of gases, the other into the nature of heat. Joule, like Bernoulli and Rumford, associated heat with the motion of submicroscopic particles of matter. Verification demanded a quantitative theory of heat. Joule took gas molecules as his submicroscopic particles. Since forces are always associated with motion, he set out to correlate their motion with the forces acting on them by applying Newton's laws of motion to the gas molecules. The fewer the forces, the simpler the problem; with gases he could ignore whatever minute forces molecules may exert on each other, thus gaining simplicity.

Suppose we have a cubical box as our container of a gas, a box whose three dimensions, *a*, *b*, and *c*, are each equal to a length that we will call *L* (Fig. 13-2). Its volume is therefore L^3. Myriads of molecules are in *random* motion in this box (Fig. 13-3). We will assume that they all are moving with the same *average* speed, *v*. We will also assume that, at any one instant, as many are moving parallel to one dimension as to either of the other two. That is, if the total number of molecules in the box is *N*, then *N*/3 are moving parallel to *ee*, *N*/3 are moving parallel to *ff*, and *N*/3 parallel to *gg*.[2] According to our fourth assumption each impact involves a rebound perpendicular to the wall without loss of speed. The average time, *t*, that it takes one molecule to move across the box and back again (a distance of 2*L*) is 2*L*/*v*, where *v* is the average speed. Mathematically,

$$t = \frac{2L}{v} \qquad [13\text{-}1]$$

We need now to calculate the force exerted by a single molecule. According to Newton's

[2] Actually the shape of the container makes no difference—our model would be very unsatisfactory if it did. We use the cubical box to make the geometry simpler. The same is true of the assumptions regarding speeds and directions of motion. However, when we carry out all calculations for any shape container and *without* the assumptions regarding average speeds and directions of motion, exactly the same result is obtained, provided that $mv^2/2$ is interpreted as the *average* kinetic energy of the gas molecules.

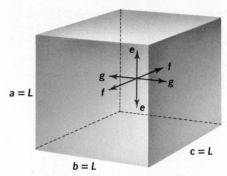

Fig. 13-2. Kinetic Theory Diagram. A cubical box contains a definite weight of a gas. Equal numbers of molecules are assumed to be traveling back and forth parallel to each of the three dimensions of the box. See Fig. 13-3.

second law, $F = ma$. This law in this form does not help us for we do not know *a* and have no way of calculating it. Neither are we sure of *m*, but we really do not need to know that, for Newton gave us his second law in another form (Eq. 7-2, p. 115):

$$F = \frac{\text{change in momentum}}{\text{time}}$$

Symbolically,

$$F = \frac{\text{change in } mv}{t}$$

Force here is thus defined as the total momentum transfer per unit time. Now we learned (p. 119) that momentum is a vector quantity; that is, it has direction as well as magnitude. A molecule moving perpendicular to one of the walls has a certain momentum, *mv*. Since it is going to make a perfectly elastic collision (assumption 4) with the wall, it is going to rebound with a momentum equal in magnitude to the forward momentum but opposite in direction. Our use of vectors requires that we call the forward one +*mv* and the rebounding one −*mv*. The difference between +*mv* and −*mv* is 2*mv*; that is,

$$mv - (-mv) = 2mv$$

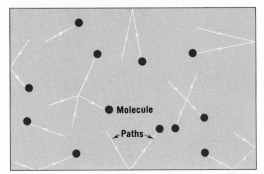

Fig. 13-3. Actual Paths of Molecules in Box. The actual paths are random, the molecules colliding with the walls at various angles and with one another and rebounding. The net effect of all these random collisions with the walls is the same as if one third of them moved parallel to *ee*, one third parallel to *ff*, and one third parallel to *gg*, as assumed in Fig. 13-2.

Thus the change in momentum is $2mv$. Therefore, the force exerted by a single molecule against the wall of the container is given by

$$F_{(per\ molecule)} = \frac{change\ in\ mv}{t}$$

$$= \frac{2mv}{2L/v} = \frac{2mv^2}{2L} \quad [13\text{-}2]$$

(We deliberately do not cancel out the 2's.)

Now the total force exerted by all of the molecules on one face of our box is the force per molecule, $2mv^2/2L$, multiplied by the number striking that face per second; this number is $N/3$. Mathematically,

$$F_{\left(\substack{total\ on \\ one\ face}\right)} = \frac{N}{3} \times \frac{2mv^2}{2L} \quad [13\text{-}3]$$

Also

$$F_{\left(\substack{total\ on \\ one\ face}\right)} = P_{\left(\substack{force\ per \\ unit\ area}\right)} \times A_{\left(\substack{area\ of \\ one\ face}\right)}$$

and the area of one face is $L \times L = L^2$, so

$$F_{\left(\substack{total\ on \\ one\ face}\right)} = P \times L^2 = PL^2$$

Substituting PL_2 for F in Eq. 13-3,

$$PL^2 = \frac{N}{3} \times \frac{2mv^2}{2L} \quad [13\text{-}4]$$

and multiplying both sides by L, we get

$$PL^3 = \frac{N}{3} \times \frac{2mv^2}{2} \quad [13\text{-}5]$$

Since $L^3 = V$ (volume of box),

$$PV = \frac{N}{3} \times \frac{2mv^2}{2} = \frac{2}{3}N \times \frac{1}{2}mv^2 \quad [13\text{-}6]$$

The Basic Equation for the Kinetic Theory of Gases

Students who skipped the mathematics involved in Eqs. 13-1 through 13-6 should examine the final equation (13-6) carefully. Its derivation was based on a hypothetical cubical box filled with the molecules of a gas, on certain reasonable assumptions about the molecules, and the application of the laws of mechanics (chiefly Newton's second law in the form stated on p. 115) to the molecules. You should read again the first paragraph under the heading Derivation of the Dynamical Theory of Heat.

In Eq. 13-6 you should recognize $\frac{1}{2}mv^2$ as the formula for kinetic energy. Here it represents the average random (translational) kinetic energy of the molecules of the gas in the box. This means that for any given number of molecules, N, the PV relationship depends on the average random kinetic energy of the molecules; that is, PV equals $\frac{2}{3}$ of the total random kinetic energy if our hypothesis is correct. Equation 13-6 yields a theoretical relationship connecting the pressure and volume of a gas with its mass and the average random translational velocity of its molecules. This equation (13-6) is the basic equation for the kinetic theory of gases.

The Kinetic Theory Definition of Temperature

In Chapter 12 we showed how both Boyle and Charles derived laws experimentally that could be combined into one ideal or general gas law, $PV \propto T$. Let us look again at Eq. 13-6. We recognize PV, the same PV that we had in Boyle's law, $PV = K$ at constant T. The K must therefore be equal to $\frac{2}{3}N \times \frac{1}{2}mv^2$. Now $\frac{2}{3}N$ is constant for any given mass of a particular gas *regardless* of its pressure, volume, or temperature. We can therefore remove this constant, and our equation is now a proportionality that says $PV \propto \frac{1}{2}mv^2$, pressure times the volume is proportional to the average random kinetic energy of our gas molecules if we keep the temperature constant. Increasing or decreasing the temperature means increasing or decreasing the average random kinetic energy of the molecules of the gas. We begin to see what temperature really is.

If we go back to the ideal gas law $PV \propto T$, and compare it with $PV \propto \frac{1}{2}mv^2$, it becomes apparent that

$$T \propto \frac{mv^2}{2}$$

That is, the absolute temperature of a gas is proportional[3] to the average random kinetic energy of the molecules of our gas. It is therefore obvious that we have our definition of temperature: *Temperature on the Kelvin scale is a measure of the average random translational kinetic energy of the molecules of a gas.* If we wish to compare the average kinetic energies of two gas samples, we simply take their temperatures using the Kelvin scale. It follows that anything that increases the average kinetic energy of molecules of a gas makes the gas hotter. Note that in all of our discussions we have been using enormous numbers

[3] Things proportional to the same thing are proportional to each other.

of molecules, and so the use of the word *average* is permissible. It is meaningless to speak of the temperature of one or of a few molecules, and it is not only meaningless to speak of hot molecules but downright silly as well. Note also that temperature is *not* the average random translational kinetic energy of gas molecules but a measure of this energy.

Note carefully that all we did to arrive at these conclusions about temperature was to take a hypothetical cubical box filled with the molecules of a gas, make certain reasonable assumptions about the molecules, and apply the laws of mechanics to them (chiefly Newton's second law). Once we had done that we were able to derive Boyle's law, Charles' law, and the ideal gas law mathematically. If these laws had not already been determined by experiment, Joule could have derived them in this manner. However, before declaring them valid, someone would have had to check them by experiment, for, as we have said, matter is not required to follow the logic of man.

One of the fruits of the derivation of $PV = \frac{2}{3}N \times \frac{1}{2}mv^2$ is that we now see what it was that had apparently declined to zero in our derivation of the Kelvin scale (Fig. 12-11). As we said then, it was neither V nor P. Our equation tells us that it was the kinetic energy of the gas molecules. At $0°K$ all random motion of molecules in gases has ceased.

The Kinetic Theory Definition of Heat

We have clarified the concept of temperature, but what about that obviously related concept, heat? We have had to repeat *average* in our previous discussions to keep you from confusing average energy with total energy. We need to remember that different quantities of the same substance at the same temperature will have the same average molecular kinetic energies but very different total molecular kinetic energies. Also the same quantities of different substances—water and iron, for example—may be at the same temperature but have very different quantities of heat; they have very different specific heats (p. 180). A gallon of lukewarm water at 50°C will contain far more heat than a short thin piece of iron wire at 1000°C.

Our problem of defining heat[4] would be far easier if the translational motions were the only ones present in a container of gas. It can be shown that molecules may also be rotating or there may be vibrational motions of the atoms (Fig. 13-4) *within* a molecule, and that energy is absorbed when these motions are increased even though they have no effect on the temperature.

Our definition of heat does not come so directly out of the mechanical model as does our definition of temperature; it has to be inferred. Suppose we have a hot oven and we put a definite quantity of cold food into it. The average random kinetic energy of the molecules of the hot air in the oven is greater than the average random kinetic energies of the molecules of the food. This fact can be checked with a thermometer. A half hour or an hour later we check again and find that the temperature of the food has risen; the bombardment of the food molecules by the air molecules has increased the average random kinetic energies of the former. (We assume that the oven is still turned "on," so that the temperature of the air remains constant.) We say that heat energy has been added to the food, but this statement does not really tell us what has been added because we have not yet defined heat energy. The only thing that has happened is that some of the motion of the air molecules has been transferred to the food molecules. Heat must therefore be molecular motion because—and

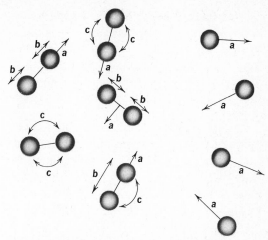

Fig. 13-4. Types of Molecular Motion. (*a*) Translational. (*b*) Vibrational. (*c*) Rotational. The latter two types are denied to single-atom molecules (rare gases). Multiatom molecules have all three types. All three types are heat, but only that of translation is registered on a thermometer as temperature.

here we repeat in slightly different words—during the heat transfer the only change made is in the molecular motions of the two bodies involved in the transfer.

We should avoid saying that heat is the kinetic energy of molecules. Consider a cold wind blowing a steady 30 mi/hr from the north, and a warm wind some days later blowing a steady 30 mi/hr from the south. Both winds are composed of masses of air molecules moving in definite directions. At 30 mi/hr these masses (and the molecules that compose them) have considerable kinetic energy owing to this movement; both masses have equal amounts of it per unit mass. This is not the randomly distributed kinetic energy that we have been talking about. The directed motions of the molecules in the winds are superimposed upon their random motions (see p. 204). That the directed motions have nothing to do with temperature is evident from the fact that both winds have the same amount of it, for both

[4]To say that heat is a form of energy is no definition at all.

are blowing at 30 mi/hr. They have widely different temperatures because the average random motions of the molecules in the wind from the south are far more rapid than those in the wind from the north. Thus it is apparent that heat is not simply the kinetic energy of molecules.

The above example of heating cold food by putting it into a hot oven should not lead one to the conclusion that mere jostling among the molecules "produces" heat. If one is prone to reach such a conclusion, possibly by remembering that Joule increased the temperature of water by stirring it (Fig. 11-7), a rereading of page 185 should clarify matters. Jostling of one set of molecules at one temperature with those of another set at a different temperature will result in an increase of average kinetic energy of one set but a corresponding decrease in the other. No "new" energy has been added.

We must be careful never to say that molecular motion produces heat. The word *produce* implies a cause and effect relationship that is not appropriate here. All we can say is that the physically observable phenomenon that we call heat is connected by the kinetic molecular theory to the nonobservable motions of molecules. We are using a theoretical construct—moving molecules—to explain an observable fact—heat. This theoretical relationship is accepted as valid because it also explains many other phenomena, as we shall shortly show. Again we say, total molecular motion *is* heat.

Bear in mind that Joule did not set out to explain temperature. There is nothing in the four assumptions of the kinetic theory that, by itself, indicates that heat and temperature are at all involved in the kinetic theory of gases. Joule *did* set out to develop a quantitative theory of heat based on molecular motions because the views expressed by Newton, Bernoulli, Rumford, and others, plus his own experiments, would not let him think otherwise. But to convince other people and to destroy forever the caloric theory of heat, a theory had to be formulated that could explain not only all of the known, obviously related, facts but also other seemingly unrelated facts, and that could, by prediction followed by experimentation and observation, lead us on to new knowledge. We will turn our attention to some of the seemingly unrelated facts that the kinetic molecular theory can explain.

Verification and Extensions of the Kinetic Molecular Theory

Deviations from the Ideal Gas Law

Our reference to the gas laws as *ideal* laws that real gases do not always obey merits special comment. Since Galileo's time the scientist has invented, in his imagination only, frictionless pulleys and wheels, blocks sliding down frictionless inclined planes, air with no air resistance, weightless weights, and unstretchable ropes and strings. After analysis he then adds the real conditions and so modifies the ideal situations that exist only in his imagination to fit those actually encountered in nature. Thus, the gas laws have been formulated to apply to ideal gases that do not exist. Most gases are very nearly ideal when the temperature is high and the pressure low. They become less and less so as lower and lower temperatures and/or higher and higher pressures are attained. If our kinetic theory is valid, it should reveal a reason for such deviations, for a fruitful theory should not only account for the phenomena that it was designed to explain but should also be applicable to other phenomena in the same field that heretofore have been unexplainable.

We have already stated that Boyle's law ($PV = K$) does not hold at low temperatures and high pressures, but we did not state why.

We idealized the concept of gas pressure in the third assumption of the kinetic theory, which states that gas molecules exert no forces on one another except at the instant of collision. We feel justified in applying this assumption to real gases because gases free to expand do so without limit. This means that in such gases the attractive forces are ineffective. However, if we compress gases, we force the molecules closer together. Since the attractive forces are intermolecular in character, it follows that the closer the molecules are, the greater these forces should be. Also at low temperatures where their average velocity is relatively low, so that the attractive forces have a longer time to act when they collide, detectable effects may be produced. When these forces become large enough the gas begins to liquefy, and eventually to solidify. Well before this stage is reached, the departure of the real gas from Boyle's law becomes considerable. Obviously no gas should exist as such at absolute zero, for a gas by definition consists of "flying" molecules that must have random kinetic energy to fly. Since at $0°K$ all random motion ceases, all flying ceases.

Since gases vary enormously in the temperatures and pressures at which they can be liquefied and solidified, the range of temperatures and pressures in which the deviation is slight also varies enormously. For nitrogen, which cannot be liquefied at a temperature above $-147°C$, no matter how great the pressure, this range is far greater than for carbon dioxide, which can be liquefied at $31°C$ and 73 atm.[5] Under any circumstances gases obey Boyle's law far more closely at high temperatures than at low because the molecules at high temperatures have a higher average kinetic energy. Their more rapid motions decrease the length of time the forces have to act as the molecules collide or move past one another. These mutual attactions of molecules for one another are called van der Waals intermolecular forces, after the man who first used them to explain the behavior of real gases.[6] Thus the deviations from the ideal gas laws are explained.

How a Gas Exerts a Pressure

When we discussed air pressure (p. 191), we stated emphatically that its cause was not its weight, but we postponed giving you the proper explanation until we studied kinetic theory. According to the theory, molecules are in constant random motion. They must therefore be constantly colliding with various surfaces such as the walls of their containers, if any, the surface of the mercury in the open receptacle of a barometer, the surface of the earth and every material object on it, including you and me, and with themselves. The number of molecules in 1 in.[3] of air at 1 atm pressure is of the order of 4 billion billion, and at room temperature they are moving with an average speed of a bit over $\frac{1}{4}$ mi/sec. These countless numbers of molecules, moving at average speeds of nearly 1000 mi/hr, bombard every surface with which they come in contact, creating a pressure of 14.7 lb/in.[2] on that surface. Put in other words, the pressure of a gas is produced by the bombardment of molecules. Note carefully that the pressure that we measure has nothing to do with the forces that are involved in the countless collisions of mole-

[5] The temperature at which gases can be liquefied at atmospheric pressure, helium excepted, varies from $100°C$ for steam to $-259°C$ for hydrogen. All can be liquefied at somewhat higher temperatures if pressure is applied, but for each there is a definite critical temperature above which the gas cannot be liquefied no matter what the pressure is. At room temperatures all of the common gases are above their critical temperatures, and all liquids below theirs. A substance in the gaseous state, but below its critical temperature, is called a *vapor*.

[6] Van der Waals formulated an improved gas law to apply to real gases by taking into consideration the fact that gas molecules occupy space and that they are not entirely free from each other's attractive forces.

cules with one another. All collisions are completely elastic, so there is no loss of kinetic energy and the molecules keep on moving forever. Pressure is, of course, proportional to the density of a given gas if we keep the temperature constant, for the more molecules per unit volume, the greater the number of impacts per unit area.

At the same temperature and at the same volume the pressure exerted by the same number of molecules of any gas is the same. Consider one mole (p. 253), 6×10^{23} molecules, of each of ten gases chosen at random and in identical containers at a pressure of 1 atm and at the same temperature. They will occupy the same volume and will exert the same pressure.[7]

Changes of Temperature by Expansion and Compression of Gases

In all of our problems concerning temperature changes by expansion and compression of gases, the key to their solutions is to be found in changes in average random kinetic energies of the molecules. If the average is reduced, cooling results; if it is increased, heating results. To solve a given problem one should first learn which change has taken place.

That compression of a gas is a heating process is attested by the manner of fuel ignition in the diesel engine. Such an engine is like the automobile engine except that it has no spark plugs. Air is drawn into a diesel cylinder and quickly compressed so greatly that the temperature of the air rises to about 700°C. Fuel is then sprayed into this hot air and is ignited by the high temperature.

[7] Barometers read gas pressures indirectly by measuring the height of a column of mercury that the gas pressure will support. At sea level this height will be 29.92 in., or 76 cm or 760 mm. This means that a column of mercury 1 in.² in cross section and 29.92 in. high will weigh 14.7 lb.

Anyone who pumps up a bicycle tire rapidly by means of a hand pump can observe another example of heating a gas by compressing it—the barrel of the pump gets hot. What is the source of the heat? Obviously, one has to do work to pump up the tire; that is, energy has to be expended—muscular energy is transformed into mechanical energy. If the law of conservation of energy is valid, we should expect this mechanical energy to be transformed into some other energy. This is merely a case of transformation of mechanical energy into heat energy.

We can also explain this phenomenon in terms of temperature, that is, in terms of average kinetic energies. From our kinetic theory definition of temperature, we see that anything that increases the average kinetic energy will increase the temperature. Consider a bicycle pump (Fig. 13-5) before the piston is made to descend. Molecules are striking the piston and the walls of the cylinder with a certain average force, rebounding from them with a certain average speed. Now, when the piston descends, its downward motion has the effect of increasing the speed of rebound just as a baseball squarely striking a bat that is moving rapidly toward it rebounds with considerably greater velocity than it would from a motionless bat. Thus, the average kinetic energy of the molecules is increased—which means that the air temperature is increased.

It is reasonable to expect that the expansion of a gas would be a cooling process if compression of a gas is a heating process. Experiments show that our expectations are correct. The explanation is given in Fig. 13-5c.

Evidence for Molecules: Brownian Movement

Despite the apparent success of our theory, we still might very well ask the questions, "Are molecules real? Is there any other evidence of molecular motion, evidence of a very different

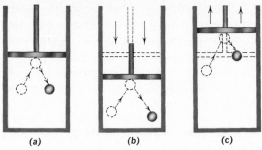

Fig. 13-5. Compression of a Gas as a Heating Process. Cross-sectional views of a piston in a cylinder are shown. In (a) the piston is motionless; gas molecules are rebounding from it without loss or gain of kinetic energy. The termperature is constant. In (b) the piston is descending and so is compressing the gas. Gas molecules and the piston are moving toward one another when they collide. The moving piston, acting like a bat when it hits a ball squarely, contributes energy to the rebounding molecules, thus increasing their average kinetic energy; the temperature rises.

Expansion of a gas as a cooling process. In (c) the piston is ascending and the gas is expanding. The gas molecules and the piston are moving in the same direction when they collide. The gas molecules impart some of their kinetic energy to the piston in the same manner that a car imparts some of its energy to one ahead (going in the same direction) if it strikes it from the rear. The gas molecules therefore lose energy, the average is reduced, and the gas is cooled.

character?" A Scottish botanist, Robert Brown, an older contemporary of Joule, looking through a microscope at plant pollen in water, saw the tiny specks of pollen *incessantly* jiggling about. The smaller the specks, the faster their seemingly random motion. The higher the temperature the faster the "dance." Put a drop of India ink in a dish of water and the black soot particles in the ink may be observed to "dance" if viewed with a high-power microscope. By means of a special device, smoke particles may be observed to do the same with a low-power microscope.

We are now sure that this irregular unceasing jiggling is due to chance bombardment of the tiny solid specks by water (or air in the case of smoke) molecules. The molecules cannot be anywhere near the size of the quivering solid particles or the latter would jump more violently. They cannot be infinitely small and infinitely numerous, for if they were the bombardment would be exactly equal on all sides, and we would see no movement. To cause a jiggle, more must hit one side of a speck than the other—in the manner we visualize molecules with random motion would do. The paths of a single particle have been mapped (Fig. 13-6) by spotting its position every two or three minutes, much as you may map the approximate path of a football player by spotting his position on the field at brief intervals.

Explanation of Avogadro's Hypothesis

About 1813, Avogadro, an Italian chemist, attempted to explain Gay-Lussac's law of combining volumes (p. 241) by assuming that equal volumes of gases under the same conditions of temperature and pressure contain the same number of particles. Why should this be?

Consider equal volumes of two different gases (say hydrogen and oxygen), both at the same temperature and pressure, which means that $V_H = V_O$, $T_H = T_O$, and $P_H = P_O$. Therefore

$$P_H V_H = P_O V_O \qquad [13\text{-}7]$$

From Eq. 13-6 we have, when we substitute for PV in 13-7,

$$\tfrac{2}{3}N_H \times (\tfrac{1}{2}mv^2)_H = \tfrac{2}{3}N_O \times (\tfrac{1}{2}mv^2)_O \qquad [13\text{-}8]$$

But $T \propto \tfrac{1}{2}mv^2$ and $T_H = T_O$. Hence the average kinetic energies are the same, that is,

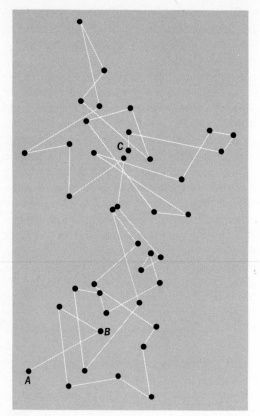

Fig. 13-6. Brownian Movement. Map (enormously magnified) of the path of a tiny particle of pollen is water as it was buffeted first one way and then another by the molecules of water. Starting at *A*, it first moved to *B* and finally wound up at *C*. Positions were determined at intervals of 2 min by observations made with a high-powered microscope. This is evidence of the reality of molecules. How else can the random motion of the grain of pollen be explained?

$(\frac{1}{2}mv^2)_H = (\frac{1}{2}mv^2)_O$, and so can be cancelled from both sides. We are left with

$$\frac{2}{3}N_H = \frac{2}{3}N_O \qquad [13\text{-}9]$$

N, as indicated on p. 206, is the number of molecules in a given sample of a gas. Thus, if we have a liter of hydrogen and a liter of

oxygen, with both liters at the same temperature and pressure, there will be the same number of molecules in each. Therefore Avogadro's hypothesis, presented in an attempt to solve a particularly knotty problem, turns out to be correct according to our kinetic theory.

The Speeds of Gases, Relative and Actual

From Eq. 13-8, if the temperatures and volumes of two gases (say hydrogen and oxygen) are the same, we get

$$(\tfrac{1}{2}mv^2)_H = (\tfrac{1}{2}mv^2)_O$$

We cancel out the $\frac{1}{2}$ from each side, and transpose as follows:

$$\frac{v^2_H}{v^2_O} = \frac{m_O}{m_H} \qquad [13\text{-}10]$$

Now, the mass of one molecule of oxygen is 16 times greater than the mass of one molecule of hydrogen; that is, their mass ratios are 16 to 1. What we want is their velocity ratios. Let us assign a velocity of 1 to oxygen. Substituting these values in Eq. 13-10,

$$\frac{v^2_H}{1} = \frac{16}{1}$$
$$v^2_H = 16$$
$$v_H = \sqrt{16} = 4$$

This means that for the average kinetic energies to be the same for the gases at the same temperature, the hydrogen molecules must be moving four times as fast as the oxygen molecules. If we are good at seeing relationships between numbers, we can see directly from Eq. 13-10 that the squares of the speeds of the molecules of any two gases are inversely proportional to the masses of the individual molecules. There are various ways of checking this. For example, we might time the rate of diffusion of two gases at the same temperature and pressure through the walls of a porous membrane or time the rate of escape of two gases through a single small opening.

The average speeds of gas molecules may be calculated from the equation,

$$PV = \tfrac{2}{3}N\left(\frac{mv^2}{2}\right)$$

Solving for v^2, we have

$$v^2 = \frac{3PV}{Nm}$$

For N we will use the number of molecules in 32 g of oxygen. Thirty-two grams of oxygen will occupy 22,400 cm³ (22.4 liters) at 0°C and a pressure of 1 atm; that is, the mass of all of the molecules of oxygen in 22,400 cm³ is 32 g. In the above equation Nm represents the total mass of the gas in the container (number of molecules, N, times the mass of one molecule). We can therefore set Nm equal to 32 in the case of oxygen. Since we must use cgs units, P must be stated in dynes (1 atm $= 10^6$ dynes/cm²).

Hence

$$v^2 = \frac{3PV}{Nm} = \frac{3 \times 10^6 \times 22,400}{32}$$
$$= 21.0 \times 10^8 \text{ cm}^2/\text{sec}^2$$
$$v = \sqrt{21.0 \times 10^8 \text{ cm}^2/\text{sec}^2}$$
$$= 4.6 \times 10^4 \text{ cm/sec}$$
$$= 46,000 \text{ cm/sec}$$
$$= \text{a little over } \tfrac{1}{4} \text{ mi/sec}$$

Changes of State

Evaporation as a Cooling Process. Evaporation of a liquid results in a change from the liquid to the vapor (see footnote 5). It is an easily observed fact that evaporation is a cool-

ing process, for a breeze on a hot summer day always feels cool to us if we stand in it while we are perspiring. Kinetic theory gives us an explanation.

The molecules of the liquid, water, for example, are in continuous motion. The temperature of the water is a measure of the average kinetic energy of its molecules. The term *average* presupposes that some of the molecules have less than average and some more than average kinetic energy. Colliding molecules mean a constant transferral of momentum and energy, some losing, some gaining. For evaporation to take place, molecules must escape from the liquid, and to escape they must break through the barrier (called *surface tension*) formed by the surface of the liquid. Surface tension is created by the topmost "layer" of molecules (Fig. 13-7) forming a free surface with no molecules close enough above them to attract them upward, whereas there is a "layer" of molecules with which they are in close contact below them to attract them

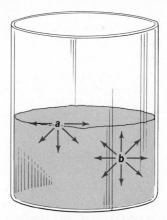

Fig. 13-7. Surface Tension. Attractions by intermolecular forces on a molecule of water at the surface (as at *a*) are greater downward than upward (because there are no molecules of water above it), whereas deeper in the liquid (as at *b*) they are equal. Therefore, molecules approaching the surface must have greater than average kinetic energy to escape.

downward. The downward forces, van der Waals or other intermolecular forces, are therefore greater, and so they hinder the escape of molecules from the surface. Thus the necessity for a greater than average velocity to "crash" the surface tension barrier.

To crash this barrier molecules must have more than average kinetic energy. Only the fastest-moving molecules have enough. When they escape, the slower-moving molecules are left behind, and the average kinetic energy is lowered, hence the temperature is lowered. Therefore, evaporation is a cooling process.

Vapor Pressure. Certain aspects of equilibrium are concerned in a number of processes that can be explained by the kinetic theory. There are two kinds of equilibrium, static and dynamic. When one weighs something on a balance like that shown in Fig. 7-16b, he establishes a static equilibrium between the two pans and their contents. Suppose two boys in an orchard are throwing fallen apples over a fence at one another. If the number of apples going each way is exactly equal, we have a case of dynamic equilibrium. In every case where we have an excess of a solid soluble in a liquid, say more sugar put in a cup of coffee than the coffee can dissolve, there is a state of dynamic equilibrium. As many molecules of sugar are coming out of solution as are going into solution, so that the excess in the bottom of the cup remains the same.

Consider now an open dish of a liquid (Fig. 13-8a). Adding heat increases the average kinetic energy of the molecules so that more have the necessary energy to escape. These escaped molecules form the vapor of the liquid. In any system a few of the escaped molecules are returned to the liquid as they are "bounced" back into the liquid through collision with air molecules. However, most of the escaped molecules do not return and are permanently lost from the liquid.

If the molecules escape into a confined space above the liquid (Fig. 13-8b), as in a well-corked bottle, the density of the escaped molecules in the region between the surface of the liquid and the cork will gradually increase until the saturation point is reached. At this stage the number of molecules escaping equals the number returning to the liquid. A dynamic equilibrium has been reached. The vapor of a liquid exerts a pressure in the manner of any gas. *Its pressure at the equilibrium stage is called the vapor pressure of the liquid;* its value for a given liquid depends only on the temperature. For water vapor at room temperature it is about 24 mm of mercury. There can never be an equilibrium stage in an open system (Fig. 13-8a) because some molecules are always escaping, not only from the liquid but also from the vessel itself.

The Boiling Process. If we heat water in an open system its vapor pressure rises as the rate of evaporation increases until its vapor pressure becomes equal to the surrounding atmospheric pressure, 760 mm on the average at sea level. The temperature of the water at this stage is its boiling point. Before the boiling point is reached, evaporation takes place only from the surface. At the boiling point evaporation takes place *also in growing vapor* bubbles that rise to escape (Fig. 13-9) and break when they reach the surface. Moreover, no liquid can be heated to a temperature higher than its boiling point in an open vessel.[8] More heat than necessary to maintain boiling simply means a greater rate of evaporation because more energy is supplied than is needed to break whatever forces, chiefly van der Waals forces, are holding the molecules in the liquid state.

The temperature at which a liquid in an open container boils depends upon the nature

---

[8]Therefore, turning up the heat under a pot of already boiling potatoes does not make them cook faster.

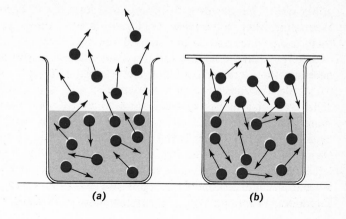

Fig. 13-8. Vapor Pressure (*a*) In an open system some of the vapor escapes from the vessel so that an equilibrium can never be established. (*b*) In a confined system a dynamic equilibrium has been reached; that is, as many molecules return as escape.

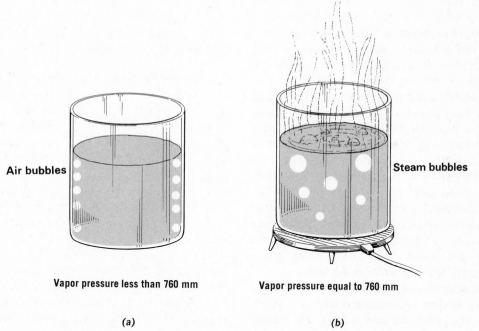

Air bubbles

Steam bubbles

Vapor pressure less than 760 mm

Vapor pressure equal to 760 mm

(a)

(b)

Fig. 13-9. The Boiling Process. (*a*) Below the boiling point air bubbles rise only along, and in contact with, the sides of the vessel. Water evaporates only from the surface. (*b*) At the boiling point steam bubbles rise all through the water. There are no air bubbles because all of the air has been driven out of solution. The steam bubbles get larger as they rise, in part because water is now evaporating from the inside surfaces of them and in part because the pressure of the water becomes less upward.

of the liquid and the atmospheric pressure. At normal atmospheric pressure liquid nitrogen will boil at $-195.8°C$, liquid hydrogen at $-252.7°C$, and liquid helium at $-269.0°C$, only a bit over 4° above absolute zero. Alcohol and ethers (and many other liquids) boil at temperatures well below that for water. We conclude that the forces holding the molecules together in all of these liquids are less than those for water.

Suppose the atmospheric pressure is reduced. In nature atmospheric pressure becomes less and less at higher and higher elevations above sea level because of the decreased density of the atmosphere. At elevations of 12,000 ft and above water boils at temperatures too low to cook certain foods. A "3 minute" egg needs to be cooked 4 or even 5 min, for, as we have seen, one cannot heat any liquid above its boiling point in an open system. In the laboratory, gas pressures can be reduced in a closed system by removing air from an otherwise closed container by means of a vacuum pump. Water can then be made to boil at room temperature. This is because the lowered pressure on the surface of the water is not great enough to keep bubbles of vapor from forming *within* the water itself.

Conversely, increasing the gas pressure on a liquid raises the boiling point; that is, the liquid cannot boil unless the temperature rises above the normal boiling point. This is the situation in a closed system, like that in a pressure cooker or a steam boiler. In an open system the gas pressure can never be greater than that of the surrounding atmosphere, whereas in a closed system it can be as high as the strength of our equipment and our source of heat will allow, perhaps 1000 atm. Here the gas pressure is furnished by the vapor of the liquid itself for it cannot escape. The pressure within the cooker or boiler is independent of the outside atmospheric pressure. The water cannot boil because the pressure

that is exerted on the water surface by the trapped vapor is too great for bubbles of vapor to form within the water. The higher the temperature, the faster the escape of molecules from the surface of the water, but these molecules instantly increase the pressure, which in turn prevents bubbles of vapor forming within the water, and so on.

The Condensation and Freezing Processes.
The change from the gaseous or vapor state to the liquid state is called *condensation*. In the open atmosphere condensation of water vapor takes place when saturated air is cooled, for cold air cannot "hold" as much moisture as warm air. Condensation takes place much more readily if there are very fine particles in the atmosphere to act as centers about which the vapor can condense. Man's attempts at rainmaking are centered about cooling air masses that are nearly at the saturation point and providing condensation points known as nuclei to act as centers of condensation.

When liquids are cooled, as in the freezing process, the average random kinetic energy decreases. If it is decreased sufficiently, intermolecular forces may be able to hold the molecules together in a rigid mass in which the molecular movements are confined to a very tiny region about each molecule. This is the solid state, and the process of bringing it about is called *freezing*.

The molecules of many substances may pass from the solid phase to the gaseous or vapor phase without passing through a liquid phase. This process is called *sublimation*.

Second Law of Thermodynamics

We have seen (Chapter 11) that heat and mechanical energy are interchangeable at a fixed rate of exchange, 4.18 joules/cal. This is the first law of thermodynamics; its extension to include other types of energy transfer is known as the law of conservation of energy. An intensive study of heat engines, such as steam engines and gasoline engines, has produced a second law of thermodynamics: *Heat does not of its own accord flow from cold regions to hot regions.* At first glance this simple statement might not seem to warrant being called a law, but combined with the first law it provides the basic theory of heat engines, including modern steam turbines and rocket motors, of heat pumps, and of refrigeration. It is also useful in understanding many other phenomena, even in dealing with heat energy of the human body.

Nonscientists commonly view science as an enormous collection of fragments of information. Some of them realize that scientists collect, sort, and build these fragments into structures of varying sizes, some of which may be likened to cathedrals, in which the building stones are united to form a harmonious whole of great beauty. One of the greatest of these cathedrals is a towering edifice known as *thermodynamics,* built to express the relationships between the concepts of work, energy, heat and temperature. First there had to be formulated the quantities that have to do with work: force, mass, acceleration, momentum, motion, potential energy, kinetic energy. Heat and temperature gave a great deal of trouble until it was agreed that heat is nothing but the vibratory motion of molecules and that temperature is simply a measure of the intensity of that part of the vibratory motion which is disordered, that is, the translational motion.

Joule announced the mechanical equivalent of heat in 1843, 41.4 million ergs/cal, a value that was remarkably close to our modern value of 41.83 million ergs/cal (4.183 joules/cal). With it came the fact that made the science of thermodynamics necessary: *one calorie of heat cannot be reconverted into 4.183 joules of work.* In other words, the process of turning work into heat is not reversible, whereas other forms of energy can be interconverted either way.

The second law of thermodynamics means that no net mechanical energy can be obtained from a medium by cooling it below the temperature of its surroundings. Any substance at a temperature greater than absolute zero possesses heat. The waters of the ocean therefore contain a great deal of heat. Why can we not use this heat for useful mechanical work? Assume for the moment that someone invented a device that could do just that. If heat energy were extracted from a part of the ocean waters, the temperature would drop; that is, it would be cooled below the temperature of its surroundings. We can do the cooling all right, by one means or another, but only *by expending* more energy than we would obtain. There is thus no *net* energy obtainable by any device. During the 19th century as many people worked as hard trying to develop such a machine as worked on perpetual motion machines. In fact, their machines have been called perpetual motion machines of the second order.

In stating that heat never flows of its own accord from a cold body to a hot one, the second law of thermodynamics implies that it will flow from a hot region to a cold one. This is perfectly obvious to everyone. However, it is not so obvious that it does this spontaneously without our being able to do anything about it. True, we can slow down the flow of heat by insulation of various kinds, including the clothing we wear. But we cannot stop the flow of heat. In running any motor—steam, gasoline, rocket, or electric—considerable heat is dissipated to the surroundings. An automobile, for example, must have a cooling system to carry away the heat produced. This heat energy is wasted, for ultimately it passes off into the atmosphere. Thus, heat energy can never be completely converted into any other type of energy, for in every conversion some heat is transferred from a hotter region to a colder one. Mechanical energy can, however, be completely transformed into heat by way of friction, as in our pile-driver example (p. 147). In fact we might say that friction is related to heat, for the only thing that frictional forces do is to increase molecular motions at the points of contact between two bodies when they are in motion relative to each other.

Degradation of Energy

We have learned that the *random* motions of molecules are heat. If in every transformation of energy some of the energy is converted into heat and dissipated to the surroundings, it follows that some ordered motion has been transformed into random disordered motion. Consider the ordered motions in a pile driver, or of a bullet striking a target, or of the piston in the cylinder of a pump. In them, a part of the order at least is transformed into disorder because a certain amount of heat is dissipated randomly into space. It is apparent to us that all we have to do to produce disorder in our daily lives is to sit and do nothing, whereas it takes work to keep our homes in order. Order is thus an unnatural state in many respects and it takes work to maintain it. In the molecular world the natural tendency is to go from a state of order into a state of disorder. We explain that the natural way for heat to flow is from hotter to cooler bodies, for the hotter a body is, the higher the state of commotion among its molecules. This commotion is passed on from molecule to molecule. Thus, heat is conducted away from its source.

The result is that all processes in nature proceed in the direction of increasing molecular disorder; that is, in all of them some random molecular motion is produced. Thus, other forms of energy are being continuously degraded to heat energy, a portion of which can never be converted back to any other form. Consider the sun and the stars and the dissipation of their heat energies throughout space. The natural conclusion is that in time all matter in the universe will be at a uniform temperature. In such a universe there can be no transfer of heat from one body to another; no life would be possible. Our natural conclusion, as stated above, may not be the correct one; certainly we do not mean to prophesy a "heat death" for the universe as a whole. Our knowledge is nowhere near complete enough to make such a prophecy. At any rate, if such a "death" is to come, it is many billions of years in the future.

Exercises

1. If matter were continuous, could it have structure?
2. State the assumptions of the kinetic theory and cite at least one item of evidence from everyday experience to support each.
3. (a) What is meant by an elastic collision?
   (b) Why *must* we assume that collisions between individual molecules of gases are perfectly elastic?
4. How does kinetic theory explain the fact that gases exert pressure on every surface with which they come in contact?
5. What happens when heat is added to a gas (a) in a closed container and (b) in an open system like our atmosphere? (c) How is the rise in temperature of the gas explained? (d) What happens when a gas is cooled?
6. What distinction can you make between a gas and a vapor?
7. How do you explain the fact that clothes will dry eventually even while frozen?

8. What conclusion is reached from the two proportionalities $PV \propto T$ and $PV \propto \frac{1}{2}mv^2$, where $\frac{1}{2}mv^2$ is taken as the average kinetic energy of gas molecules (derived from the theoretical mechanical model)?

9. According to our kinetic theory what are (a) heat and (b) temperature?

10. What meaning is given to $0°$ on the Kelvin or absolute scale by the kinetic theory?

11. What is meant by the critical temperature of a gas? What gas is most difficult to liquefy? Can you suggest a reason?

12. Helium can be liquefied only at temperatures below $-272°C$ and at 25 atm pressure. What inference can you make about the attractive forces between its molecules?

13. What is meant by the vapor pressure of a liquid? What is the vapor pressure of water at $100°C$?

14. How is the boiling point of a liquid defined?

15. On a mountain top 12,000 ft high it is impossible to cook dried beans in an open container no matter how long you boil them. Why?

16. Why does the use of a pressure cooker reduce the cooking time?

17. Why can you not heat a pan of water on the stove higher than the boiling point?

18. At a temperature a bit above $0°C$, water can be made to freeze while it is boiling. This is done by evacuating the container to a very low pressure and pumping the vapor away as fast as it forms. Explain.

19. Explain why evaporation is a cooling process.

20. Why does water evaporate faster in a warm room than in a cold one?

21. Why do you feel cooler sitting in the breeze from an electric fan than elsewhere on a hot summer day?

22. Why does alcohol in an open dish feel cooler than water in a similar adjacent dish?

23. If you put a very shallow dish of water in a pan of ether and blow air over it by means of an electric fan, the water will freeze. Explain.

24. You have samples of nitrogen, chlorine, fluorine, and oxygen, all at the same temperature.
   (a) Are the molecules in each sample moving with the same average speeds, or are their average speeds different? Explain.
   (b) Do all these samples have the same average molecular kinetic energy?

25. Students commonly ascribe the heating effect of compression of a gas to the increased collision rate between molecules. This violates one of the assumptions of the kinetic theory.
   (a) Which one?
   (b) How could you prove by experiment that the heating effect cannot be produced this way by using two containers of gas on a table, one with a pressure P, the other with a pressure $2P$?

26. By what means does an electric refrigerator produce its low temperature?

27. (a) From what you know of ether, would you say the magnitude of the van der Waals forces operating to hold its molecules together was less or greater than that in water?
   (b) Justify your answer.

28. The meniscus of some liquids, for example, water, in a narrow glass tube is concave, and in others, for example, mercury, it is convex. Explain both cases.

29. On a sweltering summer day you decide to try to keep cool by closing the doors and windows of your kitchen and leaving the refrigerator door open. Would this action be effective in reducing the average temperature in your kitchen, assuming, of course, that you are not using your stove? Explain why or why not.

30. Why can heat energy not be completely converted to mechanical energy?

31. The average speed of a molecule of hydrogen is close to 1.6 km/sec at room temperature. What is the average speed of an oxygen molecule, 16 times as heavy, at the same temperature?

32. The mass of a nitrogen atom is $\frac{14}{16}$ that of an oxygen atom. A sample of oxygen is at a temperature of 546°K. At what temperature must a sample of nitrogen be for the average kinetic energy of the molecules of both gases to be the same?

33. A volume, V, of hydrogen is compressed to a volume, $V/2$, while the temperature is held constant. How is the average speed of the hydrogen molecules affected?

34. (a) At very high pressures gases depart considerably from the ideal gas law. Why?
    (b) They do not make such a departure at very high temperatures. Why not?
    (c) How about very low temperature? Explain.

35. In a mixture of gases would you expect the average kinetic energies of the different kinds of molecules to be the same? Why, or why not? Would you expect the average velocities of all the gases to be the same? Why or why not?

36. (a) If the absolute temperature of a gas is doubled, the pressure remaining constant, what will happen to the average velocity of its molecules?
    (b) What would happen if the pressure were also doubled?

37. What evidence do we have to justify the statement that the molecules of a gas are eternally in random motion?

38. What are van der Waals forces? What role do they play in the evaporation of a liquid?

39. The energy conserved by the first law of thermodynamics is rendered increasingly unavailable by the second law. The entropy (disorder) in all nonliving systems steadily increases, moving in the direction of heat death, at which time the last temperature difference will disappear. Explain.

The Nature of Matter

Matter is the world around us—everything that we see, feel, and touch. It may have seemed thoroughly familiar to you when you began this course, but perhaps by now you are not so sure. Later you may become less sure, enough so that you can agree that the further scientists probe, the less obvious the answers become. Both early man and modern man have investigated matter; the former did so in order to use matter, the latter to understand it. Even though we have acquired an enormous knowledge of matter, fundamental mysteries remain. The likelihood is that some will always remain.

In the preceding chapter we have seen that all matter, whether gaseous, liquid, or solid, consists of enormous numbers of extremely small particles that for the time being we called molecules. So far our attention has been focused only on the general characteristics of the molecules. We paid particular attention to the gaseous state of matter because in this state the molecules are separated by comparatively

> The public was astonished to see a chemistry that sought neither philosopher's stone nor the art of prolonging life beyond the limits of nature, an astronomy that did not predict the future, a medicine independent of the phases of the moon.
> OLANS ROEMER
> (1676)

223

large distances so that the physical behavior of a single molecule is largely independent of the other molecules. This is, of course, not the case in liquids and solids, and is less true in solids than in liquids. We have seen that the degree of independence of the molecules is a function of the temperature, which in turn is a measure of the average kinetic energy of the molecules. We have also seen that the phenomena of melting and boiling involve changes in the spatial arrangements of the molecules with respect to one another without changing the composition of the individual molecules. We confined the discussions to the physical behavior of molecules under certain specified conditions.

In a general way we already know that molecules consist of smaller units called atoms. The word *atom* has appeared in our newspapers and many of our magazines almost every day during the last 25 years. Unfortunately the word has been used in a variety of ways, some correct and some incorrect, so that many people have confused concepts of its meaning. This should not surprise us, for the atom itself is so small as to defy the imagination. It would take more than a million of them, in a row, to match the thickness of this page. In the following chapters we shall attempt to clarify mistaken concepts, to learn something of the evidence for the existence of atoms, something of their physical characteristics, and something about the ways they combine to form molecules.

We have learned that Democritus (ca. 400 B.C.) advanced the discrete particle concept of matter, and gave us the word *atom* as the name of that particle. Aristotle rejected this view because it did not fit in with some of his other concepts. The atoms of Democritus were eternal, all in constant motion, and all alike in composition but different in size, shape, and position with respect to one another.

Alchemy

The first conscious attempts to change the composition of matter were made by the alchemists, probably about the beginning of the Christian era. Their beliefs that such changes could be made arose from the views of Pythagoras and Empedocles. Pythagoras—and, later, Aristotle—advanced the concept of four elements—earth (a solid), water (a liquid), air (a gas), and fire (an element more intangible than a gas)—as the constituents of all matter. Empedocles believed that by combining two or more of these elements in various proportions he could explain all of the endless kinds of substances known to man.

From the views of Empedocles came the conviction that some forms of matter could be turned into other forms by altering the proportions of these four elements. Thus arose the science of alchemy, a science that was in the beginning no different from chemistry. Alchemy seems to have originated among the Greeks in Alexandria. From there it spread into every part of the civilized world. Its purposes seem to have been twofold, one scientific—an investigation into the nature of matter—and one practical—to supply cheap imitations of expensive materials such as jewelry and fine dyes. During the Middle Ages and continuing into the Renaissance, alchemy consisted in large part of a search for the "philosopher's stone," an elixir or quintessence (a fifth element) that was supposed to be capable of turning the baser metals into gold, and of curing all human ills, thus imparting everlasting life. It was supposed to be the stuff of which the heavenly bodies were made.

The practice of alchemy persisted into the early 1700's—and even later by charlatans. Although alchemy had started off as a legitimate investigation into the properties of matter, and had been continued in part as such by a few of the alchemists for nearly 2000 years, it had contributed comparatively little to the understanding of matter. Nevertheless, what it had to contribute was important, for it advanced the science of chemistry by the better part of a century. Among its contributions were the development and refinement of many experimental techniques, several new elements (phosphorus, antimony, bismuth, zinc), several acids, alcohol, and a large number of salts.

The paucity of these contributions, considering the length of time and the great numbers of practitioners involved, is unquestionably due to the falseness of the basic underlying assumptions. Matter does not consist of four material elements plus a fifth mysterious, imponderable one. Thus, the alchemists' conceptual scheme was not fruitful; it could lead only to a dead end. This acceptance of, and adherence to, a wrong hypothesis acted as a stiffling influence on further development of their science. Not until this wrong hypothesis was discarded was further progress into the understanding of the nature of matter possible.

The First Chemist

The transition from the old alchemical view to that of modern chemistry was begun (but not completed) by Robert Boyle. Boyle, an older contemporary of Newton, was the first truly great chemist. He is better known for some of his work in physics, notably for the law that bears his name (p. 196).

Boyle started out as an alchemist, and he never did rid himself of the belief that the baser metals could be turned into gold. Nevertheless he soon rejected the Aristotelian concept of four elements, and eventually arrived at a definition of an element that is still usable, even if not in accord with modern

knowledge of the nuclei of atoms. His definition, the first modern one, was that *elements are simple bodies of matter that cannot be resolved into other bodies of matter and of which all other bodies of matter are composed.* The trouble with this definition is that it is not operational, for Boyle had no way of knowing which substances satisfied his definition and which did not. To be operational a definition of an element should describe some operation for detecting the element. Boyle recognized the difficulty but there was little he could do about it at the time. Boyle's definition of an element dealt alchemy a death blow, not instantaneous but nevertheless eventually fatal.

It was not until about 100 years later that Lavoisier (ca. 1776), the great Frenchman who has been called the father of modern chemistry, defined an element as *any substance not known to be decomposable.* This definition caused the list of elements to be revised from time to time as new knowledge was obtained. Nevertheless, within a century after Lavoisier the list became much the same as it is today. Today we substitute "that cannot be by chemical means" for Lavoisier's "not known to be" because of a far greater confidence in our modern operations.

Boyle was one of that group of illustrious men responsible for the 17th century being called the century of genius. Others were Kepler, Galileo, Huygens, Newton, Pascal, Descartes, and Leibnitz. These men helped to emancipate natural science from philosophy; they did not believe that a phenomenon could necessarily be explained philosophically just because it could be expressed quantitatively in mathematical terms. By not believing that it could, they became free to accept facts as facts even if they could not be incorporated into a general scheme of knowledge. They came to regard the acquisition of knowledge as an end in itself. It is not to be supposed that all of these men were equally free from the symbol-seeking mysticism that had pervaded Western Europe for centuries. Yet after Kepler the tendency to formulate physical laws first and to look for the symbolism afterward became more and more dominant until, by the late 18th century, we see little or no tendency for philosophical speculation to precede factual analysis.

The Properties of Matter

The properties of matter are conveniently divided into two categories, physical and chemical. In general, the physical properties are those that we can detect with our senses in one way or another. They are color, luster, smell, taste, feel, shape of the component particles, hardness, density, cleavage or fracture (how a specimen breaks), melting point, boiling point, and so on. Chemical properties are those that describe the capacity of a substance for reacting with another substance. They cannot be determined by a physical examination of a substance, nor always by means of a simple experiment. The distinction between physical or chemical properties is not always clear-cut. For example, is the sour taste of a lemon a physical or a chemical property? Or is it due to a characteristic of our taste buds?

Associated with physical and chemical properties are the terms *physical change* and *chemical change*. A change from a liquid to a solid or a gas and a change in shape due to a deforming force of some kind are physical changes. Chemical change involves chemical reaction, during which elements or compounds combine to form other compounds with totally different sets of physical properties, or the original compounds are broken up into elements or other compounds. The substances that react are called the *reactants* and those produced are called the *products*. The burning of any substance is the most obvious example

of chemical reaction. The transformation of the food we eat and the water we drink to the flesh, blood, and bone of our body is another.

To understand better that chemical changes involve chemical reactions, let us consider that most familiar of all compounds—water. Its formula, H_2O, is known to all of us and means that two hydrogen atoms are bound to one oxygen atom to form one molecule of water. We also know that hydrogen and oxygen are gases that have no physical or chemical resemblances to water. Hydrogen will burn in oxygen if it is heated to a relatively high temperature. This burning is a chemical reaction in which water is the product.

The Classification of Matter

Most matter with which we are in everyday contact is complex, far more complex than most of us realize. The air we breathe is a mixture of at least five gases, the water we drink is pure only in the health sense, the food we eat is unbelievably complex. Steel, largely composed of iron, is different from iron because of the various other substances that have been added during its manufacture to give it special qualities. Gasoline and milk are both mixtures of up to a dozen different substances. Pure substances are almost nonexistent in nature. Even artificially purified ones are rare; familiar examples are distilled water, cane sugar, and the copper used in electric wires. It is not surprising that chemistry as a true science remained so long in the embryonic state.

The concept of a pure substance is an important one. Pure substances exhibit constant composition; that is, they are so homogeneous that any small part of each has the same composition as does every other part, *even down to molecular size*. Some mixtures exhibit constant composition down to particles of microscopic size but fail when the division is carried down to particles of molecular size. Such homogeneous mixtures are called solutions. Air is a mixture of several gases in mutual solution with one another; gasoline is a mixture of about a dozen liquids in mutual solution with one another; brass is a solution of copper and zinc; brine is a solution of salt (a solid) in water (a liquid); and soda pop is a solution of a gas (CO_2) in water. None of these solutions can be called pure substances because their compositions are not constant; each has a wide range of possible compositions. Examples of heterogeneous mixtures are rocks,[1] soil, whole milk, blood, and smoke.

Pure substances are divided into elements (if they cannot be further subdivided[2]) and compounds (if they can be further subdivided). Sugar, for example, is a compound, for it can be separated into carbon and water if it is heated to a high enough temperature. Carbon cannot be further subdivided and so it is an element. By the process of electrolysis (p. 300) the water can be broken down into hydrogen and oxygen, and so it is a compound. Hydrogen and oxygen cannot be further subdivided; they are elements.

We may summarize the classification of the various kinds of matter as follows:

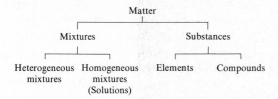

The distinction between compounds and heterogeneous mixtures is easy because simple mechanical processes can be used to separate a mixture into its components. The component

particles may be separated by sifting if they differ consistently in size or shape; by solution if only one component is soluble, as in a mixture of sand and sugar; by a magnet if only one component is attracted by a magnet; by flotation if the densities of the components are appreciably different; by melting if the melting points are far enough apart; and so on. Other methods must be used for those homogeneous mixtures that we call solutions. Most common are evaporation of the solvent if one of the components is a solid, distillation if two or more liquids are present, boiling in the case of a gas dissolved in a liquid, taking advantage of the difference in rate of diffusion in cases of gases dissolved in gases, or using the differences of temperature and pressure at which gases may be liquefied. None of these methods can effect separation of the elements that make up a compound. Chemical changes must take place in order to do that.

The Beginnings of Quantitative Chemistry

Some have called Robert Boyle the father of chemistry. Certainly he was the first to break away from the four-element concept[3] of Pythagoras and Empedocles, which Aristotle supported. He was the first to base his concepts of the fundamental nature of matter on the experimental rather than on the metaphysical. However, he never became completely emancipated from the thinking of the alchemist, and so he is another example of the observation that a man's mental processes are handicapped

---

[1] Rocks containing only one mineral, and therefore homogeneous, exist in small pieces, but rocks in the mass, like those found in nature, are always heterogeneous to some degree. Most are completely so.

[2] In this chapter whenever we say that a substance cannot be further subdivided we always mean by chemical means.

[3] A Belgian, van Helmont (ca. 1600), coined the word *gas,* which he used to replace "air." He also reduced the four elements to one. This conclusion was based on an "experiment" with a willow tree. He weighed the tree and planted it in a weighed amount of soil in a tub. For five years he carefully watered it. At the end of that time he carefully separated the tree from the soil and weighed both again. The soil weighed only 2 oz less, but the tree had gained 164 lb—just by adding water alone. His one element was therefore water.

by the mental climate of the time in which he lives.

The great Newton appears to have spent more time on alchemy and chemistry than he did on the researches for which he will forever be remembered. Newton[4] wrote no book concerning his chemical researches, so the record of his work is incomplete. It is known, however, that he accepted the atomistic view of Democritus and that he rejected the four-element concept. It is also clear that he showed greater insight into the nature of matter than did other chemists of the time (with the possible exception of Boyle). He made no striking discoveries in chemistry, however.

Antoine Lavoisier[5] more fully deserves to be called the father of modern chemistry, for almost singlehandedly he solved the problems of the composition of air and the nature of combustion. He also changed chemistry from a qualitative science to a quantitative science. Progress in the study of nature is most rapid when quantitative methods are used. The quantitative work of Galileo led directly to Newton's laws of motion and gravitation. Similarly, the quantitative work of Lavoisier led to the various laws discussed in the next chapter, and to the atomic theory upon which much of modern chemistry is based.

[4] The influence of Newton in the field of science can scarcely be overestimated; prior to 1800 over 70 books in six languages were printed about the *Principia*. It was his explanation of the property of weight of matter that mattered most to the chemists 100 years after the publication of the *Principia*.

[5] Antoine Lavoisier (1743–1794), son of a wealthy lawyer, carried on his scientific work as an avocation. The scope of his interests in both fundamental and applied science staggers the imagination. He did his work in chemistry at the same time that he worked for the local and national governments, often combining his vocation and his avocation to the advantage of France. He often used his own money to advance the public interests. Nevertheless he was beheaded in 1794 (about 100 years after the death of Boyle), during the excesses of the French Revolution, because he had once been a collector of the royal taxes. An appeal for clemency was denied with the comment, "The Republic has no need for savants."

The Phlogiston Theory

In the 100 years between Boyle and Lavoisier probably the most important development was the formulation of the phlogiston theory (the principle of fire) by Stahl of Germany from ideas advanced by Beccher. Man's interest in the process of burning probably dates back to his discovery of fire, yet his failure to understand it persisted until near the end of the 18th century. This failure undoubtedly presented an insurmountable obstacle to real progress in chemistry, for no concept of what a chemical reaction consisted of could prevail unless it explained the process of burning. The phlogiston theory was a first step in this direction.

The formation of ashes from the burning of wood and paper, the soft powders that resulted when metals were long heated to high temperatures in air, the fact that these powders became metals again when heated with charcoal, and other similar phenomena could not be imagined by Stahl and Beccher to take place without the addition or subtraction of some substance. Therefore they postulated the existence of an invisible substance that all combustible substances possessed. They named it *phlogiston*, supposing it to be an element. Their theory was very simple: during combustion phlogiston escapes; air must be present to absorb phlogiston, but its capacity to absorb phlogiston is limited.

This theory dominated the world of chemistry for about 50 years, although no one ever obtained any experimental or observational evidence of phlogiston's physical properties. Like caloric, it came to be known as an *imponderable*, that is, a substance whose physical properties are incapable of being detected by man's senses, and that can have apparently contradictory properties at the same time. Thus, on some occasions it exhibited weight, on others it appeared to be weightless, and on still others it was supposed to have negative weight. Looking backward we may wonder how such a concept could have survived among intelligent men. We must not forget the mental climate of the time; the significance of quantitative measurements had not been impressed upon the chemists, although the work of Galileo and Newton had impressed it upon the physicists. Moreover, the phlogiston theory explained many phenomena that had long gone without explanation. It was better than no theory of combustion, and supports the observation that truth is more likely to come out of error than it is out of a void.

The phlogiston theory could explain why most combustibles lose weight on burning (they lose phlogiston); why a flame goes out in an enclosed space (the air becomes saturated with phlogiston); why charcoal leaves so little residue on burning (it is nearly pure phlogiston); why a mouse dies in an enclosed space (the mouse saturates the air with phlogiston from his lungs); why some calxes (metallic oxides) turn to metals when heated with charcoal (phlogiston from charcoal is restored to calx).

The theory foundered eventually over the changes in weight that occur when certain metals are heated or burned in air to form calxes. The calx-forming process is called *calcination*. It differs from combustion in that no gas is given off in the process as it is in combustion. The modern term for calx is *oxide*. The phlogistonists believed that the calx was the element, and the metal the compound, a compound of calx and phlogiston. This belief was essential to the theory, for when a metal burned, the calx was observed to form. Consider magnesium, a metal not known at the time. It will burn with an intensely white light, forming the white powder magnesium oxide (a calx). The disconcerting thing to a would-be phlogistonist is that the magnesium calx weighs more than the metal. But how can an element (calx) weigh more than one of its

compounds? The theory had to explain such observations if it was to survive, and so a new postulate was put forth, as follows: *Phlogiston that escapes from metals has negative weight, whereas that which escapes in normal combustion has positive weight.*

The need to add a special postulate such as this to a theory to explain one lone troublesome fact is usually an indication that the theory is not going to be fruitful. This is particularly true if the postulate strains the credulity of some of its supporters.

Lavoisier vs. the Phlogiston Theory

Lavoisier's great intellect would not allow him to accept the phlogiston theory. He knew that condemnation of it would do no good; he had to have a better theory to replace it. He quickly realized that the best attack was by means of weighing both the reactants and the products of chemical reactions. To this end he had more accurate balances made than had ever been made before. His best could detect changes in weight as small as 0.0005 g, roughly $\frac{1}{100}$ the weight of a drop of water. Eventually Lavoisier was able to prove that the products of combustion always weighed more than what was burned, but for years he was unable to identify the substance that caused the added weight.

In his attempts to identify the substance Lavoisier performed a series of notable experiments with tin (Fig. 14-1). Tin is converted to a white powder (a calx) when sufficiently heated. His simplest experiment of the series consisted of heating a weighed quantity of tin in the open air for a time and then reweighing it. He found that the tin gained weight, thus verifying the results obtained by others. This result was not truly quantitative, however. To make it quantitative he placed a quantity of tin in a flask, tightly sealed it, and then weighed it. He then heated it strongly until

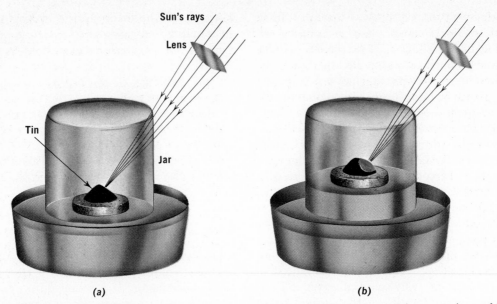

Fig. 14-1. Lavoisier's Experiment with Tin. The tin, heated by focusing the rays of the sun on it, combined with oxygen in the bell jar, thus decreasing the air pressure in the jar. As a result water rose inside the jar until the air pressure outside and inside were equal. This proved that something from the air combined with tin.

no more tin changed to calx. He weighed the still sealed flask again, and found no change. Then he carefully removed the seal, and observed that air rushed in. Using the same seal he now sealed the flask again and once more weighed it. He found that the flask had increased in weight. He concluded that the increase was due to the weight of the air that had rushed in when he first broke the seal, and was equal to the weight of air used to form the calx. As only about 20% of the air could be made to combine with tin, he knew that air was a mixture of gases. Lavoisier had established that some "atmospheric principle" had been removed from the atmosphere during combustion and calcination but he had not yet identified the "principle."

Meanwhile Joseph Priestley of England had been experimenting with various kinds of "airs," the name then used for gases. Investigation of "airs" was begun by van Helmont and Boyle, but there was little understanding of them until the time of Lavoisier.[6] Priestley had discovered a new gas by strongly heating the red calx of mercury (mercuric oxide) and collecting the released gas under water (Fig. 14-2). He found that it supported combustion far better than ordinary air. He thought it did so because it was completely devoid of phlogiston and thus could absorb more phlogiston; he therefore named it "dephlogisticated air."

[6] Stephan Hales of England had investigated hydrogen, carbon monoxide, carbon dioxide, marsh gas, sulfur dioxide, and other gases but had concluded that they were all air that had been contaminated. He prepared oxygen in 1729. Borch had prepared it as early as 1678. Van Helmont had discovered carbon dioxide in 1640. All these observations and discoveries were forgotten; they had to be made over again and their significances reinterpreted. Air was still believed to be the only gaseous element up to and beyond the time that Joseph Black discovered what he called "fixed air," which we now call carbon dioxide.

He found, also, that a mouse lived in it in an enclosed space longer than in ordinary air.

Lavoisier, on hearing of the properties of the new air, immediately suspected that it was the atmospheric principle that he was searching for. Hence he performed his own quantitative experiments—similar to those that used tin— and proved that Priestley's dephlogisticated air was the missing component of air after his calx of tin was formed. Lavoisier named it *oxygen*. He then defined the burning process as a chemical reaction in which various kinds of matter combined with oxygen.

Priestley never accepted Lavoisier's oxidation theory of combustion, preferring to continue his belief in phlogiston. His resistance to change of ingrained ideas is typical of the human mind and its inability to look at facts unprejudiced by prior opinion. Even great thinkers are troubled to some extent by this fault.

For those students who find the preceding description of Lavoisier's conclusions rather arbitrary and intellectually unsatisfying, the following material will attempt to show how carefully a true scientist must work when he wants to investigate the validity of an accepted theory, or replace a questionable theory with a better one.

Lavoisier made the truly quantitative experiments that spelled doom for the phlogiston theory. Using a setup such as that in Fig. 14-3, he heated 4 oz of mercury to near the boiling point with 50 in.³ of air in a glass retort for 12 days. As the red calx was formed, the vol-

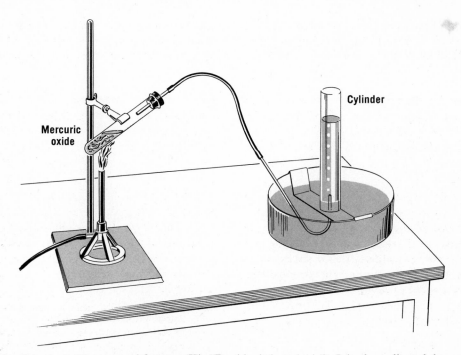

Fig. 14-2. Priestley's Discovery of Oxygen (His "Dephlogisticated Air"). Priestley collected the gas under water. Here the cylinder is first completely filled with water and inverted in the pan of water. As the gas evolves, water is displaced in the cylinder. Note that this was not a quantitative experiment as were those of Lavoisier.

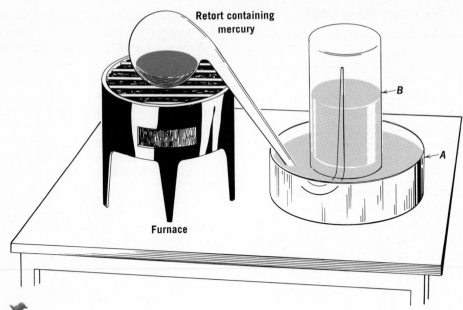

Fig. 14-3. Lavoisier's 12-Day Experiment. Mercury was heated in contact with 50 in³ of air. Part of the air combined with the mercury to form a calx. At the start the water level was at *A;* after heating it was at *B*. The volume of air above the water was reduced to 42 in³.

ume of air became less and less, allowing the water to rise in the cylinder. When the water ceased to rise, presumably because no more calx was forming, the heating was stopped. The remaining mercury and the calx were weighed and compared with the weight of the mercury originally put in the retort. The increase was 3.5 grains. (There are about 156 grains in a gram.) Next he determined the loss in weight of the air in his apparatus. He found it to be also 3.5 grains. The loss of weight of the air equaled the increase of weight due to the formation of calx; thus, there was no loss of mass during the experiment. He now tested the remaining "air" to see if it would support combustion or sustain life. The answer was *no* in both cases.

His case was not yet proved. He now strongly heated the calx that had been formed until it had all been reduced to metallic mercury. He collected the "air" given off and found it to weigh 3.5 grains. Thus, he recovered the original "air" loss—and the original quan-

tity of mercury. Again the total mass had remained constant. He now tested this recovered "air" and found that it supported combustion and sustained life much more effectively than ordinary air. Thus Priestley's new "air" was proved to be the atmospheric principle responsible for combustion, calcination, and respiration. Lavoisier gave it the name *oxygen* (meaning acid former).[7]

In this way it was finally proved by Lavoisier that a metal plus oxygen gave rise to an oxide (calx), and that an oxide heated in the presence of charcoal[8] gave a metal plus oxygen (which combined with the charcoal to form carbon monoxide or carbon dioxide). He continued his experiments and they eventually led him to the conclusion that combustion and respiration were essentially alike, the difference being essentially in their rates.

[7] Actually a misnomer, for some acids (HCl, for example) contain no oxygen.
[8] The charcoal is not needed in all cases, not in the case of mercuric oxide, for example.

Law of Conservation of Mass

Lavoisier's genius lay not only in his ability to plan and execute experiments, but also in his ability to grasp the all-important significance of them. Here we have two men, Priestley and Lavoisier, performing the same experiment but drawing different conclusions. Those of Priestley led only to a dead end, while those of Lavoisier led (to quote Galileo) to "wonderful new knowledge." Fortified by the conclusions from his experiment, Lavoisier went on to experiment with other reactions, always carefully weighing the reactants and the products. By the unimpeachable evidence of the balance he showed that the total weight of all the reaction products is equal to the total weight of all the reactants from which the reaction products were formed (within the limits of experimental error).

Newton's success in mechanics was based on his assumption that mass remained constant, and he proved that weight, although a different conception than mass, was always proportional to mass. Here we have Lavoisier showing *there is no loss of mass during chemical change*. The principle, now firmly established insofar as normal chemical reactions are concerned, is called the *law of conservation of mass*. This is one of the great fundamental laws of nature. It is the bulwark of every analytical chemist, who, it may be said, is testing it almost every day in chemical laboratories all over the world.

Exercises

1. Distinguish between physical change and chemical change by citing the differences between the reactants and the product when sodium and chlorine unite to form sodium chloride (common table salt).

2. Is the distinction between chemical and physical properties always clear-cut? Example?

3. Why did the alchemists accomplish so little?

4. (a) What was phlogiston supposed to be? (b) What was a calx supposed to be?

5. Explain each of the following by means of the phlogiston theory:
   (a) Wood burns.
   (b) A candle goes out when confined to an enclosed space.
   (c) Charcoal leaves little residue when burned.
   (d) A mouse dies in an enclosed space.
   (e) Metals form calxes when heated in air.
   (f) Metals gain weight when heated in air.
   (g) Wood, paper, and the like lose weight on burning.

6. What were the fatal flaws in the phlogiston theory?

7. How did Boyle's definition of an element differ (a) from Lavoisier's and (b) from that of the chemists of about 1900?

8. What is the difference (a) between a pure substance and a mixture and (b) between an element and a compound?

9. Describe the essentials of an experiment that provides evidence for the oxygen theory of combustion.

10. How did Lavoisier establish the law of conservation of mass?

11. What is the essential difference between combustion and respiration?

Basic Laws and Theories of Chemistry

Lavoisier's success in using the balance to settle the combustion controversy led others to its use, so that by 1800 the science of chemistry was well on its way to being put on a quantitative basis. Just as Galileo, Newton, and others had been able to establish their laws—and later, their theories—by experiments in which quantitative measurements played the leading role, so the chemists were able to establish the laws of chemical change—and later, their theories—by means of the balance and the measuring glass. A qualitative chemical theory based on little more than philosophical speculation either had to meet the challenge of these measuring tools or face rejection. From Lavoisier's time on, the chemists had to do what the physicists had been doing for 100 years; they had, as Newton stated, ". . . first to inquire diligently into the properties of things, and of establishing these properties by experiment, and then to proceed more slowly to hypotheses for the explanation of them."

> Want of time prevents me from saying anything at present respecting other points on which we differ. Those which are purely speculative will long afford room for discussion. Respecting a matter of fact, which can easily come under the test of experiment, we cannot long be at variance.
>
> A FELLOW SCIENTIST,
> in a Letter to Dalton
> (1804)

The Berthollet–Proust Controversy

The second famous controversy that the balance was called on to settle was one centered about two French chemists, Claude Berthollet (1748–1822) and Joseph Proust (1754–1826). About 1800 Proust announced that when elements combine to form compounds they do so in a fixed proportion by weight. About the same time Berthollet announced that elements combine to form compounds in ratios that are variable. To point up the controversy let us consider the case of water. Water is a simple compound that can easily be broken down into hydrogen and oxygen by electrolysis (Chapter 18). Careful weighings of the two gases show that the oxygen in any sample always weighs 8 times as much as the hydrogen. It matters not where the water comes from, the ratio is always 8:1, never 7:1 or 9:1 or any other ratio. Did this constancy of composition hold for other compounds?

When Berthollet heated copper and tin in air (in separate experiments) he got what seemed to him to be a continuous series of "compounds" of varying composition. Other evidence cited by Berthollet included solutions, alloys, and glasses—which are unquestionably variable in composition, but which today can easily be shown not to be true compounds. This was stated by Proust at the time. Berthollet cited many other examples, but Proust was able to show that in most of them Berthollet had been analyzing impure compounds.

Law of Definite Proportions

The refutation of the copper and the tin oxides proved a very different matter, but by a brilliant series of analyses of metallic oxides (and sulfides) Proust was able to prove that some metals form two oxides, or two sulfides, each with a definite composition. Berthollet's continuous series of copper oxides turned out to be mixtures in varying proportions of two of these oxides. Without a good balance Proust could never have won the controversy, could never have established the law of definite proportions (sometimes called the law of constant composition): *When two pure substances combine to form a given compound, they do so in a definite proportion by weight* (Fig. 15-1). From this we derive a present definition of a compound: A *compound* is a substance formed

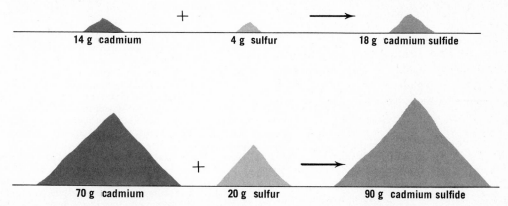

14 g cadmium   +   4 g sulfur   →   18 g cadmium sulfide

70 g cadmium   +   20 g sulfur   →   90 g cadmium sulfide

Fig. 15-1. Law of Definite Proportions. No matter how much cadmium sulfide we make, the proportion of cadmium to sulfur is always 7 to 2 by weight.

by the combination of two or more elements in definite proportions by weight.

Law of Multiple Proportions

As Proust demonstrated, some elements combine to form more than one compound. For example, carbon and oxygen combine to form either carbon monoxide (CO) or carbon dioxide (CO_2). Berthollet's doubt of the validity of the law of definite proportions arose because he failed to recognize the fact that when either tin or copper is heated in the open air for an insufficient length of time or in an enclosed vessel with insufficient air, two oxides are formed. Nitrogen will combine with oxygen under certain conditions to form at least five different compounds (Table 15-1). The law of definite proportions applies to each of the compounds mentioned above, but it leaves some things unexplained. For example, consider carbon monoxide and carbon dioxide. Let us take a fixed weight of carbon, say 12 g. Experiment shows that 16 g of oxygen will combine with the carbon to form the monoxide, whereas 32 g of oxygen are needed to convert the 12 g of carbon entirely to the dioxide. The weight ratio of oxygen in the monoxide to oxygen in the dioxide is 1:2.

Consider another example, the two oxides of copper, one red, the other black. Suppose we use a fixed weight of 16 g of oxygen. We set up an experiment that allows the 16 g of oxygen to unite with copper to form the black oxide, CuO.[1] The weight of copper needed is 63.5 g. We now set up another experiment in which the same fixed weight of oxygen is allowed to unite with copper to form the red oxide, Cu_2O. We find the weight of copper used is 127 g. This is exactly[2] twice that needed

to form the black oxide; the weight ratio of the copper in the black oxide to that in the red oxide is 1:2.

As another example we can take the oxides of nitrogen listed in Table 15-1. If we analyzed each, we would find that the weights of oxygen combined with 100 g of nitrogen (this is the fixed weight) to form each of the five compounds, would be 57 g, 114 g, 171 g, 228 g, and 286 g, respectively. Now if we divide each of these amounts by the *smallest* weight of oxygen (that is, by 57), we get simple ratios between the weights of oxygen (1:1, 1:2, 1:3, 1:4, and 1:5) present in these oxides of nitrogen.[3]

From the above experimental facts we can deduce the law of multiple proportions (Fig. 15-2): *If two elements combine to form two (or more) different compounds, then a simple ratio must exist between the two weights of one element that can combine with a fixed weight of the other.*

This law was established by John Dalton at about the same time as the law of definite proportions, which Dalton had been among the first to accept for it fitted in perfectly with some other ideas of his.

To the uninitiated the above two laws may seem to be only of passing importance. Actually they are basic to the development of the

---

[1] Chemical symbols are explained on p. 256.

[2] Here, *exactly* means "within the limits of experimental error."

[3] We used approximate weights so that the arithmetic would be easy. In an actual analysis the oxides might first have to be purified, weighed, decomposed, purified, and weighed again. At every step errors can creep in, owing to faulty techniques, imperfect equipment, and so on, all of which will cause more or less discrepancy between the final result as calculated from experimental data and the expected results as deduced from theory. These discrepancies in Dalton's time were understandably greater than those of today. How great can the above discrepancy be before it may be said that the experimental data invalidate the law? To help him make this decision the scientist learns to estimate the limits of error for each particular experiment. How he does this need not concern us here. Suffice it to say that absolute accuracy is experimentally unobtainable, so that this problem is always with the experimental scientist.

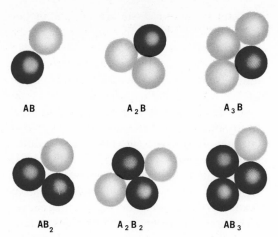

Fig. 15-2. Atomic Interpretation of the Law of Multiple Proportions. Two elements, A and B, can combine chemically to form several compounds, AB, A_2B, A_3B, and so on. The atomic ratios are 1:1, 2:1, 3:1, and so on.

science of chemistry and are fundamental clues to the existence of atoms. The law of definite proportions is of especially great importance to applied chemistry in industry and to all research laboratories, for it allows the use of just the right quantities of materials without waste in the synthesis of any compound. Or, if we speak of analysis instead of synthesis, we can say that the law of definite proportions is the foundation stone of all chemical analysis.

Dalton's Atomic Theory

We have already learned (p. 202) that the concept of matter as consisting of discrete particles called atoms was first expounded by Democritus. Aristotle disagreed with him, and because of his great influence, the concept lay dormant for many centuries. It was revived after the Renaissance when Galileo, Boyle, and Newton regarded it with favor, and the latter two used it in some of their chemical and physical speculations. They had no evidence

for the existence of atoms, but both Boyle and Newton saw that the gaseous state was most easily explained by the particulate (discrete particle) concept. It should be remembered that the formulation of the kinetic molecular theory of gases came nearly 50 years *after* Dalton put forth his atomic theory. In the 100 years between Boyle and Lavoisier the concept had no experimental verification. It began to come into its own when Lavoisier's law of conservation of mass encouraged the idea of atoms as the basic building blocks from which molecules of compounds are made.

John Dalton (1766–1844) was an elementary school teacher who was largely self-taught. He began his teaching career at the age of 12. He had no formal training in either chemistry or physics. He became interested in meteorology, which led him into a study of atmospheric and other gases. His attempts to explain the homogeneity of the atmosphere led him into thinking that the properties of gases are best explained by a theory of atoms. From the fact that under suitable conditions of temperature and pressure gases can be converted first to liquids and then to solids, it follows that they, too, should be composed of atoms. Dalton was probably the first to associate a theoretical atomic concept with the law of definite proportions. He saw that the law had meaning only if each element consisted of discrete particles, all of which had the same weight.[4] For example, if some oxygen atoms had one weight and others some other weight, how could you explain that the weight ratio of oxygen to hydrogen in a water molecule was always 8:1, no matter what the source of the water or how many samples you analyzed? Or how could it happen that in the five oxides of nitrogen the weight ratios should be as shown in Table

[4] Actually, wherever the term *weight* is used in the following discussion, we mean mass. Dalton used the term weight, and chemists to this day have commonly followed him.

15-1? This table shows that if 14 g of nitrogen (column 3) is combined with oxygen to form each of the five compounds, the weight of the oxygen used is always some multiple of 8. *Let us use the term packet for the smallest unit of nitrogen or oxygen that can exist.* Then, if we assign a relative weight of 14 to each packet of nitrogen and a relative weight of 16 to each packet of oxygen, we have, for compound A, two packets of nitrogen to one of oxygen; for B, one of nitrogen to one of oxygen; for C, two of nitrogen to three of oxygen; for D, one of nitrogen to two of oxygen; and for E, two of nitrogen to five of oxygen.

Note how the law of multiple proportions is involved here, a law that did much to establish—and cries mightily for—a theory of atoms. Taking 100 g as our fixed weight of nitrogen, then 57 g of oxygen will unite with 100 g of N to form 157 g of N_2O. The ratio 100:57 is the same as 14:8, that is,

$$\frac{100}{57} = \frac{14}{8}$$

The 100 g of nitrogen will also unite with 114 g of oxygen to form 214 g of NO. The ratio 100:114 is the same as 14:16;

$$\frac{100}{114} = \frac{14}{16}$$

The data in column 5—number of atoms per molecule as shown—cannot be deduced without additional and independent information. The lack of such information here does not matter, for if the formula of compound A was N_2O_4, it would still have a packet ratio of 1:2.

The thoughtful student may well ask why we do not assign a value of 8 to each packet of oxygen. If we could, we would use the ratios in parentheses in column 3 of Table 15-1, instead of those just preceding them. But we cannot, for doing so would indicate that a packet of oxygen weighed less than a packet of nitrogen. Actually a packet of oxygen is slightly heavier (as we shall show later) than one of nitrogen. Since the weight ratio in compound A is 1 packet of nitrogen to $\frac{1}{2}$ packet of oxygen, and since a half packet of an element cannot exist (by definition), we multiply the ratio by two to get 28:16. Note carefully that no actual weights are given for the packets, only weight ratios.

This "packet" concept is the strongest possible evidence for the existence of atoms, for we see that never is there any indication of half a packet, a third of a packet, or any other fraction of a packet, no matter what compounds or series of compounds we use. Always, the quantities of oxygen and nitrogen are multiples of 16 and 14, respectively.

Table 15-1

Com- pound	1 Weight of N in compound (g)	2 Weight of O in compound (g)	3 Weight ratios N:O	4 Packet ratio N:O	5 Formula of compound
A	100	57	100:57 = 28:16 (14:8)	2:1	N_2O
B	100	2 × 57	100:114 = 28:32 (14:16)	2:2 (1:1)	NO
C	100	3 × 57	100:171 = 28:48 (14:24)	2:3	N_2O_3
D	100	4 × 57	100:228 = 28:64 (14:32)	2:4 (1:2)	NO_2
E	100	5 × 57	100:286 = 28:80 (14:40)	2:5	N_2O_5

Note that we have used 100 g of nitrogen in each of five separate experiments. In each of them whatever weight of oxygen that was necessary was combined with the nitrogen to form the five compounds listed in column 5.

Table 15-2

Glass	Weight of sugar (g)	Glass	Weight of sugar (g)
1	4.2	6	6.3
2	3.7	7	4.2
3	2.1	8	5.2
4	2.9	9	6.8
5	4.6	10	8.4

This is such an important concept that we will use an analogy so that there will be no lingering doubts in your mind. Sugar, as you know, comes in small granules or in cubes that are much the same size and weight. For our purposes let us assume that each cube weighs exactly the same as any other. Suppose now that you take a number of glasses of water and dissolve varying amounts of sugar in each. In some you dissolve lumps of sugar, one, two, three, and so on. In others you dissolve granulated sugar, a teaspoonful, one and a half teaspoonfuls, two teaspoonfuls, and so on, making no effort to measure exactly. We now mix the glasses up so that you do not know which received the cubes, which the granules. Is there a method of finding out? Suppose we now evaporate the water from each glass and weigh the sugar that is left behind. Our results are shown in Table 15-2. We can see that the weights of sugar in glasses 1, 3, 6, 7, and 10 are all whole number multiples of 2.1, a circumstance that would make it almost infinitely improbable that these could be other than the glasses in which 2, 1, 3, 2, and 4 lumps, respectively, had been dissolved. We also come to the conclusion that each cube probably weighs 2.1 g. There is no such relation among the amounts put in the other five cups.

We can put this another way. Suppose that you did not know whether sugar came in cubes or in a "continuous" form like loose granulated sugar. If sugar had been put in ten cups of water, and you now evaporated the water,

weighed the precipitated sugar, and found that all weights were either 2.1 or some integral multiple of 2.1, then you would undoubtedly conclude that sugar came in discrete lumps, each having the same weight as every other lump.

It is difficult for us to present the actual way in which Dalton arrived at his theory or even know the exact date, for he gave his contemporaries different accounts of his methods of reasoning, all of which are inconsistent with his notebooks. Even his notebooks lead to contradictory conclusions. The time that he presented his theory was somewhere between 1805 and 1810. The assumptions of his theory, somewhat modernized as to wording, are as follows:

1. Elements consist of tiny discrete particles called atoms that cannot be divided, destroyed, or created.[5]
2. Atoms of the same element are all alike; in particular they are all alike in weight. Atoms of different elements are unlike; in particular they are unlike in weight.
3. Atoms combine with other atoms to form molecules[6] of compounds, and always in fixed simple ratios.
4. Atoms of different elements may combine in more than one ratio to form different compounds.
5. When the same elements combine in more than one ratio, the simplest compound will contain the atoms of the elements in a 1:1 ratio, the next simplest in a 2:1 ratio, and so on.

The first assumption accounts for the law of conservation of mass, and the second and

[5] The subsequent discoveries that some kinds of atoms are divisible and that not all atoms of the same element have exactly the same mass have no bearing on ordinary chemical reactions.
[6] For the present we are going to continue to use the word *molecule* to mean the smallest particle of a compound, or any gaseous element or compound, that can exist in nature and still retain the characteristic properties of the compound.

third integrate the law of definite proportions with the law of conservation of mass. If these laws had not already been derived by experiment, both would have been deduced from these first three assumptions. The third is not always true, especially in the field of organic chemistry; for example, consider the compound $C_{34}H_{39}I_3N_2O_6$. The fourth assumption accounts for the law of multiple proportions, which had been established by Dalton himself as a part of his work on the atomic theory. This law helped mightily to convince many of his skeptical opponents of the validity of the two proportionality laws.

The fifth assumption is invalid and has long since been discarded. It was stubbornly defended by Dalton right up until his death, although he had no substantial evidence for it. Its inclusion in the theory caused no end of trouble for the next 50 years. The reason for the trouble can be illustrated by the formula for water. It is the simplest compound that we know that consists of hydrogen and oxygen only. Applying Dalton's fifth assumption, its formula should be HO; that is, one atom of hydrogen would unite with one atom of oxygen, and this is what Dalton insisted it did. Since it was known by chemical analysis[7] that the weight *ratio* of oxygen to hydrogen was 8:1, Dalton's fifth assumption demanded that the oxygen atom weigh 8 times as much as the hydrogen atom. On the other hand, there is nothing in the 8:1 weight ratio that demands this. For example, suppose that the oxygen atom weighs 16 times as much as the hydrogen atom. Then if we assume that the atomic ratio is 1 oxygen atom to 2 hydrogen atoms, our weight ratio is 16:2, or again 8:1. The formula for water would then be H_2O. If we make the assumption that the oxygen

atom weighs 24 times as much as the hydrogen atom, we can also assume that the atomic ratio is three hydrogen atoms to one oxygen atom, and still have our weight ratio 24:3, or again 8:1. The formula for water would then be H_3O.

Which of these atomic ratios is correct, or which of these relative weights is correct, cannot be determined without obtaining additional and *independent* information. However, if we can determine one of the weights, we then can determine the other, for these two quantities are interdependent. There are several ways of determining one or the other of the above quantities. We will use one that is relatively easy to understand and that involves a principle mentioned in the preceding chapter. It is not the method that Dalton used, for it was not developed until about 1860 (Chapter 16), some 15 years after his death. Before we do this, however, we need to consider some other developments.

Gay-Lussac's Law of Combining Volumes

Refined techniques for handling gases developed early in the science of chemistry (beginning with Boyle in the late 1600's). At this point we must digress to remind the student that since the volume of a gas varies with its pressure and its temperature, when comparing volumes of gases we must always use the same pressure and temperature. For this purpose we reduce the volumes of all gases to the volumes they would occupy at 0°C and 760 mm of mercury, called the standard temperature and pressure, and abbreviated STP. It is always to be understood that this reduction has been

---

[7] Water had been decomposed into hydrogen and oxygen by Henry Cavendish by the process of electrolysis in the late 1700's.

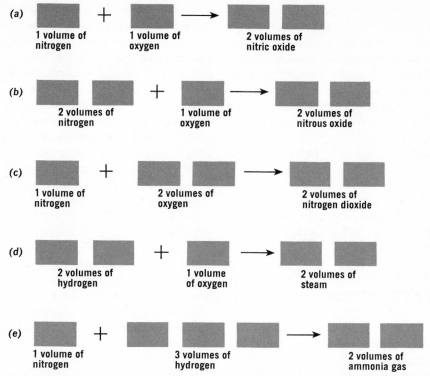

Fig. 15-3.   Volume Relations of Reacting Gases as Found Experimentally by Gay-Lussac from His Work on Gases. Gay-Lussac had no explanation for the two volumes of products (on the right) in each reaction. This does not in any way negate his experimental results.

made, even though not specifically stated.[8]

About the time that Dalton was promoting his atomic theory (1808) Gay-Lussac was analyzing and synthesizing various gases. Some of the typical volume relations that he found among both the reactant gases and the products (when they were also gases) are shown in Fig. 15-3. Each box represents one volume of a gas at STP. The number of molecules in each box (volume) was unknown at the time.

Note first only the left sides of the equations. Here we see that the volume ratios of the *reactants* in the reactions are 1:1, 2:1, 1:2, 2:1, and 1:3, respectively. From these relationships Gay-Lussac arrived at the law of combining volumes: *When two or more gases combine, the volumes of these combining gases are in the ratio of small whole numbers.* All measurements must be made at the same temperatures and pressures.

---

[8] Reduction of volume to STP (two step method):
Quantities involved—initial: V_1, P_1, T_1; final: V_2, P_2, T_2. T must be expressed in degrees Kelvin.

(1) Assuming constant temperature, by Boyle's law we calculate an intermediate volume, V':

$$V' = V_1 \times \frac{P_1}{P_2}$$

(2) Then, assuming constant pressure, by Charles' law we calculate the final volume:

$$V_2 = V' \times \frac{T_2}{T_1}$$

Now let us look at the products on the right sides of the equations. Note that in each case 2 volumes of the gas are formed, regardless of the number of volumes of reactants. Again, there are simple ratios, this time between the reactant gases and the product gases. The two volumes of products was a wholly unexpected experimental result, one which Gay-Lussac did not explain.

In 1845 Joule stated that "The discovery of Gay-Lussac, that gaseous bodies combine in equal or multiple volumes, and that the resulting compounds stand in a simple relation to their constituents, is one of the most important discoveries ever made in physical science."

The Controversy Between Dalton and Gay-Lussac

Dalton, however, refused to accept the law of combining volumes because his atomic theory could not explain this simple law of Gay-Lussac's. Dalton's insistence on the validity of his fifth assumption demanded that when hydrogen and oxygen united to form water, they did so atom for atom. He knew that 90 g of water will, on decomposition, yield 10 g of hydrogen and 80 g of oxygen. He reasoned (1) that there must be as many atoms in 10 g of hydrogen as there were in 80 g of oxygen, (2) that one atom of oxygen must weigh 8 times as much as an atom of hydrogen, and (3) that 1 volume of hydrogen will combine with 1 volume of oxygen to make 1 volume of water (in the form of steam) with neither hydrogen nor oxygen left over. Thus

$$1 \text{ vol H} \quad + \quad 1 \text{ vol O} \quad \rightarrow \quad 1 \text{ vol HO}$$

Dalton rejected all efforts to relate the law to his atomic theory. He even rejected the experimental basis of the law, accusing Gay-Lussac of careless experimental work despite

the fact that he was known as a superb experimenter, whereas he (Dalton) was known as a "coarse" experimenter. Dalton had worked on these same gases, but he had used weights instead of volumes, and he had deduced the relative weights of individual atoms of hydrogen, oxygen, nitrogen, and of other elements in accordance with his atomic theory.

Gay-Lussac was convinced that the volume regularities that are stated in his law are entirely unrelated to the weights of the combining substances, but instead are confined to the gaseous state of matter. The integral ratios as seen in the equations in Fig. 15-3, especially the first one (a), fairly "scream" for the conclusion that the particles on the left side are each composed of two atoms instead of one; that is, they are molecules and not discrete atoms. There can be little doubt that Gay-Lussac (as well as others) heard the scream but was prevented from announcing it because of the adamant opposition of Dalton, the man with the greater reputation, to any favorable consideration of Gay-Lussac's work.

Certain other factors favored Dalton. We will cite one. No reliable "picture" of the nature of a gas was at hand—the kinetic molecular theory of gases was 40 years in the future. If gas atoms or molecules were surrounded by layers of caloric that touched one another, as Dalton believed, how could 3 volumes, or 4 volumes, as in Fig. 15-3 (d and e), be compressed into 2 volumes? To him differences in gas volumes were related to differences in the sizes of the gas particles.

The controversy between Dalton and Gay-Lussac was not resolved until 1859, some 50 years later. Dalton had the bigger name (because of his atomic theory) and so the weight of scientific opinion was on his side. If Gay-Lussac had successfully explained the two volumes of products regardless of the number of volumes of reactants, he would have been the unquestioned winner of the controversy.

Meanwhile the key to the whole puzzle had been published in the most prominent journal of science in continental Europe by Amadeo Avogadro[9] in 1813.

Avogadro's Hypothesis

As soon as Avogadro learned of Gay-Lussac's law of combining volumes, he accepted it, for he saw how it could be reconciled with Dalton's atomic theory. His reasoning was approximately as follows: The third postulate of Dalton's atomic theory states that atoms combine with other atoms to form molecules of compounds, and always in fixed simple ratios. Thus

1000 atoms of N + 1000 atoms of O →
$\qquad$ 1000 molecules of NO
1000 atoms of O + 2000 atoms of H →
$\qquad$ 1000 molecules of H_2O

The second reaction is carried out at a temperature above 100°C so that water is in a gaseous state, that is, steam. The fixed simple ratios in the above two cases are 1:1 and 1:2. If these reactions are correctly stated, then

1 atom of N + 1 atom of O →
$\qquad$ 1 molecule of NO   [15-1]
1 atom of O + 2 atoms of H →
$\qquad$ 1 molecule of H_2O [15-2]

Now Gay-Lussac had found (Fig. 15-3) that

1 vol of N + 1 vol of O →
$\qquad$ 2 vol of NO   [15-3]
1 vol of O + 2 vol of H →
$\qquad$ 2 vol of H_2O [15-4]

A comparison of the second and third pairs of equations readily leads one to the conclusion that *at the same temperature and pressure equal volumes of gases contain the same number of particles.*[10] This was at first known as Avogadro's hypothesis; 50 years later it became Avogadro's law. When first advanced by Avogadro, then almost wholly unknown in the scientific world, it was little more than a brilliant guess, for there were two strong objections to it. First, the hypothesis could not by itself explain why two volumes of product gases are always formed. Also a measure of the specific gravities of reactant oxygen (Eq. 15-4) and of the water vapor revealed that the oxygen had the greater specific gravity, the ratio being 32:18. How could this be? How could any elemental gas have a greater specific gravity than any one of its compounds? Avogadro erased both objections by a second brilliant guess: *Each particle of the reactant gases consists of at least two atoms.* These particles were not single atoms, but double atoms, which we will now call *molecules.*

We may summarize Avogadro's probable reasoning as follows: Consider Eq. 15-4. The number of particles of oxygen in *one* volume is the same as the number of particles of hydrogen in *one* volume and these in turn are the same as the number of particles of water vapor in *one* volume (all are at the same temperature and pressure). But one volume of oxygen gives rise to two volumes of water vapor. Hence there are twice as many particles of water vapor as there are of oxygen. Each particle of oxygen must have split into two parts, half of the original particle going to each particle of vapor. Therefore each of the origi-

---

[9] Avogadro (1776–1857), an Italian of noble birth, was educated for the law and practiced it for a time. His love of mathematics and physics led him to desert the law to teach physics at the University of Turin.

[10] By *particles* he meant the smallest units of gases that had an independent existence. Today we use the word *molecule,* but in those days the distinction between a molecule and an atom was not clear. Furthermore, the word *particle,* in our usage, may mean either an atom, which it is in some cases, or a molecule, which it is in others.

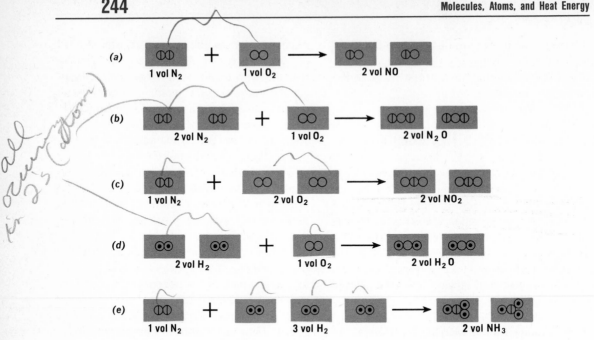

Fig. 15-4. Law of Combining Volumes. Compare with Fig. 15-3. The data on the left are consistent with those on the right if we accept Avogadro's educated guess that elemental gases consist of two atoms per molecule. (The noble gases were not known at the time.) For (*d*) and (*e*) we discarded Dalton's false fifth assumption. Note that the law of conservation of mass holds, for there are the same numbers of each kind of atom on both sides of each equation. The pictorial symbols for the atoms are those used by Dalton (p. 256). Note that the ratios of the reactant gases are those of small whole numbers in all cases.

nal particles must consist of two atoms. To see how these two hypotheses of Avogadro resolve the controversy, we have rewritten Gay-Lussac's equations showing volume relations in Fig. 15-4.

The Refusal to Accept Avogadro's Hypothesis

As we have stated, Avogadro presented his hypothesis to the scientific world in a journal where it could be read by any interested scientist. Yet he had few, if any, converts. It is instructive to see why.[11]

For one thing, Dalton's was the greater name, and the trend of opinion even in science leans toward the views of the greater "author-

ity." For another, the kinetic theory of gases had not yet been developed; a static theory prevailed that did not jibe with Avogadro's theory as a kinetic one would have.[12] Then, too, it was difficult to see how two atoms of an elemental gas could join to form a molecule. It was generally agreed at the time that atoms of the same gas repelled one another. The modern concept of the cause of air pressure had not yet been developed so the fact that it took a force to compress a gas was best explained by the repulsion of one atom of a gas for another of its own kind. Moreover, the general view that gas atoms were surrounded

[11] No significance is to be attached to the order in which these reasons are listed.

[12] The static theory pictured atoms or molecules of gases as in contact with one another, like fluffy balls of wool packed loosely in a crate. For equal volumes of gases to have equal numbers of molecules, a theory was demanded in which the molecules are widely separated, which in turn suggests motion.

by thick shells of caloric, supposedly self-repulsive, was supported by the experimental evidence from compression. Conversely, if two like atoms attract one another, why should a gas resist compression?

This is a fine example of a man being too far ahead of his time. Avogadro had no experimental evidence to support his views and to answer the objections. The result was that Avogadro's hypothesis was forgotten as the years passed, even though the difficulties of the atomic theory increased. In time, others showed that the law of combining volumes was valid, but none could reconcile it with the atomic theory. In fact, the theory came under a cloud; some chemists were talking of rejecting the whole atomic concept.

Such was the status of the atomic theory when another Italian chemist, Stanislao Cannizzaro, resurrected Avogadro's hypothesis about 1858. By use of the hypothesis, it became possible to determine easily the relative weights of atoms, and with these known, it was but a short step to the determination of the number of atoms in a molecule. These determinations involve the "weighing" and "counting" of atoms, our next topic.

Exercises

1. State the law of definite proportions.
2. What argument accompanied the establishment of the law of definite proportions and who were the chief people involved?
3. Different chemists analyzed three samples of pure table salt (sodium chloride, NaCl) from different sources. They obtained the following data for the relative weights:
   Chemist A: Na 16.5 g   Cl 25.4 g
   Chemist B: Na   5.2 g   Cl   8.0 g
   Chemist C: Na 32.3 g   Cl 49.7 g
   Show that the above data support the law of definite proportions. (To do this all you have to do is show that the ratio of Na to Cl is the same in each case.)
4. The most common ore of iron is the red oxide, hematite. Its composition is Fe_2O_3, which means that two atoms of iron and three atoms of oxygen combine to form one molecule of hematite. The weight ratio is 7 g of iron to every 3 g of oxygen. How much iron can be obtained from (a) 100 kg of hematite, and (b) 50 tons?
5. Ammonia gas (NH_3) is composed of nitrogen and hydrogen in the ratio of three atoms of hydrogen to one of nitrogen. The weight ratio is 3 g of hydrogen to 14 g of nitrogen.
   (a) If a sample of ammonia gas contains 21 g of hydrogen, what weight of nitrogen will it contain?
   (b) How many grams of nitrogen does 68 g of ammonia contain?
   (c) How many grams of ammonia can be obtained from 100 lb of hydrogen?
6. State the law of multiple proportions. Note carefully what is related to what in this law.
7. It is found that 100 g of tin will combine with 13.4 g of oxygen to form the oxide SnO; 100 g of tin will also combine with 26.8 g of oxygen to form the oxide SnO_2. Show that these facts are consistent with the law of multiple proportions.
8. State Gay-Lussac's law of combining volumes.
9. Two volumes of hydrogen combine with 1 volume of oxygen to form 2 volumes of water vapor. Show that this conforms to the law of combining volumes.
10. One volume of nitrogen combines with 3 volumes of hydrogen to form 2 volumes of ammonia (NH_3). Show that this conforms to the law of combining volumes.
11. What is there in exercise 10 that Dalton could not accept?
12. Give the assumptions of Dalton's atomic theory.
13. If Proust had not already established the law of definite proportions, it would have

been deduced from the atomic theory. Show how or why.

14. If the law of conservation of mass had not already been established, it too would have been deduced from the atomic theory. Show how or why?

15. State both parts of Avogadro's hypothesis.

16. Why was Avogadro's hypothesis not accepted at the time?

17. (a) What is meant by STP?
    (b) With what substances is it important?

18. A sample of gas has a volume of 100 liters at 25°C and 750 mm pressure. What will be its volume at STP?

19. Dalton always found that there was a mass of 8 parts of oxygen to 1 part of hydrogen in water. From these data he concluded that the atomic weight of oxygen was 8 if that of hydrogen was 1. We now know that the atomic weight of oxygen is 16 and that of hydrogen is 1. Were Dalton's data incorrect? If correct, justify (or correlate) the atomic weight ratio of 16:1.

20. Chemists use weight instead of mass as their basic unit of measurement. Why is this possible?

Weighing and Counting Atoms and Molecules

In 1857 Clausius published the first version of the kinetic molecular theory in something near its modern form. The concepts of energy, of gas pressure, and of molecules and their motions were clarified. Gone were Dalton's static model of a gas, the caloric theory of heat, the concept that gases resisted compression because of their self-repulsion for molecules of their own kind. Had Avogadro presented his hypothesis at this time it unquestionably would have won almost immediate acceptance, for the atomic theory was in a sad state. It was on the verge, in the opinion of some writers, of being abandoned because of the failure to reconcile it with Gay-Lussac's law of combining volumes. But Avogadro was dead, and so it was Cannizzaro who revived the forgotten hypothesis by presenting it to an international conference of chemists in 1858. The response was immediate; in the words of one, "It was as though scales fell from my eyes; doubt vanished, and was replaced by the feeling of calm assurance." Not long afterward, Avogadro's hypothesis (equal volumes of gases at the same temperature and pressure contain the

> The classification of the elements has not only a pedagogical importance as a means for more readily learning assorted facts that are systematically arranged and correlated but it also has a scientific importance, since it discloses new analogies and hence opens up new routes for the exploration of the elements.
> DMITRI MENDELEEV
> (1871)

247

same number of molecules) was deduced from the kinetic molecular theory (p. 213). His hypothesis thus gained status as a law, one of the utmost importance to the science of chemistry.

Atoms vs. Molecules

If we are going to count and weigh atoms and molecules, it is fitting that we understand the difference between them. Avogadro's service to science included his making the distinction between atoms and molecules. In general, *atoms are the smallest units in which an element enters into chemical combination; molecules are the smallest particles in which a compound or element can exist as an independent substance.* Thus, in a gas the individual particles are called *molecules* even though in all the rare gases[1] and in some vapors, these particles are atoms. The rare gases are therefore commonly said to consist of *monatomic molecules,* and so are called the *monatomic gases.* When vaporized, most of the metals exist as monatomic molecules. All of the other elemental gases, hydrogen, oxygen, nitrogen, chlorine, and fluorine, exist in the independent state as molecules consisting (almost always) of two atoms per molecule. They are the diatomic elemental gases. There are a large number of gases that are compounds, for example, carbon monoxide, carbon dioxide, sulfur dioxide, ammonia, the various oxides of nitrogen listed in Table 15-1, and scores of others. Their molecules consist of at least two atoms each, most of them of more than two. They might be called *polyatomic molecules.* It should be kept in mind that the terminology we employ with gases is not *necessarily* the same as that which we employ with liquids and solids. Before the method of determining molecular weights of

gases was devised, the above information was not known.

Molecular and Atomic Weights

Neither molecular nor atomic weights[2] refer to weights in the absolute sense. For example, to say that the molecular weight of an oxygen molecule is 32 tells us exactly nothing about its actual weight. If we say *also* that the molecular weight of hydrogen is 2, then we know that the weight of the oxygen molecule is 16 times greater than that of the hydrogen molecule. But we still do not know the actual weight or mass of either molecule. If we know that a molecule of either of these two gases consists of two atoms, then from the molecular weights, we know that the atomic weight of oxygen is 16 and that of hydrogen is 1. At this point we do not know the actual weight or mass of either atom. We know today that the mass of a hydrogen atom, the lightest of all atoms, is 0.00000000000000000000000166 g (1.66×10^{-24}). While this to the scientist is an interesting piece of information, and very important to modern physicists, to most chemists it is not helpful. What we are saying here is that it is the *relative weights* of atoms and molecules that are of great importance to the chemist. Since only relative weights are involved, there are obviously no units. When we say that the atomic weight of nitrogen is 14, we mean that a molecule of nitrogen weighs $\frac{14}{16}$ as much as an atom of oxygen—just that and nothing more, or, to be up to date, $\frac{14}{12}$ that of an atom of carbon.

Molecular Weights of Gases

Avogadro's law gives us an extremely simple method of determining the relative weights of

---

[1] See the column on the far right in the chart inside the front cover of this book.

[2] Strictly speaking we should use the word *masses* instead of weights. Dalton and later chemists used *weights,* and others followed along. No fundamental misunderstanding results because here on earth weights are proportional to masses.

the molecules of any gas. Since equal volumes of all gases at STP (p. 243) contain the same number of molecules, all we have to do is to compare the measured weights of equal volumes of gases. For example, a liter of oxygen at STP weighs 1.43 g and a liter of hydrogen 0.09 g. The ratio of the weight of the oxygen to that of the hydrogen is $1.43/0.09 = 16$ (within the limits of experimental error). Since there are the same numbers of molecules in both volumes, this tells us that a molecule of oxygen weighs 16 times as much as a molecule of hydrogen. If we assign a value of 2 for the molecular weight of hydrogen,[3] that of oxygen is 32.

A liter of nitrogen at STP weighs 1.26 g. Therefore, its molecular weight is $1.26/0.09 = 14$ times the molecular weight of hydrogen; that is, its molecular weight is 28. A liter of water vapor at STP weighs 0.81 g. Its molecular weight is $0.81/0.09 = 9$ times the molecular weight of hydrogen, which is 18.

The molecular weight of any gas can be determined by simply comparing the weight of a liter of it with that of a liter of hydrogen, both at STP. We could, of course, use oxygen instead of hydrogen, but the arithmetic would not be quite so simple. The actual formula, derived from Avogadro's law, using oxygen as a standard rather than hydrogen, is[4]

$$\text{molecular wt. of gas X} = 32 \times \frac{\text{wt. of liter of gas X}}{\text{wt. of liter of oxygen}}$$

It should be carefully noted that, as yet, we do not know the number of atoms in a molecule of any of the gases. Avogadro *guessed* that

[3] The reason for assigning a molecular weight of 2 to hydrogen rather than 1 is that the evidence at the time indicated that the hydrogen molecule was diatomic. Thus a hydrogen molecular weight of 1 would give us a hydrogen atomic weight of $\frac{1}{2}$—which is a less convenient number.

[4] Any other volume besides a liter could be used on the right side of the equation, as long as the same volume of oxygen was used. A liter is slightly more than a quart, 1.06 qt, to be exact.

for the elemental gases known at the time, the number was two.

Determination of Atomic Weights

Dalton was greatly interested in the relative weights (see footnote 2) of different kinds of atoms. Because of his blind adherence to the fifth assumption of his atomic theory, his conclusions about relative weights were not always valid. Not having accepted Avogadro's hypothesis, he had no easy method. There was no absolute certainty in his method even if he had not insisted that his fifth assumption held in all cases. It is not worth the time to analyze his method in detail. Suffice it to say that it involved the law of multiple proportions, the law of definite proportions, and a guess as to the number of atoms of each element per molecule. In his guessing he followed the rule of greatest simplicity:[5] When only one compound of an element was known, he assumed that its atoms were linked together in a 1:1 ratio. This may be recognized as his fifth assumption (p. 239). Sometimes it was right; it gave him the correct formulas for carbon monoxide (CO) and carbon dioxide (CO_2), but led him astray on water (HO instead of H_2O) and ammonia (NH instead of NH_3), and so forth.

Cannizzaro's Method of Determining Atomic Weights

It is now possible to go from the relative weights of gaseous molecules to the relative weights of the atoms by use of a method developed by Cannizzaro and based on Avogadro's law. We will make no attempt to reproduce the method exactly as he followed it,

[5] All scientists follow the rule of simplicity, first stated by Ptolemy (p. 12) and reiterated by many since, but not blindly. Actually the rule states that one should not introduce *unnecessary* assumptions; it does not insist that the assumptions be the simplest possible.

but will be content to outline the principles involved.

We will start with pure hydrogen. We have already seen that 1 liter of it weighs 0.09 g. For reasons that will be apparent later we will use 22.4 liters instead of 1 liter for our volume, although any volume can be used, just so long as the volume used is the same for each gas. Now 22.4 liters of hydrogen gas weighs 2.016 g. We assume that we do not yet know for certain whether these molecules of hydrogen are composed of one atom or two atoms, or even more. How do we find out?

We take 22.4 liters of steam (water vapor) at STP and analyze it. The steam weighs 18 g. We find that the hydrogen in it weighs 2.0 g. We take another hydrogen compound, hydrogen chloride gas, weigh it, and analyze it to determine the weight of hydrogen in it. Since we are going to do the same thing for a number of gaseous hydrogen compounds, let us put the data in the form of a table (Table 16-1).

There are many thousands of compounds of hydrogen; a large number are gaseous at room temperatures. No matter how many are analyzed, we would find that the weight of hydrogen contained in 22.4 liters of the compound was never less than that found in the same volume of hydrogen chloride, that is, 1.01 g. This is just *half* the weight of 22.4 liters of pure hydrogen (within the limits of experimental error). Avogadro's law says that the number of molecules in each volume is the same. This means that there is just half as much hydrogen in one molecule of hydrogen chloride as there is in one molecule of pure hydrogen. Thus, there must be at least two atoms in a hydrogen molecule. If we analyze enough gaseous hydrogen compounds and find no molecule that contains a packet of hydrogen smaller than that in a hydrogen chloride molecule, we should feel reasonably confident that the packet of hydrogen in a hydrogen chloride molecule is one atom. Our confidence seems justified when we find that the weight

of hydrogen in 22.4 liters of every one of these gaseous compounds is an integral multiple of the weight found in hydrogen chloride, that is, an integral multiple of 1.01. Looking at the last two columns in Table 16-1, we see that water must contain 2 atoms of hydrogen per molecule, ammonia must contain 3, and methane (cooking gas) 4.

We can prepare a similar table for oxygen (Table 16-2) for those who may wish to explore this method more thoroughly. We make the same assumption as before, that our group of oxygen compounds (if it is big enough) will include at least one compound whose molecules contain only one atom of oxygen. This assumption has turned out to be correct, not only for oxygen, and hydrogen, but for any other gaseous element whose numbers of atoms per molecule we wish to determine.

Following the same reasoning as for hydrogen, we find that there is just half as much oxygen in one molecule of water (or steam) as there is in one molecule of pure oxygen, and so reach the conclusion that this quantity is one atom per molecule. Fortified by our conclusion that there are two atoms of hydrogen per molecule of steam, we may now write the formula of water (or steam) as H_2O. This has been the accepted formula even since Cannizzaro showed how to determine it.

We can also set up a table like 16-1 or 16-2 for solid elements,[6] for example, carbon. In those two tables we have already listed three compounds of carbon, the two oxides and methane; Table 16-3 adds three more compounds.

Analyzing a large number of gaseous carbon compounds shows that there is never less than 12 g of carbon in 22.4 liters of any such compound, and that where there is more, it is always an integral multiple of this amount.

We have not yet completed our atomic weight determinations. From Table 16-1, column 3, we see that the least weight of hydrogen in 22.4 liters of any of the compounds listed

---

[6] All solid and liquid elements become gases if the temperature is high enough.

Table 16-1
Determination of Atomic Weight of Hydrogen

Compound	1 Volume	2 Weight of 22.4 liters at STP (g)	3 Weight of H in compound (g)	4 Col. 3 ÷ least weight, 1.01 (gives number of atoms per molecule)
Hydrogen	22.4	2.02	2.02	2
Steam	22.4	18.02	2.02	2
Hydrogen chloride	22.4	36.45	1.01	1
Methane	22.4	16.03	4.03	4
Ammonia	22.4	17.03	3.02	3
Any other gaseous hydrogen compound	22.4	—	$n \times 1.01$	n

Table 16-2
Determination of Atomic Weight of Oxygen

Compound	1 Volume (liters)	2 Weight of 22.4 liters at STP (g)	3 Weight of oxygen in compound (g)	4 Col. 3 ÷ least weight, i.e., by 16
Oxygen	22.4	32.0	32.0	2
Steam	22.4	18.02	16.0	1
Carbon dioxide	22.4	44.0	32.0	2
Carbon monoxide	22.4	28.0	16.0	1
Nitrogen trioxide	22.4	76.0	48.0	3
Nitrogen pentoxide	22.4	108.0	80.0	5

Table 16-3
Determination of Atomic Weight of Carbon

Gaseous compound	1 Volume	2 Weight of 22.4 liters at STP (g)	3 Weight of carbon in compound (g)	4 Col. 3 ÷ by least weight, i.e., by 12
Carbon monoxide	22.4	28.0	12	1
Carbon dioxide	22.4	44.0	12	1
Methane	22.4	16.0	12	1
Acetylene	22.4	26.0	24	2
Propane	22.4	44.0	36	3
Ether	22.4	74.0	48	4

is 1 g (rounded off), and that of oxygen (Table 16-2) is 16 g. Leaving off the units, the ratio of the weight of a hydrogen atom to the weight of an oxygen atom is 1:16. This method of determining the number of atoms of any particular element in a molecule of one of its compounds, and the reasoning involved, are confined to gaseous compounds. However, if we search among the possible compounds of any element, we can usually find one, or synthesize one, that is gaseous at workable temperatures. If we analyze them and tabulate the least weight (column 3 in the tables above) in 22.4 liters of *each* of the elements, we see that the smallest weight of any element in 22.4 liters of the gaseous compound is that of hydrogen. Since we are here dealing with equal volumes of gases at the same temperature and pressure, we are dealing with the same number of molecules. We also know the number of atoms per molecule (column 4). It follows that the lightest element must be hydrogen; that is, analysis shows there is always more than 1 g of any other element in 22.4 liters of that element when in the gaseous state, or in any of its *gaseous* compounds.

Molecular Weights

We have seen that the number of atoms in a molecule of pure hydrogen is 2 (column 4, Table 16-1). Its molecular weight is therefore 2. Similarly, the molecular weights of all the diatomic elemental gases are just twice their atomic weights, 28 for nitrogen, 32 for oxygen, 71 for chlorine, and 38 for fluorine. For the monatomic gases (helium, neon, argon, krypton, xenon, and radon) the molecular weight may be considered to be the same as the atomic weight. For the two elements that are normally considered liquids and so have an important vapor phase, bromine forms diatomic and mercury monatomic molecules when in the vapor state. All the elements that are solids at room temperature have unimportant vapor phases in the normal temperature range, and so we consider them to exist as discrete atoms rather than as molecules. They are therefore considered to have atomic weights only.

Compounds, since they are always composed of more than one atom (by definition), have molecular weights only. These molecular weights are always equal to the sum of the atomic weights of the atoms composing them. Thus, the molecular weight of carbon monoxide (CO) is $12 + 16 = 28$, that of carbon dioxide (CO_2) is $12 + 16 + 16 = 44$, that of sulfuric acid (H_2SO_4) is $1 + 1 + 32 + (4 \times 16) = 98$, and so on.

Some Uses of Molecular and Atomic Weights

Aside from the importance of the concepts of atomic and molecular weights to the research chemist (who could not possibly do much research without them), they are of great importance to the industrial chemist. Knowledge of atomic weights gave new impetus to the making of compounds, for the atomic weight combined with knowledge of the number of each kind of atom in a molecule made it possible to manufacture compounds without waste. Ammonia, for example, is synthesized from hydrogen and nitrogen. What proportions of these two gases should a manufacturer use? As there are three atoms of hydrogen and one atom of nitrogen per molecule of ammonia (NH_3), and as the atomic weights are 1 and 14, respectively, he knows that the *weight ratio* of hydrogen to nitrogen must be 3 to 14. This means that for every 3 g, lb, or tons of hydrogen, he must use 14 g, lb, or tons of nitrogen. Such knowledge has helped to reveal certain regularities in the way atoms combine, which in turn has been largely responsible for the synthesizing of substances that are rare or even nonexistent in nature. Thus, our vast chemical industry owes a debt to Dalton, Avogadro, Cannizzaro, and others who were curious about the relative weights of atoms at a time when such information seemed useless.

Atomic Weight Scales; Isotopes

It is convenient to have no atom with an atomic weight of less than 1. Therefore, the atomic weight of the hydrogen atom was assigned a relative value of 1. Oxygen on that scale became 16 and nitrogen 14. As more accurate methods of calculating the atomic weights developed, it became apparent that not all were whole numbers. Also, for reasons that need not concern us here, the standard of comparison was changed from hydrogen to oxygen. The atomic weight of oxygen was defined as 16.0000 and that of hydrogen became 1.008. Later, as atomic physics developed, it was discovered that not all atoms of the same element had exactly the same weight. For example, although most oxygen atoms had an atomic weight of 16, a few had one of 17 and fewer still had an atomic weight of 18. These are called isotopes; there are thus three isotopes of oxygen.[7] Carbon-12 (also written C^{12} and read "carbon twelve") comprises almost all of natural carbon—other isotopes are C^{14} and C^{13}. In 1961 the physicists and the chemists agreed to base a new atomic weight scale on C^{12}. Its atomic weight is now defined as 12.0000. The adoption of this new standard makes the atomic weight of oxygen 15.9994, a change that is insignificant to all except certain atomic physicists. That such arbitrarily made changes are possible emphasizes the fact that atomic (and molecular) weights have no absolute weight significance, that they are relative weights only.[8]

Gram Atomic and Gram Molecular Weights

Gram atomic and gram molecular weights must not be confused with either atomic weights or molecular weights, which are relative weights; when we speak of relative weights we are *never* thinking of a definite quantity of the element of compound. On the other hand, when we speak of a gram atomic or a gram molecular weight of a substance, we are speaking of as definite a quantity as when we speak of 5.01 lb of sugar.

A gram atomic weight of an element is that actually weighable quantity of the element whose weight in grams is numerically equal to its atomic weight. Thus, a gram atomic weight of oxygen is 16 g, one of carbon is 12 g, and one of uranium is 238 g. Similarly, *a gram molecular weight is that actually weighable quantity of a compound or of an elemental diatomic gas that is numerically equal to its molecular weight.* Thus, a gram molecular weight of oxygen is 32 g, one of hydrogen is 2 g, one of carbon dioxide is 44 g, one of water is 18 g, and one of sulfuric acid is 98 g. The distinctions between atomic weight and gram atomic weight and between molecular weight and gram molecular weight are of great importance in understanding elementary chemistry. The terms *gram atom* or *gram molecule* are sometimes used as substitute terms.

The Mole

Much better for most purposes is the term *mole*. Up to the time that the new atomic weight scale went into effect in 1961 a mole (from the word molecule) was synonymous with gram molecular weight. A mole is now defined as *the amount of substance containing the same number of molecules (or atoms, or radicals, or ions, or electrons, as the case may be) as there are atoms in 12 g of C^{12}.* Thus the mole is now a number that is called Avogadro's number, 6×10^{23}. It may refer to atoms, molecules, radicals, ions, or electrons.

Note carefully that the word *mole* still refers to the same quantity of any substance as it

---

[7] For further explanation of isotopes see pages 329 and 638.

[8] The whole list of elements is given alphabetically inside the back cover. Note carefully that this table does not tell you the weight (or the mass) of any atom.

did before 1961. The change is that this quantity is now expressed in terms of a number of atoms, molecules, and so on, instead of in terms of the weight of that same number of atoms, molecules, or such. Thus a gram molecular weight of oxygen (a diatomic gas) consists of 6×10^{23} molecules that weigh a total of 32 g. Also there are 6×10^{23} molecules in a gram molecular weight of any compound or diatomic elemental gas, and there are 6×10^{23} atoms in a gram atomic weight of any element; the number representing the atomic weight of any element is the number of grams that 6×10^{23} atoms of that element weigh. The diatomic elemental gases are likely to cause some confusion. There are only five of them, hydrogen, oxygen, nitrogen, chlorine, and fluorine. Learn them. They exist in nature as pairs of atoms; that is, two atoms form a molecule, written H_2, O_2, and so on. The monatomic gases are helium, neon, argon, krypton, xenon, and radon. Learn to recognize their names. We may speak of the smallest particles of them that can exist either as atoms or as molecules. It is well to note that if we want to measure out a mole of any kind of atoms or molecules, gas, liquid or solid, we must do so by weighing; we cannot possibly do it by counting.

Gram Molecular Volume

For some time we have been discussing gram molecular volumes without using the term. You may recall that on p. 250 when we began our investigation into Cannizzaro's method of determining atomic weights, we used 22.4 liters of gas for reasons that would become apparent later. If we check columns 1 and 2 in Tables 16-1, 16-2, and 16-3, we will see that the weights given in column 2 for each of the compounds are equal to the molecular weights of each of the gases listed. This

means that a gram molecular volume of a gas is the volume that will be occupied by a gram molecular weight of any gas at STP. This volume is 22.4 liters. Thus 32 g of oxygen, 2 g of hydrogen, 36.5 g of hydrogen chloride, and 76 g of nitrogen trioxide will each, when at STP, just fill a 22.4 liter container. In each container there will be one mole of molecules. It follows that to obtain the molecular weight of any gas, all we have to do is to weigh 22.4 liters of it at STP. This will, of course, give us the atomic weights for the diatomic elemental gases too by simply dividing by 2. (For monatomic gases we do not divide by 2.) Once these are determined, and once we know the number of different kinds of atoms per molecule, it is easy to determine the atomic weights of all elements that combine with any of the diatomic elemental gases.

Avogadro's Number

To make the last statement clear we must again remind you of Avogadro's law: *Equal volumes of gases contain the same number of molecules at STP.* This means that in 22.4 liters of every gas at STP there are the same number of molecules (molecules, we repeat, not atoms, except for the monatomic gases). This number is commonly designated by the letter N and is called Avogadro's number[9]—in honor of

[9] The actual value, 6×10^{23}, is a number so large that it is impossible for anyone to visualize it. We can try, however. Suppose you had an ordinary 100 watt light bulb that was a complete vacuum—not a single molecule of air in it. Now suppose you made a tiny hole in it, a hole just large enough to admit one million molecules per second. How long will it take for 6×10^{23} molecules of air to stream into the bulb at that rate? The answer is 100 million years. Let's try another way. Suppose that the maximum age of the solar system is 5 billion years. There are approximately 31.5 million seconds in a year. The number 6×10^{23} is 4 million times the number of seconds in 5 billion years. Avogadro's number is now known to a precision of 1 part in 60,000. The percentage error is about 0.0006%.

him, and not because he determined it. In fact, he never heard of it. Its value is 6×10^{23}. How this number is determined we will learn later. There are several quite different ways of determining it, all of which agree within reasonable limits of error. We repeat the following: *There are 6×10^{23} atoms in a gram atomic weight of any element and 6×10^{23} molecules in a gram molecular weight of any compound or diatomic elemental gas.*

The fact that there are the same number of atoms in a gram atomic weight of any element is apparent from the atomic weight scale alone. (The actual number, however, is not apparent.) If an oxygen atom weighs 16 times as much as a hydrogen atom, then there must be the same number of atoms in 16 g of oxygen as there are in 1 g of hydrogen, and this is the same number as in 14 g of nitrogen, 12 g of carbon, or 238 g of uranium.[10]

Let us now go back and recapitulate what we have said directly or indirectly about Avogadro's number:

1. It is the number of molecules in 22.4 liters of any *gas* at STP.
2. It is the number of atoms in a gram atomic weight of any *element,* gas, liquid, or solid.
3. It is the number of molecules in a gram molecular weight of any *compound,* gas, liquid, or solid.
4. It is the number referred to in the 1961 definition of a mole.
5. For any element in any compound in which there is not more than one atom of that element per molecule, it is the number of atoms of that element in an Avogadro's

number of molecules of that compound. That is, in 6×10^{23} molecules of hydrogen chloride, there are 6×10^{23} atoms of hydrogen and 6×10^{23} atoms of chlorine. In 6×10^{23} molecules of NaOH (sodium hydroxide) there are 6×10^{23} atoms of Na, 6×10^{23} atoms of oxygen, and 6×10^{23} atoms of hydrogen.

6. It follows that if there are 2, 3, or 4 atoms of an element per molecule of a compound then there will be 2, 3, or 4 times 6×10^{23} atoms of that element in a gram molecular weight of the compound. Thus, in 6×10^{23} molecules of H_2SO_4 (sulfuric acid) there are $2 \times 6 \times 10^{23}$ atoms of hydrogen, $1 \times 6 \times 10^{23}$ atoms of sulfur, and $4 \times 6 \times 10^{23}$ atoms of oxygen.

If these concepts are not clear to you, solving the problems at the end of the chapter should make them so.

Actual Weights of Atoms and Molecules

Once we know Avogadro's number, it is easy to calculate the actual weight of any particular kind of atom. The general formula is

$$\frac{\text{one gram atomic weight of atoms}}{\text{Avogadro's number}}$$
$$= \text{weight of one atom in grams}$$

For hydrogen,

$$\frac{1.008}{6 \times 10^{23}} = 1.65 \times 10^{-24} \text{ g}$$

We can determine the actual weights of molecules in the same manner.

$$\frac{\text{one gram molecular weight of molecules}}{\text{Avogadro's number}}$$
$$= \text{weight of one molecule in grams}$$

[10] If you have trouble seeing this, consider apples all of the same weight, and oranges all of the same weight, but let an apple weigh half as much as an orange. Suppose you have a 10 lb bag of each. You may not know how many you have of each but you can be certain that you have twice as many apples as you have oranges. You also know that to have the same number of oranges as you have apples you would have to have a 20 lb bag of them. You might assign an atomic weight of 1 to apples, and 2 to oranges. It follows that there are as many oranges in 2 tons of them as there are apples in 1 ton.

Chemical Symbolism

We have been using chemical symbols for some time and you should already be familiar with some of them. Dalton used pictorial symbols. Berzelius, the great Swedish analytical chemist, dropped the pictorial symbols for the first letter of the name of the element, or if two elements began with the same letter, he added one of the other letters in the name, for example, C for carbon, Cl for chlorine, Ca for calcium, Cr for chromium. What, you may ask, about Na for sodium, K for potassium, Fe for iron, Cu for copper, Au for gold, and a few others? These elements were first given Latin names, for almost up to 1800 Latin was the language of the scholars. Na stands for natrium, the Latin name for sodium, K for kalium, Fe for ferrum, Au for aurum, Ag for argentum (silver), and so on.

These symbols always represent one atom, and one only, of the element. In conjunction with its atomic weight, the symbol for an element signifies one atom of the element and gives us (1) an abbreviation of the name of the element, (2) the weight of one atom relative to that of the C^{12} atom, (3) the weight in grams of 6×10^{23} atoms of the element, (4) the least weight (in grams) of the element found in 22.4 liters of any of its gaseous compounds.

In order to write the chemical formula of a compound we need to know two things, the elements composing it and the number of atoms of each element per molecule. Chemical analysis gives us the first, and the method discussed in the preceding section gives us the second. For the five elemental diatomic gases the formulas are H_2, O_2, Cl_2, and F_2, for all occur in the free state as double atoms. You have already seen how formulas in general are written, H_2O, CO_2, N_2O_3, HCl, H_2SO_4, $C_4H_{10}O$, and so on. The formula of a compound gives us a shorthand method of writing the compound. It tells us the kinds of atoms composing the compound and the number of each kind of atom present. In conjunction with the atomic weights of the various atoms in the compound, we can determine how many grams of the compound make a mole, the weight of 6×10^{23} molecules of it, and the percentage composition by weight of the various elements composing it. Thus, from the formula, H_2O and the atomic weights of 1 and 16 for H and O, respectively, we see that the molecular weight is 18, and that $\frac{2}{18}$ of any given weight of water is hydrogen and $\frac{16}{18}$ of it is oxygen.

Chemical Equations and Formulas

Chemical symbolism helps us to write chemical reactions. Such reactions are written in the form of equations, with an arrow taking the place of an equal sign. Thus,

$$iron \ + \ sulfur \ \rightarrow \ iron \ sulfide$$

becomes

$$Fe \ + \ S \ \rightarrow \ FeS$$

Other examples are

$$Zn \ + \ Cl_2 \ \rightarrow \ ZnCl_2$$

and

$$C \ + \ O_2 \ \rightarrow \ CO_2$$

These equations tell us that one atom of zinc combines with one molecule (two atoms) of chlorine to form one molecule of zinc chloride, and one atom of carbon combines with one molecule (two atoms) of oxygen to form one molecule of carbon dioxide.

In the equation

$$2H_2 \ + \ O_2 \ \rightarrow \ 2H_2O$$

we see that two molecules of hydrogen combine with one of oxygen to form two molecules of water vapor. A formula represents a molecular unit, often called a formula unit, and the number in front of it (called a coefficient) applies to the whole unit, as does the 2 in $2H_2O$. On the other hand, the number placed as a subscript after the atomic symbol applies only to that particular kind of atom. Thus $2H_2O$ means two molecules of H_2O, each molecule having two H atoms and one O atom.

To write an equation one must know whether or not the substances involved will react and, if they do, one must know what products will be formed. Furthermore, the law of conservation of mass applies, so that there must be the same number of each kind of atoms on both sides of the equation. Seeing that there are is called *balancing* an equation.

Thus the equation

$$H_2 + O_2 \rightarrow H_2O$$

is not balanced. However,

$$2H_2 + O_2 \rightarrow 2H_2O$$

is balanced. Similarly,

$$Na + O_2 \rightarrow Na_2O$$

and

$$Al + O_2 \rightarrow Al_2O_3$$

are not balanced.

In balancing equations, it is always assumed that the formulas for the compounds formed are correctly written. Therefore, the subscripts are always assumed to be correct; you need only to determine the coefficients. Knowledge of the combining power of atoms (valence) is necessary in the balancing of any but the simplest equations.

From the formulas H_2O and Na_2O we see that hydrogen and sodium have the same combining power, since 2 atoms of each combine with 1 atom of oxygen. If that of hydrogen is 1, then that of sodium must be 1, and that of oxygen must be 2. Therefore, just as it took 4 hydrogen atoms to combine with 2 oxygen atoms to form 2 molecules of water, it takes 4 sodium atoms to combine with 2 oxygen atoms to form two molecules of Na_2O. Hence, the balanced equation is

$$4Na + O_2 \rightarrow 2Na_2O$$

Following the same general line of reasoning we balance the other equation by writing

$$4Al + 3O_2 \rightarrow 2Al_2O_3$$

Carefully examine the following equations to see how they are balanced.

$$Zn + 2HCl \rightarrow ZnCl_2 + H_2\uparrow$$
$$AgNO_3 + NaCl \rightarrow AgCl\downarrow + NaNO_3$$

The arrow pointing upward indicates that the hydrogen is given off as a gas, whereas the arrow pointing downward indicates that a solid has been "thrown out," or *precipitated* from solution (because it is insoluble in the solvent). No arrow is placed with the $ZnCl_2$ and the $NaNO_3$ because they remain in solution. Substances rarely react if both are in the solid state. Most reactions are carried out in solution, using water or some other convenient solvent.

Naming of Compounds

The naming of compounds is for the most part systematic; the name tells something about the composition. Over the years a pattern of conventional usage was built up, and there is now a standardized system that was established by an international committee.

Any compound composed of two elements has the suffix -ide for the second element. Examples are hydrogen chloride (HCl), sodium chloride (NaCl), carbon dioxide (CO_2), potassium iodide (KI), and calcium carbide (CaC). The order of writing the constituents of a compound is a matter of convention. The metal is usually written first as can be seen in these examples. It would not be wrong to write the nonmetal first in simple compounds, but in writing the formulas of more complicated compounds the order of the chemical symbols is important.

Certain groups of atoms have strong tendencies to maintain their identity as a group in chemical reactions, for example

$$H_2SO_4 + Zn \rightarrow ZnSO_4 + H_2\uparrow$$

$$2HNO_3 + Mg \rightarrow Mg(NO_3)_2 + H_2\uparrow$$

$$CaCl_2 + Na_2CO_3 \rightarrow CaCO_3 + 2NaCl$$

Here the groups are SO_4, NO_3, and CO_3. They are called sulfate, nitrate, and carbonate, respectively. Note that these groups appear on both sides of the equations and so maintain their identities even though they are hooked up with different elements. Other common groups of this type are OH (hydroxide), PO_4 (phosphate), NO_2 (nitrite), SO_3 (sulfite), NH_4 (ammonium), and ClO_3 (chlorate). Thus NaOH is sodium hydroxide, $Ca_3(PO_4)_2$ is calcium phosphate, and $MgSO_3$ is magnesium sulfite. Note that the -ate group contains more oxygen than the corresponding -ite group.

Where two elements form more than one compound, the suffixes -ous or -ic occur in the name of the first element. Examples are mercurous oxide (Hg_2O) and mercuric oxide (HgO), ferrous oxide (FeO) and ferric oxide (Fe_2O_3), and cuprous sulfide (Cu_2S) and cupric

sulfide (CuS). Note that the compound in each pair that has the largest proportion of the metal per oxygen atom is the -ous compound; the others are -ic compounds.

Note also that some acids are -ic compounds even though they contain no metals, for example, hydrochloric (HCl), nitric (HNO_3), sulfuric (H_2SO_4).

Prefixes such as mono-, di-, tri-, tetra-, penta-, are given to the second element in a compound to indicate the number of atoms of that kind present per molecule of the compound, for example, carbon monoxide, carbon dioxide, sulfur trioxide, carbon tetrachloride, phosphorus pentachloride.

These examples form only a small part of the system, a system made necessary by the tens of thousands of inorganic compounds, let alone the hundreds of thousands of organic compounds. The naming of the organic compounds can become singularly complex. For example, the compound $C_6H_4COOCH_3COOH$ is acetylsalicylic acid, a name that tells the organic chemist a great deal about its composition whereas its common name, aspirin, tells him nothing.

Classification and the Periodic Table of the Elements

We are going to make only a brief excursion at this time into the area of classification of the elements and the periodic table—which is really a marvelous classification scheme. Both will occupy much more of our time in Chapter 25 where they will have more meaning than they would here. We present here only those aspects of classification and the periodic table of which we will need a rudimentary knowledge in the intervening chapters.

Classification is a very important kind of scientific activity. It is the first step that man must take to make order from chaos. No one can talk intelligently or for long about any large group of items, be they chemical elements or compounds, kinds of life, cloth, or even people, without using some system of classification. Furthermore, to be of value a classification system must be widely used by other people; otherwise confusion results. In science, the systems used are world-wide so that scientists of most countries can intelligently communicate with one another. In the classification of life, for example, the names of the various classes, orders, families, genera, and species are the same in all languages. Not until some classifying has been done is it possible to see relationships, to speculate intelligently, devise hypotheses, formulate laws, and develop theories about the various kinds of matter.

It should be realized, however, that all classification systems are man-made, that they are made for particular purposes, and that if better systems are invented, the old ones are usually discarded. Just as the pathways of science are strewn with discarded hypotheses and theories, so they are also strewn with discarded classification systems. The making of a classification system involves definitions of the various categories of materials with which we are working. As our knowledge increases, differences that appeared important earlier may turn out to be trivial, and vice versa. Our definitions may turn out to be inadequate, or even invalid, and so new ones have to be made that are in accordance with new facts.

The Problem of Classification of the Elements

No progress was made or could be made in the classification of matter as long as the belief that there were only four elements— earth, fire, water, and air—prevailed. We have seen (p. 225) how Robert Boyle started the science of chemistry by attempting to classify matter into elements and compounds. His trouble was his lack of an operational definition of an element; that is, his definition did not include any operation for detecting an element. An operational definition of an element could come only with time, and, needless to say, the list of elements had to be revised as it continued to grow. In a list published in 1789 Lavoisier included 23 that have stood the test of time. Once a proper theory of combustion and an acceptable atomic theory had been formulated, the science of chemistry developed at a faster rate. More and more elements were added, some because of new developments in other fields. For example, the invention of the battery led to the discovery of sodium and potassium via electrolysis, and, later, the developing science of spectroscopy added rubidium and cesium to the list. By 1870 about 65 elements were definitely known, with a few more in the doubtful column.

Ever since it was realized that the elements held the key to the understanding of all matter, chemists have been largely concerned with the study of their physical and chemical properties, and with investigations that would reveal which elements react with which, and under what conditions, what compounds were formed from them, and the nature of these compounds. The knowledge accumulated for a time at an ever-increasing rate, but as more elements were discovered and the number of known compounds increased prodigiously, this knowledge became burdensome; the need for a basis of classification grew.

There had to be some system; there could not be a never-ending number of elements, for this would be a denial of law and order in the universe. The belief that the number of elements was limited grew as it became increasingly difficult to add to the list. The common elements were known early; the new ones were rare elements. Today the list has increased to 88 for the elements occurring naturally here on earth. A dozen or more artificially made elements have been created.

The long quest for simplicity in nature has been at least partially fulfilled, for the chemist is now reasonably certain that there are no more new naturally occurring elements to be discovered *anywhere in the universe*. This sounds like a very dogmatic statement and it probably will be viewed with scorn by many people. But every chemist and every physicist in the whole world believe that it is as definitely established as the law of gravitation; they have to, or else admit that the enormous body of evidence we have concerning the structure of the atom is completely false. Before you reach the end of this course this evidence will be presented to you.

Under the stimulus of Dalton's atomic theory, with its emphasis on the relative weights of atoms, the atomic weights of many elements had been determined. As early as 1815 the Englishman William Prout noticed that the atomic weights, as then determined, were close to integral multiples of the weight of a hydrogen atom. He therefore suggested that hydrogen was the primordial stuff of which all other matter is made. However, as more accurate determinations of atomic weights became available, the deviations from exact multiples of that of hydrogen became greater. The popularity of his hypothesis declined and was forgotten, only to be revived again in our own century, albeit in somewhat different form.

The Periodic Table

Many—in fact, we might say most—of the chemists who lived and worked during the first two thirds of the 19th century were aware of many of the similarities and regularities among the elements known at the time. Progress toward dividing the elements into groups was handicapped at first by too few of the possible members of a group being known. By 1870 about 65 of the 88 naturally occurring elements were known, enough so that most of the regularities became fairly obvious to the serious students of classification. By far the best known of these students was Dmitri Mendeleev (1834–1907), a brilliant Russian chemist who was the first to recognize clearly the need for a widely accepted classification scheme in order to identify the properties responsible for the regularities already known. If these were known perhaps the physical and chemical behavior of the elements would be better understood, perhaps other regularities and periodicities would become apparent.

Toward this end he first arranged all of the known elements in order of their atomic weights. He then arranged them in horizontal rows and vertical columns, still keeping them in the same order, and taking care to place those with similar physical and chemical properties in the same vertical column.[11] What he had—when his table had been worked over and altered sufficiently to take into consideration not only new knowledge but the lack of knowledge that left gaps for elements yet undiscovered—was a table similar to that displayed on the inside of the front cover of this textbook. He had to violate the order of atomic weights in two cases, cobalt and nickel for one, and tellurium and iodine for the other, in order to keep these elements in their proper families. With the discovery of argon a third case arose—with potassium.

The vertical columns of the table are families of similar elements, the horizontal rows are the periods, so called because certain characteristic properties recur at regular intervals; each period (except the first) starts with an alkali metal and ends with a monatomic gas. The periodic table of the elements, as it is now

[11]In his original chart he put these elements in horizontal rows.

called, is by far the most important table ever concocted by scientists. It contains all the elemental kinds of matter known to man. Its arrangement and the reasons therefore have occupied the attentions, directly and indirectly, of a multitude of physical scientists for 100 years. The discovery of the reasons for this arrangement is one of the crowning glories of science. How this solution came about and some of its consequences is the major aim of most of the rest of this course. But before we can start, we must first investigate another aspect of matter, its electrical nature, an aspect that is fundamental to the understanding of the periodic table and most of the questions it raises.

Exercises

1. How are atoms and molecules defined in this chapter?
2. What is meant by atomic weights? From what assumption does the concept of atomic weights arise?
3. The oxygen (at STP) in a quart container weighs 1.39 g. What would be the weight at STP of (a) a quart of hydrogen and (b) a quart of nitrogen?
4. Let us assign a value of 2 for the molecular weight of hydrogen. How do we determine the atomic weight of oxygen?
5. (a) At STP 22.4 liters of butane (bottled gas, formula C_4H_{10}) weighs how much?
   (b) How much does the hydrogen in it weigh?
   (c) How many molecules of butane are there in 22.4 liters?
   (d) How many atoms of hydrogen are there in 22.4 liters of butane?
   (e) How many atoms of carbon?
6. What is the weight of 6×10^{23} atoms (a)

of gold (Au), (b) of lead (Pb), (c) of sodium (Na), (d) of helium (He)?
7. How many atoms are there in 1 mole of (a) gold, (b) lead, (c) of sodium, and (d) helium?
8. One liter of a gas X weighs 0.715 g at STP. Under the same conditions a liter of oxygen weighs 1.430 g. Calculate the molecular weight of gas X.
9. How many grams are there in 1 mole (a) of NaCl, (b) of H_2SO_4, (c) of $C_{12}H_{22}O_{11}$ (cane sugar), (d) of a compound whose formula is $Fe_3Al_2(SiO_4)_3$?
10. Refer to Table 16-1. At the end of it add the data for butane (exercise 5).
11. A liter of an oxide of sulfur weighs 2.81 g at STP and by analysis is found to consist of 50% S and 50% O_2 by weight. Calculate its formula.
12. Refer to exercise 5. What is the percentage by weight of hydrogen in butane?
13. From the following data determine the atomic weights of chlorine, hydrogen, and carbon:

Compound	Molecular weight	Percent of chlorine
Hydrogen chloride (HCl)	36.5	97.3
Chlorine (Cl$_2$)	71.0	100.0
Carbon tetrachloride (CCl$_4$)	154.0	92.2
Chloroform (CHCl$_3$)	119.5	89.0

14. How many moles are there in (a) 140 g of nitrogen, (b) in 69 g of sodium, (c) in 256 g of SO_2?
15. Learn the symbols for hydrogen, helium, oxygen, nitrogen, fluorine, chlorine, bromine, carbon, sulfur, phosphorus, sodium, potassium, calcium, magnesium, alumi-

num, iron, copper, zinc, lead, mercury, and silver.

16. Write the names of the following compounds: HCl, HNO_3, H_2SO_4, NaCl, NH_3, NaOH, KOH, CO, CO_2, SO_2, FeO, Fe_2O_3, HgO, Hg_2O, Cu_2O, CuO, KCl, $MgCl_2$, $AlCl_3$, $FeCl_2$, $FeCl_3$, Na_2SO_4, $CaCO_3$, and H_2S.

17. Write the formulas for the following compounds: sodium nitrate, magnesium sulfate, silver chloride, sodium oxide, magnesium oxide, carbon tetrachloride, potassium sulfide, sodium carbonate, calcium sulfate, and sodium nitrite.

18. Balance the following equations if they are unbalanced:

$$Na_2O \ + \ H_2O \ \rightarrow \ 2NaOH$$
$$CaO \ + \ H_2O \ \rightarrow \ Ca(OH)_2$$
$$K \ + \ Cl_2 \ \rightarrow \ 2KCl$$
$$Al \ + \ HCl \ \rightarrow \ AlCl_3 \ + \ H_2$$
$$Na \ + \ H_2O \ \rightarrow \ NaOH \ + \ H_2$$

19. Learn the groups OH, SO_4, CO_3, NO_3, and NH_4.

20. Write chemical equations for each of the following:
    (a) One molecule of nitrogen combines with three molecules of hydrogen to form two molecules of ammonia.
    (b) One atom of lead combines with two atoms of chlorine to form one molecule of lead chloride.
    (c) Two atoms of lithium (Li) combine with one molecule of sulfuric acid to form one molecule of lithium sulfate plus free hydrogen.

21. If there are 2.7×10^{22} molecules in one liter of hydrogen at STP, how many molecules are present in one liter of oxygen at STP?

22. Chlorine has two isotopes, Cl^{35} and Cl^{37}. If chlorine as found in nature were composed of 50% Cl^{35} and 50% Cl^{37}, its atomic weight would be listed as 36 even though Cl^{36} does not exist. Actually the atomic weight of chlorine is 35.5. What per cent of each of its isotopes compose chlorine?

23. (a) What is a gram molecular volume?
    (b) How many molecules of a diatomic gas, elemental or otherwise, are there in a gram molecular volume?

24. (a) What are the elements in the vertical columns of the periodic table called? Why?
    (b) What are the elements in the horizontal rows called? Why?

PART IV

The Electrical Nature of Matter

Electric and Magnetic Energy

Those two great theories, the kinetic molecular theory and the atomic theory, together give us a picture of matter as consisting of tiny moving particles whose freedom of motion determines the state of that matter in bulk, that is, whether it will be gaseous, liquid, or solid. The two theories supplement one another. The kinetic theory is a purely mechanical one—as was Newton's planetary theory—explaining a large number of diverse physical phenomena in terms of moving particles and the forces exerted by or acting on them. The atomic theory, also essentially mechanical in nature, relates more to the chemical properties of matter than to the physical. However, neither theory gives us much fundamental information about the nature of atoms or molecules. Both allowed for attractive forces between the particles, but neither provided any explanation of the origin or the nature of these forces.

The first suggestion that these forces were electrical in nature was made about 1817. Berzelius, the great Swedish analytical chemist,

Many philosophers cite the lodestone and also amber whenever, in explaining mysteries, their minds become obfuscated and reason can no farther go.
**WILHELM GILBERT
(1600)**

probably was the strongest early advocate of this view. Experiments involving the electrolysis of certain solutes (Chapter 18) added to the evidence without offering an acceptable explanation of these electrical forces. In fact, all early attempts to explain them were entirely mechanical; they were based on the properties of a supposed imponderable fluid, reminiscent of caloric and phlogiston. Until about the beginning of the present century all fruitful physical theories were mechanical in nature. There was therefore no compelling reason to believe that all phenomena in nature could not be interpreted in terms of other mechanical theories.

In the closing years of the 19th century and the early years of the 20th, scientists began to realize that the electrical nature of matter could not be explained in terms of a mechanical model. The phenomena of electricity and magnetism depend on a new fundamental property of matter itself, the electric charge, and not on an external imponderable fluid. The concept of charge cannot be defined in terms of more elementary concepts; it has to be intuitively arrived at just as were the concepts of mass, length, and time. In the final analysis, this means that we cannot state in so many words what charge really is. However, we must understand the concept if we are to learn about the fundamental nature of atoms and molecules. We can do this only by studying the behavior of charges, by measuring their magnitude, and by learning the laws that govern their behavior. We therefore turn to a study of the more important aspects of electricity and magnetism. Ultimately we will learn (1) that these two are intimately related in an entirely unexpected manner, (2) that electricity is particulate in nature (this will be explained in the next chapter), and (3) that electricity forms a link between matter and energy (to be explained in Chapter 20).

Historical Development

As far back as the time of Thales or before, man was familiar with four phenomena that we now know to be electrical in origin. These are (1) the power of amber (fossil resin) that had been rubbed against one's garments to attract bits of straw or other light objects, (2) lightning, (3) the phenomenon of St. Elmo's fire,[1] and (4) the ability of the torpedo fish and the electric eel to stun their prey by contact. The ancients saw no connection between these phenomena. Little new knowledge was added from the time of Thales to the time of Queen Elizabeth I, over 2000 years later. It was then that William Gilbert, best known for his work on magnetism, added many nonmetallic substances to the list of those that had the power of attraction. Such bodies were said to be *electrified* or *charged*.

Somehow Gilbert failed to discover that some electrified bodies could repel one another, even though he must have observed repulsion many times.[2] A number of later experimenters observed this power of repulsion, among them Otto von Guericke, best known for his Magdeberg hemispheres experiment. In the early 18th century an English experimenter, Stephen Gray, was able to conduct a charge over a distance of more than 650 ft by means of a damp twine. Gray also showed that the power of attraction could be transferred from one metallic object to another.

About the same time, Charles Dufay of France was able to demonstrate that there were two, and only two, kinds of electricity.

---

[1] The pale glow sometimes seen on the tips of pointed objects, such as ships' masts, aircraft propellers, wings, or other projecting parts, especially during thunderstorms.

[2] This is undoubtedly a case of the mind seeing only what it is prepared to see. There was no place for repulsion in Gilbert's theory of electricity. He therefore entirely missed "seeing" the repulsion.

One, which he called the vitreous kind, was produced on glass by rubbing it with silk; the other, which he called the resinous kind, was produced on amber by rubbing it with wool or fur. He also discovered that each of the two kinds had an attraction for the other, but that both were *self-repulsive*. In more modern language, *like charges repel one another and unlike charges attract*.

Theories of Electricity

Dufay's Theory

Dufay's work led to the first theory of electricity that was capable of explaining the facts known at the time. The theory assumed that each kind of electricity was a subtle imponderable fluid present in all uncharged matter in equal amounts. Each could be transferred to other objects by rubbing. Thus, rubbing an amber rod with fur transferred some of the resinous fluid to the amber, leaving the fur with an excess of vitreous fluid, the amber with an excess of resinous fluid. Both the amber and the fur were now charged. The rubbing created nothing; it simply redistributed the two fluids. Any of the charged substances could now be used to attract bits of paper, straw, or other light objects. A few years later John Canton discovered that he could produce the resinous kind on perfectly clean glass by rubbing it with new flannel. This made the terms vitreous and resinous meaningless. Not long after, Benjamin Franklin called the vitreous kind *positive,* the resinous kind *negative.*

Franklin's Theory

Benjamin Franklin (1706–1790) reasoned that there was no need to assume two fluids to explain the facts. He thought that perhaps neutral matter contained a "normal" amount of a single fluid. More than this normal quota would give one kind of electrification (or charge), less than normal, the other kind.

Franklin used the term *positive charge* to refer to the kind on a glass rod rubbed with silk, and *negative charge* to the kind on an amber rod rubbed with fur. He guessed that during the transfer from one of these bodies to the other the charge transferred was the kind he had labeled positive. Thus the direction of charge movement was from positive to negative; that is, the movement is that of the positive charges only. Actually the designations positive and negative were purely arbitrary, for he had no way of knowing which kind was associated with the excess fluid and which with the deficiency; he could only guess. He could have hoped that the glass rod actually contained the excess fluid and that the amber rod had a deficiency, for the term positive suggests the former and the term negative suggests the latter. If so, his hopes were dashed, for we now know that he guessed wrong.

Franklin's theory of a single electric fluid suggests another conservation principle. If charge is produced on one body by the addition or removal of electric fluid from another body, there can be neither a net gain nor a net loss of charge in the whole system.

Modern Theory

Both Dufay's two-fluid and Franklin's one-fluid theories can be used to explain all the phenomena of electrostatics that have been described so far—and many more. Franklin's was preferred because it was simpler yet explained all of the facts equally well. Franklin's theory persisted down to the turn of the present century, and some aspects of it are still in use. Practical electricians may still refer to electricity as "juice," and they use the terms positive and negative as Franklin used them. Thus, when charges are transferred, as in an electric current, they assume that the direction of the current is from positive to negative.

Our modern theory substitutes particles called electrons for the fluid. *Electrons* are extremely small parts of all neutral atoms; they have both mass and charge. Their charges are always negative. (We will learn more about them in several of the later chapters of this book.) The number of electrons in naturally occurring atoms varies from 1 (in hydrogen) to 92 (in uranium). Some electrons are easily removed by various methods from some kinds of atoms. This leaves these atoms with a deficiency, and hence positively charged. The removed electrons may attach themselves to another atom (of the same kind or a different kind), giving it an excess and hence leaving it negatively charged, or the electrons may be left to exist in the free state for a time.

Whenever excess negatively charged electrons are transferred from one body (or place) to another body (or place) by means of a connecting wire,[3] an electric current arises, momentary though it may be. Since all electrons carry a negative charge, an electric current in a wire is a flow of negative electricity. Electrons have similar charges, and so repel one another. Therefore it is logical to assume that, given an opportunity, they will move from a region of excess electrons to a region of deficiency. This movement is directly opposed to the assumption of Franklin that the transfer is that of the positive charges. It is also opposed to what most sources of information on electrical circuits give concerning the flow of electricity. However, the flow of negative charges in one direction is equivalent in effect to the flow of positive charges in the other, so that nothing is lost by the continued use of Franklin's terminology.

We do not reverse the definitions of the terms positive and negative, but instead call the Franklin direction of flow the *conventional current.* The vast majority of electrical phenomena can be explained by using it. For phenomena that cannot be explained by it, the scientist uses the term *electron current,* which is from negative to positive. We do not change the definitions because of two difficulties. One is the problem of re-educating a host of practical electricians; the other is the trouble it would cause to scientists reading the earlier literature. But, you may ask, if we continue to teach Franklin's terminology, aren't we teaching something that isn't true? The point involved here is what we expect of a theory. If it is useful, adequate, and consistent with all of the known observations, must it also be true? If you insist upon "truth," then you are insisting upon more than the scientist demands in his theories, for he knows that it is frequently impossible to decide what truth really is in this context. He does insist, however, upon truth in his observations.

Since electrons are negative charges, neutral atoms must possess the same number of positive charges as they do electrons. However, these positive charges are not transferable from one atom to the other in the manner that electrons are, and so they are entirely irrelevant to our present discussion. So are the mass and the amount of charge on an electron. These topics will be discussed after we "discover" the electron, an event that happened a little over 100 years after Franklin's death in 1790.

Conductors and Insulators

We have already noted that the list of substances that can be charged by rubbing *as you hold them in the bare hand* consists entirely of nonmetals. The fact that charges can be rubbed off glass by silk suggests that the glass

---

[3] Electric currents through gases and liquids may involve particles with either positive or negative signs.

holds some of its charges less tightly than does silk. Similarly, fur must hold some of its charges less tightly than does amber, for amber removes them from the fur. The fact that *metal* rods held in our bare hands cannot be charged no matter what we rub them with is due either to the tightness with which metals hold their charges or to the looseness with which the charges are held. If the charges are held too loosely, they may escape through our bodies. The problem is easily solved; we wear rubber gloves—and find that we can charge any metal rod because rubber is an insulator, and the charges can no longer escape through our bodies. Furthermore, we find that we can charge metals either positively or negatively, something that we could not do with non-metals—some of which can be charged only positively, others only negatively.

This discussion suggests that various substances have different abilities to hold their charges. This is true, but more significant is the ease with which charges may move about through various substances. Those materials through which charges move easily are called *conductors;* the others are called *insulators.* The metals are all good conductors, although there is great variability among them. The best are silver, gold, copper, and aluminum; they are far better than iron, mercury, lead, or zinc. The nonmetal carbon is an indifferent conductor. The other nonmetals are insulators, some better than others, the best being sulfur. Other excellent insulators are glass, amber, rubber, bakelite, mica, and air. The human body, fortunately, is a rather poor conductor, but, like many other things, it is a better conductor when wet than when dry. That rare commodity, pure water, is an excellent insulator, whereas ordinary water is a relatively good conductor because of the dissolved materials in it. The poorer conductor a substance is, the better insulator it is. There is no sharp boundary line between conductors and insulators. There is no perfect conductor and no perfect

insulator at ordinary temperatures. Near absolute zero some metals lose almost all of their resistance to an electric current; they become "superconductors."

We can now understand why insulators held in the bare hand may be charged by friction whereas conductors cannot—not because charges cannot be transferred from or to them but because they "run off" to the ground[4] as fast as they are transferred. If a person holding a conductor in his bare hand is insulated from the ground or floor, both he and the conductor may be given a heavy charge (as can be done with the Van de Graaff machine).

Experiments in Electrostatics

That like charges repel one another and unlike charges attract can be shown by a variety of simple experiments (Figs. 17-1 and 17-2). Pith balls[5] (and other bodies) can be charged by induction or by contact. The methods are explained in the captions to the figures. Anyone can verify the above experiments if he has the patience. It will take more patience in summer than in winter, and more patience on a humid day than on a dry day. In fact, if the humidity is really high, you may find your patience will do you no good, for you may be unable to charge a glass rod because of the affinity of glass for atmospheric moisture. In any case there is a tendency for the charges to leak off the ball or the rod. Given time enough this always happens, and so we always have to recharge from time to time if we wish to maintain the charge.

---

[4] A *ground* in this context is anything that has great capacity to hold both positive and negative charges. The earth is the best of all, hence the name. To dispose of an electric charge, we simply ground it. The human body acts as a good ground for small amounts of charge.

[5] Pith balls are commonly made from pieces of thoroughly dried raw potato and then coated with aluminum paint. The thread by which they are suspended insulates them from their surroundings.

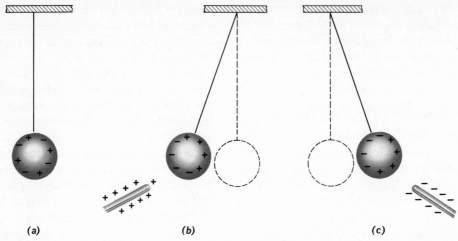

Fig. 17-1. Charging a Pith Ball. (*a*) An uncharged pith ball. Note the distribution of the charges. (*b*) A pith ball attracted by a positively charged glass rod and (*c*) by a negatively charged amber rod. Note the redistribution of the charges on the pith balls in both cases.

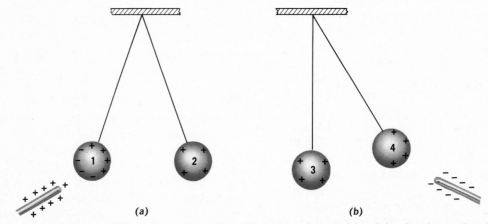

Fig. 17-2. Charges on a Pith Ball. (*a*) The pith ball is attracted to position 1 by the glass rod and then is allowed to touch the rod. It becomes positively charged and so is repelled to position 2. (*b*) When the glass rod is removed, the ball moves to position 3. A negatively charged amber rod brought near attracts it to position 4.

The Electroscope

We will be able to perform a greater variety of experiments if we have an instrument that will not only detect a charge but, if the sign on the instrument is known, will detect the sign of any other charge. An electroscope is one such instrument (Fig. 17-3). Commonly we use a bottle or a flask with a rubber stopper, through which a metal rod projects. Inside the bottle the rod is bent at a right angle so that a gold leaf[6] can be bent double and hung over it. The outside end of the rod is a metal knob. The bottle or flask shuts out air drafts. This gold-leaf electroscope is considerably more sensitive than the pith balls.

Distribution of a Charge on a Conductor

With an electroscope we can also prove that electrical charges distribute themselves only over the *outer* surfaces of conductors. Suppose we take an uncharged electroscope into a well-grounded metal cage (Fig. 17-4)[7]—or a

[6]A gold leaf is used because gold can be hammered to an unbelievable thinness without breaking, and so a leaf of it is extremely light in weight. Aluminum foil is often used at present. It is far thicker than the gold leaf, but its density is far less.

[7]Such cages are called Faraday cages, after the great scientist who discovered their properties.

solid metal box. No matter what kind or how violent an electrical disturbance is taking place on the outside of the cage, the electroscope on the inside would show no evidence of it. Lightning could strike the cage but the electroscope, no matter how sensitive, would never show it. This is explained by the repulsion of like charges for one another. If our cage is negatively charged, as it would be if a positively charged thundercloud were above it, the excess negative charges can get farther away from one another if they remain on the outside of the cage than they could if they were on the inside. This makes such cages excellent places to be during a thunderstorm. It explains why people inside buildings with a steel framework are never hurt by lightning and why the interior of such a building is never damaged.

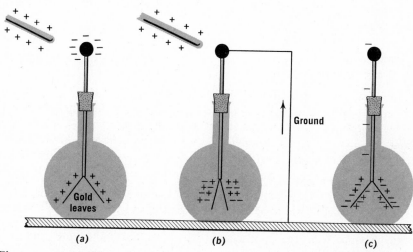

Fig. 17-3. Electroscope. (*a*) When the charged glass rod is brought near, the leaves diverge. (*b*) With a wire leading from the knob to the ground, negative charges are attracted up to the knob and enough go down to the leaves to neutralize the charge there, causing the leaves to collapse. If the ground is broken while the glass rod is still near the knob, some of the negative charges brought up from the ground are trapped in the knob. (*c*) Removal of the glass rod allows these charges to redistribute themselves, but there are now more negative charges than positive ones. Hence the leaves diverge again.

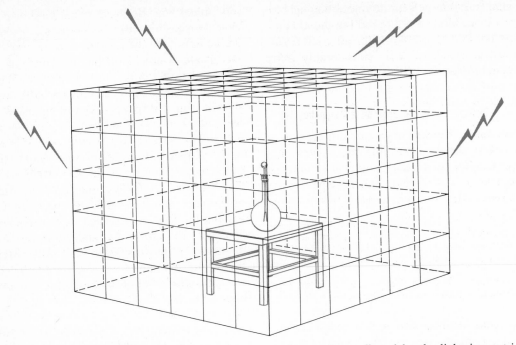

Fig. 17-4. A Faraday Cage. Note that the electroscope is entirely unaffected by the lightning outside, even though it may strike the cage.

Distribution of Charge vs. Shape of Conductor

An electroscope can also be used to prove that, on a spherical insulated conductor, the charge is evenly distributed over the outside surface, whereas on an egg-shaped conductor it is not (Fig. 17-5). All we need to do is to charge two such conductors and bring them separately near an electroscope. It matters not how we rotate the spherical one; the electroscope will behave in the same manner as long as we keep the distance from the knob constant. With the egg-shaped one, however, the electroscope clearly shows a greater charge on the end with the smaller radius of curvature. The more pointed this end is, the greater the concentration of charge. There is no easy explanation of this phenomenon in terms that we have developed so far and so we will not attempt one.

Lightning as Electricity

Probably Franklin's most important work was that in which he positively identified lightning as electricity. The idea was not new with him, but it took his famous kite experiment to prove it.[8] He showed that the charge which traveled through his kite string had the same properties as charges produced by friction. It was Franklin's knowledge of the peculiarity of pointed conductors that led him to the invention of the lightning rod. Charges are

[8]He flew a kite during a thunderstorm. Some of a cloud's charge, or that induced in the earth directly below, traveled through the twine. Franklin was able to prove that this electricity had exactly the same properties as that produced by an ordinary electrical machine, which "generated" charge by friction. Franklin was extremely fortunate that he received no injuries while performing his kite experiments. Several Europeans who attempted to repeat his experiments were severely shocked, and one was killed.

constantly leaking off any charged body. The rate of leakage under any given set of physical conditions is determined by the concentration of the charge. This fact limits the size of the charge that can be placed on a body. If the concentration becomes great enough, it will leak off in a fraction of a second, causing a spark if a conductor is brought near. Since the concentration is greatest at points or edges (if any) of conductors, the leakage is greatest there. In fact, the leakage is so rapid that a charge of spark proportions never builds up on a conductor with sufficient points or edges. The escape of the charges from points or edges of conductors during a thunderstorm at night accounts for the phenomenon called St. Elmo's fire. It also explains lightning rods.

Lightning rods are pointed metallic rods, connected together and well grounded, placed on the high parts of buildings. In a thundercloud considerable friction is developed between the condensing water droplets falling through the cloud and the upward-rushing air currents. The exact process is not clearly understood. The final result may be a flash of lightning between two oppositely charged parts

of the same cloud, from one cloud to another, or between a cloud and the earth.

Consider a positively charged cloud. Such a charge causes a negative charge to be induced on the surface of the earth directly beneath the cloud. Since air is a better insulator than almost anything else one is likely to encounter in nature, electrons from the earth will "climb" up the highest tree below the cloud, or the highest chimney or steeple, or any other object that projects above the general level of the ground beneath the cloud. This includes you, which is why you should get away from these high objects, or, if you cannot and are alone on a level surface, land or water, you should lie down as flat as you can. If the charge on the cloud and that on the high object below it becomes concentrated enough the resistance of the air is overcome; vast numbers of electrons may flash from the earth to the cloud as a stroke of lightning. If the cloud is negatively charged, electrons will flash from the cloud to the earth. If such a cloud is above a house adequately equipped with lightning rods (Fig. 17-6), the induced charge on the earth flows up the ground wire and leaks rap-

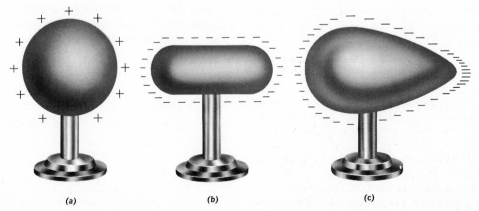

(a)   (b)   (c)

Fig. 17-5. Distribution of Charge on Conducting Objects of Various Shapes. Note that density of charge is greater at points of sharper curvature so that greater leakage of charge into the atmosphere tends to occur at such points.

idly off the points into the atmosphere where they rise to neutralize the charge on the cloud. After the initial stroke, charge may flow back and forth several times; the path has been made easier.

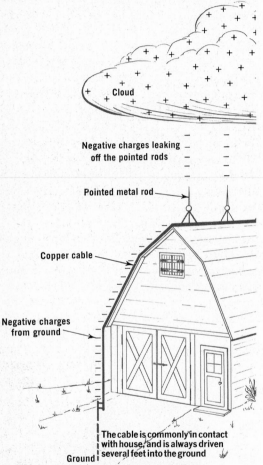

Fig. 17-6. Lightning Rod. Positive charges on the cloud induce an accumulation of negative charges on the house. The concentrations of the two kinds of charge may become great enough for a discharge to occur between the house and the cloud if the house is not protected by lightning rods. This instantaneous discharge is a flash of lightning. If the house is protected, the charges leak off the points so rapidly that no concentration of charges can develop.

In general, we may state that the charges on the cloud, in flashing to or from the earth, follow paths of least resistance. Hence any place indoors is normally safer than outdoors, low places are safer than hills, hollows or pits are safer than level ground, low trees are safer than high trees, no trees are better than one tree, and land is safer than water. Wire fences, lone trees, and wide open spaces, or bodies of water should be avoided. One hundred per cent safe, or nearly so, are houses properly equipped with lightning rods, buildings or towers with steel frames sunk into the ground, steel bridges with steel supports, and the inside of automobiles, all of which are, in a sense, Faraday cages.

Coulomb's Law

Apparatus like that used by Cavendish to measure the force of gravitation (Fig. 7-15) may be used to measure the magnitude of the force between two charges. The principle is exactly the same (Fig. 17-7), and the law that resulted is in the same form; that is, it is an inverse-square law.

This law, known as Coulomb's law, states that *the force between two small charged bodies is proportional to the product of the charges carried by each and is inversely proportional to the square of the distance between them.* Mathematically,

$$F \propto \frac{q_1 q_2}{d^2}$$

where q_1 and q_2 represent the two charges.[9] Writing this proportionality as an equation, we have

$$F = \frac{K q_1 q_2}{d^2} \qquad [17\text{-}1]$$

[9] Coulomb had no way of knowing the absolute magnitude of the charges carried by the two bodies.

Coulomb did the experimental work leading to the law two or three years after Cavendish measured the gravitational constant, G. Coulomb's apparatus did not need to be as sensitive as that of Cavendish, for electrical forces are far greater than gravitational forces.[10]

Note that the force of gravitation is one of attraction only, whereas that between charges may be one of either attraction or repulsion. There is one other difference between the forces. If any substance, perhaps a piece of glass, is placed between two charges in an attempt to shield them from one another, the force is somewhat reduced. The amount of reduction is a characteristic of the shielding medium. It follows that the force is greatest in a vacuum. There is no such shielding effect in gravitation. This is shown by the fact that the attraction between the moon and the sun is the same when the earth is squarely between

the two (as in a total lunar eclipse) as it is at other times. If this were not so, the moon would follow a somewhat different curve after the eclipse from that before.

Units of Charge

Coulomb's law is used to define the unit of charge. If two equal charges are of such magnitude that when they are placed 1 cm apart in a vacuum, they exert a force of 1 dyne on each other, then each charge is defined as 1 electrostatic unit (esu). Since the dyne is a very small unit, 1 esu is very small. A larger unit, the coulomb, consists of 3×10^9 esu.

K is a constant of proportionality whose numerical value depends on the units used. In our equation for Coulomb's law, $K = 1$ if q_1 and q_2 are each 1 esu and d is 1 cm. If q_1 and q_2 are in coulombs, then K is very close to 9.0×10^9 newtons-meters^2/coulomb^2, and Coulomb's law thus becomes

$$F = (9 \times 10^9)\frac{q_1 q_2}{d^2} \qquad [17\text{-}2]$$

[10] So much greater, in fact, that the gravitational effects are negligible within atoms when compared with electrical effects. On a cosmic scale, however, gravitational effects are vastly more significant.

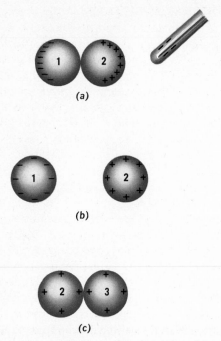

Fig. 17-8. Method of Charging Two Identical Metal Balls Equally. (*a*) Two balls in contact as a charged rod is brought near. (*b*) While the rod is still near, the two balls are separated, leaving one positive, the other negative. A third ball, uncharged, is brought in contact (*c*) with one charged ball. The two balls become equally charged and remain so after separation. During the whole process the balls, being metal, must be insulated from any ground.

if F is expressed in newtons (p. 116) and the distance d in meters. If the charges q_1 and q_2 have the same sign, the force is one of repulsion; if they have opposite signs it is one of attraction. The method of charging two identical bodies equally is illustrated in Fig. 17-8.

Electrostatic Discharge

The charge that can be developed on a glass or amber rod by rubbing it with silk or fur is small, and only a small fraction of it is transferred to another body by contact, for charges do not move freely on or from an insulator. The small amounts of charge that are transferred give little or no visible sign of such transfer. However, if we put a moderate amount of charge on an insulated metal conductor, and then bring it close to a grounded conductor, a visible spark may be seen—and heard. Such a spark gives off light and heat energy. Remembering our law of conservation of energy, we might well ask where this energy comes from.

Remember that when we discussed charging an object, the object at first had no net charge; it was neutral—that is, it had equal amounts of positive and negative charge. In order to charge the object, the positive and negative charges must be separated from each other. Since there is a force of attraction between these opposite charges, work must be done (energy must be expended) to separate them. It is this energy that reappears in the spark as light and heat.

There are several types of machines, some operated by hand, some by motors, that can separate quantities of charge large enough to cause sparks from a few inches to several feet long. One such device is the Van de Graaff generator which comes in several sizes and designs. In all of them a charge is built up on an insulated metal ball of a size appropriate to the charge-separating capacity of the machine. It is the mechanical energy expended in separating the charges that reappears in the sparks produced. The larger the charge that is developed on such a conductor, the greater the rate at which it leaks off into the atmosphere. Hence, there is a limit to the amount of charge that can be placed on any conductor.

Potential Difference

The concept of potential difference is as important to static electricity as it is to current electricity—which is why we develop it here.

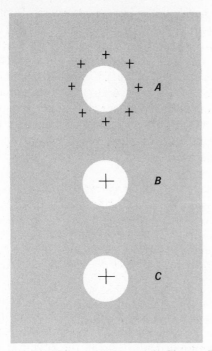

Fig. 17-9. Difference of Potential. Charge *B* has more electric potential energy with respect to *A* than does charge *C* because it experiences a greater force of repulsion. It therefore can do more work in moving away (spontaneously) from *A* than can charge *C*. We therefore say that *B* is at a higher potential than *C*.

The term is a short way of referring to a difference in electrical potential energy per unit charge, and is often abbreviated PD. The analogy with gravitational potential energy is nearly perfect. Just as work must be done on a body to give it gravitational potential energy, so must work be done on a charge to give it electrical potential energy.

Consider a positively charged body, *A*, in Fig. 17-9. A positive charge at *C* will experience a force of repulsion by *A*. (Consider *B* to be absent.) The magnitude of this force can be calculated from Coulomb's law. If we now move the charge from *C* to *B*, we are moving it against this repulsive force, and so we are doing work. The energy that we expend in

doing this work is stored up in the charge as electrical potential energy. The amount of work that it can now do in returning to *C* is a measure of the difference in electrical potential energy of the charge at *B* and at *C*. Furthermore, since the charge has more potential energy at *B* than at *C*, we say that *B* is at a higher potential than *C*. If free to do so, a positive charge will spontaneously move from *B* to *C* because of the mutual repulsion of like charges.

Remembering that we can measure energy only in terms of work that is or can be done by that energy, we can define *potential difference as the quantity of work done during the transfer of 1 unit of positive charge from one point to another*. In other words, potential difference is equal to the difference in potential energy per unit charge of the object when at position *C* as compared with position *B*. The practical unit of potential difference is the volt. *If we do 1 joule of work while transferring 1 coulomb of charge from one point to another, say, from C to B, then the potential difference between C and B is 1 volt*. If we do 2 joules of work while transferring 1 coulomb of charge, then the potential difference is 2 volts, and so on. Thus

$$\text{potential difference (in volts)} = \frac{\text{work (in joules)}}{\text{charge (in coulombs)}}$$

In symbols

$$V = \frac{W}{Q} \qquad [17\text{-}3]$$

Thus, the voltage of any electrical system represents the energy transfer per coulomb. In charging a 12 volt automobile storage battery 12 joules of work must be done to transfer 1 coulomb of positive electricity from an outside source to the positive terminal of the battery. The battery can then do 12 joules of work for each coulomb of charge transferred from the positive terminal to the negative terminal via the electrical system (starter, lights, horn, radio) of the car. Ordinary households in the United States are provided by the electric power company with a difference of potential of 110 or 120 volts. This means that *for each coulomb of charge* that passes from one wire in an outlet to the other wire of that same outlet, 110 (or 120) joules of work can be done (or 26.3 cal of heat can be produced) by any appliance connected between the two wires.

Current Electricity

So far our interest has been chiefly in electric charges at rest. True, they moved from charged rods to pith balls or to insulated charged conductors, or along short wires connected to electroscopes, but our interest was not in the motions themselves. Any movement these charges made was practically instantaneous, erratic and noisy—lightning, for example. Such is the nature of static electricity.

There is no fundamental difference between charges (electrons) at rest and charges (electrons) in motion as they travel in a quiet, orderly, and continuous (for an appreciable time at least) manner through conductors —except that when they are in motion they possess a set of properties that they do not have when at rest. These properties are such that they light our lamps, run our electric motors, make possible our radios, television sets, telephones, and so on. We have already stated that an electric current is a flow of negatively charged particles (electrons). We may speak of a flow of electrons, but never of a flow of electric current because an electric current is a flow of electrons. *The moving electrons are the current.* Electrons do not flow except through conductors arranged to form

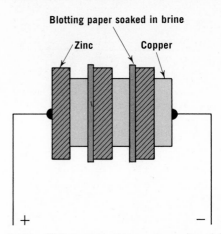

Fig. 17-10. Voltaic Cell. Alternating pairs of disks of copper and zinc are separated by blotting paper soaked in brine. A difference of potential develops between the zinc and the copper. If the two open ends of the wires are connected, a current will flow. The brine-soaked blotting paper takes the place of the frog's leg used by Galvani.

a complete circuit.[11] Break the circuit at any point and the flow ceases. Electric switches are made to open and close electrical circuits at will.

The generation of current electricity had its inception in a chance observation made near the end of the 18th century by an Italian medical professor, Luigi Galvani. He noticed that a frog's leg spontaneously contracted when near a machine for generating static electricity. Investigating further, he found that if two dissimilar metals were in contact while one was touching a nerve of the frog's leg and the other a muscle, the same contraction of the muscle was observed. He attributed this (falsely) to "animal electricity."

Another Italian, Alessandro Volta, carrying this research further, discovered that the frog's leg was not necessary to produce the electricity.

[11]For important exceptions, see photoelectric effect (Chapter 22) and thermionic emission (Chapter 18).

All that was needed were two dissimilar metals, for example, copper and zinc. A greater current was obtained by making a pile of alternating pairs of copper and zinc plates (or any two dissimilar metals, although some are more effective than others), each pair separated by paper moistened with water or brine. The brine (salt solution) is the better conductor. This was originally known as a voltaic pile (Fig. 17-10). Actually it was the first crude electrical cell or battery. With this invention (in 1800) a steady continuous flow of electric charge could be maintained for the first time. The current generated is direct current (DC); that is, it flows constantly in one direction.

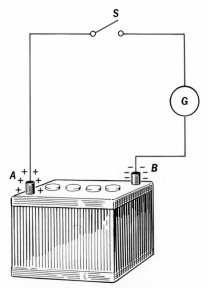

Fig. 17-11. Modern Battery. Because of chemical action within, the cell maintains an excess of positive and negative charges on the two terminals, *A* and *B*. Mutual repulsion of like charges on each terminal limits the potential difference between *A* and *B*. If the two terminals are connected by a wire and the switch, *S*, is closed, a current will flow. The current can be detected and measured by the galvanometer, *G*. The direction of the conventional current is from *A* to *B* through the wire.

Electrical Circuits and Electric Energy

In all circuits a difference in potential must exist between two points, and these two points must be connected by a conductor if there is to be a current. For a continuous current some means must exist to maintain the difference in potential. Only an electric generator, of which the battery (Fig. 17-11) is one type, can do that. Such generators may be called *sources*. Every conductor offers a certain amount of resistance to the flow of charges. Light bulbs, electrical appliances of various sorts, electric motors, and such, inserted in the circuit are called *resistances* because they have more resistance than the connecting wires.

Suppose we follow the charges through a complete circuit. The source will consist of a series of batteries, enough to give us 110 volts. We will put in two resistances, an electric iron, and a motor. Hordes of negative charges (electrons) leave the source in a steady stream, well endowed with 110 joules of potential energy per coulomb, energy obtained by the conversion of chemical energy in the batteries which they expend in traveling through the circuit. Through the copper wires of the circuit they can move with little loss of energy. When they reach the wires of the electric iron they have a more difficult time because these wires are made of a special alloy which has a higher resistance than the copper wires. The result is analogous to greatly increased friction between the atoms in the wire and the moving charges. More energy is required to move the charges through these wires. This energy is converted into heat that causes the special alloy wires to heat the iron.

When the charges encounter the motor, a different phenomenon appears, one which will be described later. At this time we shall merely say that the effect is as if the charges had to push uphill against a contrary force. In the process, some of the remaining energy of the charges is converted into mechanical energy, causing the motor to turn. The charges move on, returning to the batteries bereft of much of their original potential energy because of the work they have done en route. In the batteries the charges receive a fresh supply of energy so that they can make the round trip again.

Whence comes this energy? Joule discovered that the same amount of energy was released through chemical changes just by throwing the ingredients of the battery cases into a beaker of acid—only in the beaker the energy is released as heat instead of as electric energy.[12] Thus the electric energy released from a battery is transformed chemical energy, energy that in turn is ultimately transformed via electric energy into heat energy (in the iron) and mechanical energy (in the motor).

How much energy does each coulomb deliver? We have already seen that this energy transfer per coulomb is expressed in volts. Instruments called *voltmeters* measure the number of volts. Voltmeters are best thought of as electrical pressure gauges (Fig. 17-12), since they measure the potential energy delivered by each coulomb in some chosen part of the circuit, just as a water-pressure gauge measures the potential energy per unit volume of the water at a particular point in a pipe or tank. Compare Figs. 17-12*a* and 17-12*b*.

Equation 17-3, $V = W/Q$, gives us the energy transfer per coulomb. If the potential difference in our circuit is 110 volts, it means that every coulomb of charge that passes through it will accomplish 110 joules of work. Now if we know the number of coulombs

---

[12] This was one of the things that Joule did in determining the mechanical equivalent of heat, 4.18 joules/cal.

flowing through the circuit per second, we can calculate the total energy transfer per second— or per time *t*—for obviously energy (or work) per coulomb × number of coulombs = total energy (or work). This total divided by the time (in seconds) will give us the energy transfer per second. The number of coulombs per second is given by

$$\frac{\text{total charge (in coulombs)}}{\text{time (in seconds)}}$$

The number of coulombs per second is a *rate* of flow. It is designated the current. The unit of current, symbolized by the letter I, is the *ampere*, which is defined as a flow of 1 coulomb/sec. In symbols,

$$\frac{Q}{t} = I \qquad [17\text{-}5]$$

Thus, if 20 coulombs passes through a conductor in 4 sec, the current, I, is calculated as follows:

$$I = \frac{Q}{t} = \frac{20}{4} = 5 \text{ amperes}$$

An ammeter inserted in the circuit will indicate the number of coulombs flowing through the circuit per second. Note that an ampere is a measure of the *rate* of flow; it is not a measure of the total flow. The principle on which the ammeter works is described in Fig. 17-21.

The second thing we need to know is voltage. To date we have defined voltage, V, in terms of energy transfer per coulomb, and we have defined the rate of transfer, I, in terms of coulombs per second.

It follows that the total energy transfer per second is obtained simply by multiplying Eq. 17-3 by Eq. 17-5, as follows:

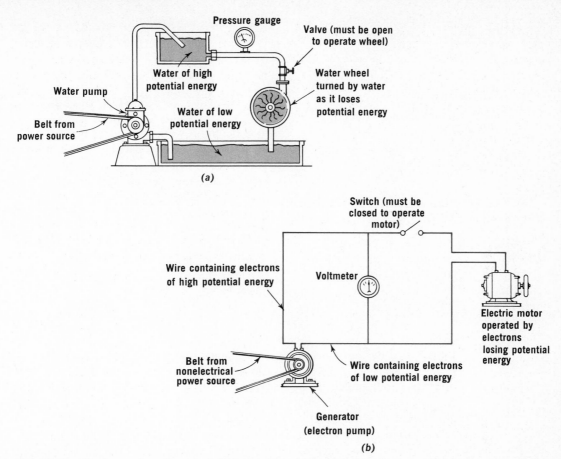

Fig. 17-12. Analogy of an Electrical System with a Water Pressure System. The generator keeps the electrons circulating just as the pump keeps the water circulating. The voltmeter is analogous to the pressure gauge, the switch to the valve, and the wires to the pipes. A battery could be used as an electron pump instead of the generator.

$$\text{volts} \times \text{amperes} = \frac{\text{joules}}{\text{coulombs}} \times \frac{\text{coulombs}}{\text{seconds}}$$

$$= \frac{\text{joules}}{\text{seconds}} \qquad [17\text{-}6]$$

for the coulombs cancel out. In symbols,

$$VI = \frac{W}{Q} \times \frac{Q}{t} = \frac{W}{t} \qquad [17\text{-}7]$$

Now joules per second (W/t) is the rate of doing work; that is, it is (by definition) power, symbolized by the letter, P. Hence,

$$P = \frac{W}{t} = VI \qquad \text{or} \qquad P = VI \quad [17\text{-}8]$$

The unit of power is the watt. By definition it is 1 joule/sec. All electrical appliances are rated in watts because the number of watts tells us the rate at which the appliance uses electrical energy. A 100 watt light bulb uses 100 joules of energy for every second it is lighted. If we burn it for 1 hour, it consumes 100 watt-hours (360,000 joules) of energy. If we burn it for 10 hours, it consumes 1000 watt-hours or 1 kilowatt-hour of energy. This is what the power company bills us for—kilowatt-hours of energy, not the amount of electricity (charge) that we use.

Ohm's Law

Resistance to the flow of electricity is a property of every substance, including conductors. The relationship between potential difference, current, and resistance was first studied in the 1820's by George Ohm, a German schoolmaster. The ratio of the potential difference across the ends of a wire to the current in the wire is called the *resistance* of the wire.

Resistance in a circuit is designated by R. For any one circuit it is a constant. Ohm made wires (by hand) of different sizes and lengths, and of different metals, varying only one factor at a time in the manner of any good scientist. Batteries and thermocouples were still the only means of obtaining an electric current. Despite these handicaps he finally established the law justly named in his honor.

Ohm's law states that for a given conductor the current is proportional to the voltage across the ends of that conductor. In symbols, $I \propto V$. With the proportionality constant R, we can write

$$V = RI \qquad [17\text{-}9]$$

If V is in volts and I in amperes, then R is expressed in ohms. An *ohm,* our unit of resistance, is defined as *the resistance that will allow a current of 1 ampere in a conductor under a potential difference of 1 volt*. Ohm's law applies only to our most common types of electrical circuits, mainly metallic conductors at ordinary temperatures.

Heating Effect of a Current

Joule, in his work on the mechanical equivalent of heat, investigated the relationship between the heating effect and the current, keeping all other factors constant. He found that if he doubled the current the amount of heat produced was increased by a factor of 4, that if he tripled the current, by a factor of 9. Thus *the amount of heat produced is proportional to the square of the current*. It is also, of course, proportional to the time the current flows. Hence

$$W \propto I^2 t \qquad [17\text{-}10]$$

Introducing a proportionality constant, R, we can write

$$W = RI^2 t \qquad [17\text{-}11]$$

This is sometimes referred to as Joule's law.

If Ohm had not performed the experiments necessary to establish his law, it would have been deduced from Joule's law ($W = RI^2t$) as follows:

$$W = VIt \qquad [17\text{-}12]$$

Hence

$$VIt = RI^2 t$$
$$V = RI \qquad [17\text{-}13]$$

Ohm's law says that a potential difference of 220 volts will cause twice as many coulombs to flow through an appliance per unit time as does a potential difference of 100 volts. But Joule's law says that doubling the current will increase the heating effect four times, a desirable effect in electric stoves and clothes dryers but highly undesirable in most other appliances made to withstand a lesser temperature.

A short circuit means just that. Commonly, it is a circuit made short by a defect that allows the current to bypass a resistance. This reduces R almost to zero in that circuit, and since V is about 110 volts in our homes at all times, I must become enormous for the product of RI to equal 110. The heating effect therefore may be increased 100-fold or even 1000-fold. If the circuit is not protected by a fuse, the heat developed will melt or burn the insulation off the wires and can start a fire if the wire is in contact with anything flammable.

A fuse is a short piece of wire of low melting point inserted in the circuit at an appropriate place to prevent a fire if a short circuit occurs. Melting it has the same effect as "pulling the switch." Too heavy a load, caused by plugging too many lights or appliances into the same parallel circuit, will also cause the fuse to blow. We have seen that most houses are wired for 110 to 120 volts. The appliances plugged into a circuit protected by a 15 ampere fuse should not use more than 1650 watts (110 × 15). Substituting a fuse with a greater capacity in order to allow the circuit to carry a heavier load without burning out the fuse is dangerous. To bypass a burned-out fuse by insertion of a penny, or other piece of metal, is not only folly but well-nigh criminal. Modern wiring jobs commonly use circuit breakers in place of fuses.

Electricity and Magnetism

The relationship of magnetism to electricity is an entirely unexpected one. Only two observations even suggested any relationship at all. One was that lightning discharges occasionally had been noted to magnetize a piece of steel or to demagnetize a magnetic needle. The other was the observed similarity in the behavior of static electric charges and magnetic poles. Without these observations it is unlikely that the relationship would have been discovered so soon (1820). Even so, no one suspected how fundamental the relationship was.

Magnetism

We are all familiar with ordinary magnets. A freely suspended magnet will always turn so that one end (pole) points approximately north. This is the north-seeking pole and by definition is called the north pole. In the vicinity of Cincinnati, Ohio, the north pole of a compass needle points directly to the true geographic pole (point of emergence of the imaginary axis of the earth), whereas in New York City it points nearly 12° to the west of true north and in Denver it points somewhat over 12° to the east of north. Correlation of a large number of such determinations from points all around the earth locates the magnetic pole in the north as lying north of Hudson's Bay some 1400 mi from the geographic pole. It is interesting to note that the locations of the earth's magnetic poles have changed many times during the history of the earth. The reason for the earth's magnetism is still being investigated.

From a *practical* viewpoint only a few metals can be magnetized. Chief among them are iron and steel. Others are nickel, cobalt, and certain alloys; for example, one of aluminum, nickel, and cobalt makes the finest of permanent magnets. All "permanent" magnets eventually lose their magnetism.

Units of Magnetism. The forces of repulsion and attraction found between like and unlike poles, respectively, are similar to those between like and unlike electric charges. That is, *like magnetic poles repel and unlike poles attract.* Coulomb found that these forces of repulsion and attraction between two poles obeyed the same general inverse-square law as did electric charges:

$$F \propto \frac{p_1 p_2}{d^2}$$

where F is the force of attraction or repulsion, p_1 and p_2 represent the strengths of the two poles, and d is the distance between them. Written as an equation,

$$F = K \frac{p_1 p_2}{d^2} \qquad [17\text{-}14]$$

As usual, we need to define a unit magnetic pole in order to have some basis for measuring p_1 and p_2. This unit of pole strength is defined as follows: If two like poles of equal strength are placed in a vacuum 1 cm apart and the force of repulsion between them is 1 dyne, then each pole is defined as a unit pole. Thus, in the above equation, if p_1 and p_2 are both unit poles, and d is 1 cm, then F is 1 dyne, and K becomes 1.

Theory of Magnetization. Magnetic poles occur only in pairs. There is no such thing as a magnetic pole existing all by itself. This is proved by breaking magnets into any number of parts (Fig. 17-13). Each part, no matter how

Fig. 17-13. A broken magnet develops new poles instantaneously at the broken ends.

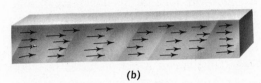

Fig. 17-14. (*a*) Molecular magnets in an unmagnetized steel bar are randomly oriented. (*b*) During the process of magnetization the molecular magnets line up parallel to the external field, producing poles at the ends of the bar.

small, will have a north pole and a south pole. Thus magnetism seems to be a property of the smallest particles of certain substances. This suggests that atoms or groups of atoms (called *domains*) are tiny magnets that in unmagnetized pieces of iron, and such, are haphazardly arranged. The domains are assumed to be microscopic units in which the atoms composing the unit have identical or nearly identical orientations. When most of the domains are lined up the same way the substance is magnetized (Fig. 17-14). Thus nothing has been added during the process of magnetization except orientation—which has, of course, required an input of energy. Note, however, that there is nothing in this theory that ultimately explains magnetism.

Magnetic Fields and Magnetic Lines of Force

Suppose we place a sheet of glass on a bar magnet and sprinkle iron filings lightly on the glass.[13] If we now tap the glass lightly, we will

[13] The glass is to prevent the filings from sticking to the magnet.

Fig. 17-15. Patterns Formed by Iron Filings near Three Bar Magnets. The filings align themselves in the direction of the lines of force passing through them.

see the filings arrange themselves along imaginary lines of force in one of the patterns shown in Fig. 17-15. Other arrangements of magnetic poles give other patterns. Note that the directions of the magnetic fields are outward from the north poles, as shown by the arrows in Fig. 17-16, and inward toward the south poles. This is a matter of convention. The density of the lines of force is an indication of the force exerted. Thus the lines are denser near the poles because experiment shows that the magnetic forces are greatest there.

If we place a magnetic pole in a certain region of space, that space appears to have been altered from what it was before. It is altered because any piece of iron brought into it will now experience a force that it will not experience if the magnet is removed. A field of force exists in this altered region of space, for a force is exerted on any magnetic body[14] brought into the field. This field extends presumably for infinite distances in all directions, but from a practical viewpoint the force becomes negligible in relatively short distances from the magnetized body because of the inverse-square law. The magnetic field inten-

sity (strength) is designated by the letter H. If the magnetic body brought into the field is another small bar magnet or the magnetic needle of a compass whose ~orientation is known, the magnetic field will be found to have direction. By definition the direction of this field at any point is given by the direction of the force exerted on a north pole at that point.

The field concept originated with Michael Faraday, one of the greatest experimenters in electric and magnetic phenomena that ever lived.[15] Faraday applied the field concept to electric charges as well as to magnetic poles.

Place an electric charge in the vicinity of another charge and it experiences a force, either of attraction or repulsion, just as does a magnetic pole in the presence of another

---

[14] A magnetic body need not be another magnet; any metal attracted by a magnet is a magnetic body.

[15] Faraday (1791–1867) was apprenticed to a London bookbinder for seven years. He became interested in physics and chemistry by reading some of the books that he bound. He had little formal education. In 1813 he became assistant to Sir Humphry Davy, director of the Royal Institution of Great Britain (founded by Count Rumford), where he started out as little more than a bottle-washer. His experimental genius quickly showed itself, so much so that when Sir Humphry Davy, who among other successes discovered sodium and potassium, was asked what his greatest discovery was, he replied, "Michael Faraday." Twelve years later (1825) Faraday became director of the Institution, a position he occupied until his death in 1867.

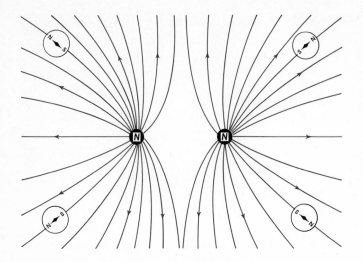

Fig. 17-16. Lines of Force About Two Like Poles. Small compasses are used to indicate the orientation of the magnetic field. If we substitute two like electric charges for the two like poles, we have an electric field instead of a magnetic field; both can be represented in the same manner by similar diagrams.

magnetic pole. An electric field of force exists in this space about the charge (Fig. 17-16). The electric field intensity (strength) is designated by E and its direction at any point is given by the direction of the force exerted on a unit positive charge in that field. The magnitude of the force on the charge is given by

$$F = qE$$

If F is in newtons and q is in coulombs, then E is in newtons per coulomb.

On Fields in General

We have seen that the field concept can be applied to gravitational, magnetic, and electric forces. A gravitational field surrounds every material body, a magnetic field surrounds every magnetic body, and an electric field surrounds every electrically charged body. Curiously enough, the same space can have a gravitational field, a magnetic field, and an electric field at one and the same time without the fields interfering with one another.

Gravitational fields are of one kind only, so the only forces acting are those of attraction.

No material body in the whole universe can exist without a gravitational field surrounding it. In the normal state material bodies are electrically neutral, but an electric field can be created about any material body under the proper circumstances. From the practical viewpoint magnetic fields can be created about only a few electrically neutral metals or metallic alloys.[16] The strength of the gravitational field is extremely weak compared to the strength of electric and magnetic fields. Gravitational attraction becomes enormous only as the sizes of the bodies become enormous. The gravitational field cannot be destroyed or neutralized, nor can an object be shielded from its effects, whereas electric fields are easily neutralized, magnetic fields can be either created or neutralized by various means, and both can be shielded from their surroundings in various ways.

Although magnetic and electric fields are similar in ways that have been already mentioned, their differences are significant also. If free to move, magnets align themselves in

---

[16] A magnetic field also exists about any moving electric charge. See Oersted's experiment (p. 287).

a north-south direction, whereas there is no tendency for any sort of alignment among single stationary charges. Positive charges may be isolated from negative ones and vice versa, but north poles cannot be isolated from south poles. Charges move readily from one body to another along conductors; there is no corresponding movement of magnetism. Insulated charged conductors will share their charges with neutral insulated conductors, with the result that their electric fields become weaker. A magnetized piece of steel will magnetize any number of other pieces of steel without itself losing any of its magnetic field strength.

Magnetism from Electricity

Oersted's Experiment

It was Hans Christian Oersted, a Danish professor of physics, who discovered that magnetic fields could exist where there were no magnets. In a series of experiments in which he was using an unusually large Voltaic pile (battery) so as to produce a large current, he happened to note that a compass in the near vicinity was behaving oddly. Further investi-gation showed that the compass needle always oriented itself at right angles to the current-carrying wire (Fig. 17-17a), and that it reversed its direction if either the direction of the current was reversed, or the compass was changed from a position below the wire to one above (Fig. 17-17b). Note carefully that the movement of the compass needle is at right angles to the current-carrying wire; it is not toward the wire, nor away from the wire; that is, the force is neither one of attraction nor one of repulsion.

That all currents are surrounded by magnetic fields was an important discovery, for many experiments by many investigators had shown that stationary charges and magnets had no effect on each other. Previous experiments had shown that charged bodies such as glass or amber rods show no magnetism. We must conclude that it is the movement of the charges (electrons) that causes the magnetism. The problem now was to find out how and why. We have already learned that one magnetic field will interact with another. It seems reasonable therefore to suspect that the electrons passing through the wire have set up a magnetic field about the wire. To check we

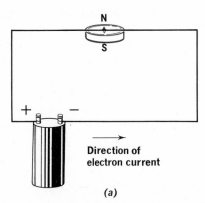

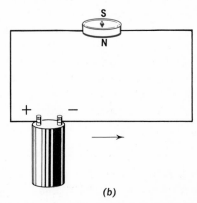

Fig. 17-17. Oersted's Experiment. (*a*) The compass is below the wire. When a current is flowing through the coil, the needle orients itself at right angles to the direction of the current. Reversal of the current causes the needle to reverse its direction. (*b*) The direction of the compass needle is also reversed as the compass is moved from a position below the wire to one above.

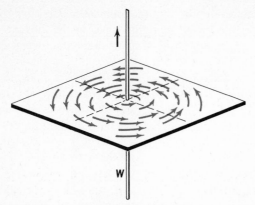

Fig. 17-18. Current-carrying wire (W) has a magnetic field in which the lines of force are concentric about the wire. If the current stops, the field disappears. If the current is reversed, the field is reversed. Would a compass needle point toward the wire?

orient a current-carrying wire vertically through a horizontal board and sprinkle iron filings about it; we find that the filings form concentric circles about the wire (Fig. 17-18). A number of tiny compasses placed alongside the wire orient themselves at right angles to the radii of these concentric circles. Therefore, the lines of force are circular about the wire—since compass needles always line up with the lines of force. If the current is reversed, the compass needles reverse their directions. Eventually the conclusion was drawn that all magnetic fields arise from electric currents, that is, that the ultimate source of every magnetic field is an electric current.

Practical Results of Oersted's Discovery

Electromagnets. If instead of a straight wire, we use a loose coil of wire (called a *helix* (Fig. 17-19) if no current is in it, and a *solenoid* if a current is), sprinkling iron filings as before, we see that the filings take much the same form as they do around a bar magnet. Moreover,

if we check with a compass, we will find that one end of the solenoid acts as a north pole, the other as a south pole. If mounted to swing freely, the solenoid would orient itself as does a compass needle. Even a single loop of wire will have a north-seeking side and a south-seeking side. The more loops in the coil, the greater the strength of the field. This makes electromagnets possible.

Electromagnets more powerful than any permanent magnet of the same size are made by inserting soft iron cores inside closely wound coils. The core greatly strengthens the magnetic field, for the core itself becomes magnetized, and the lines of force that pass through the coil are gathered into a smaller volume within the core. Electromagnets today have countless uses, from the small ones used in hearing aids, telephones, doorbells, and so on, to the giant ones used to load and unload scrap iron, railroad rails, and other heavy equipment. Of enormous importance are the facts that electromagnets can be demagnetized simply by pulling a switch that shuts off the current, and that the poles can be reversed simply by reversing the direction of the current through the coils.

Galvanometers, Ammeters, Voltmeters. As soon as Oersted's discovery was announced, experimenters everywhere went to work to exploit it. Investigation showed that the extent of the movement of a compass needle depended on the strength of the current passing through the wire. This fact made the galvanometer possible. In the first one the magnet was movable and the wire fixed, but it wasn't long before the wire, made into a coil, was made movable and the magnet fixed. (That it makes no difference which is movable and which is fixed could be deduced from what law?) A current passing through the wire makes the coil an electromagnet (Fig. 17-19) with one end (or face) of the coil a north pole,

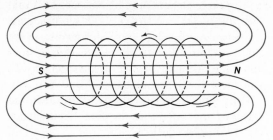

Fig. 17-19. Magnetic Field of a Current-Carrying Coil. The magnetic fields of the individual loops of wire are all in the same direction and thus reinforce each other.

the other a south pole. In Fig. 17-20 a very light wire spring may be added, with one end attached to the coil, the other to a part of the frame. This light spring (not shown in Fig. 17-20) allows the coil to turn in an attempt to orient its poles with those of the horseshoe magnet but resists the turning to such an extent that complete orientation is impossible. The greater the current, the greater the force attempting to turn the coil. A pointer is attached to the coil in somewhat the manner shown in Fig. 17-21b, and a calibrated scale can then measure the current in the coil by measuring the amount of stretch in the spring.

If a small coil is made of many turns of very fine wire, if an independently mounted soft

iron core is placed inside the coil, and if the suspending wire is of extremely fine gold, we will have a highly sensitive instrument for measuring the current in the wire, a current as small as a billionth of an ampere. Such a galvanometer is too delicate for ordinary use. More rugged ones, but still too sensitive[17] for normal use, are made by modifying the suspension. The still more rugged ammeter has a wire of low resistance in parallel with the coil so that the major part of the current, say nine tenths, will pass through it. Thus, only one tenth of the current passes through the

[17] Because of the heating effect of currents, such fine wires will easily get hot enough to melt if ordinary currents are passed through them.

Fig. 17-20. Behavior of a Flat Coil of Current-Carrying Wire in a Magnetic Field. A current in the coil causes the coil to become an electromagnet. This magnet will attempt to orient its magnetic field with that of the horseshoe magnet. If we attach a light spring to the coil in such a way that the coil cannot fully orient itself, then add a scale and a pointer (see Fig. 17-21b), we have a device that will measure the current in the coil by measuring the force acting to turn the pointer. This is possible because the force is proportional to the current. This is the principle of the galvanometer. If, on the other hand, we leave the coil free to orient its poles with those of the magnet, but then "frustrate" the attempt by changing the direction of the current in the coil, we have an incipient electric motor. If we continue the frustration and time the reversals of current direction correctly, the coil can be kept turning in the same direction. Mounting the turning coil on an axle gives us an electric motor.

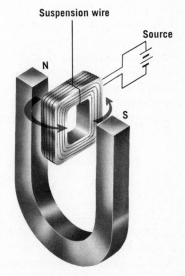

Suspension wire

Source

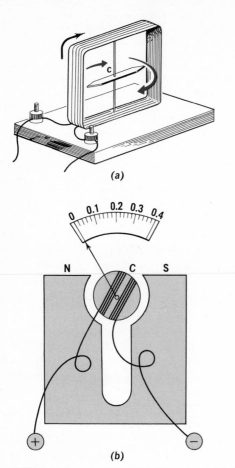

(a)

(b)

Fig. 17-21. Galvanometers and Ammeters. (*a*) A magnetic needle, *c*, is mounted within a fixed coil of wire attached to a source. The needle will tend to orient its magnetic field with that of the coil. More commonly the magnet is fixed and the coil free to move as in (*b*), where coil, *C*, and the magnet are shown in cross section. When current passes through the coil it turns to the right, moving the pointer attached to it along the scale. The greater the current, the farther the coil turns. A known fraction of the current passes through the coil; most flows through the shunt (not shown), a wire of low resistance connected electrically in parallel with the coil. Note that movement of the needle in (*a*) or of the coil in (*b*) is due to the motor effect.

coil, so large currents can be measured without burning out the coil (Fig. 17-21*b*). The scale is, of course, designed to read the full current through the system. Ammeters are always connected directly in the line in which the current is to be measured.

Galvanometers can easily be modified to measure the difference in potential between any two points in a circuit; that is, they can be converted to voltmeters. Since $V = RI$ (Ohm's law), V can be measured if the product $R \times I$ is known. All we need is to know R and I, R by a previous separate measurement, I by the galvanometer itself, and then to devise a scale that will automatically multiply R by I. As the coil twists, a pointer indicates the product on the scale.

Since P (power) $= VI$, the power supplied by a circuit can be obtained by the readings of an ammeter and a voltmeter. The total energy supplied to the circuit is found by multiplying the product of these readings by the time the current flows. For actual measurements to households and industry, a watt-hour electric meter is more convenient, and is exclusively used for that purpose.

Electric Motors: The Motor Effect. The motor effect, that is, the sideways push given a current-carrying wire in a magnetic field, is the principle that causes galvanometers, ammeters, and voltmeters to work. However, we found it easier to explain these instruments without naming or describing the principle in the manner that we will now do. The principle, based on Oersted's discovery and established by Faraday, is as follows: *If an electric current is made to flow through a conductor in a magnetic field, there will be exerted a force at right angles both to the magnetic field and to the direction of the current* (Fig. 17-22).

To explain, let us start with no current in the coil in Fig. 17-20. The flat coil is suspended

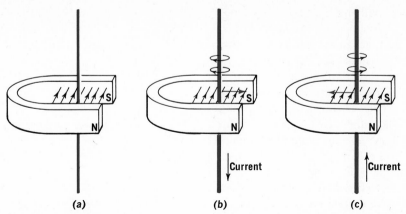

(a)   (b)   (c)

Fig. 17-22. Magnetic Deflecting Forces Acting on a Current-Carrying Conductor. The directions of the current, the magnetic field of the U-magnet, and the deflecting force are at right angles to each other.

and oriented between the poles of a magnet as shown. No force is acting on it to change its orientation until a current sent through the wire of the coil transforms it into an electromagnet. We then have two magnets and two magnetic fields that interact instantaneously in a specific way. Suppose the current is such that the instant it is turned on, the side of the coil facing the reader becomes a south pole, the other side a north pole. Then, south pole will be adjacent to south pole and north pole to north pole, and the predominant forces acting are those of repulsion of like poles. These forces cause the coil to turn and as it turns through more than 90°, the forces of attraction between unlike poles take over. If we keep the current constant, the coil would, because of inertia, swing a bit past the equilibrium position (Fig. 17-20) and then swing back, finally coming to rest after having turned through 180°. We have seen the motor effect take place but we have no motor. Now suppose we change the direction of the current in the coil the instant before the coil, having swung through a bit more than 180° because of inertia, starts to swing back. Instantly repulsion replaces attraction with the result that the coil

does not swing back but continues to turn towards the south pole of the horseshoe magnet. Again its inertia carries it a bit past the equilibrium position, and again we frustrate its attempt at orientation by changing the direction of the current at the crucial moment. Repeatedly doing this twice every revolution, causes the coil to keep on turning—and we have a potential electric motor. The reversal of the polarity of the electromagnet is accomplished by using alternating current (AC) for the electromagnet. Such current in the United States is generated to switch the polarity—that is, to reverse the current—120 times per second (60 cycles). Thus, the coil is given 120 "kicks" in the same direction per second, enough to cause it to spin rapidly, which is what we want in a motor.

For an effective motor we must redesign the setup. The suspension wire is replaced by a sturdy axle on which coarse wire is appropriately wound. Alternating current is fed through the coil, causing the polarity of the coil to be changed 120 times a second. The axle with its coils of wire, called an armature, is thus kept spinning. A pulley put on the end of the axle to which a belt may be attached, or a gear that will mesh with an appliance gear, and the motor is ready to convert electrical energy into mechanical energy (and some of it into the inevitable heat energy).

Note that we used the same diagram to explain electric motors that we used to explain galvanometers (Fig. 17-20). The only essential difference is that a light spring and a scale are necessary for galvanometers and axles are not. Note also that there are three elements in the system, the magnetic field, electric current, and motion. In the electric motor we put the magnetic field and the current into the system and take out motion. (Compare with the electric generator, Fig. 17-23.)

Electricity from Magnetism

Again it was Faraday who first successfully pondered the question, "If an electric current is capable of producing magnetism, is it not possible that magnetism can be used to produce electricity?" It took him nine or ten years of sporadic experimentation to discover how.[18] Part of the difficulty was due to the crudity of the instruments available; part was due to the fact that only a feeble momentary current could be produced, so that it could easily go undetected. To add to the difficulty, a stationary wire in a closed circuit and in a stationary magnetic field generates no current. If, however, either the wire or the field is moving, a current is generated, but only if the wire is made to cut *across* the field. If the wire moves parallel to the field—remember magnetic fields have direction (p. 285)—there will be no current. The speed of the movement, the strength

[18]Joseph Henry of the United States independently discovered how at about the same time (1831), but Faraday is usually given the credit because of priority of publication.

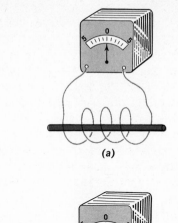

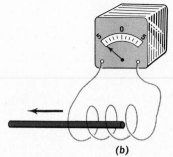

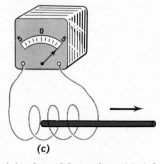

Fig. 17-23. Electricity from Magnetism. (*a*) A bar magnet at rest in a coil of wire produces no current, as can be seen by the galvanometer. (*b*) When the magnet is quickly moved to the left, the galvanometer registers a current through it. (*c*) If the magnet is moved to the right, the galvanometer registers a current in the opposite direction. In any case the needle swings back to 0 the instant motion stops. Note that a current is generated in the wire by the latter's motion across the magnetic field. This is the principle of the electric generator.

of the magnet, and the number of loops of wire, are all factors that govern the amount of current generated.

The principle involved is illustrated and explained by Figs. 17-23 and 17-24 and their captions. An electric current is a stream of electrons moving through a conductor (a copper wire in both cases). These electrons are parts of the atoms that compose the wires. Not more than one or two electrons in each atom are free to move with the expenditure of very little energy, even though there are 29 of them in each atom of copper. However, there are 6×10^{23} atoms in 63.5 g of copper (a bit over 2 oz). To generate a current this vast multitude of electrons must all move in the same direction in the wire. To get them to do so we use mechanical energy to move the magnet and its magnetic field *relative* to the wire. When we move the wire across a magnetic field, we move its free electrons with it. Each moving electron experiences a force perpendicular to the motion and perpendicular to the field. The force is therefore along the wire, pushing them

along the wire in the same direction, and giving rise to a potential difference.

Faraday's Law of Electromagnetic Induction

In explaining Faraday's law of electromagnetic induction we will repeat to some extent what we have said in the preceding paragraphs. From Faraday's experiments we may generalize the behavior of moving wires and magnetic fields as follows: *When a conductor cuts across magnetic lines of force, or the magnetic lines of force cut across a conductor, the electrons in the conductor experience a sideways push that causes them to move through the conductor as an electric current.* As stated the assumption is made that the conductor is part of a closed circuit, as in the secondary coil in Fig. 17-24. A briefer but less explanatory statement of the law is as follows: *A potential difference is induced in a conductor only while the conductor is in relative motion across lines of magnetic force.* The emphasis is on the words "relative motion across."

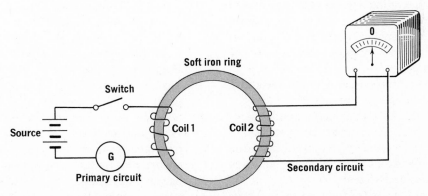

Fig. 17-24. Electromagnetic Induction. Faraday used apparatus like this to generate electricity by electromagnetic induction for the first time. Opening and closing the switch of the battery will produce a changing magnetic field about coil 1 and in the soft iron ring. The changing field in the ring, cutting back and forth across the wires of coil 2, will induce a current in the wires of that coil. Keeping the switch closed will allow a current from the battery to flow through the primary circuit, but none will be induced in the secondary. This apparatus also illustrates one type of electrical transformer.

Exercises

1. A glass rod is rubbed with silk. What charge appears on the silk?
2. A hard rubber rod is rubbed with fur. What charge appears on the fur?
3. In terms of electrons explain what happened during the rubbing in exercises 1 and 2.
4. In terms of electrons explain what happens when the charged glass rod is brought near an uncharged electroscope.
5. Do the same for the charged hard rubber rod.
6. The charged glass rod is made to stroke the metal rod of the uncharged electroscope, giving it a charge. What is the sign (positive or negative) of the charge?
7. If the rubber rod is used in place of the glass rod, what is the sign of the charge?
8. From your answers to exercises 6 and 7, we may generalize as follows: When an object is charged by contact with a charged body, the sign of the transferred charge will always be (the same as) (different from) that of the original charge. Cross out the wrong choice.
9. Suppose a rubber rod is used in place of the glass rod. What is the sign of the charge?
10. Why should television and radio sets with outside aerials be grounded?
11. In giving an object a "permanent" charge by induction, does it matter if the finger (or other ground) is removed from the object before or after the charging body is removed? Explain.
12. Why cannot a metal rod be given a charge while held in the bare hand?
13. Why may it be dangerous to turn on an electrical appliance while in the bathtub or standing on wet ground?
14. A person inside a building with a steel frame is safe from lightning. Explain.
15. Why are lightning rods made with sharp points?
16. A positively charged cloud drifts over a building protected by lightning rods that are well grounded in damp earth. No flash occurs, although one would have occurred if there were no lightning rods. Explain how the rods protected the building.
17. From what you have already learned about electric charges, criticize the old adage, "Lightning never strikes twice in the same place."
18. Two unlike charges 6 cm apart attract each other with a force X.
    (a) If they are moved so that they are 3 cm apart, they will now attract each other with what force?
    (b) If they are placed 12 cm apart, what will the attracting force be?
19. Two negative charges of 1 coulomb each are placed 1 m apart. Calculate the force in newtons.
20. How does an electrical potential difference arise?
21. What is the relationship between electrical potential difference and work?
22. What is a volt? What is the mathematical relationship among potential difference, work done, and charge transferred?
23. If 550 joules of work are done in moving 5 coulombs of charge from point A to point B, what is the potential difference between these two points?
24. Franklin's invention of the lightning rod precipitated the erection of a large number of such rods on houses in England, chiefly because of Franklin's popularity there. King George III, probably because of jealousy, decreed that every such rod should have a ball on its upper end instead of a point. What effect, if any, would this have on the efficiency of the rod?
25. The Empire State Building in New York City has been struck by lightning many

times, but no one within it has ever been injured as a result. Why?

26. You are safe from lightning in a closed modern automobile during a thunderstorm. Why? (Do not bring the rubber tires into the argument).

27. What limits the charge that can be placed on a thoroughly insulated small body? Explain.

28. How can you charge an electroscope negatively with only the help of a positively charged rod?

29. What is the difference between a static discharge and an electric current?

30. What is the relationship between the current in a wire and the potential difference between the ends of the wire?

31. Since $V = RI$, what happens to I if R drops to near zero and V is a fixed amount?

32. If 480 coulombs of charge passes through a resistance in 2 min, what is the current?

33. An electric lamp carries a current of 2 amp under a potential difference of 110 volts for 30 sec.
    (a) How much energy is supplied to the lamp.
    (b) In what form, or forms, is this energy delivered?

34. How many amperes does a 100 watt lamp draw on a 110 volt circuit?

35. The wire of the heating element in an electric stove, toaster, or iron gets red hot, but the wire running from the outlet to the stove, toaster, or iron does not. Explain.

36. By mistake you plug a radio into a 220 volt outlet and find that it burns out all the tubes. Explain precisely why.

37. Which of the following combinations of electric devices could be plugged into the same 100 volt outlet and all turned on at the same time without burning out a 15 ampere fuse in a parallel circuit?

(a) A 1000 watt toaster and a 400 watt coffee percolator.

(b) A 140 watt electric blanket, a 60 watt radio, three 100 watt lamps, and a 2 watt electric clock.

(c) A waffle iron having a resistance of 15 ohms, an electric refrigerator with a $\frac{1}{5}$ horsepower (150 watt) motor, a 750 watt electric iron, and a 50 watt radio.

38. Which has the greater resistance in each case?
    (a) The filament in a 25 watt bulb or that in a 100 watt bulb.
    (b) The filament in a 100 watt bulb or the heating element in your toaster.
    (c) Two 50 watt bulbs or one 100 watt bulb.

39. A 100 watt bulb is a more efficient light giver than two 50 watt bulbs. Why?

40. A 100 watt lamp burns steadily for 24 hr. At a rate of 5¢ per kilowatt-hour, what is the cost?

41. In a certain experiment 96,500 coulombs is sent through the apparatus. If the current is a steady 5 amperes, how long must it remain turned on?

42. In the home, electric lights are commonly turned on and off in one of several ways. They include (a) "flicking" a switch, (b) turning plastic knob, (c) pushing button or a small plastic rod, and (d) pulling a chain. Which of these devices should never be installed in a bathroom? Why?

43. In some homes, light may dim momentarily when the motor of a refrigerator starts. Explain.

44. In the 1950's an advertisement appeared in a New York City newspaper for an electrical gadget that would save the user considerable money. The argument of the advertiser went as follows: Electricity consists of two parts, volts and amperes. Ordinary electric devices were built to use only volts; the amperes were simply

wasted. His device made them use both, thus saving electricity because it did not waste the amperes. Criticize the argument.

45. How is the north pole of a magnet defined?

46. (a) Could you locate the geographical North Pole by means of a compass? Explain.

   (b) In which direction would the north end of a compass point at the North Pole?

47. Would you be wise to try to determine directions with a compass while standing (a) alongside an automobile, (b) near a wire fence, (c) on a steel bridge, and (d) beneath a high-voltage electric power line (with copper wires)? Explain in each case.

48. The deep interior of the earth consists of a core 4000 mi in diameter presumed to be composed largely of iron and some nickel. It is probably, in part at least, molten. This molten iron has been said to be the *direct* cause of the earth's magnetism. Show why it cannot be.

49. Note that it was Coulomb who produced the evidence that the forces of attraction or repulsion between electric charges and between magnetic poles follow inverse-square laws. State both of these laws, in words and mathematically.

50. The field concept applies to three types of forces.

   (a) What are they?

   (b) Who originated the field concept?

   (c) How can you detect the presence of a magnetic field?

   (d) Of an electric field?

51. There are at least three differences between a gravitational field, on the one hand, and electrical and magnetic fields, on the other. What are they?

52. Two unit poles are 2 cm apart. Let the force between them be represented by F. What will be the value of the force if the distance is (a) increased to 4 cm, (b) increased to 6 cm, (c) reduced to 1 cm?

53. (a) What sorts of things may be magnetized?

   (b) What is the easiest way to demagnetize a magnet?

   (c) Once it is demagnetized, how might you magnetize it again?

   (d) What is actually happening according to our theory of magnetism when you magnetize a steel bar?

   (e) Why should tapping the bar during magnetization process help?

54. Describe Oersted's experiment. State exactly what his discovery was.

55. (a) What is the motor effect?

   (b) In what way is it related to Oersted's discovery?

   (c) What devices depend upon it for their operation?

56. Suppose that in a particular setup a flat current-free coil of wire is suspended between the poles of a horseshoe magnet in such a way that the plane of the coil passes through the poles. Both coil and magnet are free to move. The current is then turned on.

   (a) Describe precisely what will happen and why.

   (b) What will happen if the direction of the current in the coil is reversed? Explain.

57. How does a generator (dynamo) generate electricity?

58. How can a changing magnetic field be produced in a wire without moving either the wire or a magnet?

59. Suppose that you had a stream of electrons, not confined in a wire, traveling a straight course through air or a partial vacuum.

   (a) Would their path be altered, and if so, how, if they passed the north pole of a magnet?

   (b) The south pole of another magnet?

   (c) A positively charged metal plate?

(d) A negatively charged metal plate?

60. Distinguish between AC and DC. What is meant by 60 cycle current?

61. Complete the following statements:
    (a) Magnetic fields are created through the movement of _____ .
    (b) Every change of an electric field produces a _____ .
    (c) The physicist calls these two connected fields the _____ .

62. What is (are) the effect(s) of changing electromagnetic fields in or about a loop of wire?

63. Small outboard motor boats normally carry no batteries and obviously have no outside source of electricity. They are usually started by turning the engine over by the operator pulling a cord. (Large motors use batteries to operate a self-starter). How do the small boats get the electricity needed to fire the gasoline?

64. In what fundamental respect is the electric motor similar to the electric generator (dynamo)?

65. You have two iron rods that are identical except that one is magnetized and the other isn't. How can you determine which is which without using any apparatus of any kind whatever (except the rods themselves)? (Don't forget Newton's third law).

66. In which of the following would you expect to find AC and in which DC?
    (a) The filament in a light bulb in your home.
    (b) The filament in a light bulb in your car.
    (c) In the circuit of your portable radio.
    (d) In the circuit of an outboard motor.

The Fundamental Unit of Electricity

So far we have said that electricity consists of charges, positive and negative, that are always associated with matter. The thoughtful reader will realize that such a statement tells us almost nothing about what electricity really is. The early investigators experimented to find out (1) how electricity behaved and (2) what could be done with it. The true scientists among these investigators wanted something more; they wanted to find out the fundamental nature of electricity.

The object of all science is to coordinate our experiences and bring them into a logical system.
ALBERT EINSTEIN

Passage of a Current Through Liquids— Electrolysis

Experimenters began passing electric charge through various solutions shortly after Volta invented the battery in 1800.[1] The greatest of

---

[1] You will recall that before the invention of the battery a steady uniform flow of charge was impossible. Only static electricity—a violent, riotous, discontinuous flow of charge—was possible.

these experimenters was Faraday. The process of passing an electric charge through a solution, together with any accompanying changes due to the migration of solute particles, is called *electrolysis.* Chemical changes always occur if any charge passes through the solution. In the following discussions we will center our attention on water solutions and pure molten salts such as NaCl and KCl. It was by electrolysis that some compounds were broken up that heretofore had resisted separation into their component elements. Potassium and sodium were obtained by electrolysis in 1807 by Sir Humphry Davy (the mentor of Michael Faraday) from potash (K_2O) and soda (Na_2O), which at that time were both still considered elements. Chlorine was also discovered in this way. The source is always direct current.

The essence of the process of electrolysis is as follows: In any liquid solution the solute particles (molecules, atoms, ions), that is, the particles of the material in solution, wander about as individuals among the particles of the solvent. Some solutions are good conductors and so are called *electrolytes.* Water solutions of salts, many acids, and most bases are excellent electrolytes. The pure molten salts themselves are also good conductors. If we remember that electric current in a wire consists of a stream of charged particles (electrons), then it is obvious that the passage of electric current through a solution is also a stream of charged particles that is carried in some manner from one electrode[2] to the other.

Observation of the process reveals that one kind of charged particle moves toward one electrode, while a charged particle of opposite

sign moves toward the other. Faraday called these charged particles *ions,* from a Greek word meaning "to travel." Experiment reveals that hydrogen ions[3] (H^+) and metallic ions such as sodium (Na^+) always travel toward the cathode (Fig. 18-1) proving that they carry positive charges, whereas nonmetallic ions such as chloride (Cl^-) and oxide (O^{2-}) ions and radicals such as NO_3^- and SO_4^{2-} always travel toward the anode, proving that they carry negative charges. It is the ions that carry the charges from one electrode to the other; there is no stream of electrons as such flowing through the solution. Electrons are transferred, of course, since no current through the solution is possible without such transfer.

Electrolysis of Molten Sodium Chloride

The process of transfer of electrons can best be illustrated if we pass a current through pure molten NaCl in which there is no water present to complicate the electrolytic process (Fig. 18-1). Sodium chloride is ionic not only in solution, but in the solid and molten states as well. The ions that come into contact with an electrode become neutral atoms; the positively charged sodium ions do so by acquiring an electron from the cathode, and the negatively charged chloride ions by giving up an electron to the anode. The resulting sodium atoms are deposited on the cathode as sodium metal. The chlorine atoms immediately pair up to form molecules, and these pairs escape in groups as tiny bubbles of gas, which may be collected with proper apparatus.

The electrons released at the anode pass through the connecting wire to the battery; the battery in turn furnishes electrons to

---

[2] An electrode is the conducting surface through which an electric current enters or leaves an electrolyte. Usually the electrodes are thin plates of metal attached to the conducting wires. The electrode by which the electron current enters the solution is called the *cathode,* the one by which it leaves is the *anode.* The anode is positive, the cathode negative (see p. 268).

[3] Positively charged ions are written as H^+, Na^+, Mg^{2+} (or Mg^{++}), Al^{3+}, and so on, the superiors indicating the number of positive charges. Negatively charged ions are indicated by minus signs instead of plus signs.

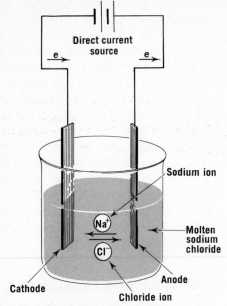

Fig. 18-1. Process of Electrolysis of Molten Sodium Chloride. Because of electrostatic attractions the positively charged sodium atoms (ions) move to the cathode where they become neutral atoms and are deposited on the cathode. The negatively charged chlorine atoms (ions) move to the anode, where they become neutral atoms and are released as a free gas.

the cathode. The reaction at the cathode is

$$Na^+ \ + \ e^- \ \rightarrow \ Na$$

and that at the anode is

$$2Cl^- \ \rightarrow \ Cl_2 \ + \ 2e^-$$

where e^- is an electron. The combined reaction may be written

$$2Na^+ + 2Cl^- + 2e^- \ \rightarrow \ 2Na + Cl_2 + 2e^-$$

Note that the electrons cancel. The net effect is transfer of two electrons from $2Cl^-$ (Cl atoms each with an extra electron) to $2Na^+$ (Na

atoms each shy one electron) by use of electrical energy, thus decomposing NaCl into free metallic sodium and chlorine gas.[4] It should be obvious that the number of electrons acquired by the sodium at the cathode must exactly equal the number released by the chlorine at the anode. If each sodium ion acquires one electron and each chloride ion gives up one, then it follows that the number of sodium atoms deposited on the cathode exactly equals the number of chloride ions liberated at the anode. Therefore, if we collect one gram atomic weight of sodium (23 g) at the cathode, we should also collect one gram atomic weight[5] of chlorine (35.5 g) at the anode, for there are the same number of atoms in a gram atomic weight of any element. What will this number of atoms be?

Electrolysis of Water

Pure water is not an electrolyte; it will not carry an electric current.[6] To electrolyze water, then, a little acid, base, or salt (usually sodium sulfate, Na_2SO_4) is dissolved in it. It is commonly said that the salt is added to "carry the current," but the details of the process are far from being understood. At least, the chemists are far from agreement on them. There is no doubt about the end result and that is all we will be concerned with here.

The process is not nearly so simple as the electrolysis of molten NaCl, where there are only two ions to reckon with. In our Na_2SO_4 solution there are Na^+, H^+, SO_4^{2-}, and OH^-

[4] Sodium metal and chlorine gas are produced industrially by this process. Electrolysis is also used for some other metals, notably aluminum.

[5] We use gram atomic weight here rather than mole because we measure the amount of the elements liberated by weighing them, not by counting the molecules or atoms released. You will recall that there are 6×10^{23} atoms in a mole of atoms, and the weight of this number of atoms in grams is numerically equal to the atomic weight of the particular kind of atom under discussion.

[6] Water is not completely un-ionizable, since one molecule in about 550 million breaks up spontaneously into H^+ and OH^- ions at room temperature.

ions, as well as molecules of water. In general, the process is one of oxidation-reduction (Chapter 25) during which one of the above species is oxidized (loses electrons) and released at the anode, and another is reduced (gains electrons) and released at the cathode. The usual rule is that these processes tend to follow the path of least resistance or that, other things being equal, the process or processes that involve the least energy change will take place. The net result at the cathode is

$$2H_2O + 2e^- \rightarrow H_2 + 2OH^-$$

or, multiplied by 2 (in order to balance the overall equation below),

$$4H_2O + 4e^- \rightarrow 2H_2 + 4OH^-$$

Hydrogen gas (H_2) is liberated at the cathode and the solution near the cathode becomes basic.[7] The net result at the anode is

$$2H_2O \rightarrow O_2 + 4H^+ + 4e^-$$

Oxygen gas (O_2) is liberated and the solution about the anode becomes acidic. The overall reaction is obtained by adding the above two equations, remembering that H^+ ions and OH^- ions combine to form H_2O:

$$4H_2O + 4e^- \longrightarrow 2H_2 + 4OH^-$$
$$2H_2O \longrightarrow O_2 + 4H^+ + 4e^-$$

$$2H_2O \xrightarrow{electrolysis} 2H_2 + O_2$$

Faraday's Laws of Electrolysis

Michael Faraday was the first to investigate quantitatively the electrolytic process. He

found that the amount of the element liberated at an electrode was directly proportional to the strength of the current and to the time that the current was allowed to pass through the solution. From these facts he formulated his first law of electrolysis: *When an electric current passes through a solution, the total mass of the particular element deposited (or liberated) is directly proportional to the total charge passing through the solution.* This must mean that each ion of a given element carries a definite amount of electric charge.

The next step was to investigate the relative amounts of electric charge carried by ions of different elements, for it was quickly apparent that these amounts varied from one element to another. This can be done as follows: Suppose we have separate beakers of HCl solution, molten NaCl, molten $MgCl_2$ and molten $AlCl_3$. Let us connect these four beakers in series with a battery, a switch, and an ammeter. Since the solutions are in series, the same number of coulombs will pass through each of them. The ammeter, together with a clock, will determine the number of coulombs, since $Q = It$. We close the switch and open it only after 1.008 g of hydrogen has been collected at the cathode.[8] A check of our ammeter and the total time the current was passing through the various solutions allows us to calculate that 96,500 coulombs of charge was transferred while 1.008 g of hydrogen was being collected. Note that the same amount of charge was passed through each of the solutions (for they are connected in series).

We now weigh the products deposited at each of the electrodes in all four beakers. The results are summarized in Table 18-1. Let us examine the results one by one to see what

---

[7]The role of the Na^+ and the SO_4^{2-} ions is to prevent the repulsive effect of ions of the same sign of charge from stopping the reaction. At the cathode, where OH^- ions are causing the solution to become basic, the Na^+ ions move in and neutralize the solution. At the anode the solution is kept neutral by the SO_4^{2-} ions moving in.

[8]We can determine the weight of hydrogen collected either by weighing, or by measuring its volume. Since 1.008 g of hydrogen is one gram atomic weight, or one half gram molecular weight (mole) of it, its volume at STP will be one half of 22.4 liters.

Table 18-1

	ANODE			CATHODE		Total charge passed (coulombs)
Beaker	Element	Weight released (g)	Element	Weight released (g)	Atomic weight	
1	Cl	35.5	H	1.008	1.008	96,500
2	Cl	35.5	Na	23.000	22.990	96,500
3	Cl	35.5	Mg	12.162	24.312	96,500
4	Cl	35.5	Al	9.000	26.981	96,500

conclusions we can draw. We note that for beaker 1, one gram atomic weight of hydrogen and one gram atomic weight of chlorine were collected at their respective electrodes. Since the number of charges released at the anode must be the same as the number released at the cathode, and since there are the same number of atoms in a gram atomic weight of any element, it follows that each hydrogen ion carried the same quantity of charge as each chloride ion.

For beaker 2 we see that one gram atomic weight each of sodium and chlorine was released. Following the same reasoning as before, we conclude that the sodium and chloride ions carry the same amount of charge. It follows that the sodium and hydrogen ions carry the same amount also.

The situation in the other two beakers is different with respect to the weights of the metals released, *although the amount of chlorine is the same*. We find that the weight of magnesium released is half a gram atomic weight and that the weight of aluminum released is one third of a gram atomic weight. This means that only half as many atoms of magnesium and only one third as many atoms of aluminum were released as there were atoms of chlorine by the same quantity of charge. Since the number of electrons given up by the chlorine at the anode must equal the number acquired by each of the metals, it follows that each magnesium ion acquired two electrons in becoming an atom, and that

each aluminum ion acquired three electrons. This means that the magnesium ion carries twice the charge of a chloride ion and an aluminum ion carries three times the charge. We also note from the formulas of their chlorides that the valence of magnesium is 2 and that of aluminum is 3.

Investigation of other elements by electrolysis of their salts reveals (1) that no ion carries a smaller charge than an ion of hydrogen or chlorine and (2) that 96,500 coulombs[9] of charge will release one gram atomic weight of any monovalent element, one half gram atomic weight of any bivalent element, and one third gram atomic weight of any trivalent element. We further note that the charges on all of these ions are in the ratios of small whole numbers and that the number of charges on any ion of an element is equal to the valence of that element. We therefore feel justified in concluding that the charges carried by atoms are even multiples of some fundamental unit charge, a unit charge that is associated with atoms of elements whose valence is one. We may now state Faraday's second law of electrolysis: *The same amount of charge will release different weights of different elements, and these weights are proportional to the atomic weights and inversely proportional to the valence.* Another way of stating the law is to say that the weights of different elements liberated by the same quantity of electricity are directly pro-

---

[9] This quantity of charge is now known as 1 faraday.

portional to their equivalent weights. (The equivalent weight of an element is defined as its atomic weight divided by its valence. Equivalent weights are sometimes referred to as combining weights.)

If there is a fundamental unit of charge—that is, if the charge on the electron is the smallest unit of charge that can exist—and if we know the charge carried by one electron, then we can calculate the number of electrons in 1 faraday (96,500 coulombs) of electricity. The charge on the electron is 1.6×10^{-19} coulomb (for method of determination, see p. 310). Therefore the number of electrons in 1 faraday is

$$\frac{96,500}{1.6 \times 10^{-19}} = \frac{9.65 \times 10^4}{1.6 \times 10^{-19}}$$
$$= 6.023 \times 10^{23} \quad [18\text{-}1]$$

You will note that this is Avogadro's number, the number of atoms in a gram atomic weight of any element (or in a gram molecular weight of any compound or diatomic gas). We see now why it is that 96,500 coulombs of electricity will liberate one gram atomic weight (6×10^{23} atoms) of any monovalent element.

We must not think that Faraday knew all this. He made the experiments and formulated the laws of electrolysis, but he knew nothing of electrons, or the absolute quantity of charge on the ion, or of Avogadro's number. *The fundamental concept in Faraday's laws is that the smallest charge that can exist is that associated with monovalent ions.* Can we infer, then, that electricity, like chemical elements, consists of unit particles comparable to atoms? Faraday himself came very near making that inference but was held back, perhaps by a belief in the indivisibility of atoms.

In 1874, Johnstone Stoney expressly stated that *the charge on a monovalent ion was the smallest charge that could exist.* His argument

was as follows: A given weight of an element consists of a definite number of atoms; a definite quantity of charge liberates a definite number of atoms of that element; therefore, the total charge must be evenly distributed among the atoms. If matter comes in packets that we call atoms, then *electricity must also come in packets* (which Stoney proposed to call electrons). *Electricity is therefore particulate in nature just as are matter and radiant energy.* Thus, each negative ion carried 1, 2, or 3 extra electrons, and each positive ion was missing 1, 2, or 3 electrons, the number depending upon the valence. In 1881, Helmholtz clearly stated that Faraday's laws imply the existence of "atoms" of electricity. Yet still another 15 years were to elapse before the electron was discovered to be a universal constituent of all matter.

Passage of an Electric Current Through Gases

Experimental work of major consequence on the passage of electricity through gases came much later than that on its passage through liquid solutions, most likely because normally gases are rather good insulators. Any insulator will conduct electricity if a large enough potential difference is applied. At ordinary atmospheric pressure it takes a potential difference of 30,000 volts to make a spark jump from one charged electrode to another 1 cm away.

Experimental work on the passage of electricity through gases also had to await the invention of the gas discharge tube (1853). It was simply a partially evacuated glass tube with a metal electrode sealed in each end (Fig. 18-2) and a small branching tube with an opening so that a vacuum pump could be attached to reduce the gas pressure when desired. The common tubes used for fluorescent lighting or for advertising signs are types of

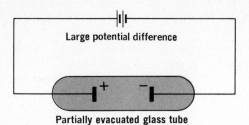

Partially evacuated glass tube

Fig. 18-2. Simple Gas Discharge Tube. A hole, not shown in a longitudinal section, is commonly present in each electrode.

discharge tubes. In all of them an electric current is passed through a gas under low pressure. The current is carried by ions, positive and negative, just as it is through an electrolytic solution (Fig. 18-3).

How do the ions originate? In the electrolysis of molten NaCl, we said that sodium and chlorine are both ionic, that is, exist as ions, in either liquid or solid NaCl. There is no need to create ions; the whole molten mass consists entirely of ions. However, in our discharge tube, there is nothing but molecules of a gas, along with a few ions that are always present in air (or any other gas) for various reasons. Collisions[10] between some of the more energetic neutral molecules result in some of them

losing a charge, thus becoming positively charged ions. Other neutral molecules pick up the freed charges, thus becoming negatively charged ions. Thus ions are created in pairs, one positive and one negative. Ions of opposite sign attract one another, and so commonly recombine to form neutral molecules when they collide. However, more are being formed all the time, so that at any given temperature there is an equilibrium between ion formation and ion recombination. This equilibrium may be upset by applying a higher potential difference to the electrodes. This increases the energy of the ions already present, the positive ions are accelerated toward the cathode and the negative ions toward the anode.

Air is such an excellent insulator that if normal air pressure is maintained in the tube, no detectable current will pass through the tube except at a very high voltage. We therefore use the vacuum pump to reduce the pressure. The current will now rise rapidly for two reasons: (1) the mean free path of the ions present is greatly increased so that more of them reach the proper electrode per unit time even though some ions are being removed by the pump, and (2) these accelerated ions are more effective creators of new ions. Let us continue to evacuate the discharge tube.

The two-way migration of ions constitutes the current in the early stages of the evacuation. An ammeter inserted in the circuit does not record a current immediately because not

---

[10] There are countless collisions among the vast hordes of molecules in the tube, 2.7×10^{19} per cubic centimeter at normal air pressure with an average velocity of $\frac{1}{3}$ mi/sec. The collision rate is of the order of 5 billion per sec per molecule; the mean free path (distance traveled between collisions) is of the order of 8.5×10^{-6} cm.

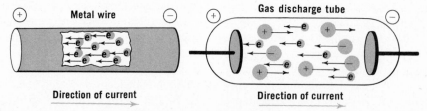

Fig. 18-3. Current in a Wire vs. Current in Gas Discharge Tube. In the wire electrons move from negative (−) to positive (+); this is the *electron* current. In the gas discharge tube the two-way migration of ions constitutes the current. The *conventional* current is from positive (+) to negative (−) (see p. 268).

enough ions are present. As the vacuum pump decreases the molecular population, the collisions become more effective creators of new ions (for reasons already stated). The ammeter soon records a current. When the pressure is sufficiently low a fascinating and beautiful series of events take place in the tube. First a narrow branching beam of reddish purple light writhes and twists across the tube from one electrode to the other. The vacuum pump continues to reduce the pressure as this beam of light thickens to fill most of the tube— except for a blue glow near the cathode and a dark space at the anode. At still lower pressures the blue glow is replaced by a thin red sheath of light. A dark space develops to the right of it, followed by a band of light, blue light that gradually fades into another dark space that occupies the middle portion of the tube. Nearer the anode is a broad band of weak red-violet light. When the vacuum pump has reduced the pressure to less than a millionth of an atmosphere these colored lights all fade and disappear. The ammeter reading drops to zero. We conclude that there are no longer enough ions at this low pressure to form a detectable current. Then almost at once the glass wall of the inside of the tube near the anode begins to glow with a soft green fluorescent light. The ammeter registers a low current again.

We can explain the fading and disappearance of the light by assuming that the vacuum pump has reduced the density of the ions until there are no longer enough to produce a detectable flow. We can explain the soft greenish glow and the resumption of a current reading on the ammeter *only* if we assume that something other than ions is now constituting the current, perhaps some kind of rays that cause the glass to fluoresce as they impinge on the glass. Pending further identification these rays were called cathode rays. That the rays come from the cathode can be proved in

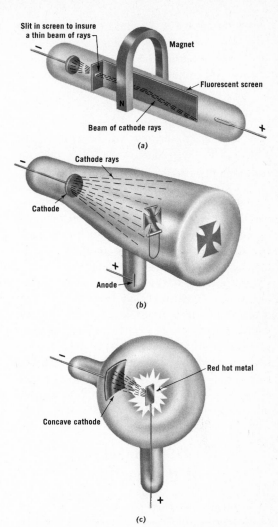

Fig. 18-4. Cathode Ray Tubes. (*a*) Magnetic deflection of cathode rays by Thomson was accomplished in such a tube as this. Note that the beam is deflected downward and that this direction is at right angles to the magnetic field of the magnet. The fluorescent screen is to make the beam visible. (*b*) Cathode rays cast a sharp shadow of a Maltese Cross on the screen on the inside of the front end of the tube. This indicates that the rays travel in straight lines. (*c*) A beam of rays is focused on a piece of metal in the center of the tube. The metal gets red hot; this proves that the rays have considerable kinetic energy.

a number of ways. The most obvious is by switching the polarity. Doing so causes the most intense part of the greenish glow to shift towards the other end of the tube—for the anode has now become the cathode. If an opaque object, such as a maltese cross is properly placed in the tube with a screen (Fig. 18-4b), a sharp shadow will be cast on the screen. The sharp shadow indicates that the rays follow straight lines.

For a time some scientists thought that these rays were a form of light rays comparable to ultraviolet or infrared radiation. However, it was soon shown that they could be deflected in magnetic fields, and, later, in electric fields. The directions of these deflections showed that the rays carried negative charges (Fig. 18-4a). It was also shown that they could convey momentum and so had inertia, mass and kinetic energy. While it was eminently reasonable to expect them to be particles, one or two quantitative tests of the rays would remove any last lingering doubts. The obvious measurements to be made were those of mass and magnitude of charge.

Thomson's Discovery of the Electron

Although a German physicist had observed the phenomenon of cathode rays for the first time in 1858, and many others had experimented with them in the intervening years, it remained for J. J. Thomson to perform the crucial series of experiments that proved the rays were universal constituents of all matter and to determine the ratio of their charge to their mass, a ratio commonly known as e/m (to be read as e over m). His method was brilliant but simple. To determine the ratio, he had first to calculate the velocity. He did this by employing both electric and magnetic fields of known strength, for a beam of charged

particles can be deflected by either electric or magnetic fields. In electric fields the deflection is one of electrostatic attraction or repulsion, whereas in a magnetic field, the deflection is at right angles both to the direction of the field and to the direction the rays are traveling (see p. 290 and Fig. 17-22). It can be shown that the force acting on a beam of charged particles moving in a magnetic field is given by the following equation:

force = magnetic field strength
$\qquad$ × charge × velocity

Symbolically,

$$F = Hev \qquad [18\text{-}2]$$

It can also be shown that the force acting on the same beam in an electric field is given by

force = electric field strength × charge

Symbolically,

$$F = Ee \qquad [18\text{-}3]$$

Thomson subjected the beam to both electric and magnetic fields at the same time by passing it between two charged plates and between the poles of an electromagnet (Fig. 18-5). The plates were charged so as to deflect the beam one way and the magnet oriented so as to deflect it the opposite way. By regulating the strength of the two fields the two forces could be made equal so that there was no deflection. Thus,

magnetic field strength × charge
$\qquad$ × velocity = electric field strength
$\qquad\qquad\qquad\qquad$ × charge

or in symbols,

$$Hev = Ee \qquad [18\text{-}4]$$

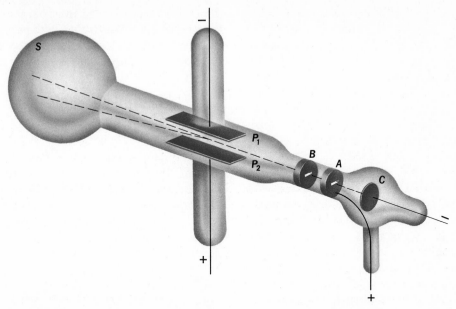

Fig. 18-5. Thomson's Apparatus for Determination of e/m (somewhat modernized). C, cathode; A, anode with a hole in it; B, plate with a hole in it to provide a narrow beam of cathode rays; P_1 and P_2, plates charged so as to deflect the rays downward; S, a fluorescent screen to make the rays "visible." Not shown is the electromagnet, whose field lies at right angles to the plane of the paper and is oriented so as to deflect the rays upward. If the two deflecting forces are equal, there is no deflection.

Since the charge, e, appears on both sides, it cancels out. This was no doubt disappointing to Thomson, for e was one of the two quantities he sought. However, he had an equation for v, and this might help him in his quest. Transposing,

$$v = \frac{E}{H} \qquad [18\text{-}5]$$

The electric field strength, E, is determined by placing a voltmeter in the circuit with the charged plates, and the magnetic field, H, by slightly more complex means if an electromagnet is used. From Eq. [18-5], v is determined. For the particular tube he was using, Thomson found the velocity of the rays to be about 10,000 mi/sec. Knowing the velocity of the rays, he could perform a second experiment to determine the ratio e/m.

In this second experiment he used the deflection in a magnetic field only. The rays are deflected at right angles to the direction in which they are moving. If the magnetic field is uniform and large enough, the beam is continuously deflected; the resulting path is an arc of a circle. Recall that a change of direction is an acceleration, and that an acceleration at right angles to the direction of motion is a characteristic of uniform circular motion; it is apparent that the equations for uniform circular motion (p. 124) will apply. These equations are

$$a = \frac{v^2}{r}$$

and, substituting for a in $F = ma$,

$$F = \frac{mv^2}{r}$$

However, Eq. [18-2] is also an equation for the force acting on the beam in a magnetic field. Hence, the two expressions can be equated.

$$\frac{mv^2}{r} = Hev \qquad [18\text{-}6]$$

Transposing,

$$\frac{e}{m} = \frac{v}{Hr} \qquad [18\text{-}7]$$

The quantities v, H, and r can be measured, v as already described, H as already indicated, and r by measuring the deflection of the beam in the field. The quantity v/Hr comes out to be 176 million (1.76×10^8) coulombs/g of particles. This value for e/m means that 1 g of the particles moving through a wire will furnish 1.76×10^8 coulombs of electricity.[11]

Thomson had to be content with the ratio alone, for he could conceive of no way of measuring e or m. He used many different substances as his cathode and found that the e/m of the rays was the same regardless of the source.[12] Cathode rays soon came to be known as *electrons,* the name that Johnstone Stoney had suggested for the charge on a monovalent ion. The "atomicity" of electricity seemed proved.

Thomson was very reluctant to advance the idea that atoms are not the indivisible particles envisaged by Dalton but are complex mechanical systems composed of positively and negatively charged parts. It was only after repeated experiments had convinced him that

he said: "There is no escape from the conclusion that we are here dealing with particles far, far lighter than atoms." At first he had very few converts. Further evidence was needed.

Confirming Evidences for Electrons

A number of phenomena had long been waiting for explanations; perhaps the discovery of electrons would furnish the key to them. But measurement of either the charge or the mass of the electron would go a longer way in convincing the skeptical of the reality of electrons.

Millikan's Oil Drop Experiment

In the years following Thomson's discovery of the electron attempts were made, first by Thomson and then by others, to measure the charges carried by very small amounts of matter. The object was to measure the charge on the electron, for if the charges on enough samples were determined, perhaps one sample would be found that carried a single charge. One difficulty was that of being able to recognize such a sample; perhaps some other sample would carry a smaller charge. No one was naive enough to think that he could isolate a single electron and measure its charge.

The principles involved are really quite simple. The mass of any body can be determined by a measurement of the force acting on it when it is accelerated (for $F = ma$). Similarly, the charge on a body can be measured by the force it experiences in an electric field. It is neither practical nor necessary to measure the force on a single electron. However, the total number of electrons on a body must be small enough so that a change of one electron makes a noticeable difference. Since the force on the charged body is most likely to be very small, the body itself must be very light. The

---

[11] This is enough electricity to keep a 100 watt light bulb burning 24 hours a day for nearly 6 years.

[12] It is interesting to turn this ratio upside down so that it reads m/e. It is equal to about 0.00055 g/faraday. This means that if Thomson had continued his experiment collecting the electrons until 96,500 coulombs had passed through the circuit, the total weight of the electrons emitted from the cathode would have been 0.00055 g. The corresponding figure for hydrogen is 1.008 g/faraday. If we now divide 1.008 by 0.00055 we get 1833. This means that it takes 1833 electrons to weigh as much as one hydrogen atom, the lightest of all the atoms.

fact that the force of gravity must be reckoned with also demands that the body be very light if the very small electric force is not to be masked by a relatively large gravitational force. Optimum conditions will exist if the electric and gravitational forces are nearly the same order of magnitude.

For the body to carry the charges, an American physicist, Robert A. Millikan, used oil drops from the mist sprayed from a small atomizer of the type used for perfume. These spherical drops were so small that they could be observed only in a beam of light and by the use of a microscope (Fig. 18-6). A drop that small falls slowly through the air because of countless collisions with air molecules. However, the velocity of such spherical drops can be determined by the application of Stokes' law, the derivation of which will not concern us here. Suffice it to say that such drops accelerate only briefly after they start to fall and then attain a constant velocity.[13] This constant velocity, called the terminal velocity, is far easier to determine than an acceleration, and it is a measure of the forces acting on the body.

Millikan brought the measurements of the charges on the drops to a high degree of precision and was able to present convincing evidence that he had determined the charge on the electron. His method was ingenious. He started with two parallel metal plates connected to a source of direct current whose voltage he could carefully control. Thus, he could vary the charge on the plates at will. The upper plate had a tiny hole drilled in it so that if oil were sprayed in the region directly *above* the plates, an occasional drop would drift downward through the hole into the space

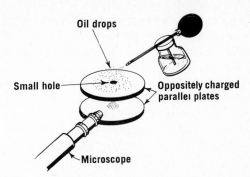

Fig. 18-6. Schematic Representation of Millikan's Oil Drop Apparatus for Measurement of the Charge on the Electron.

between the plates. This region was strongly illuminated so that Millikan, by means of a small microscope, could see the droplet as it wafted downward slowly because of air friction. The droplet would probably be charged by friction as it was sprayed from the nozzle of the atomizer, and so be attracted by one charged plate and repelled by the other. The whole apparatus was enclosed to protect the droplets from air currents. Once a droplet came into view, Millikan could close the hole to prevent any others from coming through. He then charged the plates, giving the upper one a charge that was opposite to that which was on the drop. If this plate were given a charge exactly large enough to counteract the gravitational attraction, the droplet would remain stationary if there were no collisions with air molecules. There are, however, billions of collisions per minute with air molecules, so many that the Brownian fluctuations (p. 213) are negligible. Millikan was able to watch one drop continuously for 18 hours.

In such a situation the upward electrical force, Eq, would equal the downward gravitational force, mg. Hence,

$$Eq = mg \quad \text{and} \quad q = \frac{mg}{E} \quad [18\text{-}8]$$

E, the strength of the electric field, is deter-

---

[13] A constant velocity is attained by any body falling through the atmosphere from a great enough height, a height such that the gravitational force acting on the body is equal to the force of friction with the atmosphere. The net force is then zero. In accord with Newton's first law, the body falls with constant speed.

mined from the voltmeter reading and the distance between the plates, m is the mass of the drop, and q is the charge on the drop. Millikan could determine m from Stokes' law, which relates the terminal velocity of a spherical drop falling through air to the mass of the drop, the density of the material composing the drop, and the viscosity of the air. Since the last two quantities are known and the terminal velocity can be measured directly as the drop slowly falls between the plates, the mass is easily calculated. This leaves q as the only unknown, and so it is easily found.

Millikan not only measured the charge on scores of droplets, but he also varied the experiment in many ways. One way was to ionize the air between the plates by means of X rays or other radiation. The droplets would pick up one or more of the ions, thus acquiring a new charge. This would upset the balance between the electric and the gravitational fields, and a new equilibrium would have to be made by changing the value of the charge on the plates. The difference between the original charge and the new one gave the charge on the ion, or ions, acquired by the drop. He also varied the experiment by using oils of different viscosities, by using atomizers that gave smaller or larger drops, by using different gases in his enclosed apparatus, and in several other ways.

Millikan made thousands of such measurements; he worked for six years before he began to get consistent results. When he tabulated and analyzed his results, he found that all his charge measurements were, within the experimental limits of error, whole number multiples of a certain number that *might* or *might not* be the constant minimum charge on the electron. Some representative examples are listed in Table 18-2. The work of Millikan on this problem demonstrates the role of "perspiration" in scientific work.

Obviously, the charge on the electron cannot be the smallest of the values in the table, for

Table 18-2
Charges on Oil Drops, q
(coulombs) [Millikan]

1.	3.2×10^{-19}	6. 8.0×10^{-19}
2.	9.6×10^{-19}	7. 20.8×10^{-19}
3.	6.4×10^{-19}	8. 11.2×10^{-19}
4.	14.4×10^{-19}	9. 17.6×10^{-19}
5.	19.2×10^{-19}	10. 12.8×10^{-19}

3.2 is not evenly divisible into all the other values. It must therefore be smaller than 3.2×10^{-19}. Numbers greater than 0.01 that are evenly divisible into 3.2 are 1.6, 0.8, 0.4, 0.2, and 0.1. We can eliminate the last four by noting that the values in the table (assumed to be representative) do not include values that are not also evenly divisible by 1.6. For example, if the value is 0.8, why are there not values such as 4.0×10^{-19}, 5.6×10^{-19}, 2.4×10^{-19}, and the like, values divisible by 0.8 but not by 1.6? *Thus, the charge on the electron, e, is* 1.6×10^{-19} *coulomb*. Millikan obtained multiples of this unit, some up to nearly 200 times it. Many measurements have been made by many experimenters since Millikan first announced his results in 1910. The accepted modern value for the charge on an electron is $(1.601864 \pm 0.000025) \times 10^{-19}$ coulomb.

Mass of the Electron. Once e was known, the mass of the electron could be calculated from Thomson's e/m ratio:

$$\frac{e}{m} = 1.76 \times 10^8 \text{ coulombs/g} \quad [18\text{-}9]$$

Transposing,

$$m = \frac{e}{1.76 \times 10^8}$$

$$= \frac{1.6 \times 10^{-19} \text{ coulomb}}{1.76 \times 10^8 \text{ coulomb/g}}$$

$$= 9.1 \times 10^{-28} \text{ g} \quad [18\text{-}10]$$

The more accurate value is $(9.1084 \pm 0.0004) \times 10^{-28}$ g. It takes nearly 2000 electrons to equal the mass of a single hydrogen atom, the lightest of all the atoms (see footnote 12).

Avogadro's Number. Confirmation of the size of the charge on the electron was made by measurements of the amount of charge carried by monovalent ions in liquid solutions. The basic constant, Avogadro's number, could now be computed by using the above value of e.

You will remember the faraday as the number of coulombs needed to liberate one gram atomic weight of any monovalent element by electrolysis. If we assume that each monovalent negative ion in solution had one excess electron whose charge is 1.6×10^{-19} coulomb and that this electron is liberated during electrolysis, then dividing the total charge by the unit charge will give us the number of monovalent atoms liberated by the total charge.

Dividing the faraday by e, we get

$$\frac{96,500 \text{ coulombs}}{1.6 \times 10^{-19} \text{ coulomb}} = 6.023 \times 10^{23}$$

[18-11]

Avogadro's number has been verified in a number of quite different ways. Thus, the "atomicity" or particle concept of electricity rests on a sound basis.

Thermionic Emission of Electrons

Strong support for the electron concept also came from its ability to explain another phenomenon that had gone unexplained since its discovery in 1883 by Thomas Edison. Edison was attempting to improve the electric light bulb. The observation, now called the Edison effect, was not further investigated by Edison, however, for he could see no way in which it would help him improve his bulb.

We can illustrate the phenomenon by building a metal plate into an ordinary light bulb

at the time of its manufacture. A wire leads from the plate through a sealed hole in the bulb to the outside (Fig. 18-7). The pressure within the bulb is about 10^{-6} atm. The wire leading from the plate is then attached to a galvanometer, which in turn is connected to a power source, say to the positive terminal of the battery that supplies the current to the bulb. If the circuit is now closed, the bulb lights up, but the galvanometer shows no instantaneous deflection. Then, suddenly it does, showing that a current has begun to flow even though the plate is connected to nothing inside the bulb; we conclude that the current must be flowing across the gap between the plate and the filament of the bulb.

How does the current get across the highly evacuated space between the filament and the plate? There was no adequate answer at the time because the electron had not yet been discovered. It cannot be by ions of gas in the bulb, for we have seen from our cathode ray experiment (p. 305) that there are insufficient ions to form a current at the very low pressure of the gas inside the bulb. Moreover, if we connect the plate to the negative terminal of the battery, no current flows. Thus, the current is unidirectional. If we now decrease the current flowing to the bulb filament so that the filament is no longer heated to incandescence, no current is detected by the galvanometer even when the plate is connected to the positive terminal. Conversely, the hotter the filament, the greater the current flowing across the gap up to a point called the saturation point. We temporarily conclude that electrons are being ejected from the hot filament.

That the current flowing across the gap between the plate and the filament is actually a flow of electrons was later demonstrated by Thomson, who measured their e/m and found it to be the same as for cathode rays. This provided a ready explanation not only for thermionic emission but also for the concept

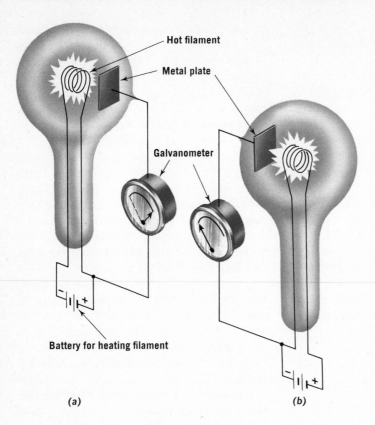

Hot filament

Metal plate

Galvanometer

Battery for heating filament

(a)

(b)

Fig. 18-7. The Edison Effect: Thermionic Emission of Electrons. (*a*) Metal plates are inserted in ordinary electric light bulbs. They are connected on the outside of the circuit that lights the bulbs. The plate on the left is connected to the positive side of the battery so that the plate is positively charged. When the filament is hot, electrons are ejected from it, and the galvanometer shows that a current is flowing despite the lack of any physical connection between the plate and the bulb. The circuit is completed by the stream of electrons ejected from the filament traveling from the filament to the plate because of their attraction for it. In (*b*) the plate is connected to the negative side of the battery. No current flows. Why not?

of an electric current consisting of a flow of electrons. The phenomenon of thermionic emission can be explained as follows: Electrons are negatively charged particles that are attracted toward positively charged bodies and repelled by negatively charged bodies. Thus, when the plate in the bulb is positive the emitted electrons are attracted to it and so the circuit is completed. When the plate is negative the electrons are repelled from it so that the circuit is incomplete. Therefore, the plate must always be positively charged. As such, it is a one-way street that allows electrons to move across the gap only from filament to plate. Direct current (DC) crosses the gap unhindered. But consider alternating current (AC), in which electrons are alternating directions

120 times per second (in 60 cycle current). Electrons can cross the gap only when their direction is from filament to plate, never from plate to filament. Thus AC is converted to DC. Every radio or TV set that operates with tubes has one tube that operates in this manner to change the normal AC supplied to your house into DC. It is called a *rectifier.*

Perhaps we will gain a deeper insight into thermionic emission if we compare it to the evaporation of a liquid. In a liquid the molecules that escape (evaporate) are those that have gained extra energy. Heat provides the extra energy, and the hotter the liquid, the faster the evaporation up to the boiling point. The rate of evaporation at a given temperature varies with the liquid.

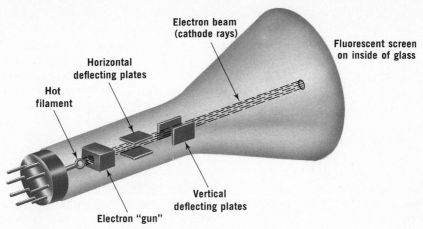

Fig. 18-8. Common Television Tube. The hot filament ejects electrons (thermionic emission) which are given high energy by the high voltage produced in the electron gun. The two sets of plates deflect the electrons as they are alternately given positive and negative charges by whatever is coming in over the aerial. These deflected electrons form the picture on the fluorescent screen.

Electric Charges vs. Electrons

Previous to Thomson's work on e/m all electric phenomena were explained as a flow of charges. Essentially it was Franklin's theory that was used. The term *charge* is a nondescript and vague term. The concept of an electron as a particle having a definite mass and a fixed amount of negative charge is intellectually far more satisfying.

With electrons now regarded as definite parts of atoms, some of which can be removed more or less easily, a better understanding of conductors and insulators is possible. The atoms forming conductors hold some of their electrons very loosely so that they can move about readily. Hence they can be made to move all in one direction, forming an electric current. Atoms of insulators hold their electrons relatively tightly and so a current cannot

be set up in them, or, at best, only with difficulty.

The quantitative data amassed about electrons plus the ability of the electron concept to explain many diverse inexplicable phenomena made the scientific world—except, perhaps, for a few die-hards—willing to accept the divisibility of the atom. Moreover, the inference that had been drawn from Faraday's laws of electrolysis by Johnstone Stoney—that electricity was particulate in nature, and that the electron was its fundamental unit—received firm experimental support.

Exercises

1. (a) How are the charges transported through a solution during electrolysis?
   (b) How does this differ from the transportation of charges through a wire?
2. To what electrode are (a) metallic ions

and (b) nonmetallic ions transported during electrolysis?

3. How does an ion (a) at the cathode and (b) at the anode become a neutral atom?

4. State Faraday's laws of electrolysis.

5. (a) What purpose does the battery serve in the process of electrolysis? Be explicit, please.

   (b) Could a source of alternating current instead of direct current be used? Explain.

6. (a) How much charge is 1 faraday?

   (b) How can the magnitude of the charge be determined?

7. A current of 2 amperes is passed through a molten salt for 80 min (4800 sec).

   (a) How many faradays (approximately) passed through?

   (b) How many electrons were transferred at the cathode? How many at the anode?

   (c) How many atoms of a monovalent metal would be deposited at the cathode? How many of a bivalent element? Of a trivalent element?

   (d) If the salt was a chloride, how many *atoms* of chlorine would be released at the anode? How many *molecules*?

   (e) What would this amount of chlorine weigh?

8. How many coulombs are required to liberate 1 mole of iron (a) from $FeCl_2$ and (b) from $FeCl_3$?

9. (a) How many molecules of chlorine would be released in the process of liberating 1 mole of iron from $FeCl_2$?

   (b) What is this number called?

10. (a) How many atoms of iron would be liberated from $FeCl_3$ by $\frac{1}{10}$ coulomb, and how many *atoms* of chlorine?

    (b) Suppose the solution to be $FeCl_2$. How many atoms of iron and how many atoms of chlorine would be liberated?

11. For compounds of magnesium, copper, iron, and so on, water solutions can be used to obtain the metals by electrolysis. We cannot obtain metallic sodium and potassium by use of their water solutions but have to use their compounds in the molten state. Why?

12. State the argument for the existence of "atoms" of electricity (as shown by Faraday's experiments).

13. Why is a high voltage necessary to pass an electric current through gases?

14. Why does a reduction of the pressure in a gas discharge tube result in better conductance of a current?

15. (a) What is meant by a ray of radiation?

    (b) How could you distinguish an electromagnetic ray from a particle ray? Would this method apply to all kinds of particles? Explain.

16. What did J. J. Thomson do with respect to cathode rays that previous investigators had not done?

17. How much does 6×10^{23} atoms of hydrogen weigh? What is the ratio of the weight of an electron to that of an atom of hydrogen (approximately)?

18. (a) What are positive rays?

    (b) How are they related to cathode rays?

19. (a) What is meant by *thermionic emission* of electrons?

    (b) Why is there no current if the plate is connected to the negative terminal of the battery?

20. What practical uses are made of thermionic emission?

21. Why does a radio or television set that uses tubes not work instantly when you turn it on?

22. A rectifier is a tube in some "plug-in" types of radio and television sets (as opposed to battery-operated sets). It changes alternating current to direct current. Explain how it does this.

23. (a) What are ions?

(b) What is the charge on a monovalent ion?

24. Why didn't J. J. Thomson calculate the value of e, the charge on the electron?

25. What is Avogadro's number?

26. What were J. J. Thomson's final conclusions concerning cathode rays?

27. In measuring the charge on the electron, Millikan measured the charge carried by oil drops. Did he have to make certain that he had a drop with just one charge on it?

28. If he had an oil drop with just one charge on it, how would he recognize that fact? Explain.

PART V

Structure of Matter

The Divisibility of Atoms

Chapter 19

The investigations into the structure of atoms followed two apparently unrelated paths, which we may call the *particle path* and the *wave path*. Ultimately the two paths join, the junction made possible by a great many scientists working independently in apparently totally unrelated fields. We might show the two paths and their junction as follows:

Particle path
- Faraday and electrolysis
- Discovery of the electron
- Discovery of radioactivity
- Rutherford's theory of the nucleus

Wave path
- Electromagnetic theory of light
- Spectra
- Planck's, quantum theory
- Einstein's photon theory

Bohr theory of the hydrogen atom

Union of the two paths in the Bohr theory and the immediate consequences led to the electronic configuration of atoms, which gave a

> The value of any working theory depends upon the number of experimental facts it serves to correlate, and upon its power of suggesting new lines of work.
> **LORD RUTHERFORD**
> **(Nobel Prize, Chemistry, 1908)**

logical basis for the groups and the periods of the periodic table. It also led to electronic interpretations of the various kinds of chemical reactions.

We have already discussed the first two parts of the particle path, the work of Faraday in the early 1830's, and that of Thomson in the late 1890's. We will proceed to the other parts after a brief review of the early development of the modern concept of atoms. The wave path and the Bohr theory are treated in Chapters 20 and 22.

Atoms vs. Ions and Electrons

John Dalton had formulated his atomic theory in the early 1800's. It was accepted at once even though it ran into trouble because of its failure to explain Gay-Lussac's law of combining volumes (Chapter 15). It had reached a low ebb in the 1850's and would probably have been abandoned if there had been anything better to replace it, but scientists would rather tolerate a "lame" theory than have no theory at all. Even a lame theory could help them make progress, slow though it might be. Then up rose Cannizzaro with his resurrection of Avogadro's hypothesis—and the law of combining volumes was reconciled with the atomic theory. The theory was rejuvenated; the "scales fell from the eyes" of the chemists, enabling them to find their way out of the blind alley Dalton had created for them by his stubborn insistence on his fifth assumption; and the science of chemistry bloomed again.

Meanwhile Michael Faraday had discovered ions in his work on electrolysis. What was the relationship between atoms and ions? Certainly Faraday did not know. The uncertain status of the Dalton theory at the time did not help him any, and its uncertainty may have prevented him from speculating on the possibility that a negative ion with its extra

charge(s) was a "bit more" than a neutral atom, and a positive ion with not enough charge(s) was a "bit less" than a neutral atom, even though the belief in an atom's indivisibility was well-nigh universal. The "bits" were, of course, the electrons that J. J. Thomson was to "discover" nearly three quarters of a century later, and that Johnstone Stoney was to name more than 20 years before they were discovered (p. 303). Thomson, even after discovering that cathode rays were ejected from many different kinds of atoms and noting that they were "particles far, far lighter than atoms," was still reluctant to advance the idea that atoms are not the indivisible particles envisaged by Dalton. It takes about 1830 electrons to weigh as much as one hydrogen atom, the lightest of all atoms. The atomic weight of hydrogen is 1.008 and $\frac{1}{1830}$ of 1.008 is so small a quantity that for many purposes we say that the mass of the electron is zero. This "tearing loose" of electrons from atoms of many kinds was the first direct evidence that atoms were divisible.

Radioactivity

Even if Thomson's discovery of the electron had not been made until much later, revision of the atomic theory would have been necessary because of a very different sort of discovery. In 1896 Henri Becquerel of France was working with fluorescent minerals to see if they emitted X rays (which had been discovered only a few months previously). He had been exposing well-wrapped photographic plates to certain fluorescent minerals in full sunlight. Because of a spell of cloudy weather, he placed his minerals and a new set of unexposed well-wrapped plates in a drawer. Some days later he returned to his experiments, and, being a careful experimenter, he did not want to use plates that had been in the vicinity of his fluorescent minerals for several days. However, he decided to develop these plates without further exposing them. He found them fogged.

"I thought at once," he said, "that the action might be able to go on in the dark." Accordingly, he placed a new well-wrapped plate in the drawer with the same minerals. On developing it he found it was intensely fogged. He began testing the minerals to find out which was emitting some kind of radiation that was capable of passing through opaque materials. It turned out to be a uranium mineral called pitchblende, whose composition is U_3O_8. Since oxygen is known not to emit such radiation, the emitter of the rays was probably uranium. Pure uranium, put in a drawer with unexposed plates, not only proved this but also showed that it was more effective, gram for gram, in fogging plates than was the oxide. Other minerals were tested and all those containing either uranium or thorium were found to produce the same effect. Becquerel failed to understand the meaning of the observations at the time even though he was working on the problem of the highly penetrating X rays.

There were two fundamental differences, however, between this radiation and that of X rays. One was that the radiation flowed steadily from the uranium while it was resting on the table or in a dark drawer with no external source to excite its atoms. The other—not immediately known, of course—was that nothing that man could do would stop it, slow it down, or speed it up. The rate at which it *spontaneously* emitted this radiation was found to be proportional to the amount of uranium present, and it mattered not whether this uranium was in the elemental state or chemically combined with other atoms.

The Work of Marie and Pierre Curie

Becquerel turned the problem over to Marie Curie, who was one of his student assistants. She and her husband, Pierre, ultimately found that the radiation emitted from pure uranium oxide was less intense than that emitted from its ore.[1] Marie rightly concluded that there must be some other substance (or substances) in the pitchblende that was more powerfully radioactive[2] than uranium. She and her husband began the long and arduous labor of extracting the element (or elements) responsible. Marie Curie processed six tons of pitchblende by hand in a leaky shed with a dirt floor. She obtained one tenth of a gram of the radioactive component(s). The percentage of the unknown material was indeed small. Two years of hard labor, false leads, misinterpretations, and discouragements followed, but eventually the Curies isolated two new elements, polonium (in 1898) and radium (in 1902), both highly radioactive. Far more important than the isolation of two new elements was the discovery that certain atoms, chiefly those of high atomic weight, break down *spontaneously* into other kinds of atoms by the emission of the same radiation that fogged Becquerel's photographic plates. In their investigations the Curies had identified several other minerals that emitted radiation of the same sort. All of them contained uranium and/or thorium.

Identification of Radioactive Rays

First attempts to identify the radiation showed that it consisted of two distinct types that, pending further identification, were called alpha rays and beta rays. Later a third type was detected, and called gamma rays. The same problem arose with these rays as with

[1] An ore is a naturally occurring mineral aggregate from which one or more metals may be extracted at a profit. Pitchblende is an ore of uranium.
[2] This term is applied to all substances that emit an energetic radiation (of waves or particles) of some sort spontaneously, that is, without the necessity of an outside source of energy.

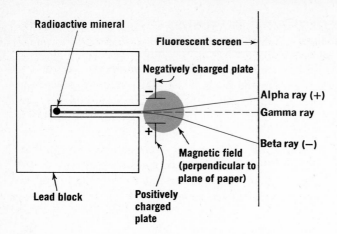

Fig. 19-1. Analysis of Rays Emitted from Radioactive Mineral. The lead block absorbs all rays except those traveling directly towards the screen. The rays pass through an electric field on their way from the block to the screen, with the deflections shown. A magnetic field is then substituted for the electric field. Alpha and beta rays are proved to be particles, charged as shown. Gamma rays could be either waves or uncharged particles. Further analysis proves them to be waves.

cathode rays: Were they particles or were they waves? The question was settled in the same way, by passing them through magnetic and electric fields (Fig. 19-1). The alpha (α) and beta (β) rays were found to be particles, and gamma (γ) rays were found to be a type of wave radiation.

The beta rays were the easiest to identify. They were deflected in electric and magnetic fields in the same manner as electrons. They had the same e/m, and so were correctly identified as electrons. They differed from Thomson's cathode rays in three ways: (1) in the manner in which they were produced,[3] (2) in their great speed, and (3) in their enormous kinetic energies. Their speeds were found to vary enormously, depending upon the particular radioactive mineral from which they were ejected. The maximum speed for any one species of mineral was constant, however. Some beta particles had velocities approaching that of the velocity of light, 3×10 cm/sec. Curiously enough, the e/m of these enormously fast beta particles was found to be only about $\frac{1}{20}$ of the standard value, 1.76×10^8

[3]Cathode rays and beta rays both consist entirely of electrons, but these are not terms that can correctly be used interchangeably because of this difference in method of production.

coulombs/g. This is surprising, for if the charge e is constant—and there is a wealth of evidence that it is—then the mass of these high-speed electrons must be *increasing with the speed* (for further discussion of this phenomenon see Chapter 21).

The alpha rays were found to carry a double positive charge but were only slightly deflected in a magnetic field, suggesting that their charge was small in comparison with their masses. Comparisons with the e/m ratios of hydrogen and helium ions suggested that they were helium ions. However, positive evidence was needed. The radiations were allowed to stream from a radioactive mineral into a small evacuated tube for months on end. Eventually spectroscopic analysis revealed that helium atoms were inside the tube. Alpha particles were indeed helium ions—helium atoms that have lost two electrons, and so carry a double positive charge.

Although alpha particles are emitted from the cores of radioactive atoms with a speed of about 1.5×10^9 cm/sec, their range is only a few centimeters in air, and sheets of metal 0.01 cm thick stop them completely. They produce intense ionization of the air through which they move; that is, air molecules are broken up to form positive and negative ions.

The man who did most of the work on this problem was Ernest Rutherford,[4] later Lord Rutherford, probably the greatest of the investigators into the structure of atoms.

Gamma rays proved not to be particles. They pass through glass as easily as does light, even through several centimeters of lead, a substance that is extremely effective in stopping all kinds of radiation. Gamma rays carry no charge and so are not deflected in electric and magnetic fields. They are indifferent ionizers of gases. Their velocity is that of light. In time they were found to be an invisible form of light, a kind of super X ray[5] with a shorter wavelength and a higher frequency.

Importance of Discovery of Radioactivity

Thus the picture of the atom as an indestructible basic building block of all matter collapsed when the experimental physicists subjected Becquerel's "uranium rays" to a searching analysis. Another world inside the atom had been opened up by the study of natural radioactivity. The fact that all three of these highly energetic radiations were spontaneously emitted from the cores of heavy atoms naturally raised the question: Whence comes the energy?

The answer will have to await further investigation into the structure of atoms. We cannot logically complete our discussion of radioactivity here. We introduced it here for two reasons. The first is that it played a prominent part in changing the viewpoint concerning the indivisibility of atoms, for there could be no doubt that these three types of rays were disintegration products of certain heavy elements. The second is that the discovery of radioactivity gave scientists a tool for further investigations into the structure of atoms. Before the nature of alpha particles had been worked out, Thomson had "discovered" electrons. It was not long before scientists were "firing" electrons at other atoms to see if other parts could be knocked loose from them. They failed because electrons were too light and too small. They penetrated matter but that was all. The alpha particle weighed about 7500 times as much as the electron, and so was therefore far more effective as an atomic "bullet." It turned out to be the first really effective disrupter of other atoms.

Rutherford's Nuclear Theory of the Atom

That an atom had so definite a structure that scientists could confidently refer to its different parts had now become certain. Electrons with their negative charges had been proved to be universal constituents of all matter, the existence of positive rays carrying positive electricity had been demonstrated, and alpha and beta particles, the first with a double positive charge, the second with a single negative charge, had been proved to be ejected from certain kinds of heavy atoms. Attention naturally turned to what the rest of the atom consisted of, and to the number and spatial arrangement of the electrons. Probably of greatest interest was the distribution of the

---

[4] Rutherford was a New Zealander who came to the famous Cavendish Laboratory in Cambridge, England, in 1895, at the time when it was the Mecca of physicists from the British Empire.

[5] Wilhelm Röntgen of Germany discovered X rays accidentally while he was investigating cathode rays by means of a gas discharge tube. At one stage of his investigations he noticed that certain crystals that were on his desk some distance away began to glow. He knew that cathode rays did not have enough energy to penetrate the distance from his tube to the crystals. He investigated to see if the fluorescence was caused by a new radiation with exceptional penetrating ability. This supposition proved correct. All attempts to determine whether the radiation was particle-like or wave-like met with defeat. Hence he called the rays X rays. For more information see Chapter 23.

positive charge(s) necessary to insure the electrical neutrality of an atom.

In 1898 J. J. Thomson, who had just "discovered" the electron, advanced the so-called "raisin cake" theory of the atom (also called the plum pudding or currant bun theory). The electrons were the "raisins" (or the plums or the currants), which were assumed to be scattered throughout a spherically shaped droplet of matter that formed the cake proper (or the pudding or the bun). This droplet was electrically positive. Its total charge, uniformly distributed throughout, equaled the sum of the negative charges carried by the embedded electrons. The system was thus held together by electrical attractions. The electrons were most strongly attracted by the center of the cake but were also repelled by one another, so that each was "assigned" to a certain area within the cake. However, at least one of them occupied a position at or very near the surface so that it was possible for it (or them) to escape from the system, thus leaving the atom a positive ion. Conversely, free electrons could enter the cake, making it a negative ion. The possibility that there was a greater concentration of the positive charge nearer the center than elsewhere was considered but not generally accepted at the time.

Various other theories about the distribution of the positive charge(s) were advanced, none of them based on crucial experiments of any kind, so we will not review them here. One of the problems was the vastly greater amount of matter associated with the positive rays compared to that associated with the electrons. The belief was general, however, that all atoms contained positively charged hydrogen ions, which were called *protons* (meaning "primary"). Neutral matter contained electrons, as shown by Thomson. It therefore also had to contain equal amounts of positive charge. A variation of this concept was first advanced by William Prout, a British chemist, about 1817.

He made the suggestion that hydrogen was the primordial substance out of which all other atoms were made. His evidence was that atomic weights of many elements, as then known, were almost even multiples of the atomic weight of the hydrogen atom. The idea was abandoned when more careful atomic weight determinations were made. We will see later how close to being right Prout was, although in a way that would have surprised him.

The alpha particle owed its effectiveness in causing ionization not only to its mass but also to the fact that it was ejected from radioactive atoms with velocities of about 10,000 mi/sec, and so had an enormous kinetic energy. At the time no way was known to see what actually happened to the alpha particles as they traveled through the air. It was known that if the particles of certain salts, for example, zinc sulfide, were struck by cathode rays, they would fluoresce. Experiments showed that alpha particles would also make them fluoresce. Moreover, if alpha particles are fired at a screen coated with zinc sulfide, their individual effect can easily be seen if a low-power microscope is used in a completely darkened room, for each produces a tiny flash of light on hitting the screen. This discovery that the impact of individual subatomic particles could be observed meant that research on single atomic events could, in part at least, replace that which previously had to be based on the average behavior of large numbers of atoms. By varying the distance of the screen from the source of the particles, their range could be determined. The rather amazing discovery was soon made that if a very thin metal foil was placed between the source and the screen, most of the alpha particles passed through the foil almost as if it were not there. All were stopped completely, however, by slightly thicker foils.

Rutherford decided to use gold foil in his experiment to "see" inside the atom, for it is

Fig. 19-2. Rutherford's Gold Foil Experiment. The apparatus is much like that shown in Fig. 19-1 except for the presence of the gold foil. The beam, *B*, consists of alpha particles radioactively ejected from *R*. Note how some are deflected from a straight-line path after passing through the foil, whereas the great majority go straight through. In the actual experiment the screen is moved almost completely around the foil.

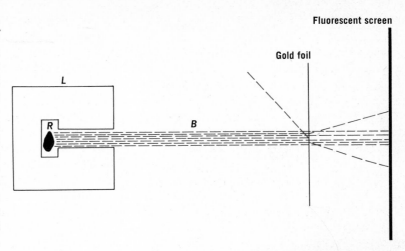

the most malleable substance known and can be hammered out, without tearing, into sheets so thin that a pile of about 250,000 sheets is only an inch thick. Nevertheless, each sheet, thin enough for alpha particles to go through it, is still several thousands of atoms thick. For his source of alpha particles he used a speck of radium. By use of the apparatus shown in Fig. 19-2 he was able to obtain a thin pencil of particles. At first these were allowed to impinge directly on the screen. All of the hits were within a small circle whose diameter was approximately that of the beam.

The gold foil was then placed directly in the path of the beam. The whole apparatus was enclosed in a good vacuum, so that collisions of alpha particles with air molecules would be extremely unlikely. Most of the alpha particles were deflected by small amounts, so that the spot on the screen that included most of the "hits" had a diameter slightly greater than that which was made by the thin pencil of alpha particles when the gold foil was absent. Some flashes were observed on the screen far out from this central spot. This indicated that on passing through the gold foil some of the particles were scattered somewhat (Fig. 19-2), so this experiment is sometimes referred to as Rutherford's scattering of alpha particles ex-

periment. Since some particles were, very surprisingly, deflected to the edge of the screen and possibly beyond, the screen was moved in a circle (Fig. 19-3) about the gold foil in an effort to determine the maximum angle of scattering. A very few were found to be deflected 180°; that is, they seemed to have hit something head-on without going through the foil so that they bounced right back in the direction whence they came. How was this experimental result to be interpreted in terms of a model? Rutherford could not interpret it by any "raisin cake" or "plum pudding" model of the atom. An advocate of such a model would have no trouble explaining why almost all of the alpha particles passed through the foil with scarcely measurable deflections, but he could not possibly explain the fact that a very few underwent large-angle scattering. The distribution of the charges would not allow it. Rutherford therefore had to introduce a theory in which he assumed that the whole of the massive positively charged part of the atom was concentrated in a very small region of the atom, which he termed the *nucleus*. The nucleus was very tiny, about $\frac{1}{10,000}$ the diameter of the atom itself, which had been estimated by other methods to have a diameter of 10^{-8} cm. This makes the volume of the nucleus

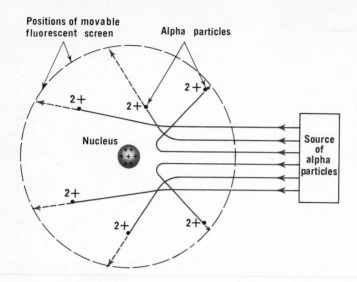

Positions of movable fluorescent screen

Alpha particles

2+

2+

2+

Nucleus

2+

2+

2+

Source of alpha particles

Fig. 19-3. Schematic Diagram of Rutherford's Alpha Particle Scattering Experiment. The alpha particles are scattered by the repulsive forces of the similarly charged nucleus. Those that approach closest to the nucleus are deflected the most, some almost reversing their paths.

about a millionth of a millionth the volume of the atom as a whole. The nucleus was assumed to be surrounded by a swarm of electrons, each carrying a negative charge. The total number of the electrons equaled the number of unit positive charges on the nucleus. An atom was therefore largely empty space.

From this model Rutherford could calculate that no direct hits or head-on collisions were actually made, for the alpha particle and the nucleus carry charges of the same sign and would repel each other. We *now* know that gold has 79 of these charges, the alpha particle only 2. Therefore, a particle headed for a direct hit with a nucleus would encounter an intense electric field, and so be slowed down to a stop by the repulsive force before it reached the nucleus and would then be accelerated directly back along the same path. Its deflection would therefore be 180°. Others whose paths would carry them near to the edge of a nucleus would be deflected through smaller angles ranging from less than 180° down to near 0°. Since most particles were scarcely deflected at all, the distances between the nuclei must be very large, relatively. The mass of an electron and

its electric force were considered much too small to cause any appreciable deflection of the alpha particles because the mass of the alpha particle is about 7500 times that of an electron.

Using foils made of atoms with fewer charges on the nucleus, for example, foils made out of aluminum, it was found that the average angle of scattering remained the same but the number scattered at any given angle was less. Using Coulomb's law, Rutherford predicted quantitatively how many alpha particles would be scattered (1) at different angles and (2) from different targets (foils). He also predicted the scattering of alpha particles with different energies (obtained by using different radioactive minerals as a source of his particles). His experiments agreed extremely well with his predictions. He was then able to announce his nuclear model (theory) of atoms, which we have already described.

In science the solution of one problem begets another, or as is more likely, several of them. The most obvious problem in Rutherford's case was the distribution of the electrons about the nucleus. Rutherford adopted the suggestion of a Japanese physicist that the electrons revolved about the nucleus, forming a miniature planetary system. The revolving was necessary to explain why the electrons did not "fall" into the nucleus, just as the earth would fall into the sun if it stopped revolving. Another problem immediately arose. An electron is a charge and it is being accelerated as it revolves about the nucleus. (Recall that a change in direction is an acceleration just as much as a change in speed is.) According to Maxwell's electromagnetic theory an accelerated charge should radiate "light," losing energy as it does so. As it loses energy, the electron should move closer to the nucleus, gradually spiraling down into the nucleus. It is obvious that under ordinary conditions the electron does none of these things. How could it revolve without radiating, since energy was being used to cause it to change its direction, according to Newtonian mechanics?

A second problem involved the structure of the nucleus. The nucleus contains practically the whole mass of an atom. How did nuclei of light atoms, for example, hydrogen and helium, differ from nuclei of heavy atoms such as uranium? What was the relationship of the positive charges to whatever it was that formed the mass? How could a large number of charges all of the same sign be held together in so small a nucleus against their repulsive forces? These are all physical questions, and their solutions would undoubtedly give rise to others, let alone the associated chemical questions. Despite all these unsolved difficulties, the nuclear theory was soon widely accepted, for the interpretations of Rutherford could not be disputed. Its acceptance was a great step upward on the seemingly endless path that led hopefully to the understanding of matter and its associated energy. Partial answers to the questions listed above came quickly, but reasonably complete answers had to await the passage of 20 years.

The Concept of Atomic Number

The *atomic number* of an element originally referred to the position of that element in the periodic table. It was the "serial number" of an element when the elements were arranged (with one or two reversals) in order of atomic weight, due allowance being made for undiscovered elements by leaving gaps with serial numbers assigned to the gaps. The many regularities in the table excluded the possibility of elements being discovered that would fit anywhere except in one of the gaps, or at the high end of the table. Thus, the serial numbers represented a "natural" order of the elements, but they did not represent any property or quantity that changed regularly from one element to the next element; that is, they had no more significance than the numbers given to houses to identify them on a street. Actually the term used to refer to an element was not *atomic number,* but simply *number.* The former term did not come into use until after Moseley's work had been announced.

The concept of a definite number of charges in the nuclei of atoms had been "kicking around" for some time before 1913. The number of electrons surrounding the nucleus had been estimated by various men, the general conclusion being that it was probably related serially to the order of the elements in the periodic table. Since atoms were electrically neutral, the number of positive charges on a nucleus had to be the same as the number of electrons surrounding it. Rutherford, in his work on his nuclear theory, had estimated that the total charge was about equal to half the atomic weight. He guessed that the number of positive charges was the same as the serial number in the periodic chart (see inside of front cover).

In the same year (1913) that Rutherford did his work on the atomic nucleus, one of his assistants, H. G. J. Moseley, made a systematic study of the number of positive charges on nuclei by means of X rays. The original order of the elements in the periodic table was the order of increasing atomic weight except for the three cases in which the atomic weight decreased from one element to the next. Moseley found a regularity (which we will explain when we learn more about X rays) in the results of his experiments that allowed him to arrange the elements in the same order and that also explained the reversals. He was convinced that the regularity was due to an orderly increase in the number of charges on the nucleus. Moseley said, "We have here a proof that there is in the atom a fundamental quantity, which increases by regular steps as we pass from one element to the next. This quantity can only be the charge on the central positive nucleus." When the periodic table is made by arranging the elements in order of nuclear charges, the reversals are explained, for the elements fall naturally into their correct places. Moseley's work gave us a new definition of an element: *All atoms that have the same atomic number* (same number of charges on the nucleus) *are the same element.* This was a great step forward, but it still left us without information about the particles that carried these positive charges. These particles obviously existed, but they had not yet been isolated and identified.

Positive Rays and Isotopes

Cathode rays were first discovered in 1859, but they were not shown to be the fundamental particles of negative electricity, the electron, until about 40 years later (1898). Investigators into the nature of cathode rays used gases of various kinds; they knew that in the early stages of evacuation of their gas discharge tubes, the current consisted of a two-way migration of oppositely charged ions (p. 304). In their attempts to find out more about them,

specially constructed cathodes with holes—channels, canals, slots—in them were made. In 1886 some of the rays that had enough energy to pass through these channels into the space behind the cathode despite the strong attractions between them and the cathode were collected and analyzed.

It was easy enough to prove that these rays (or ions) carried a positive charge, but identifying them was another matter. Attempts to measure their e/m, ratio of charge to mass (hereafter called q/m) ran into difficulties. One of them was that not all q/m's for atoms of the same element were the same. A second was the fact that after accelerating the rays in an electric field they did not all have the same velocity. To measure their q/m it was necessary to pass them through a magnetic field. Now a magnetic field exerts a strong force on a rapidly moving particle and a much weaker force on a slowly moving one of the same mass. A velocity selector had to be developed first—by J. J. Thomson when he began to devise new methods of positive ray analysis in 1907. It was found that the q/m for a positive ray was much less than the e/m for an electron. This meant that the rays were far more massive than electrons, for the charge was the same but of opposite sign. Also the q/m depended on the kind of gas in the discharge tube. When it was hydrogen, the q/m was greater than for any other elemental gas, an expectable result if hydrogen is the lightest of all elements. Comparison of the q/m of hydrogen with the e/m of the electron revealed that the mass of the former was 1836 times greater than the mass of the latter. This observation was the beginning of mass spectroscopy by means of which the various isotopes and rays are identified. In fact, it is this that makes positive rays important in unraveling the structure of atoms. The study of them revealed that not all atoms of the same element have the same atomic weight, something that previously had never been suspected. This introduces us to isotopes again, but we cannot give the proper explanations here; that will have to wait until after we have discussed some other aspects of atomic structure.

The Discovery of Protons

Research on the structure of the nucleus was continued by Rutherford and others, chiefly by bombarding various kinds of atoms with alpha particles (doubly charged helium ions) from a radioactive source. Rutherford used such ions to bombard nitrogen atoms in a closed tube. The approximate atomic weights of helium and nitrogen are 4 and 14, respectively. Now a light ball with a fixed velocity that strikes a much heavier ball head on cannot propel that heavier ball nearly as far as it could if it struck a ball lighter than itself (laws of conservation of energy and of momentum). Therefore Rutherford expected to find that the alpha particles would be stopped by collisions (even if not head on) with the heavier nitrogen atoms.

To see if they were, he placed a movable fluorescent screen in the tube. Alpha particles cause a flash of light (scintillations) to be emitted when they strike the screen. Few flashes could be observed farther than a distance of about 7 cm. These few could be observed when the screen was more than 30 cm away. This could happen only if the particles causing the flashes had greater velocity than the alpha particles. Momentum considerations ruled out the possibility that they could be nitrogen atoms.

Rutherford tried other gases, but found they produced no long-range scintillations. For all of them, alpha particles had very nearly the same range. Clearly then, the effect was one related to the particular gas, nitrogen, and equally clearly, the particles causing the long-range scintillations were particles smaller than alpha particles. The only particles smaller than alpha particles that could produce this effect are hydrogen nuclei, which have masses about one fourth those of alpha particles. He therefore isolated[6] some of the unknown particles and tested their behavior in a magnetic field. He found that they had the same charge and the same mass as hydrogen nuclei. They must therefore be hydrogen nuclei. They were called *protons*. Thus the particles carrying the positive charges were isolated and identified. They are now known to be fundamental building blocks of atomic nuclei, each carrying a charge of +1.

The Discovery of Neutrons

The mass number[7] of the hydrogen nucleus (a proton) is 1, whereas that of helium is 4. If it is the proton that carries the positive charge, then helium's two protons account for only half of its mass. What constitutes the other half? Two possibilities exist. It can consist of one particle with a mass equal to 2 amu[8] or of two particles each with a mass equal to 1 amu. That there were two particles each approximately equal to 1 amu instead of one particle of 2 amu could be inferred from the fact that beryllium has a mass of 9 amu, 4 of which can be accounted for by its 4 protons, the other 5 either by 1 particle of 5 amu (which can easily be disproved) or by 5 particles of 1 amu each. By reasoning such as this it was suspected that the unknown particles could not have masses of two amu each. The unknown particle was first inferred to be some sort of a proton-electron combination. Such a particle would be about the right size, it would be electrically neutral, and it would account

---

[6]The separation is effected by passing the charged particles in the tube through electric and magnetic fields.

[7]The mass number of an atom is the whole number nearest its atomic weight.

[8]An amu (atomic mass unit) is defined as $\frac{1}{12}$ the mass of one atom of the isotope of carbon that we call carbon-12. It is equal to 1.67×10^{-24} g.

for the source of the beta particles (electrons) emitted during natural radioactivity. It would also explain why the ejection of a beta particle would increase the atomic number of the atom by one; the proton left behind with no electron to neutralize it would add an extra charge to the nucleus. This hypothetical proton-electron combination was named the *neutron* even before it was discovered. The search for it continued for years. In 1930 Marie Curie's daughter, Irene, and her husband, F. Joliot, were bombarding the metal beryllium with alpha particles. No protons were ejected, but a new type of radiation of greater energy than any yet known was detected. If a plate of paraffin (a hydrocarbon) was placed in its path, the new radiation ejected protons from it. This new radiation was wholly unaffected by electric and magnetic fields. The discoverers came to the conclusion that this radiation was electromagnetic in character.

In 1932 Chadwick, a former assistant of Rutherford's, proved that the high energy of this radiation could not be accounted for by assuming that it was electromagnetic in character, but that the energy could be explained by assuming that the radiation was composed of particles with masses slightly greater than that of protons, but with no charge. Further research convinced the investigators that it was the long-sought-for neutron.

The difficulty of the neutron's detection lies in its tiny size and in its electrical neutrality; it has a mass number of 1 and zero charge. Because of these properties it has great penetrating ability; neutrons cannot be contained in any container. Having no charge, a neutron does not ionize a gas except by a direct hit and so does not readily lose its energy (since the bulk of the atom is empty space); it experiences no electrical force of repulsion or attraction on approaching a nucleus. In a head-on collision with a proton, all or nearly all of its energy is transmitted to the proton.

Protons and neutrons have very nearly the same mass. Since they are the two building blocks that form atomic nuclei, they may both be referred to as *nucleons*.

Exercises

1. Compare the weight of an atom of hydrogen with that of an electron.
2. (a) What was the first decisive evidence that atoms were divisible?
   (b) The second such evidence?
3. (a) What is radioactivity?
   (b) Name three radioactive minerals.
4. Of what does the radiation from such minerals consist?
5. (a) What is another name for alpha rays?
   (b) What use was made of them?
6. What convinced Rutherford (and others) that atoms carried positive charges?
7. What was his method of investigation to discover these positive charges?
8. What inferences could Rutherford make from the results of the above experiments?
9. Rutherford's "bullets" never actually crashed into the center of an atom. Why not?
10. Why did Rutherford postulate electrons circling about the nucleus like a miniature planetary system?
11. How did this planetary concept conflict with Maxwell's electromagnetic theory of light?
12. The diameter of a nucleus is only about $\frac{1}{10,000}$ that of the atom. The volume of a sphere varies as the cube of the diameter. What is the volume of the nucleus compared to the volume of the atom?
13. What was Rutherford's method of investigating an atomic nucleus?
14. With what atom was he successful in the above investigation?

15. What is (a) a hydrogen ion, (b) a proton?
16. What, in general, happens during a nuclear reaction?
17. What is (a) a mass number, (b) an atomic mass unit?
18. (a) What is an isotope.
    (b) Why are two isotopes of oxygen not two different elements?
19. Why did researchers search for neutrons; that is, what made them believe that neutrons existed?
20. What made it so difficult to identify the neutron?
21. Contrast neutrons with protons.
22. We may write the symbol for gold as $^{197}_{79}Au$ or $_{79}Au^{197}$. Explain these numbers.
23. In what way do radioactive atoms differ from nonradioactive atoms?
24. (a) Atoms of what element were used by Rutherford in his investigation of the atomic nucleus?
    (b) Why these and not some other kinds of atoms?
25. What are (a) alpha rays, (b) beta rays, and (c) gamma rays?
26. Which kind of ray will fog a photographic plate?
27. What important difference in the ability to fog such a plate is there between alpha, beta, and gamma rays on the one hand and ordinary light rays on the other?
28. What important fact about atomic structure did the presence of isotopes reveal?
29. What is meant by e/m?
30. What does q/m means? How does it differ from e/m?

Electromagnetic (Radiant) Energy

20

We have been discussing radiation in the last chapter without formally defining it. *Radiation,* as currently used in physics, refers to the emission and propagation of energy through empty space or through a material medium by means of waves or by submicroscopic particles of matter. We may divide radiation into two kinds, wave radiation and particle radiation. The difference between them must be clearly understood because a very large part of modern physics deals with one or the other of them. We have already encountered both types and we saw that their discoverers had difficulty in determining which type they had discovered. Particle radiation is much the simpler; we may compare it to a jet of water shot out of a nozzle. The ejection of cathode rays[1] from a cathode forms one example, and that of alpha and beta particles from the nuclei of radioactive atoms is another. Wave radiation is much more complex because nothing of a material nature is radiated, and the medium through which the

I have a new electromagnetic theory of light which until I am convinced to the contrary I hold to be great guns.
JAMES CLERK MAXWELL
(ca. 1860)

[1] A ray in this context is a beam of submicroscopic particles or a beam of waves. Also see Fig. 9-4.

energy is propagated may consist of any kind of matter, or it (the medium) may be non-existent; that is, it may be a very good vacuum. Sound and light are examples of wave radiation, but sound needs a medium; it is transmitted mechanically, and light is not. Our interest here is in light as an electromagnetic phenomenon.

Waves and Wave Media

We discussed some of the fundamentals concerning waves and wave motions in Chapter 9. We restricted our attention there very largely to mechanical waves as transmitters of energy away from a source region without involving any transport of matter to carry the energy. We saw that all mechanical waves, whether longitudinal or transverse, have a number of fundamental characteristics in common, namely frequency, wavelength, velocity, and amplitude, all of which were defined and illustrated in Chapter 9. All mechanical waves need a medium for their transmission, matter in any state for sound waves (which are longitudinal), matter in a solid state for transverse waves (such as waves in a rope), and a liquid-gas interface for surface waves, for example, water waves (which are combinations of longitudinal and transverse waves).

We also mentioned electromagnetic waves as waves that can be propagated through any medium, at least to some extent, that do not make use of media in their propagation, and that are most rapidly propagated through a vacuum. From this we may conclude that physical media are a hindrance rather than an aid to the propagation of electromagnetic waves. Thus a problem was posed for the physicists of the 19th century, for, in their eyes, the transport of energy without a transport of matter depended upon the presence of a medium between the source and the receiver to act as the carrier of the wave energy motions. They could not visualize—any more than can we—waves traveling through a vacuum, as the light from the sun and the stars must, if light is a wave motion.

Consequently, the concept of the *ether*,[2] first advanced by Aristotle, was revived in somewhat different form by Christian Huygens, who believed light was a wave motion. It was another imponderable, like phlogiston and caloric, with many diverse, contradictory, and mysterious properties. It filled all space in the whole universe, even the spaces between atoms and molecules, and its sole use was to act as a medium for the transport of light waves. It had to be as rigid as steel and yet offer no resistance to the planets as they moved through it. The ether concept began to fall into disrepute after the crucial Michelson–Morley experiment in 1887, an experiment that was especially designed to detect it but yielded only negative evidence. Belief in the ether concept still persisted in some quarters until Einstein dispelled it in 1905 with his special relativity theory (Chapter 21). From that time on the ether theory was as passé as the phlogiston and caloric theories.

Corpuscular vs. Wave Theories of Light

The two methods of transporting energy, one with a transport of matter from the source to a receiver and the other without, found their expression with respect to light in the corpuscular theory of Newton and the wave theory of Christian Huygens of Holland.

Newton believed that light consisted of par-

[2] The word is still used occasionally in connection with radio and TV broadcasting.

ticles of extremely small size, but he believed it with no great degree of positiveness, and he failed to specify the characteristics of the corpuscles. He rejected the wave theory because he could not detect diffraction (p. 339), an essential characteristic of any wave motion.[3] Huygens, a contemporary of Newton, was a strong advocate of the wave theory and formulated the first well-rounded theory in 1678. According to Newton's theory light should travel faster through water—or a solid—than through air, whereas the reverse should be true of the wave theory. A way to measure these speeds was not found until about 1850 when Foucault—the French physicist who used a pendulum to give evidence that the earth rotates on an axis—found that the velocity of all light in all media that he tested was slower than in a vacuum, thus deciding the issue conclusively in favor of the wave theory. We shall see later that this conclusion does not prove the wave theory to be unqualifiedly correct but only ruled out corpuscles of matter that obeyed the laws of Newtonian mechanics and that are speeded up as they enter a denser medium. The most impressive argument in favor of Huygens' wave theory was that two light beams can cross through each other without "colliding."

Meanwhile Newton's theory prevailed—because of his greater reputation—until about 1805, when both Thomas Young of England and Augustine Fresnel of France demonstrated that light definitely showed both diffraction and interference effects. The weight of opinion thus shifted to the wave theory.[4] Before proceeding further we need to learn a bit more about the behavior of light as a wave phenomenon. A quick review of Chapter 9 is relevant for all students at this time.

---

[3] There were other, less compelling, reasons.
[4] Neither theory explained the fundamental cause of light.

Reflection and Refraction

We are all more or less familiar with the fact that water waves may be reflected from a wall, light waves from a mirror, and sound waves from a cliff or other surface. The last we term an *echo*. We are also familiar with such terms as *transparency* and *opaqueness* referring to the varying degrees with which objects reflect, absorb, or transmit light waves. We are not so likely to realize that they apply equally well to most other kinds of waves, especially to other types of electromagnetic waves. Thus, metals reflect radio waves, but glass, brick, and wood—if not too thick—are largely transparent to them. If this were not so, outdoor aerials for television and radio would always be necessary. Substances are said to be opaque if either absorption or reflection is complete or nearly so.

Waves of all kinds are also refracted; that is, their rays are bent as they pass *obliquely* from one medium to another in which their speed is different (Fig. 20-1). Accompanying the refraction is a change in the velocity; in fact, the velocity change is the cause of the refraction. If the boundary between the two media is at right angles to the path of the rays, there is a change in velocity but no bending. Thus, if one stands in clear water waist deep and looks down at his legs, they seem to be curiously shorter than they actually are. If he looks at the flat bottom all around him, it appears to be shallower away from him in every direction, so that he seems to be standing in a depression. Ponds of clear water never appear as deep as they actually are.

An understanding of how refraction is produced by differences in speed along the wavefront may be obtained by watching the behavior of long water waves far out from shore and moving obliquely toward shore. Ocean waves are caused by the wind, and if the wind is blowing obliquely toward shore, the waves will

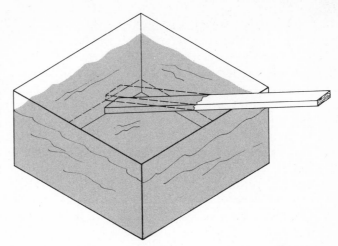

Fig. 20-1. Refraction. A stick partially immersed in water, when *viewed at angle* to the surface of the water, appears bent because of the bending of the light rays as they pass from the denser water medium to the less dense medium of air. Note also that refraction causes the bottom of the water container to appear higher than it really is.

move obliquely also. One end of such a wave will be nearer the shore than the other end, and so will reach shallow water first. Friction with the bottom will slow this end while the other end is still advancing at the original speed. As the advance continues, more and more of the wave will be slowed by the shallowing bottom, allowing the far end to catch up. If the shallow water zone is broad enough, that is, extends seaward far enough so that the near end has not yet broken, all parts of the wave will progressively swing around to bring the whole wave front approximately parallel to the shore; its direction has been changed. The wave has been refracted because the near part of the wave has been forced to move for a time slower than the far part. The frequency of these waves remains the same but the wavelength decreases; the equation $v = f\lambda$ still applies. The apparent bending of the stick in Fig. 20-1 is due to the difference in the speeds of light waves in air and in water.

Refraction and Dispersion of Light

If we pass ordinary white light (sunlight) through a glass prism (a wedge-shaped piece of glass), the light rays are refracted on entering the glass and again on leaving it. The light leaving the glass is not white, but all the colors of the rainbow (Fig. 20-2). Newton, who was the first to perform this experiment (1669), believed that the colors were due to the dispersion (spreading out) of the various components of white light; that is, that white light is made up of the colors of the rainbow.

To prove this he placed another similar but oppositely oriented prism (Fig. 20-3) in the path of the rays coming from the first prism. These colors were recombined into white light, proving his belief. He also placed a screen with a narrow slit in it between two properly oriented prisms (Fig. 20-4). Through this slit he could admit any one of the colors coming through the first prism and bar the others. He allowed these colors, one by one, to pass through the second prism, oriented in different ways, to see if each could be broken up any further. He found that they could not. The colors emerging from the first prism are red, orange, yellow, green, blue, and violet.

How do we explain these facts? How does a prism break white light up into different colors? The answer is by the refraction of the components of white light. White light consists

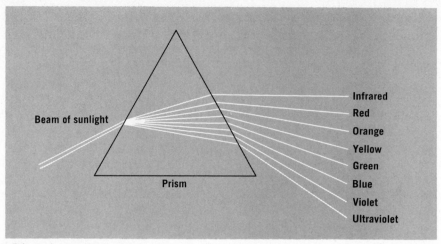

Fig. 20-2. Dispersion of White Light. The velocity is slowed as the beam of light enters the prism, so the rays are bent, the shorter wavelengths more than the longer. This difference in the amount of bending is the cause of the dispersion.

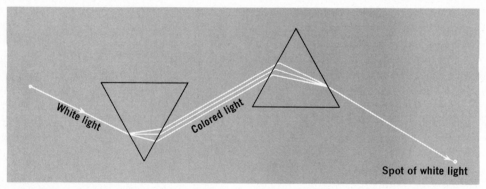

Fig. 20-3. Newton's Proof of the Composition of White Light. White light passing through the first prism was dispersed into colored bands. These were then recombined to form white light again by passing through an oppositely oriented prism.

of the colors of the rainbow—red, orange, yellow, green, blue, and violet, each color having a different band of frequencies and wavelengths. On entering the glass prism (a different medium), the lower frequencies (red) are refracted less than the higher. Thus, the prism sorts out the rays according to their frequencies forming a band of colors called a *spectrum* (Plate I, at p. 346). Each color in a

continuous spectrum consists of a group of frequencies that the human eye translates into color. These frequencies range from 7.5×10^{14} cycles/sec (on the violet side of the spectrum) to 4×10^{14} cycles/sec (on the red side).[5] There are also frequencies in ordinary sunlight that

---

[5] The quantity "cycles/sec" is now designated by the unit called the *hertz,* abbreviated Hz.

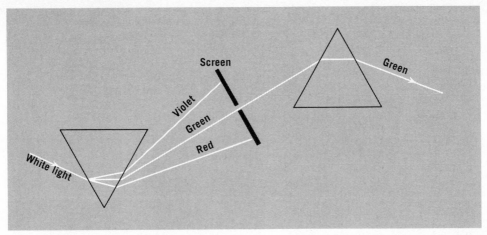

Fig. 20-4. Newton's Proof That Dispersed Color Bands Are Primary. One of the colors of the continuous spectrum was passed through another prism to see if it could be broken up. The screen with a slit was used to select the desired ray.

are higher than the violet; these are the *ultraviolet*. The human eye is not constructed to translate them to visible light, but they can be detected by other means. The frequencies immediately lower than the red are called *infrared*. Our eyes do not register them as light, but our bodies detect them as heat.

This last statement should raise a question in our minds. If heat is molecular motion, why do our bodies register the electromagnetic radiation we call infrared as heat rays? If our definition of heat means anything, the answer should be that these infrared rays have the ability to increase molecular motions. This justifies calling them heat rays.

Polarization of Transverse Waves

A wave motion is a vibratory disturbance traveling through a medium, except that no medium is necessary for electromagnetic waves, of which light is one kind. In ordinary light the vibrations are in random directions, up and down, sideways, and at all angles that are perpendicular to the direction the wave is traveling. Such light is unpolarized. If we pass this light through a tourmaline crystal oriented vertically, all the sideways (horizontal) components of the vibration are absorbed; only the vertical components are transmitted (Fig. 20-5 gives a rope wave analogy for light waves). Such light is polarized. If we turn the crystal 90°, the vertical components are absorbed and the horizontal components are transmitted. If we send the light through two crystals, one oriented vertically and one horizontally, the first crystal will transmit only the vertical vibrations, but these will be absorbed by the second crystal—which would transmit only horizontal vibrations—therefore all the light will be absorbed and none transmitted (Fig. 20-6). Some crystals other than those of tourmaline will also polarize light, as will the substance called polaroid, used in some sunglasses.

Longitudinal waves cannot be polarized because the vibrations producing them are all parallel to the direction of travel. Polarization therefore is a means of distinguishing trans-

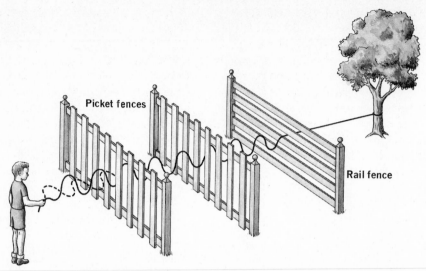

Fig. 20-5. Polarization of Waves. The rope is vibrating in a vertical plane so that the waves can pass through the two picket fences without diminution. However, the waves are stopped by the horizontal rails of the third fence. If the rope vibrates in a horizontal plane, the waves are extinguished by the first picket fence, although they could pass through the rail fence without effect. In either case the waves are said to be polarized because the vibrations are all in the same plane. If the hand has a random motion, the vibrations will be random, some vertical, some horizontal, some in between. The picket fence then will act as a polarizer, for it will allow only the vertically oriented components of the waves to pass through.

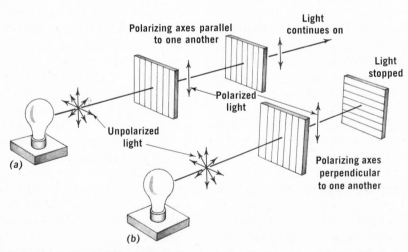

Fig. 20-6. Polarization of Light Waves. The vibration of ordinary white light is unpolarized, as shown. (*a*) A polarizing type of crystal put in its path allows vibrations parallel to its polarizing axis to pass through. This polarization blocks out half of the light; the rest continues on. (*b*) If another crystal with its polarizing axis turned at right angles to the axis of the first is also placed in the path of the light, all light is stopped.

verse waves from longitudinal waves. It is also strong evidence for the wave theory of light; Newton's corpuscular theory could not explain polarization. Curiously enough, it seemingly never occurred to Newton or Huygens that light could be a transverse wave. More than 100 years elapsed before Thomas Young realized that the case for light as a wave motion would be clinched if light were a transverse wave, for then it could be polarized.

We may summarize the concept of polarization as follows: (1) Light consists of transverse waves in which the vibrations are in a plane perpendicular to the direction in which the light is traveling. (2) Light from the sun is unpolarized. Its vibrations are in all directions within the plane just described. In polarized light the vibrations are restricted to one direction within that plane (see Fig. 20-6). The concept of polarization is meaningless if light consists of Newton's corpuscles.

Diffraction of Light

The phenomenon of diffraction of mechanical waves has been discussed in Chapter 9. We learned that the amount of bending of the wave on passing through an opening depends upon the ratio of the wavelength to the width of the opening. The diffraction is more marked the greater the wavelength and the smaller the aperture. Hence to show prominent diffraction effects small wavelengths need small openings; for light they must be very small indeed, for the wavelengths of visible light lie between 10^{-4} and 10^{-5} cm. It is this aspect of the effective size of an opening that makes diffraction of light so difficult to observe. Even the great Newton missed seeing it, or seeing it, misinterpreted it.

Grimaldi of Italy, an older contemporary of Newton, did neither; he did not miss it or misinterpret it. He placed an opaque screen

containing a tiny hole in the path of a beam of light and noted that the spot on the opposite wall was slightly bigger than he expected on the assumption that the light rays had passed through the hole in straight lines. The edges of the spot were not sharp but bounded by narrow fringes of color. To him this meant that the beam had spread out a tiny bit and so had been diffracted. Thus he concluded the beam was not a beam of particles, but a beam of waves. This conclusion was ignored at the time and soon forgotten.

Diffraction gratings are made to diffract light and cause it to interfere so that the wavelength of the light can be measured. Diffraction is closely related to interference, so we will leave further discussion of diffraction and diffraction gratings until after we have discussed the interference of light.

Interference of Light

The phenomenon of interference has been discussed with respect to mechanical waves in Chapter 9. Just as two sound waves can be added together to produce either greater loudness or virtual silence, so two light waves can be added together to produce either greater brightness or darkness. Interference can occur whenever a wave disturbance can be propagated from a source to a receiver by two or more paths of different lengths. A beam of light may be separated into two parts, then made to follow somewhat different paths and then brought back to form a single beam. The two parts may arrive completely in phase, completely out of phase, or partially in and partially out (Fig. 9-9). If the two paths differ in length by a whole (integral) number of wavelengths, the two beams will be completely in phase; complete reinforcement (constructive interference) results. If the two paths differ in length by any fractional number of wavelengths, the two beams will not be in phase. If completely out of phase, complete cancellation (destructive interference) results, and if partially out of phase the interference will vary from constructive to destructive at different points, depending on the amount of phase difference, which, of course depends on the difference in length of paths. Interference, like diffraction, is so characteristically a peculiarity of wave motion that it is a test to distinguish wave radiation from particle radiation.

Interference accounts for the color patterns when white light, striking a thin transparent film, is reflected to the eye. The film may be a soap bubble, a film of oil on a water surface, and so on. Some light is reflected from the front or top surface of the film and some light from the back or bottom surface. These two beams arrive together at the retina of an eye. The difference in the distance traveled by the two beams is equal to twice the thickness of the soap film (Fig. 20-7). If this difference in path is an odd number of half wavelengths of red light, then the red component of white light will not be seen because the crests of the red wave coming from one surface of the film

are canceled by the troughs of the red wave coming from the other. What is seen is white light minus the red component. This is the complementary color of red, that is, green to bluish green. If the difference is an odd number of half wavelengths of yellow light, then the yellow component of white light is canceled, and so forth. Because the film varies in thickness, different components are canceled out in different places, thus giving a multicolored pattern.

Huygens' Principle

The essence of this principle is that every point on a wave front may be considered as a new source of waves. Consider a screen with two narrow openings of the same width a millimeter or less apart (Fig. 20-8). Light waves that have fronts that are parallel to the screen impinge periodically on the screen with its two openings. Small parts of each wave pass through the two openings simultaneously. Because of diffraction a succession of new waves emerge from each opening; that is, each opening acts as a new source of waves. It is easy to

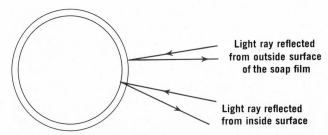

Fig. 20-7. Interference of Light Waves. It is seen that a ray of light reflected from the inside surface of the soap bubble to the eye has a longer distance to travel than one from the outside surface. If this path difference is equal to one wavelength or multiple thereof, the two waves will reinforce one another if they travel the same path, giving greater brightness. If the path difference is one half wavelength or any odd multiple thereof, the two waves will cancel one another, causing darkness (if the light is monochromatic). If the light is white, some wavelengths will be cancelled, giving white light minus one or more of its component colors. Since all such films vary in thickness, various colors are seen.

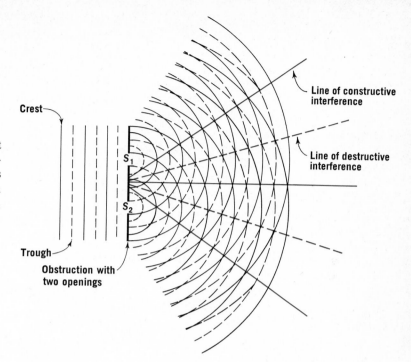

Crest

S₁

S₂

Trough

Obstruction with
two openings

Line of constructive
interference

Line of destructive
interference

Fig. 20-8. Wave Front Representation of Interference. Note that the waves from S_1 and S_2 interfere, in some places constructively, in others destructively.

see (Fig. 20-8) that as the waves spread from each opening, they will interfere with one another. It is equally easy to see that whether they will interfere constructively or destructively (p. 161), other factors remaining constant, will depend upon the distance between the two openings and the position of the observer relative to the openings.

Young's Interference Experiment

Thomas Young of England was one of the most brilliant and versatile men who ever lived. By the time he was four years old he had read the complete English Bible twice, at 13 he had read the Hebrew Bible, and when he was 14 he had mastered seven languages. As an adult he practiced and taught medicine, deciphered Egyptian hieroglyphics, and did superior research in several fields in physics, the

most famous of which was his pinhole experiment in which he demonstrated the interference of light. This experiment spelled doom for Newton's corpuscular theory and firmly established Huygens' wave theory. His actual experiment made use of a screen with two closely spaced pinholes in it, but essentially the same results are obtained if we substitute two equally spaced slits for the pinholes. These two slits correspond to the two narrow openings discussed under Huygens' principle, but in our screen they should not be more than 0.5 mm apart. Fig. 20-9 shows how the interference of the two sets of light waves coming through the two slits in the screen can occur.

The light coming through the two slits falls on a second screen. If the room is dark we will see a series of alternating bright and dark lines on the screen. The bright lines are formed by the constructive interference of the two

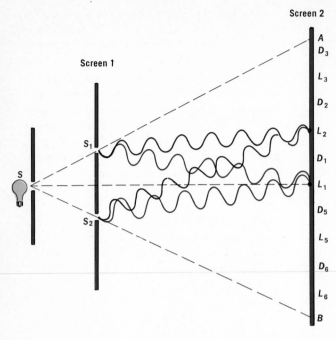

Screen 2

A
D_3
L_3
D_2
L_2
D_1
L_1
D_5
L_5
D_6
L_6
B

Screen 1

S_1

S

S_2

Fig. 20-9. Young's Double Slit Experiment. It was designed to show that light has the characteristics of a wave motion. If light is a stream of particles, then spots of light should appear on screen 2 only at A and B. The two slits, S_1 and S_2, each act as a new source of light (Huygens' principle). The point L_1 is equidistant from each slit, so that the two beams arrive at L_1 in phase (crest meets crest and trough meets trough), causing constructive interference. The two beams are again in phase at L_2, L_3, and so on because L_2 is one wavelength farther from S_2 than it is from S_1, and so on. The point D_1 is one half wavelength farther from one slit than from the other; hence crest meets trough, producing destructive interference. Thus on screen 2 a series of alternating dark and light lines are seen. In actual practice the two slits are very close together.

beams, one from S_1, the other from S_2, and the dark lines by the destructive interference of two beams coming from the same sources. Young showed his genius by correctly interpreting the alternating dark and bright lines as the result of interference. These lines are thus easily explained by the wave theory but are utterly inexplicable by Newton's corpuscular theory.

We see then how interference not only establishes the wave nature of light but also furnishes a method for measuring the wavelength. We will examine this method, not only because it is simple but because it will allow us to present further evidence against the corpuscular theory.

Consider Fig. 20-9. Everything in it is greatly magnified except perhaps the distance between screen 1 and screen 2, which are shown on edge. The two parallel slits, S_1 and S_2, are shown in cross section, and so here look like holes. The slits are very close together, and

each acts like a new source of waves (Huygens' principle); the slits are so narrow that the waves are diffracted through large angles. Note that the rays S_1L_2 and S_2L_2 interfere constructively at L_2. They travel slightly different paths to L_2, S_2L_2 is longer by a whole number of wavelengths, so crest meets crest at L_2. The same thing would be true of S_1L_3 and S_2L_3. Also at L_1 there will be constructive interference because S_1L_1 and S_2L_1 are equal. Now, rays from S_1 and S_2 also reach points D_1, D_2, and so on. The path S_2D_1 is longer than path S_1D_1 by an odd number of half wavelengths (an even number of half wavelengths is the same as a whole number of whole wavelengths), and so these rays interfere destructively. Crests meet troughs at points marked D; the waves cancel and so give dark lines there. Young's apparatus is known as the two-slit diffraction grating and illustrates the basic principles of operation of the practical diffraction grating. Most diffraction gratings used in scientific apparatus have about 15,000 slits per inch. Such gratings are made by scratching very fine, very closely spaced lines on glass. The spaces between the lines constitute the slits.

Speed of Light

Any satisfactory theory of light must take into account a question that had been debated since the time of the ancient Greeks, namely, does light travel at a finite or at an infinite speed? The Greeks had assumed that light had a finite speed simply because moving means going from one place to another, which takes time. Galileo had tried without success to measure the speed of light in the simple way that speeds of finite objects are measured. That he could detect no time interval between the source and an observer several miles away could mean either that the speed was infinite or that it was too great to detect by ordinary

means. The Danish astronomer Roemer settled the question of finiteness in 1676, and at the same time measured the speed with something like modern accuracy.

His method was simple. One of Jupiter's moons, Io, disappears behind Jupiter and reappears regularly as it revolves about Jupiter. The time interval between appearances should be constant if the speed of light is infinite, no matter where the earth is in its orbit. However, observation showed that when the earth is farthest from Jupiter, Io reappears about 16 min (1000 sec) later than when the earth is nearest Jupiter (Fig. 20-10). Roemer explained the lateness was due to the greater distance that light had to travel, a distance equal to the diameter of the earth's orbit (2 × 93 million mi).

$$v = \frac{d}{t} = \frac{186{,}000{,}000 \text{ mi}}{1000 \text{ sec}} = 186{,}000 \text{ mi/sec}$$

These are modern figures. Roemer's figure was 192,000 mi/sec. His error was due to inade-

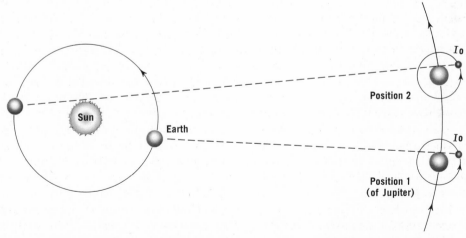

Fig. 20-10. Roemer's Method of Measuring Velocity of Light in 1676. One of Jupiter's moons, Io, is observed to be coming out of eclipse at two different times six months apart (during which time Jupiter has moved on its orbit). The time between appearances of Io can be calculated. It arrives 16 min late in the second position because the light has to travel farther to reach the earth (2 × 93 million mi farther).

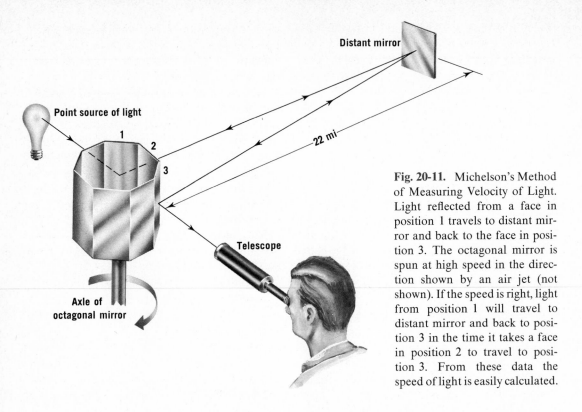

Point source of light

1
2
3

22 mi

Distant mirror

Telescope

Axle of
octagonal mirror

Fig. 20-11. Michelson's Method of Measuring Velocity of Light. Light reflected from a face in position 1 travels to distant mirror and back to the face in position 3. The octagonal mirror is spun at high speed in the direction shown by an air jet (not shown). If the speed is right, light from position 1 will travel to distant mirror and back to position 3 in the time it takes a face in position 2 to travel to position 3. From these data the speed of light is easily calculated.

quate knowledge of the earth's distance from the sun. The method was not entirely convincing to everyone.

The American physicist Albert Michelson made the first highly precise measurement of the speed of light by improving on a laboratory method used by Fizeau in 1849. The principle used by Michelson is shown in Fig. 20-11. A precision-built octagonal mirror was mounted on an axle and rotated at high speed by a jet of compressed air. Three of the eight faces of the mirror were labeled 1, 2, and 3. Consider the situation to be as follows before the mirror starts to rotate:

Light from a strong point source strikes face 1 of the octagonal mirror, which reflects it to another mirror about 22 mi away; this distant mirror reflects it back to face 3 of the octagonal mirror, which in turn reflects it into the lens

of a fixed telescope, where it is focused on the crosshairs in the eyepiece. If the octagonal mirror is now turned slightly, the image of the light disappears from the telescope. Suppose that we turn the air jet on so as to give the octagonal mirror moderate speed. No light will be observed in the telescope. But if the speed of rotation is increased sufficiently, face 2 will move from the position shown into the position occupied by face 3 in exactly the same time as it takes the light to go from face 1 to the distant mirror and back again. The image of the light therefore reappears in the telescope and, if the speed of rotation is just right, it will be focused on the crosshairs. This speed of rotation can be measured and the time for one eighth of a rotation calculated. This gives the time for the light to travel to the distant mirror and back again, a distance of 44 mi.

Michelson also measured the speed of light in other media and found it to be less than in air. This was in accord with the wave theory and in opposition to the corpuscular theory. He also found that red light travels at a considerably greater speed through liquids and solids than does blue light, yet travels at the same speed through a vacuum.[6] Michelson received a Nobel prize for his work on the speed of light.

The most modern measurement is 2.99876×10^{10} cm/sec. This is equal to 186,464 mi/sec. The speed of light in a vacuum is a most important constant, for it enters into calculations of the sizes, distances, motions, and energies of and within atoms. It is also a basic yardstick in astronomy. For almost all purposes we may round the figures off and remember them as 3×10^{10} cm/sec and 186,000 mi/sec.

Electromagnetic Theory of Light

The electromagnetic theory of light was first advanced in 1864 by James Clark Maxwell (1831–1879), an Englishman of Scottish descent, with wealthy parents and a long line of distinguished ancestors. He received the finest education available in England. He became one of the greatest mathematicians and one of the finest theoretical physicists that ever lived. His first paper in mathematics was read to the Royal Society of Britain when he was 15; he was considered too young to appear personally before the Society.

Maxwell's theory of electromagnetic radiation had its inception in Faraday's concept of electric and magnetic fields. In contrast to Maxwell, Faraday (1791–1867) was self-educated. His father was a blacksmith; he was

apprenticed to a bookbinder before he finished elementary school. At the age of 22 he went to work in the science laboratory at the Royal Institution of London under the tutelage of Sir Humphry Davy, its director. Twelve years later he became its director. In all he spent 54 years at the Royal Institution. His first work was in the field of chemistry, but he soon started research in electricity. He quickly became one of the greatest of all experimenters in electricity and magnetism. In 1831 he discovered how to use a current in one circuit to produce a current in an entirely different circuit (see Fig. 17-24).

Maxwell's first step in his study of electricity was to read Faraday's *Experimental Researches*. He was a great admirer of Faraday, and he read the whole of Faraday's works on electricity and magnetism with enthusiasm *before* he proceeded to translate Faraday's concepts into mathematical terms. He was intrigued by Faraday's field concept (p. 285).

Gilbert (Chapter 17) in the 1600's had shown that small elongated pieces of certain kinds of matter, such as iron filings (or pieces of paper or thread), aligned themselves in characteristic patterns about magnets (or about charged objects) (see Figs. 17-15 and 17-16). Most, if not all, investigators prior to Faraday had been satisfied to explain the forces of attraction and/or repulsion exhibited by magnets and electrified bodies simply as action at a distance; the space about such bodies was considered to be devoid of anything tangible or intangible that required analysis. Faraday wanted a mechanical model to explain how these forces acted. Maxwell wrote, after he had read Faraday's *Researches,*

. . . Faraday, in his mind's eye, saw lines of force traversing all space where the mathematicians saw centers of force attracting at a distance; Faraday saw a medium where they saw nothing but distance; Faraday sought the

---

[6]Through air all colors travel at practically the same speed. The difference is less than 0.03%.

seat of the phenomena in real actions going on in the medium, [whereas] they were satisfied that they had found it in a power of action at a distance. . . .

Maxwell agreed with Faraday that a field devoid of a material existence of its own was unsatisfactory. The notion of an ether (p. 333) was in full bloom as a familiar conceptual device that was useful in explaining how radiations of heat and light could be transmitted through the vast empty spaces between the stars, and especially between the sun and the earth. Both men were under the influence of the ether concept. Faraday wrote:

It is not at all unlikely that if there be an ether, it should have other uses than simply the conveyance of radiations.

The differences between the approaches of the two men to the problem, one essentially experimental, the other essentially mathematical, were great, yet Maxwell wrote,

When I had translated what I considered to be Faraday's ideas into mathematical form, I found that in general the results of the two methods coincided, so that the same phenomena were accounted for, and the same laws of action were deduced by both methods. . . .

Maxwell had found that his equations lacked a certain "consistency" unless he assumed that something "occurred" in the empty space about moving electric charges and moving magnets. To a nonmathematician he was as vague about this empty space as Faraday was.

Faraday's Interpretation of His Experimental Data

Faraday probably reasoned somewhat as follows: Charges at rest have stationary electric fields and electric lines of force about them, and magnets at rest have stationary magnetic fields and magnetic lines of force about them. The charge and the magnet have no influence on each other.

As soon as a charge is accelerated, its stationary electric field becomes a changing electric field with its electric lines of force, and this changing electric field gives rise to a changing magnetic field with its magnetic lines of force. We now have a magnetic field that is independent of a magnet, and this is the magnetic field that we will include in the remainder of our discussion.

Maxwell's Interpretation of Faraday's Data

Together these two fields of force constitute Maxwell's electromagnetic field. Minus his mathematics Maxwell probably reasoned somewhat as follows: Moving charges carry their fields with them, their lines of force move with them like a man's whiskers with their owner. Also moving charges in a conductor constitute an electric current. If the movement of the charges that form this current is uniform—that is, steady, not being accelerated (or decelerated)—both the moving electric field and its accompanying magnetic field are steady. No electromagnetic waves will be radiated into space. Such an electric current as this is direct current (DC). Of course, when we start the charges (electrons) moving—that is, when we turn the switch to the *on* position—the charges are briefly accelerated, our stationary electric and magnetic fields become changing fields, and a few electromagnetic waves are radiated. However, the current becomes steady in less than a second (usually), the situation becomes static again and remains so until we turn the switch off. The current dies away, the charges are decelerated, we again have changing electric and magnetic fields for an instant or two, and a few electromagnetic waves are radiated.

If you will review our account (p. 293) of how an electric current in one circuit (primary) induces an electric current in an entirely different (secondary) circuit, you will find that the method used is exactly as described above.

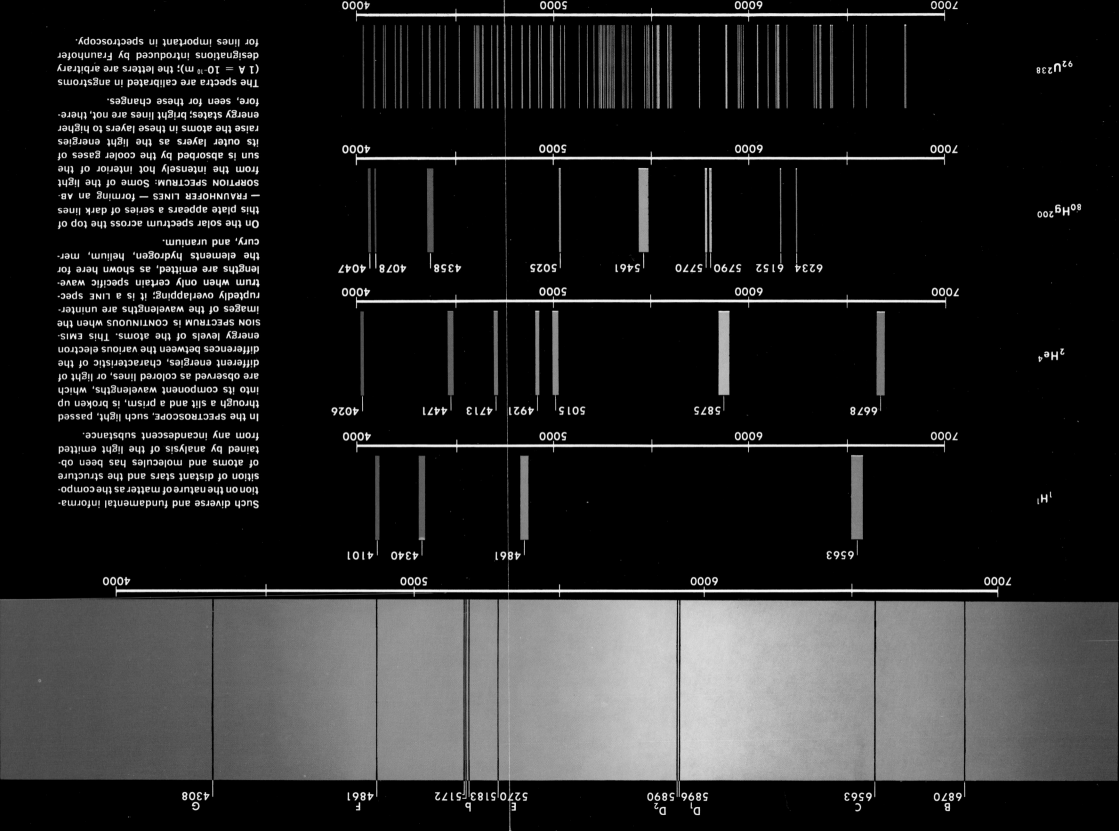

In the SPECTROSCOPE, such light, passed through a slit and a prism, is broken up into its component wavelengths, which are observed as colored lines, or light of different energies, characteristic of the differences between the various electron energy levels of the atoms. This EMISSION SPECTRUM is CONTINUOUS when the images of the wavelengths are uninterruptedly overlapping; it is a LINE spectrum when only certain specific wavelengths are emitted, as shown here for the elements hydrogen, helium, mercury, and uranium.

On the solar spectrum across the top of this plate appears a series of dark lines — FRAUNHOFER LINES — forming an AB-SORPTION SPECTRUM: Some of the light from the intensely hot interior of the sun is absorbed by the cooler gases of its outer layers as the light energies raise the atoms in these layers to higher energy states; bright lines are not, therefore, seen for these changes.

The spectra are calibrated in angstroms ($1\ \text{Å} = 10^{-10}$ m); the letters are arbitrary designations introduced by Fraunhofer for lines important in spectroscopy.

Such diverse and fundamental information on the nature of matter as the composition of distant stars and the structure of atoms and molecules has been obtained by analysis of the light emitted from any incandescent substance.

There we were describing the production of an induced current, whereas here we are describing the production of an electromagnetic wave.

Now, just as we had to have a constantly changing electric field to keep an induced current in the secondary circuit (p. 293), so we have to have a constantly changing electric current to keep electromagnetic waves radiating. We do not have to worry about the necessary changing magnetic field, for if we have the changing electric field we automatically have the changing magnetic field (p. 346). It is impossible to have the former without the latter.[7] The easiest way to produce a changing electric field is to use alternating current (AC). In it the charges (electrons) are constantly being accelerated and decelerated not only by their direction reversals but also by their changing speeds, which alternately rise to a maximum and then drop to zero.

Instead of using the language that we have used to describe the generation of electromagnetic waves, Maxwell used the terms *electric field intensity,* represented by the letter E, and *magnetic field intensity,* represented by the letter H. Both E and H were made vector quantities by assigning directions as well as numerical values to them. If we stop to think about the relation of magnetic fields to electric fields, then it is easy to see that E and H must travel in the same direction together even though their vectors are at right angles to one another, both rising to a maximum and declining to zero together. If we also remember that the direction of the electric field, the direction of the associated magnetic field and the direction of the current are mutually perpendicular to one another (p. 290), then the representation of electromagnetic waves as they are shown in Fig. 20-12 should be under-

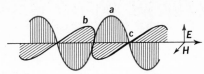

Fig. 20-12. "Model" of the Electromagnetic Wave. An electromagnetic wave may be viewed as an electric wave and a magnetic wave always in phase and at right angles to each other as they travel through space. The electric wave is shown in the vertical plane (in color), the magnetic wave in the horizontal. The electric field intensity, E, and the magnetic field intensity, H, reach their maximums (at a and b, respectively) simultaneously; their minimums (c) are also simultaneous.

standable. "The changes in each field maintain the other field, with a sort of mutual back-slapping, so they continue to travel."[8]

We know that energy is transported by waves of all kinds. Electromagnetic waves are no exception. What is the source of the energy that they transport? We know that a vibrating source is necessary for any wave. We have seen that the alternating current that we are using consists of electrons that are being accelerated and decelerated rapidly. As they slow down and stop before reversing their direction some small fraction of their kinetic energy is converted into the radiant energy of an electromagnetic wave. To use Maxwell's terminology, it is the values of E and H that change cyclically as the waves wing their way through space. These fluctuating fields will influence other charges that may be encountered, as, for example, the electrons in an antenna of a radio or television set. These electrons absorb some of the energy carried by the waves, so that they vibrate with the same periodicity as the transmitter's original oscillations.

The crux of Maxwell's work was that he took the relationships between electric and magnetic fields and all the other information that

---

[7] It is also impossible to have the latter without the former under certain conditions, but this fact is not relevant to the present discussion.

[8] Eric M. Rogers, *Physics for the Inquiring Mind,* Princeton Univ. Press, Princeton, N.J., 1960, p. 564.

he could get from Faraday and other experimenters, blended and condensed them into ingenious yet simple mathematical equations. These equations are too much for us, but from them he deduced that these electromagnetic waves should travel with the speed of light and predicted that in other respects they would behave like light, traveling indefinitely through space just as does the light from even the most distant stars. He predicted the existence of other electromagnetic waves, for example, radio waves, that would differ from light waves only in their frequency and wavelength. Their existence was not unexpected, for if vibrating electric charges can send out the combined electrical and magnetic disturbances that we call electromagnetic waves in the frequency range of visible light, there seems no reason why vibrating charges of higher and lower frequencies should not send out waves with somewhat different characteristics. But the existence of electromagnetic waves was not proved; they were still only a prediction from theory. There was as yet no concrete evidence to show that Maxwell's theoretical waves and the waves that our eyes interpret as light were one and the same thing.

Predicting the Existence of Electromagnetic Waves

It was easy enough to set up apparatus that would produce electric oscillations in wires, but obtaining frequencies that were high enough to give visible light was a very different matter. Modern electric circuits can produce frequencies up to 10^{12} cycles/sec (1000 billion per second), but to produce red light we need 4×10^{14} cycles/sec (400,000 billion per second). You might ask how commercial radio broadcasts that range from 550,000 to 1,600,000 cycles/sec (far below those needed to produce visible light) are produced. No man-made mechanical device can be made to vibrate with anything like such frequencies.

It has been discovered that crystals, for example, quartz crystals, have certain natural periods of vibration of their own, and these frequencies fall in the above ranges. This natural frequency is governed by the composition of the crystal, and its size and shape, in much the same way as the pitch (frequency) of a church bell is determined by its composition, size, and shape. Therefore, crystals of quartz are ground to the correct size and shape to produce the desired frequency of the waves emitted from the antenna of the broadcasting station. The smaller the crystal, the higher the frequency it emits. If the size is small enough, the frequency leaves the range of the ordinary radio for that of the short-wave radio. Still smaller crystals emit frequencies in the radar range.

It might seem possible to get down into the infrared invisible light ranges by choosing still smaller crystals. The trouble is that below the radar range the crystal size is too small to handle. If we calculate—and we can—the size a crystal must be in order to emit infrared waves, we find that it must be of *molecular* size.

By further reasoning and calculation we can conclude that to produce frequencies as high as those of visible light and beyond we will need particles smaller than molecules and atoms, which means that no crystals can do the job. Thus, according to Maxwell's theory of electromagnetic radiation, visible light, ultraviolet light, and *any possible radiations of still higher frequencies must be emitted by oscillating electric charges within atoms.* We will return to this conclusion later in this chapter. Remembering that infrared waves are heat waves, and, from kinetic theory, that heat is a kind of molecular motion, we should not be unduly surprised. Rather, we should feel gratified, for here we see how two apparently different concepts of heat, the molecular theory of heat and the wave theory of heat, can be completely reconciled.

Demonstrations of Electromagnetic Waves

Maxwell had suggested the type of apparatus needed to make a direct test. Although Maxwell published his theory in 1873, it did not attract much attention in the scientific world for more than fifteen years. What was needed was someone to make a direct test. In 1888 Heinrich Hertz of Germany, an unusually fine experimenter, decided to see if he could determine whether or not Maxwell's predictions were valid. He felt certain that his apparatus could not attain the necessary frequencies to give visible light, but he thought it possible to confirm Maxwell's other predictions. His apparatus was a simple spark-gap device (Fig. 20-13) sufficiently charged to cause a spark to jump from one highly polished electrode to the other. According to Maxwell's theory, electromagnetic waves should be sent out every time a spark jumped; and these waves should be capable of causing electrons to move the same way in a secondary circuit some distance away, provided it were "tuned" to the original circuit. The original circuit was thus a transmitter, consisting of a source, two polished metal spheres as the electrodes, and an induction coil[9] (not shown) to build up large charges on the metal spheres. The secondary circuit was a receiver, consisting merely of two similar electrodes connected to each other by a wire. Current was actually induced in this circuit, observable as a spark between the receiver electrodes, whenever the spark jumped across the transmitter electrodes.

The experiment was an historic triumph, not only for Hertz but more so for Maxwell, who

[9] An induction coil is used with direct current, a transformer with alternating current. The principle is the same, except that an induction coil must have a device that rapidly makes and break the circuit. Why?

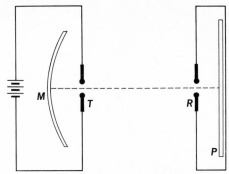

Fig. 20-13. Hertz's Proof of Electromagnetic Waves. Spark gap devices served as a crude transmitter, T, and receiver, R. A high voltage source was necessary for the transmitter to emit a strong spark. A weak spark jumped the gap at R when a strong one jumped the gap at T. Energy was thus transmitted from T to R by means of a wave motion. M and P are concave and plane reflecting mirrors, respectively, which were used to prove the waves had the properties of light waves.

unfortunately had died nine years previously at the age of 48. (Incidentally, Hertz died at the age of 37). Hertz measured the wavelength of the transmitted waves, and from his knowledge of their frequency and the equation $v = f\lambda$ (p. 156) found their velocity to be about 3×10^8 m/sec $(3 \times 10^{10}$ cm/sec), which is the speed of light in air.

Thus Hertz verified the major predictions of Maxwell. These waves were called Hertzian waves; we now call them radio waves. The fact that, unlike light waves, they will pass through opaque nonconductors if they are not too thick explains why indoor aerials for radio and television sets work very well. The fact that they are reflected or absorbed from metal surfaces explains why car radios are dimmed when crossing a metal framework bridge. In 1898, Marconi achieved reception and transmission of Hertzian waves over distances of many miles and, in 1901, sent and received them successfully across the Atlantic Ocean. Thus, radio is the result of the combined efforts of Faraday the experimenter, Maxwell the theorist, Hertz the experimenter, and Marconi the inventor and engineer.

Maxwell was responsible for the fusion of two apparently completely unrelated branches of science, light, on the one hand, and electricity and magnetism on the other. By his brilliant use of mathematics

> . . . he achieved a success which must be counted among the greatest miracles of the human intellect. He succeeded, by pure thought, in luring away secrets from nature which were only partly brought to light a generation later by laborious discerning experiments.[10]

You should not feel defeated if you cannot picture electromagnetic waves winging their way through empty space, for no one else can do that either. Scientists freely admit that they do not know what electromagnetic waves "are." The "are" is in quotes because the word implies that these waves exist as such; we do not know that. In fact, no expert thinks that they do exist, certainly not as we (or anyone else) have described them. However, we do know that changing electric and magnetic fields cause radiant energy to travel through space with a velocity of 186,000 mi/sec, that some of this energy is intercepted by our radio and TV aerials to give us the news of the world, fine music, and other worthwhile entertainment—unfortunately, too, a vastly greater quantity of pure drivel. This energy has the properties of a transverse wave, for it can produce diffraction and interference effects as all waves do, and it can be polarized as only transverse waves can. Furthermore, electromagnetic "waves" can be exactly and quantitatively described by equations that have the same mathematical form as those that describe visible mechanical waves.

[10] From the writings of Max Planck, who helped create the image of modern physics.

Mechanical Models. One of our troubles is that we cannot help trying to picture a phenomenon for which there is no picture; that is, we try to visualize a mechanical model that we can analyze. Even Lord Kelvin, an original thinker and a preeminent scientist, said in 1884 in reference to Maxwell's explanation of light:

> I am never content until I have constructed [in my mind] a mechanical model of the object I am studying. If I succeed in making one, I can understand; otherwise I do not. Hence, I cannot grasp the electromagnetic theory of light. I wish to understand light as fully as possible, without introducing things I understand still less.

It is true that mechanical models, even though they are incorrect, may give us a great deal of information that would not be obtainable otherwise. Consider a map of the world. In a sense it is a mechanical model. It is not the world, nor is it even a small replica of it. In fact, it has little or no real resemblance to the physical world. Yet we can learn far more about the physical world from this map in an hour or two of study of it than we could from years of actual exploration of the earth. Thus we justify the use of mechanical models that may bear little resemblance to reality.

We can sympathize with Lord Kelvin's difficulty in trying to understand Maxwell's explanation of light, for which no model could be constructed. It would be interesting to know what his thoughts were on learning that Hertz, four years later, demonstrated electromagnetic waves, and that Marconi, fifteen years later, had sent messages from Europe to America by means of them.

The use of Maxwell's theory advanced our knowledge of visible and invisible light far beyond what would have been possible otherwise. It has served, and still does, as a unifying concept for many phenomena concerning light. It has been one of the most fruitful of all scientific theories, even though it cannot provide a complete explanation for all phenomena of light. The paper that announced this theory to the world in 1873, a paper synthesizing electricity, magnetism, and light, was probably the greatest scientific publication since Newton's *Principia*. Maxwellian electrodynamics was added to Newtonian mechanics to form the foundations on which all future advances in physics must rest—or so it seemed at the time.

Radiation from Hot Bodies

That hot bodies should radiate heat is known to all of us. We also know that if the temperature is high enough, they also emit light. The radiator in our room may emit heat but never light; the heating element of our electric stove glows a dull red as it emits a lot of heat but little light, and the electric light bulb emits considerably more light (of the white variety) than does the heating element of the stove. We note the same phenomenon if we place a poker in a hot fire—after brief heating we detect heat radiated from it long before it is hot enough to emit light.

These radiations are the infrared or heat waves that have frequencies too low to affect our optic nerves, but still high enough to be absorbed by our skin, where their energy is converted to molecular kinetic energy, raising the temperature of the skin. Continued heating of the poker increases the amount of heat radiated, and soon the poker begins to glow red as frequencies are emitted sufficiently high for our eyes to detect. As heating continues, the red color gradually changes first to orange, then to yellow, and finally to white. This means that the higher frequencies responsible for the green and blue colors are increasing in amount faster than those responsible for the red.

If we should continue the heating until the

poker turns blue[11] (a temperature we cannot attain in the laboratory, but one that is attained in the hotter stars), the proportion of waves due to frequencies corresponding to blue would be greatly increased.

From these facts we can easily make the deduction that the production of higher frequencies requires greater energy than the production of the lower ones (Fig. 22-1). Note carefully that the total energy emitted by the infrared does not decrease with an increase in temperature. It actually increases, but red no longer determines the color that we see because the number of higher frequencies emitted has increased. Thus, the intensity of light that a heated body emits increases as its temperature increases, and the color of it shifts from the red toward the blue end of the spectrum. In the interests of clarity, let us try to explain this in another way.

Without specifying its characteristics, let us call whatever it is that is emitting radiation from within the glowing body an emitter. It is apparent that there must be enormous numbers of such emitters in the body, for the size of an emitter is easily demonstrated to be below the limits of visibility of our best instruments. It is also evident, as has been shown, that emitters are not all alike, some emitting low frequency radiation, some high frequency. When the temperature is high enough for significant amounts of radiation to be emitted, it is the low frequency emitters that emit first. Higher temperatures bring the high frequency emitters into play. Thus, as the temperature continues to rise, more emitters of all frequencies are brought into play. Since the high-frequency emitters carry more energy than the low, the radiation peak shifts toward the shorter wavelengths. It is therefore easy to see that the color of the light emitted by an in-

[11] At this temperature the poker would quickly melt and then vaporize.

candescent body is an index of its temperature. In this way the astronomer can estimate the temperature of stars, and foundry workers can estimate the temperature of the molten metal with which they work.

Spectra

We remember that it was Newton who, in 1669, dispersed ordinary white light (sunlight) into its component frequencies, into the colors of a continuous spectrum (Plate I, at p. 346), by passing the light through a wedge-shaped glass prism.[12] The dispersion is accomplished by the process of refraction (p. 335), which is a bending of the light rays, the violet more than the red, due to differences in velocity changes as the medium changes (from air to the glass of the prism and back to air again). The band of colors forms, as we have said, a continuous spectrum in which there are no gaps; that is, all of the wavelengths present in sunlight are represented.

A continuous spectrum can also be produced by solids, liquids, and highly compressed gases that have been heated to incandescence, that is, until they glow and so emit light of their own. We have concluded that light is an electromagnetic phenomenon, that it is propagated in the form of electromagnetic waves. Now, all waves have their origin in vibrating sources. We learned that the electromagnetic waves propagated by the apparatus of Hertz had their origin in oscillating electric charges as they "sputtered" back and forth across the spark gap in the electrical circuit he used. But here in these incandescent substances there is

no electrical circuit. We begin with cold matter, heat it sufficiently and it emits light. We must conclude that the vibrating source must be the atoms, molecules, or ions that compose our glowing solids, liquids, or compressed gases. It is important to keep our history straight—electrons had not yet been discovered, nor had radioactivity. Atoms were still indivisible in the eyes of all late-19th-century scientists.

Incandescent bodies in which the atoms are so close together that they interfere with one another while vibrating emit continuous spectra. A great mixture of electromagnetic waves of many frequencies and wavelengths is emitted. When this mixture is sent through a prism, the waves are sorted out to form a continuous spectrum. In an incandescent gas (or vapor) under low pressure, the atoms are much farther apart than they are in incandescent liquids and solids so that they do not interfere with one another; each can emit its own characteristic wavelengths. Certain sharp frequencies of light appear in the spectrum, and no light is emitted at other frequencies. The result is the discontinuous spectrum of isolated lines—a *line* spectrum. If the rarefied gas is composed of atoms all alike—that is, if it is an element—the line spectrum may be called an *atomic spectrum,* or an *emission line spectrum* (Plate I). Each element gives off a characteristic pattern of lines of specific frequencies. Thus a line spectrum is formed of lines of one color each and these lines cannot be dispersed into light of other colors. Such a one-color light is said to be *monochromatic.* We may say that this one-color light corresponds to a pure tone on a musical instrument. Carrying the analogy further, we may say that white light represents a mixture of visual wavelengths just as common noise represents a mixture of auditory wavelengths. Thus, line spectra represent certain specific wavelengths of light just as pure musical tones represent certain specific wavelengths of sound.

---

[12] We insist on the word *ordinary* here because "unordinary" white light can be made by blending complementary colors such as yellow and blue, or red and bluish green. We also note that the light Newton analyzed came from a hot glowing body, the sun.

The Spectroscope

The spectroscope is an instrument used for analyzing light according to its distribution of frequency and color. Commonly the light is passed through a prism and a system of lenses (Fig. 20-14). Light from a source enters a slit and its rays are made parallel by the first lens before it passes through the prism where it is refracted and separated into its various wavelengths (p. 336). It then passes through the focusing lens to the eye or to a photographic plate. Some spectroscopes use a diffraction grating (p. 342) in place of a prism. The optical system forms an image of the slit for each frequency of light present. When not all wavelengths are present, a discrete set of slit images is formed that are called spectral lines. What we have is a *bright line spectrum*.

Commonly a third tube is added for the purpose of admitting light to illuminate a scale. This scale permits the positions of the spectral lines with respect to one another to be described. Spectroscopes vary in their resolving power depending on how they are made. One of low resolving power may show a broad line in a particular place in a spectrum, whereas one of high resolving power may split this broad line into two or more narrow lines of the same color but representing slightly different wavelengths.

Flame Spectra vs. Bright Line Spectra

Consider sodium. If we vaporize it in an open flame, we see an ill-defined mass of yellow light. Let us look at this light through a spectroscope. We see only a part of that light as one or two bright yellow lines whose length and width is determined by the dimensions of the slit through which the light enters the spectroscope. Similarly, if we vaporize lithium we will see a mass of reddish light. In the spectroscope we see only a part of that mass as a bright red line because the slit through which the light enters is the shape of that line. If we vaporize a compound containing both sodium and lithium our *unaided* eye would see a mass of orange light (a mixture of red and yellow). Through the spectroscope we see no orange lines but the same yellow and bright red lines that we saw with sodium and lithium

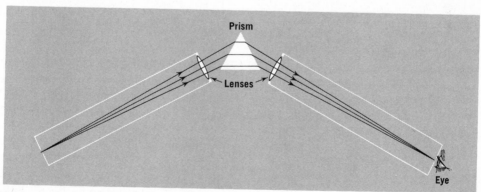

Fig. 20-14. Essentials of Spectroscope. Light enters at the left via a slit, is dispersed by refraction into its component wavelengths by the prism, and is focused for the eye by the lens at the right. If monochomatic light enters the slit, the eye will see a bright band or line of light whose width depends on the width of the slit, and whose position depends on the amount of refraction. The prism can be rotated to bring widely dispersed rays into the viewing tube. The actual effect of the lenses and prism on paths of the light rays is not shown.

alone. The spectroscope has separated the two colors in the orange light by refraction as it passed through the prism. Yellow light is refracted more than red, so we see them separated into lines. We chose sodium and lithium for our examples because they each emit one-color light only at the vaporizing temperature. Many elements when vaporized emit light of many frequencies (Plate I, at p. 346), which the prism (or diffraction grating) of a spectroscope sorts out by refracting or diffracting some colors (frequencies) more than others.

Bright line spectra are remarkably different with different emitters, that is, with different kinds of gases and vapors; each kind of atom has its own characteristic pattern. Since any solid or liquid element may be converted to a vapor if it is heated to a high enough temperature, its bright line spectrum is a means of identification. The patterns of the spectra of the various kinds of atoms differ in the number of lines present, in the variety of the colors shown, and in the spacing of the lines, not only in the visible range but also in the infrared, ultraviolet, and X-ray regions. Thus, mercury vapor has two thin red lines, two intense lines close together in the yellow range, one intense line in the green, and several less intense in the blue and purple ranges. The relative order of the colors of the various lines is obviously the order in which they occur in the continuous spectrum. Sodium vapor has but two strong, closely spaced lines in the yellow range, which in a spectroscope of low resolving power commonly appear as a single line. Contrast this with iron vapor, which shows over 6000 lines. Clearly, the bright line spectra are the fingerprints of the atoms and for that reason are often termed atomic spectra.

The discovery that the spectrum of any one kind of atom is unique made chemical analysis by flame spectra, that is, by heating in a hot flame, possible for many of the metals. Salts of sodium, for example, give the same yellow line as does sodium heated alone. Two new elements, cesium and rubidium, were discovered by spectroanalysis of ores containing these metals. Later, helium was discovered in the sun some twenty years before its discovery here on earth. Astronomers are able to tell the composition of stars by their spectra. Thus we justify our statement elsewhere that our periodic chart contains all of the elements in the visible part of our universe. Some types of adulteration of food and other products may be detected by spectral analysis. Line spectra of substances that are gases at room temperatures are not produced by heating in a flame because gases cannot ordinarily be heated to incandescence. Instead, their spectra are produced by electric excitation in a gas discharge tube.

Absorption Spectra

Absorption spectra are observed in the spectroscope when ordinary white light from an incandescent source is filtered through a relatively cool gas before entering the spectroscope. Such a spectrum consists of a pattern of dark lines or bands in the otherwise continuous spectrum of the light transmitted through the medium. Consider the continuous spectrum of the sun (Plate I, at p. 346). The sun has an envelope of relatively cool gases and vapors surrounding it. This envelope is the filtering medium. The light being filtered is emitted by atoms of many elements in the outer part of the sun. Among these elements is sodium, which we will use as an example. The sodium in the sun is in the form of a very hot glowing vapor emitting the sodium frequencies (in the yellow part of the spectrum) in every direction away from the sun. The outer part of the envelope contains cooler sodium vapor, which is not hot enough to glow and so does not emit radiation. Now these sodium atoms in the cool vapor can absorb some of the frequencies (energy) that they themselves could emit if their vapors were hot enough. Those atoms that absorb enough such energy begin to radiate the same frequencies *in every direction,* even back into the sun itself. This limits the amount of energy that is radiated in the *proper direction to reach a spectroscope.* Therefore, the amount of energy that does enter the spectroscope is not enough to form a visible line in the spectrum, so we see a dark line in the yellow part of the continuous spectrum.

Joseph von Fraunhofer in 1814 noted these dark lines in the spectrum of the sun; they are known as Fraunhofer lines. Fraunhofer was a maker of optical glass. His interest was initially a practical one, that of improving the quality of the glass he was using to make spectacles. In this research he laid the foundations for solar and stellar chemistry. He constructed a "map" showing 576 of these dark lines in the spectrum of the sun and made other maps of various stars. He invented the forerunner of the modern spectroscope and diffraction grating, and in doing so, laid the foundations of the whole science of spectroscopy.

Problems of Bright Line Spectra

The great variety of patterns presented great problems to the early students of spectra, problems that were not resolved until after the first decade of the present century. That light is emitted by gases or vapors when their atoms are excited was known in the 18th century. The first flame spectra were studied about 1750. Line spectra were first studied about 1800. Aside from that of Fraunhofer, not much significant work was done until the 1850's, when Kirchhoff and Bunsen began the work that shortly led them to the conclusion that each element had its own characteristic line spectrum.

Maxwell's electromagnetic theory of light (p. 345) holds that accelerated charges send

out radiant energy in the form of waves. The accelerated charges—electrons were not yet known—oscillated (vibrated) back and forth between two points, causing energy to be emitted. The problem was to identify the oscillator, for all waves had to have an oscillating source. The only possibility at the time seemed to be charged atoms, the ions of Michael Faraday, but how could they account for the multiplicity of the lines and patterns in bright line spectra? Why the different wavelengths represented by the different lines, and why the exact line patterns? Why did atoms in the incandescent gaseous state emit these different bright line spectra, whereas these same atoms in the form of glowing liquids or solids emit continuous spectra only, and these all alike no matter what the element, if the temperature is the same? [13] Why should sodium show only one or two (depending upon the resolving power of the spectroscope) yellow lines in the visible range, whereas iron vapor could give about 6000 lines? What complex arrangement of emitters could possibly give that many lines? Why should some closely similar elements, sodium and potassium, for example, have such different patterns? Why was there no progressive change in the patterns from element to element in the periodic chart? Why should the number of lines for any one element depend upon the intensity of the heating?

Clearly, these problems could not be solved until the structure of the atom was better understood, and, conversely, it is easy to see that no picture of the atom that failed to explain line spectra could be seriously considered. We must turn our attention to the structure of atoms in order to find the answer, but before

---

[13] We now know that the reason they are all alike at the same temperature is that in liquids and solids, or even in the dense gaseous core of the sun, the incessant mutual collisions among the atoms blur the individual characteristics, just as springs connected together in large groups can no longer vibrate with their own frequencies.

we do so we will consider two developments concerning spectra, each of which added to our knowledge but at the same time created problems of its own.

We should also keep in mind one other fundamental problem, one more fundamental to this course than the explanation of spectra or the unraveling of the structure of the atom. We must not forget that we are engaged in a study of matter and energy, that energy, insofar as we know at the present time, does not exist apart from matter. Up to this point in our study, all matter has been considered to consist of indivisible atoms. If, to understand bright line spectra, this concept of structureless atoms is to be abandoned in favor of atoms that have parts—and hence a structure[14]—then the prevailing concepts of radiant energy will also have to be altered. Any new concept of atoms will have many other things to explain, most of them related to the understanding of the periodic table, which contains all of the elemental kinds of matter in the whole universe. Among them is the orderly arrangement of the elements into periods and groups (or families). Why the groups? Why the periods? Why the transition elements? Why do the various elements combine with each other as they do? Why do some refuse to combine at all? In short, what is there in the structure of atoms that governs the behavior of matter? Our search for the cause of line spectra will not be fruitful unless it also opens up a path that will eventually lead us to a reasonably complete understanding of the periodic table.

Balmer's Empirical Formula

In the 1870's and 1880's there was feverish research to find a numerical relation between the spacings of the spectral lines, to find some mathematical key to decode the secrets of the lines. In 1885 Johann Balmer (a Swiss schoolteacher who was neither a research scientist nor a recognized mathematician) made the first important break in the problem. By a straight trial-and-error method, he hit upon a formula that related the four principal (visible) lines of hydrogen (red, green, blue, and violet) to their wavelengths. Balmer's formula is as follows:

$$\lambda \text{ (in cm)} = c\left(\frac{n^2}{n^2 - 2^2}\right) \qquad \text{[20-1]}$$

where λ is the wavelength, n is an integer $(1, 2, 3, 4, \ldots)$, and c is an empirically determined constant whose value is 3645.6×10^{-8} cm. Specifically, for the hydrogen lines, n is 3 for the red, 4 for the green, 5 for the blue, and 6 for the violet. Let us calculate the wavelength of the red (alpha) line by substituting 3 for n and the numerical value of c in the equation:

$$3645.6 \times 10^{-8}\left(\frac{3^2}{3^2 - 2^2}\right)$$
$$= 6562.08 \times 10^{-8} \text{ cm} \qquad \text{[20-2]}$$

The experimental value obtained for this red line by Anders Ångström, who had made the most careful wavelength measurements of his time, was 6562.10×10^{-8} cm, or 6562.10 Å.[15] The agreement is remarkably close, considering the difference in methods used by Balmer and Ångström. However, the agreement loses much of its strangeness when we learn that Balmer started with Ångström's experimental

---

[14] A structure in this context refers to the arrangement of the parts.

[15] Instead of expressing wavelengths in centimeters, it is now customary for simplicity's sake to do so in ångström units (abbreviated Å; named in honor of Ångström); 1 Å = 10^{-8} cm.

value and worked backwards from it, juggling figures in a cut-and-try fashion until he came up with the right answer. Note carefully that he did not obtain his results by the formulation of a theory and/or by mathematical analysis. Balmer could give no reason for the success of his formula.

Far more remarkable is the fact that Balmer's formula is almost equally good for the wavelengths of the green, blue, and violet lines of hydrogen, and even for lines beyond the visible part of the spectrum, that is, in the ultraviolet region, where the value of n is $7, 8, 9, \ldots$. Moreover, as the value of n gets bigger, the formula demands that the lines get closer and closer together. This is readily seen from the quantity $n^2/(n^2 - 2^2)$ in the formula. For example, when n is 3, the value of this quantity is 1.80; when n is 4, it is 1.33; when n is 5, it is 1.19; when n is 6, it is 1.12. It is thus seen that the difference between successive wavelengths becomes less and less which means that the lines in the spectrum of hydrogen are getting closer and closer together as the ultraviolet region is approached, for the spacing is a function of the differences in wavelengths. All of this is in agreement with the observed spectrum of hydrogen (Fig. 22-7).

The wavelengths of all of the lines of hydrogen mentioned so far are given by the Balmer formula by varying the value of n while keeping the 2^2 in the denominator; all such lines are grouped together as the Balmer series. Balmer speculated on the possibility that there might be other series of hydrogen lines in the invisible parts of the spectrum, that is, in the infrared and ultraviolet. In them the wavelengths should be given if we replace 2^2 with 1^2, or 3^2, or 4^2, and so on. Such series were eventually found as improvements in apparatus and techniques took place. The first series, whose wavelengths are given when 2^2 is replaced by 1^2, is in the ultraviolet region of the

spectrum; the others are in the infrared region.[16]

However, the formula had to be altered in some respects. If it was to give the wavelengths of these lines, a new constant had to be determined. This constant, R, is called the Rydberg constant in honor of the great Swedish spectroscopist (R is approximately equal to 4 divided by the previous constant, c). If we rewrite Balmer's formula to give the reciprocal of the wavelength (instead of the wavelength) and use the new constant, the equation then becomes:

$$\frac{1}{\lambda} = R\left(\frac{1}{2^2} - \frac{1}{n^2}\right) \qquad \text{[20-3]}$$

The value of R is 109,677.58 cm^{-1} (the superscript, $^{-1}$, in this constant simply means "reciprocal of"). The equation applies only to the Balmer series. We may now write the formula in the more general form, so it will be applicable to all of the series, as follows:

$$\frac{1}{\lambda} = R\left(\frac{1}{n_1{}^2} - \frac{1}{n_2{}^2}\right) \qquad \text{[20-4]}$$

Here n_1 is a fixed integer $(1, 2, 3, \ldots)$ for any one series, and n_2 is another integer $(2, 3, 4, \ldots)$ that varies within the series (as n did in the original form of the equation) but can never have a value smaller than $n_1 + 1$, that is, $n_2 \geq n_1 + 1$. It should be noted that the equation does not apply directly to spectra of elements other than hydrogen. This should not surprise us, considering the range of the numbers of lines and the diversity of the patterns of atomic spectra. Yet it served as a basis for the development of other formulas of simi-

---

[16] That in the ultraviolet region is called the Lyman series; those in the infrared region are the Paschen, Brackett, and Pfund series, all named after their discoverers.

lar form for the spectra of other gases and vapors.

It should also be noted that the Rydberg constant appears in all of the formulas. These similarities suggest that all bright line spectra are caused by the same basic physical mechanism, a mechanism that must be extraordinarily complex in order to explain the great variety of spectral lines and spectral patterns. The understanding of this physical mechanism was not much advanced by Balmer's formula; such understanding had to await a better knowledge of the nature of light and a model of the structure of the hydrogen atom.

The Electromagnetic Spectrum

We remember that Newton and Huygens advanced conflicting theories during the latter half of the 17th century concerning the method by which light was transmitted from a source to a receiver. Most students of light accepted Newton's method largely because of his reputation. In the very early 1800's Thomas Young demonstrated interference and diffraction properties of light, and the weight of scientific opinion swung away from Newton and over to Huygens. The last "diehards" were convinced of the wave theory when Fizeau and Foucault (about 1850) both demonstrated that light traveled faster in a rare medium—air, for example—than it did through water or glass. Maxwell's electromagnetic theory did not reject the wave theory, for it dealt essentially with the origin of light rather than with its transmission. Its origin was something that the wave theory did not even consider.

We have already stated that Maxwell's equations (really wave equations) did not preclude electromagnetic vibrations with frequencies other than those giving rise to visible light. It was Hertz who demonstrated radio waves in the laboratory and Marconi who first used them for commercial communication. Infrared and ultraviolet radiations were known to be parts of the solar spectrum since the early 1800's (see Fraunhofer, p. 355). The infrared radiations have wavelengths that are longer than those of visible red but shorter than those of radio, and the ultraviolet has shorter wavelengths than the violet but longer than those of X rays (Chapter 23).

We did little more than mention X rays because we did not yet have the background to understand their origin. We still do not, and will not have it until after we have discussed the Bohr theory. X rays form a significant part of the electromagnetic spectrum; their place is in the high frequency–high energy portion beyond the ultraviolet. They are a most useful form of radiation to man, and a very dangerous form if improperly used.

Since the turn of the present century other additions have been made to what we now call the electromagnetic spectrum (Fig. 20-15). All electromagnetic waves have the same velocity in air, 3×10^8 m/sec, or 3×10^{10} cm/sec. Differences in their behavior are due to differences in frequency (or wavelength). All have their uses in our society. The longer radio waves travel around the earth in a way that the shorter cannot, for the longer are reflected and diffracted back to earth when they strike the lower boundary of the ionosphere (Chapter 30), whereas the shorter wavelengths (higher frequencies) go straight on in straight lines. Television waves belong in this category and so the limit of their reception is bounded by the horizon.

Our eyes are constructed so as to receive a limited number of frequencies. Various devices have been constructed to receive other parts of the spectrum, each being restricted to certain ranges. Radar and walkie-talkie sets, short-wave radios, television, and ordinary radio receivers are all used to detect wavelengths greater than about 1 cm. Especially

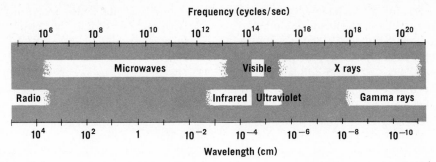

Fig. 20-15. Electromagnetic Spectrum. In all cases frequency $\times$ wavelength equals 3×10^{10} cm/sec, the velocity of light.

synthesized films of one sort or another will detect all wavelengths that are a bit shorter than 1 cm. Those wavelengths longer than 1 cm have an obvious connection with electricity, for we are all familiar to some extent with the broadcasting of radio and television waves. Those shorter than about 1 cm have no such obvious connection with electricity; nevertheless, we have already seen from Maxwell's theory that these shorter wavelengths should also be produced by oscillations of electric charges. To explain how this is done by electric charges that reside within the atom is one of the ultimate aims of Chapter 22. But before we do so, we are going to take a short diversion into the theory of relativity.

Exercises

1. The phenomenon of reflection is of little or no interest to us in our search for a better understanding of light, but the phenomenon of refraction is. What did refraction reveal about the nature of ordinary sunlight?
2. The fact that light can be polarized tells us what about the nature of light?
3. How may ordinary light be dispersed?
4. Monochromatic light cannot be dispersed. Why not?
5. Visible light has approximately what range of (a) frequencies, and (b) wavelengths?
6. Distinguish between the theories of light formulated by Newton and by Huygens. Do either of these theories deal with the origin of light?
7. Why did Newton reject Huygens' wave theory?
8. Why do we now follow Huygens rather than Newton?
9. In what way is diffraction of light (a) similar to and (b) different from refraction?
10. What two phenomena can be explained by the wave theory but not by the particle theory?
11. Distinguish between particle radiation and wave radiation.
12. In exercise 11, we asked about the differences between particle radiation and wave radiation. How is this question related to diffraction and interference of light?
13. Express the speed of light in cm/sec and in mi/sec.
14. What is the relationship between color and frequency?
15. Which has the greater frequency, red or violet light? Which has the greater wavelength?
16. Define (a) a spectrum, (b) a bright line

spectrum, and (c) a flame spectrum. (d) How may a flame spectrum be obtained?

17. (a) How did Maxwell's theory of light differ from that of Huygens?
    (b) Did Maxwell's theory add anything to our understanding of the origin of light?

18. Was Maxwell able to demonstrate his theory?

19. For what purpose was the ether invented?

20. In Maxwell's electromagnetic theory, what do E and H represent?

21. How is an electromagnetic wave generated?

22. Lord Kelvin objected to the electromagnetic theory. Why?

23. What kind of spectrum is emitted by (a) a glowing solid or liquid, and (b) a glowing vapor or gas?

24. We learned earlier that heat is molecular motion. Why, then, are we justified in speaking of infrared rays as heat rays?

25. (a) Would you expect DC electricity flowing through a wire to send out electromagnetic waves?
    (b) How about AC? Explain.

26. Does Maxwell's theory contradict Huygens' theory? Why, or why not?

27. What is the most necessary part of a spectroscope? What is the function of this part?

28. What contribution did Hertz make to Maxwell's theory?

29. What was Balmer trying to do when he discovered what is known as his formula?

30. What was the one great problem, or perhaps we should say, what was the one great group of problems, of line spectra?

31. Calculate by means of Balmer's formula the wavelength of the violet line in the hydrogen spectrum.

32. What determines the frequency of the radiation emitted by glowing atoms?

33. The bright line spectrum of sodium as viewed with an ordinary spectroscope consists of a single yellow line. The flame spectrum of sodium viewed by the naked eye consists of a "mass" of yellow light.
    (a) Why is the first a "line," whereas the second is a "mass" of light?
    (b) Why are these spectra yellow? (The answer should include how these spectra are produced.)

34. Luminous hydrogen has a reddish hue but is not pure red. How do you account for this?

35. In what state must an element be in order to obtain its bright line spectrum?

36. What is the difference between a continuous spectrum and a line spectrum? How are line spectra produced?

37. Visible light constitutes a very small part of the electromagnetic spectrum. Man has developed several artificial sense organs with which he is able to pick up many messages from the universe around us. Name as many of them as you can.

38. A stove poker heated white hot emits what colors of light?

Relativity

The theory of relativity examines the nature of space and time and their relationships to light and other electromagnetic radiation. Since the modern concepts of space and time, as expressed by Einstein's special theory of relativity, arose out of studies on the motion of light, it is appropriate that we discuss the subject here, immediately after our presentation of the electromagnetic theory of light.

The popular attitude toward relativity includes the notion that it is much too difficult for those of us who are neither good scientists nor excellent mathematicians. The difficulty is not with the concept itself, but with our reluctance to re-examine, and ultimately to abandon, some of our strongly held ideas about the universe. This reluctance is common to scientist and nonscientist alike—witness the time it took scientists and philosophers of the 16th and 17th centuries to get used to the idea that the earth is not the fixed center of the universe.

> The views of space and time which I wish to lay before you have sprung from the soil of experimental physics, and therein lies their strength. They are radical. Henceforth space by itself, and time by itself, are doomed to fade away into mere shadows, and only a kind of union of the two will preserve an independent reality.
> **HERMAN MINKOWSKI**

Relativity of Motion

The ancient Greeks and later followers of the geocentric hypothesis had no problem with the relativity of motion because they had an easy absolute reference point, the center of the earth, which was also the center of the universe. To them the earth was in a state of absolute rest; therefore all motion was absolute motion that could be measured relative to the fixed reference point, the center of the earth.

The need for a reference point against which motion can be measured is not apparent to the average person in his normal everyday life. To a scientist who needs to understand all of the subtleties of motion to keep his thinking straight while studying it, the presence or absence of an absolute reference point becomes all-important.

Reference Frames

As an example, consider the concepts *up* and *down*. Down is the direction of motion of a falling object, a vertical path directed approximately toward the center of the earth. Up, obviously, then is the opposite direction. If the earth were flat, vertical could be taken as an absolute direction. But the earth is round, and so different points on it have different verticals; in fact, verticals in some places are perpendicular to those in some other places. Therefore, up and down have no precise meaning unless the point on the earth's surface to which they refer is defined.

Consider another case. You are seated on a train that is moving at uniform velocity. You observe the conductor drop a coin. From your point of view it drops straight down, just as it would if the train were motionless in the station. A person standing outside the train also sees the coin drop, but he observes that the coin falls downward along a curved path,

that of a parabola (compare Fig. 6-2). To him the coin's motion is the resultant of two motions, a downward one due to gravity and a forward one due to the motion of the train. (See "Projectile Motion" in Chapter 6.) We conclude that the coin moved in a straight line relative to the train and in a parabola relative to the earth's surface.

The heliocentric theory of Copernicus changed things from the ancient Greek view, for the earth could no longer be viewed as a body in a state of absolute rest. To Copernicans the reference point became the center of the sun, supposedly at absolute rest in the center of the universe. Newton's contributions to scientific knowledge again altered the concept of an absolute reference frame. Newton recognized that the sun is not necessarily at rest at the center of the universe. Therefore, needing a wider frame of reference, he conceived an abstract *absolute space* in terms of which any motion could be given meaning. His absolute space was completely uniform in all directions and extended infinitely in all directions. Hence any motion relative to the reference frame of absolute space could be considered an absolute motion.

In fact, experience tells us that it is impossible to determine whether a body is at rest or is moving uniformly in absolute space. Assume the following: You are on a train that is on one of two closely spaced parallel tracks. The train is capable of giving you a vibrationless ride. All window shades are tightly drawn except on the window by your seat. You know the train is standing still because objects on the station platform are not changing positions relative to you. Suppose now that you take a short nap. When you wake up and look out of your window, you see another train on the other track. It appears to you to be standing still because it is not changing position relative to you. The conductor comes along and you ask him when your train is going to start. For an answer he raises the shade on a window on the other side of the aisle, and you see the scenery rushing by at a mile a minute. You realize then that the other train is also moving at exactly the same speed as yours, so that relative to you and your train its speed is zero. You conclude that one can perceive a state of rest or a state of motion only in relation to some other frame of reference. If one of the two trains were moving faster (or slower) than the other, a glance out of your window would tell you at once.

Inertial Reference Frames

This example of the two trains shows that one cannot determine one's absolute motion when one is moving at uniform speed. This is a necessary consequence of Newton's first law of motion. This law states that a net external force is necessary to change the speed or direction of motion of an object. Suppose you are on a train that is moving with uniform velocity on a smooth track. If you place a ball at the center of a level table in the train, the ball will remain motionless until a force is applied to it. Such a reference frame (the train), in which a body remains in a state of uniform motion unless acted on by a force, is called an *inertial reference frame*. Note that you do not have to concern yourself with the motion of the inertial reference frame itself; you merely look for change of motion (or absence of such change) in objects relative to the reference frame.

Of course, not all reference frames are inertial reference frames. For example, let us suppose that the train, still traveling at uniform speed, starts around a long smooth gradual curve. If there is very little friction between the ball and the table, the ball will start to roll toward the edge of the table even though

no apparent unbalanced external force is acting on it. This reference frame (train on curve) produces an effect that appears to you, on the train, to contradict Newton's first law; that is, the motion of the train results in your observing an acceleration although you do not see a force being exerted. Such a reference frame is noninertial. Noninertial reference frames are discussed further under "General Relativity" later in this chapter.

The distinction between inertial and noninertial reference frames is an important one. In a noninertial reference frame, the motion of a body (such as the ball on the table) will appear to violate Newton's laws—namely, the ball will appear to accelerate in the absence of a force. In an inertial reference frame all bodies obey Newton's laws. Moreover, it can be shown that Newton's laws of motion have the same form in all inertial reference frames. This means that there is no "privileged" reference frame with respect to uniform motion; all systems at rest or moving uniformly relative to one another "obey" Newton's laws. In other words, it is impossible to detect absolute motion of objects by any difference in the laws of motion between the reference frames of which they are a part.

Although any inertial reference frame is suitable for ordinary measurements of relative velocities, the scientists of the 19th century continued to feel the need for an absolute frame of reference. Various solutions were proposed, none of them satisfactory. Then Maxwell's newly developed electromagnetic theory gave rise to a new possibility of finding an absolute frame of reference. Although Newton's laws of motion do not change their form from one inertial reference frame to another, Maxwell's equations of the electromagnetic field do change. Perhaps it might be best to abandon attempts to determine the absolute motion of material objects and turn instead to an investigation of the relationships between light and motion.

The Ether an Absolute Reference Frame?

Maxwell and his early followers believed that light had to be carried by some medium that pervaded all space. Faraday had assumed that the ether, or some variety of it, was the substance that transmitted electric and magnetic forces across empty space (p. 346). In his view it made action at a distance possible. Maxwell accepted Faraday's assumption because it helped to explain light as an electromagnetic phenomenon. One of the major difficulties of the electromagnetic theory of light was the lack of any observable medium for the transmission of light waves and other electromagnetic waves. Physicists agreed that light was a wave motion because it showed diffraction and interference effects. All waves other than electromagnetic waves need a physical medium for their transmission (p. 154), but there was no obvious medium to transmit light and other electromagnetic waves. In fact, experiments showed that these waves were best transmitted in a vacuum. Physicists therefore turned to the ether as a medium in which light could spread, much as sound spreads in air.

The ether was another of those special fluids, like phlogiston, caloric, and electrical fluid, that were introduced to explain certain specific phenomena. All of them had one property in common, that of complete elusiveness or undetectability. The ether also had to have some special properties. First, it had to permeate all space, even the empty space we call a vacuum, because light from the stars passed through all space. It had to be a solid because light was a transverse wave and so could not

pass through a gas or a liquid (p. 155). It had to be a rigid solid because of the great speed of light, yet all material objects had to move through this solid without resistance.

Although the ether was postulated originally to serve as a medium for the transmission of light, this fantastic "substance" gained a wider acceptance than it would have otherwise because some scientists thought that it might serve as an absolute frame of reference more fixed than the stars. If the ether is at rest, we must be moving through it. Many physicists began a search to detect the ether by means of experiments in electrodynamics, the most important of which was the Michelson–Morley experiment.

The Michelson–Morley Experiment

The purpose of the Michelson–Morley experiment was to detect the motion of the earth through the ether. If the ether is at rest—as most 19th century scientists assumed—the earth must be moving through it. Or—since motion is relative—we can consider the earth to be at rest and the ether to be blowing past like a wind. It is reasonable to assume that the velocity of light would be affected by this motion. We represent the velocity of light by c and the velocity of the ether wind by v. Then, using vector addition (Chapter 5) of velocities, we have $c + v$ for the velocity of light moving in the direction of the wind and $c - v$ for the velocity of light moving in the opposite direction.

Now if such a difference in velocity existed—and if someone could develop an instrument that would detect it—there would be evidence for the existence of the ether. But the velocity of light, 186,000 mi/sec, is so great compared to ordinary velocities that an extremely sensitive instrument would be needed to detect the difference between $c + v$ and $c - v$.

The Michelson Interferometer

In 1879 Maxwell suggested to the physicist A. A. Michelson that he attempt to measure the speed of the ether wind relative to the earth. For this purpose, Michelson invented a device, the Michelson interferometer (Fig. 21-1), for measuring small differences in the speed of light with great precision. Light from a monochromatic (single wavelength) source is directed against a "half-silvered" mirror.

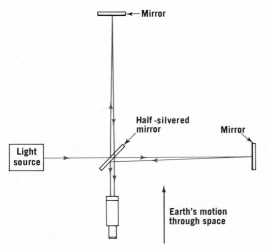

Fig. 21-1. The Michelson Interferometer. The central "half-silvered" mirror has an extremely thin coating of reflecting metal and is therefore partially transparent. The thickness of the coating is such that the mirror reflects half the light impinging on it and transmits the other half. The two outer mirrors are thickly coated to reflect substantially all the light they receive. To simplify deriving the mathematical relationship between the travel times from the central mirror to each of the outer mirrors and back, we assume that the outer mirrors are equidistant from the central mirror. In performing an actual experiment, however, this equality is not necessary.

Such a mirror has the property of reflecting only half the light falling on it and transmitting the other half through it. The mirror is placed at such an angle that the reflected light goes off at 90° to its original direction while the transmitted light continues in its original direction. Each beam reaches an ordinary optical mirror and is reflected back to the half-silvered mirror. Again, by partial reflection and partial transmission, part of each beam reaches an optical viewing device, which is basically a low power microscope with a set of crosshairs. The two light beams meeting here produce a set of interference lines, similar to those in Young's double slit diffraction grating (Fig. 20-9). The positions of the interference lines in relation to the crosshairs are affected by one or both of two factors: the relative distances between the central and outer mirrors and the relative travel times of the light beams over these distances. This interferometer was accurate enough to measure changes in distance of the order of 3×10^{-7} cm.

Now, if there is an ether wind, it will take the light a bit longer to travel a given distance to and from a mirror along a path parallel to the direction of the wind than along a path at right angles to the direction of the wind.

For students who want a mathematical proof of the preceding statement, we offer the following brief summary.

We represent the time required for a light beam to travel to and from one mirror parallel to the direction of the ether wind by t_1 and the time required for a light beam to travel to and from the other mirror at right angles to the direction of the wind by t_2. The ratio of travel times is then

$$\frac{t_1}{t_2} = \frac{c}{\sqrt{c^2 - v^2}}$$

where c is the velocity of light and v is the velocity of the ether wind. (The derivation of this relationship can be found in most physics textbooks and is omitted here.) It can be seen that for any value of v other than zero the parallel travel time, t_1, will be greater than the perpendicular travel time, t_2. However, if there is no ether wind, so that $v = 0$, then

$$\frac{t_1}{t_2} = 1 \quad \text{and} \quad t_1 = t_2$$

Thus the travel times would be equal.

The difference in travel times could be verified by observing the change in the ratio of travel times that would result from changing the position of the interferometer in relation to the ether wind. Michelson's plan was to set up the apparatus in one position, for example, that indicated in Fig. 21-1, and note the positions of the interference lines in relation to the crosshairs. Then he would change the position of the apparatus—rotate it 90°, say—and again note the positions of the interference lines. Michelson was convinced that the ether wind existed, so he expected that a 90° rotation of the apparatus would produce a different travel-time relationship. This would be reflected in a change in the positions of the interference lines.

The Negative Result

In 1887 Michelson, together with E. W. Morley, performed this experiment. The result was remarkable; the interference lines did not change position. This meant that the travel-time relationship did not change. Therefore either the velocity of light is not affected by the ether wind—which contradicts the principle of the vector addition of velocities—or there is no ether wind. This second alternative means that the earth must be stationary with respect to the ether.

As another alternative, it was proposed that the the ether moves along the earth and with

every moving object. This had to be rejected in view of Fizeau's experiment demonstrating that the speed of light in running water is the same as the speed of light in still water. (This meant that the ether is not carried along by the moving water.) The hypothesis of a moving ether also was incompatible with the observed phenomenon of the aberration of light (Fig. 2-10).

All attempts to account for the negative result of the Michelson–Morley experiment met with failure. Numerous repetitions of the experiment always gave the same result. Other experiments were designed to detect the motion of other objects, such as the sun and other stars, with respect to the ether, and these all yielded a negative result. All of these unsuccessful attempts to measure the motion of light relative to the ether led to the inescapable conclusion that the velocity of light and other electromagnetic waves in empty space is always the same, no matter what the motion of the source or of the observer.

No experiment could be devised that could detect the velocity of any object relative to the ether. This gave rise to the possibility that the ether does not even exist. However, scientists were reluctant to abandon the concept of the ether because it was so useful in explaining the transmission of light through otherwise empty space.

The Special Theory of Relativity

Einstein insisted that hypotheses and theories must be built on observation and experiment; what cannot be measured must be discarded. This meant that the concept of the ether had to go, for no experiment could detect it. Further, since the motion equations of Galileo and Newton were satisfactory for comparatively low speeds but failed to explain phenomena occurring at or near the velocity of light, it was necessary to change the laws of science to accommodate the new knowledge. This Einstein did in his formulation of the special theory of relativity, which was published in 1905.

The special theory of relativity has two simple postulates:

1. The laws of physics must be written in the same form in all inertial reference frames that have uniform motion relative to each other.
2. The velocity of light in a vacuum is constant regardless of relative motion between source and observer.

The student can easily see that, like all great theories, Einstein's postulates are based on the work of his predecessors. However, from these simple postulates Einstein was able mathematically to derive equations predicting that, at very high speeds, the properties of mass, length, time, and velocity would be different from those described by Newtonian equations.

In 1905, when Einstein published his theory, there were no means of testing his theoretical equations by experiment. However, as laboratory methods and apparatus were improved in the course of several decades, experiments were devised that confirmed most of Einstein's theoretical predictions. We will examine briefly some of these.

The Relativity of Simultaneity

Einstein also considered the question of whether two observers, moving with uniform linear motion relative to each other, can both reach the same conclusion about the simultaneity of two events. His conclusion was that they could not. Let us see why this should be.

Suppose we have a long and absolutely straight stretch of railroad track. We will set up an electric light bulb at each end of this straight track and connect the bulbs to a switch at the exact midpoint, M, of the straight stretch so that when an observer at M closes the switch, both bulbs light up simultaneously. Now imagine a train traveling rapidly along this track from one end, A, of the straight stretch toward the other end, B. The exact midpoint, M', of this train is also known and an observer is stationed there. When M' is alongside M, the observer at M closes the switch. He sees both bulbs light simultaneously. Does the observer at M' also see both lights as simultaneous? The answer is no! How can this be?

The observer at M is stationary with respect to A and B and equidistant from them. There is no question about his observation of simultaneity. However, M' (on the train) is moving toward the light coming from B and away from the light coming from A. Therefore that observer will see the light emitted from B earlier than he will see that emitted from A. The observer at M' will then state that the bulb at B lit before the bulb at A.

Our conclusion must be that events that are simultaneous with reference to the track are not simultaneous with reference to the moving train. If the two observers meet and compare results, the one from M' will say that his measurement of time intervals in the direction of his travel gave different results than similar measurements made at M; that is, he saw the bulb at B light before the bulb at A. It could be said that measures of time intervals (clocks) in "moving" systems are slow—that is, indicate a smaller time lapse—when compared with the same measures in "stationary" systems.

It follows that the measurement of a time interval by a moving observer will give a different result when compared with the same measurement in a "stationary" system, that is, stationary with respect to the event being measured. Einstein summarized it by saying that every reference frame has its own particular time; in other words, time is a *relative* quantity, having different values for different observers moving relative to one another.

The relativistic equation for this relationship is

$$t = \frac{t_0}{\sqrt{1 - v^2/c^2}} \qquad \text{[21-1]}$$

where t_0 is the time measured by the "stationary" observer; t is the time measured by the moving observer, and v is the velocity of the moving observer relative to the event being measured. Note that when v is very large, t becomes large as compared with t_0; that is, what would be a small time interval for the "stationary" observer is a large time interval for the "moving" one. Thus time appears to slow down for the moving observer compared to the stationary observer. This apparent slowing down of time is called *time dilation*.

Experimental confirmation of time dilation comes from a study of certain subatomic-sized particles called mesons, which are produced by cosmic ray (p. 635) reactions high in the atmosphere. Mesons are unstable and, at low speeds, break up spontaneously in about a millionth of a second. Mesons "born" of cosmic rays have very high velocities, commonly more than 99% of the speed of light. Yet even at these speeds, it would take a meson about $\frac{1}{100,000}$ sec—the equivalent of 10 meson "lifetimes"—to arrive at the surface of the earth from its "birthplace" in the upper atmosphere. How, then, can we explain the detection of such mesons here on the earth's surface? The answer is given by the time dilation effect: at 99% of the speed of light *relative to the earth*, the physical processes that determine the meson's disintegration *appear* to be slowed up by a factor of 10 *as measured by earth clocks*. Therefore the high-speed meson appears to last ten times as long as a low-speed meson and can reach the surface of the earth before it disintegrates.

The Length Contraction

Once two observers are unable to agree upon whether two events occur simultaneously, they are bound to disagree about other measurements. In particular, two observers will not agree on the length of an object if they are moving relative to one another. Suppose one observer, who is stationary with respect to the object whose length is being measured, finds that the object has a length l_0. Using the postulates of relativity, Einstein showed that an observer moving with a velocity, v, relative to the object will measure a different length, l, according to the equation

$$l = l_0 \sqrt{1 - v^2/c^2} \qquad \text{[21-2]}$$

Since l is smaller than l_0, it follows that an object appears to shrink when it is being measured by someone moving relative to it. Thus length, like time, becomes a relative quantity.

Mass-Energy Relationships

The first postulate of the theory of relativity requires that the laws of physics have the same form in all inertial reference frames. This applies, of course, to the principles of conservation of energy and momentum. Thus, if two observers, one stationary and one moving, examine the same interaction, both observers must find that energy and momentum are conserved.

Einstein proved that in order for this to be so, the mass of an object must appear to be larger to a moving observer than to an observer who is stationary relative to that object. The equation is

$$m = \frac{m_0}{\sqrt{1 - v^2/c^2}} \qquad \text{[21-3]}$$

where m_0, the *rest mass,* is the mass measured by a stationary observer (in whose reference frame the object is at rest), and m is the "moving mass" measured by an observer moving with a velocity, v, relative to the object.

It can be seen that if v is equal to c, the denominator of Eq. 21-3 becomes equal to zero and m becomes infinite. And from $F = ma$, the force needed to accelerate it to this velocity would also be infinite. This is obviously an impossibility. Thus one corollary of the special theory of relativity is that no material object can attain the velocity of light.

The mass equation (21-3) and its corollary have been experimentally verified. Subatomic particles (for example, electrons in a cathode ray tube or a particle accelerator) have been accelerated experimentally to speeds greater than 99% of the speed of light, but speeds equal to c have not been attained. Furthermore, these particles have been found to have increased masses in accordance with Eq. 21-3. The masses of such charged particles are determined by observing their motion in a magnetic field in which they follow a curved path. The radius of curvature (Fig. 36-1) varies with the mass and velocity of the particle. Charged particles were sent through the field at different speeds. It was found that the radius of curvature varied in such a way that could only be explained by an increase in mass as predicted by Eq. 21-3. For example, at 10% of the speed of light, the increase in the mass of the moving electron over its rest mass is 0.5%, at 50% of c the increase is 15%, and at 90% of c the mass increase is over 100%.

The student may well ask where the increase in mass with increased velocity comes from. The law of conservation of mass (p. 233) says that matter cannot be created or destroyed. However, to accelerate the particle from rest to some given velocity, a certain amount of energy is required. Not all of this energy goes to the kinetic energy of the particle; some portion of it, ΔE, appears as an additional amount of mass, Δm, over and above the original rest mass, m_0, of the particle. Thus the mass is increased at the expense of energy. Einstein showed that the increase in energy (ΔE) is related to the increase in mass (Δm) by the equation $\Delta m = \Delta E/c^2$. From this follows the famous relationship $E = mc^2$, which relates the energy of a body to its mass. For a body at rest, $m = m_0$; thus, each body possesses a residual amount of energy, $E = m_0 c^2$, even when it is not in motion.

Relativistic Addition of Velocities

The limitation on maximum velocity, as described in the special theory of relativity and confirmed by high-velocity particle measurements, is in contradiction to the common concept of unlimited velocities. For example, let us assume that we are in a spaceship traveling at $\frac{8}{10}$ the speed of light ($0.8c$) relative to the earth. If this spaceship were to fire off an auxiliary rocket vessel in a forward direction at $0.7c$ relative to the spaceship, then by ordinary velocity addition, the auxiliary vessel would have a forward velocity relative to earth of

$$v = v_1 + v_2$$

or $\qquad 0.8c + 0.7c = 1.5c$

This velocity would be greater than the speed of light. But experiments show that, as predicted by the special theory of relativity, there can be no velocities greater than the speed of light. The common sense addition shown above may hold at ordinary low speeds but is experimentally invalid at speeds that are an appreciable fraction of the speed of light. Such high speeds, of course, are not attained in every-day life but only reached in modern laboratories.

For experiments involving velocities near the speed of light, it has been found that we must use the relativistic velocity addition equation:

$$v = \frac{v_1 + v_2}{1 + v_1 v_2 / c^2} \qquad [21\text{-}16]$$

Substituting in this equation the velocity values given in the previous example, we have

$$v = \frac{0.8c + 0.7c}{1 + 0.56c^2/c^2} = \frac{1.5c}{1.56} = 0.96c$$

This is less than the velocity of light.

The General Theory of Relativity

The special theory of relativity is limited to reference frames moving with uniform velocity relative to each other. The general theory extends the concept of relativity to accelerating frames—that is, to noninertial reference frames. It is primarily concerned with the relationship of gravitation, motion, and space.

The Principle of Equivalence

We have seen (p. 132) that all objects at the same place on or near the surface of the earth have the same gravitational acceleration even if their masses are different. This has been explained through the balancing of gravitational attraction (weight) against inertial resistance (mass). There was, however, another question associated with these concepts that puzzled physicists for many years: Why should the mass of an object be the same when determined by two unrelated methods? By Newton's second law, $F = ma$, the mass (m) is measured by the force necessary to give it a certain acceleration. This is *inertial mass*. By Newton's law of gravitation, $F = G(Mm/r^2)$, m is measured by comparing the earth's gravitational pull on it—that is, its weight—with the weight of an arbitrary standard mass. This is

gravitational mass. In all measurements of the mass of an object by both these methods, it has always been found that the inertial mass is equal to the gravitational mass. Now, there is nothing in the laws of Newtonian mechanics that requires that mass measured by these two different methods should be the same, nor is there anything in Newtonian theory that explains this coincidence.

The Einsteinian view of mass is best given by an example. Imagine a spaceship traveling through free space. Various unattached objects are floating freely in the interior of the ship. Suddenly all these free-floating objects start moving in one direction within the ship. What can have caused this motion? Let us suppose that an astronaut inside the spaceship has no way of viewing his external surroundings. Then, according to Einstein, he can conceive of only two causes, each as plausible as the other:

1. The ship has entered into an external gravitational field.
2. The ship is accelerating.

From this, Einstein derived the *principle of equivalence:* an accelerated reference frame is equivalent to an inertial (uniformly moving) reference frame on which a gravitational field is superimposed. In other words, the effects of acceleration cannot be distinguished from the effects of gravitation. Here Einstein applied a principle used by all great scientists: if we cannot measure any basic difference between two phenomena, they must be the same. Therefore, in agreement with experimental fact, inertial mass and gravitational mass must be equal and there is not even a theoretical basis for any difference between them.

Postulates of the General Theory

The basis of the general theory can now be summarized in the following nonmathematical statements:

1. The laws of physics must have the same form in both inertial and accelerating frames.
2. It is impossible to distinguish between an inertial reference frame in a uniform gravitational field and an accelerating reference frame.

As with the special theory, Einstein used purely mathematical methods to make predictions that cannot be verified within the realm of everyday experience. Nevertheless, observations have since been made that conform to his theoretical predictions, and applications of the theory have led to useful results.

The Gravitational Red Shift

From our brief statement of the general theory it is not difficult to conclude that a uniform gravitational field is equivalent to an accelerating reference frame and that measurements of length, mass, and time made in strong gravitational fields should show the same relativistic changes as similar measurements made between two accelerating reference frames. For example, an event occurring in a gravitational field will be subject to the relativistic time dilation effect (p. 368); that is, the time duration of the event will be increased, as measured by an observer outside that gravitational field.

Let us suppose that we have some excited atoms in a strong gravitational field, for example, light-emitting atoms in the sun. Einstein predicted that since light can be treated as an electromagnetic wave motion, the time dilation effect would cause the time for one vibration of the electromagnetic emitter to be increased. This is equivalent to decreasing the frequency of the emitted light and would cause a shift of the spectral line toward the red end of the spectrum. This phenomenon has in fact been observed and is known as the gravitational red shift. It is an indication of the probable validity of the general theory of relativity.

Light and Relativity

Light itself, as distinguished from the emitter of light, is affected by gravitational fields.

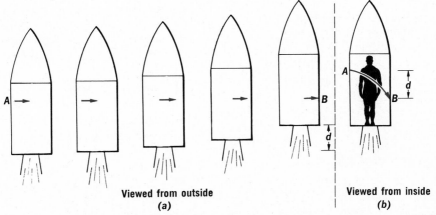

Fig. 21-2. Path of Light Across an Accelerating Spaceship. (*a*) As seen from outside. The spaceship rises through the distance *d*. Light enters at *A*, travels across in a straight line and leaves at *B*. (*b*) As seen from inside. The light enters at *A*, traverses a parabolic path (like a projectile under the influence of gravity), and leaves at *B*. To the inside observer, the acceleration manifests itself only as a force pushing him down toward the floor, just like gravity, and pulling the light beam down in a similar manner.

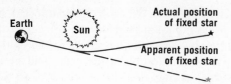

Fig. 21-3. Influence of Gravitation on Light. Light from a fixed star that passes closely by the sun is deviated by the sun's gravitational field. Therefore, to an observer on the earth, the image of the star appears somewhat displaced from the sun.

A simple example can illustrate this. Consider a wide spaceship accelerating upward. Suppose a light beam starts from A on one side of the spaceship and moves horizontally toward the other side (Fig. 21-2a). Because of the time that elapses as the light crosses the spaceship and the upward acceleration of the spaceship during this time, the beam strikes the other side at B, which is somewhat lower than the level of A. From the viewpoint of an astronaut inside ths spaceship, then, the light follows a curved (downward) path as shown in Fig. 21-2b. Thus for observers in accelerated reference frames, light appears to bend.

By the principle of equivalence, light should also bend in gravitational fields. This gravitational bending of light has been observed during solar eclipses as an effect on the position of the stars whose light passed close to the edge of the sun (Fig. 21-3). Such bending has also been predicted by other theories but not as accurately as by the general theory of relativity. Here we have another indication of the probable validity of the theory.

Relativity and the Planets

Mercury revolves about the sun in an orbit that is more eccentric than that of any other planet except Pluto (p. 60). Newtonian theory predicts a slight precession of the axes of this ellipse, but the observed precession is greater.

The prediction that is made by relativity theory is more accurate than that made by any other theory.

Theory vs. "Common Sense"

The physical theories of the 17th century were accepted because they fitted the quantitative knowledge available in those times. Einstein's theories are acceptable now because they agree with our more detailed and accurate observations. That they contradict "common sense" observations is because of the crudeness of such observations. Science is not completely accurate, but it is far more exact than common sense.

Exercises

1. For objects moving freely over long distances it can be observed that the earth is not a true inertial frame reference frame. (a) Name and describe this phenomenon. (b) What causes it?
2. In the system of ball in train on curve described on p. 363, the ball appears (to an observer on the train) to roll off to one side. What force, if any, causes the ball to roll? Explain.
3. How does the Michelson–Morley experiment contradict Galilean relativity?
4. Referring to Fig. 21-1, would there be a greater length contraction perpendicular to the earth's motion through space or parallel to that motion?
5. How did Einstein resolve the contradiction between the Michelson–Morley experiment and classical relativity?
6. Suppose an SST flies past you at 1800 mi/hr.

(a) By what percentage does its length appear to contract?

(b) From a practical viewpoint, what do you think is the possibility of measuring this contraction?

(c) If you could observe a clock inside this passing SST, it would appear to be running slow. By what percentage would it appear to be slow?

7. Define the terms (a) inertial mass and (b) gravitational mass.

8. How did Einstein explain the fact that the inertial mass of an object is always equal to its gravitational mass?

Planck's Quantum Theory of Radiation and Its Consequences

The first movement toward a better understanding of the nature of light came about through the work of Max Planck (1858–1947) of Germany. Planck was not only a superior theoretical physicist but also an exceptionally able mathematician. About 1900 he became interested in the energy distribution of the radiation from hot solid bodies—which we discussed (p. 351) as a prelude to our study of bright line spectra. The problem was to relate, in accordance with Maxwell's theoretical principles, the amount of radiant energy emitted from a hot solid to the temperature of the solid and to the frequency of the radiation. The actual energy radiated and the energy predicted on the basis of Maxwellian principles, Newtonian mechanics of waves, and other known laws did not agree. These, if correct, should have explained the emission of energy in all parts of the electromagnetic spectrum.

In order to reach the truth, it is necessary, once in one's life, to put everything in doubt—so far as is possible.
RENÉ DESCARTES

Formulation of the Quantum Theory

We learned in Chapter 20 that the radiation from all hot solids and liquids was much the same if the temperature was the same, regardless of the chemical composition of the substance. Therefore, it seemed possible to formulate a single theory of radiation applicable to all such hot bodies. The first step in the building of such a theory was to find an ideal surface to act as an absorber and as an emitter of radiation; the ideal surface would be capable of emitting as much as it absorbed. (Analogously, an ideal mirror is one that reflects 100% of the light falling on it.) No such ideal surface exists, but in 1895 a suitable substitute was found and the experimental physicists went to work to gather the required data. From these data they constructed distribution curves, energy against wavelength (Fig. 22-1), and compared them with a curve constructed on theoretical grounds. None succeeded in making experimental data agree with theory.

Meanwhile Planck, the brilliant theorizer, but no experimenter, was at work on the problem. He obtained the best experimental data available and applied his great mathematical talent to them. He tried by every method he could conceive to derive a formula from classical physics that would fit the curves obtained from the experimental data. None of the mechanical models made by adhering to classical ideas succeeded. Planck then tackled the problem in reverse by setting up an empirical equation that fitted the experimental data for the complete energy-distribution curve at any temperature. This procedure is somewhat like that of a student looking up the answer to a problem in the back of the book and then working backward to the problem. Planck could not derive his empirical equation from classical theory, and this was not at all satisfying to him—

nor would it be to any true scientist. He continued his reverse tactics by asking himself a question: What minimum modification of the classical theory will make it fit the facts? Perhaps some alterations of its assumptions would solve the puzzle without destroying anything fundamental to the Maxwellian theory.

Planck's Assumptions

Planck, familiar with the work of Hertz, believed that light must have its origin in submicroscopic vibrations within atoms, each of which emitted radiation of its own frequency. There must be vast numbers of emitters (p. 351), since all frequencies were present in the emitted radiation, giving a continuous spectrum. Somewhere among the classical concepts there had to be a flaw. A careful check, point by point, left him with two fundamental assumptions of Maxwell, as follows:

1. The energy E of an individual oscillator (vibrator) can be any amount from zero upward, and the oscillator can absorb or radiate any amount of energy.[1]
2. Any electric charge emits radiation whenever it is accelerated; it therefore must radiate all the time that it is vibrating (because to vibrate it must accelerate).

Now Planck saw that if either or both of these fundamentals were wrong, he might be able to solve the original problem. He replaced them with two new assumptions, which we will label A and B to distinguish them from Maxwell's assumptions (1 and 2).

A. Each oscillator can emit only certain definite energies, energies that are integral multiples of a quantity hf, where h is a con-

---

[1] For an analogy consider an ordinary pendulum started swinging in air. It loses energy by friction, so that its amplitude decreases gradually and *continuously* from its initial value down to zero, at which point it is at rest.

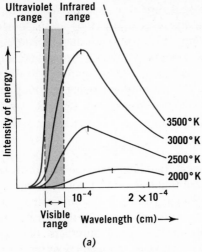

(a)

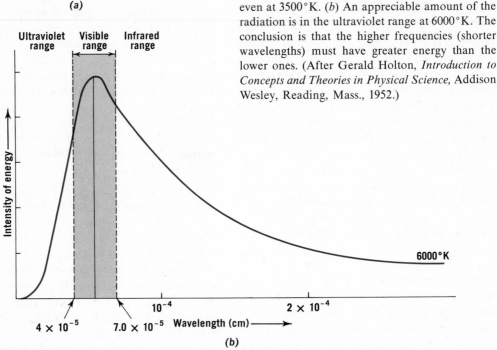

(b)

Fig. 22-1. Distribution of Electromagnetic Energy from a Glowing Ideal Emitter (p. 375). The area below each curve represents the total energy at the given temperature. (*a*) Note that almost all of the energy is in the infrared at the low temperatures, that the total energy rises in all ranges with increasing temperature, and that the proportion in the ultraviolet and visible ranges increases more rapidly than that in the infrared. An object barely begins to glow at 500 to 550°K. This is shown by the small amount of energy in the visible range. Not much of the total emission is in the ultraviolet even at 3500°K. (*b*) An appreciable amount of the radiation is in the ultraviolet range at 6000°K. The conclusion is that the higher frequencies (shorter wavelengths) must have greater energy than the lower ones. (After Gerald Holton, *Introduction to Concepts and Theories in Physical Science,* Addison Wesley, Reading, Mass., 1952.)

stant (Planck's constant) and f is the frequency of the oscillator. Written as an equation.

$$E = nhf$$

where n is any integer. Thus the total energy of the oscillator is "quantized" into a whole number n of packets of magnitude hf each. Any change, ΔE, in the energy of the oscillator must therefore be in integral (whole number) units of energy, each unit having a magnitude of hf. The energy change of an oscillator can be hf, $2hf$, $5hf$, $8hf$, or any similar *whole* number of hf units but no fractional amounts such as $1.3hf$ or $3.9hf$.

B. An oscillator radiates only when it is emitting one or more of these discrete packets, that is, when it changes from a higher energy value to a lower one. This packet of energy is emitted as a pulse of radiation called a *quantum*. This means that an oscillator does not necessarily radiate while undergoing acceleration, that is, changing its speed or direction.

The Quantization of Energy

Note how contradictory assumptions 1 and 2 of Maxwell are with respect to assumptions A and B of Planck. Number 1 says that when an emitter is either emitting or absorbing energy, the process (either emission or absorption) is continuous, like a steady stream pouring in or out, whereas A says it is discontinuous, a packet at a time. Maxwell's number 2 says that if an oscillator is being accelerated, it *must* radiate, whereas Planck's B says that it may or may not. Maxwell says that no matter how much or how little energy an oscillator has it can radiate all of it or any part of it, whereas Planck says that it can radiate energy of a given frequency, f, only if it possesses an amount of that energy that is at least equal to hf.

Now, we know that there are a great many frequencies available in the electromagnetic spectrum. Let us arbitrarily select three frequencies that we shall indicate as f_1, f_2, and f_3, where the increasing subscripts mean increasing frequencies; that is, $f_3 > f_2 > f_1$.

If some oscillator has a total energy content greater than hf_3, it can emit quanta having energies of hf_3 or hf_2 or hf_1.[2] If the oscillator

[2] As we shall see later, this simplified example is severely limited by the structure of the oscillator.

had an energy content between hf_3 and hf_1, it could emit quanta of energies hf_2 or hf_1 but not hf_3. If its energy were less than hf_2, yet more than hf_1, the only quantum it could emit would have an energy of hf_1. Of course, many other examples could be made up using other frequencies and other total available energies. Moreover, the oscillator cannot absorb just any quantity of energy but must do so one particulate (discrete) packet at a time. If this is so, then energy is particulate in nature (p. 303), just as matter and electricity are. There is, then, a basic discontinuity in nature: Matter comes in individual atoms, ions, or molecules; electricity comes in the discrete units we know as electrons; and here we now have radiant energy coming in discrete units (quanta) proportional to hf.

An Analogy.   To better understand how an oscillator can absorb or emit energy in packets of certain sizes, but not in other sizes, let us consider the vibrations of a stringed musical instrument. The strings are tightly stretched between two points of attachment. Pluck one of the strings in the middle, and a wave motion in the strings results; the string vibrates as a whole. The distance between the two points of attachment is half the wavelength λ. Let us represent this distance by l, which is also the distance between two nodes (for the points of attachment act as nodes). The string can be caused to vibrate in two, three, four, or more sections (Fig. 22-2). If it vibrates in one section—that is, as a whole—the distance between two adjacent nodes is $l/1$: if in two sections, the distance between two adjacent nodes is $1/2$; if in three sections, the distance is $l/3$; if in four sections, the distance is $l/4$; and so on. The distance between two adjacent nodes is always l over some integer. We might say that the vibrations are quantized. The quanta are $l/1$, $l/2$, $l/3$, $l/4$, and so on. There is no possibility whatever of the string vibrating in

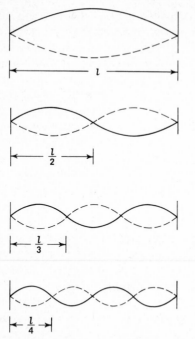

Fig. 22-2. The Quantization of Modes of Vibration of a String.

any other way. Just so, radiant energy is quantized; there is no possibility that it can be absorbed or emitted in units of a size other than hf.

Planck's Constant, h

Planck's constant is an extremely small quantity. Its units are erg-seconds or joule-seconds (1 joule = 10^7 ergs). Its dimensions are energy times time, sometimes called *action*. The actual size in cgs units is $h = 6.6 \times 10^{-27}$ erg-sec; in mks units $h = 6.6 \times 10^{-34}$ joule-sec. It was obtained by trial so that by use of it "prediction fits the facts beautifully."

Planck's constant, h, turned out to be one of the great universal constants of nature. It now appears in many different physical theories.

The Sizes of Quanta

Let us see how h is used with respect to light energy. Red light has a frequency of 4×10^{14} cycles/sec (approximately); violet light, 7.5×10^{14} cycles/sec; and ultraviolet light, 10×10^{14} cycles/sec and up. Since $E = hf$,

for red light:

$$4 \times 10^{14} \times 6.6 \times 10^{-34}$$
$$= 2.64 \times 10^{-19} \text{ joule}$$

for violet light:

$$7.5 \times 10^{14} \times 6.6 \times 10^{-34}$$
$$= 4.95 \times 10^{-19} \text{ joule}$$

Thus a quantum of violet light has nearly twice the energy of a quantum of red light. X rays come in huge quanta, up to 2000 times as much as a quantum of red light, and some gamma rays up to a million times as much (Fig. 22-3). The absorption of such a single large quantum can change an inheritance gene in a living cell, or even kill the cell.

Troubles of a Radical Concept

Planck's idea that radiant energy is quantized was a radical concept, far more radical than the concept of light as an electromagnetic phenomenon. Lord Kelvin, whose many scientific accomplishments we honor by assigning

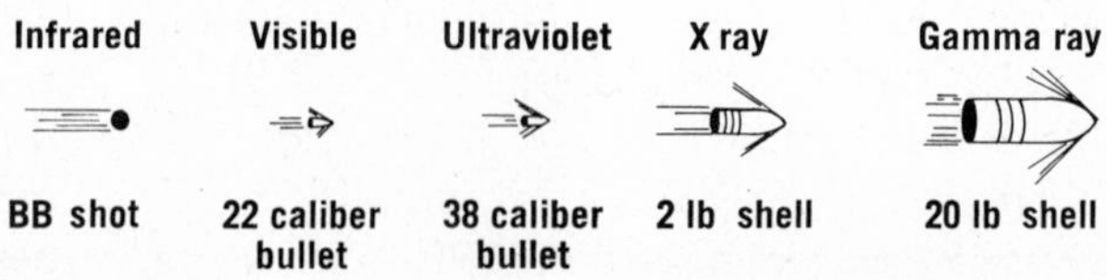

Fig. 22-3. Energies of Quanta. Projectile energies are analogous to the relative energies of quanta.

Infrared	Visible	Ultraviolet	X ray	Gamma ray
BB shot	22 caliber bullet	38 caliber bullet	2 lb shell	20 lb shell

his name to the absolute temperature scale, and whose comment on a mechanical model for electromagnetic waves we quoted on p. 350, would have been in more of a quandary than ever trying to construct an adequate model that could explain the emission of light in separate packets.

He was no different from most other scientists of the time, who were unwilling to accept such a departure from well-established principles. Even Planck himself was loath to accept the verdict of his own brain, for how could you explain diffraction and interference of light by his quantum theory? (Even today we call on the wave theory to explain these phenomena.) Planck still looked upon light as an electromagnetic radiation even though the mechanism of its creation remained obscure. He believed that the emitters of light were atoms, that within them were the vibrators or oscillators that "created" light when the absorption of outside energy set them to vibrating or oscillating. He thought that there was some mechanism within the atoms that caused them to "spit" their energy out in discontinuous bits, but that, once spat out, the energy traveled as a wave. It was Einstein who advanced the idea that it was the radiation itself that was propagated in the form of quanta. This meant that every quantum with an amount of energy hf could be regarded as a particle as long as it continued to move.

A new and difficult concept does not usually attract much attention until someone else comes along and shows that the new concept can explain some phenomenon that has long gone unexplained. A theory made to suit one specific set of facts can probably be adjusted to fit that particular set of facts even though some flaws are present. However, the likelihood of that theory being universally applicable is very slender unless a very different phenomenon can be explained by the same theory. This is especially true if no adequate

explanation of this different phenomenon has been yet devised. The strengthening of the evidence for Planck's quantum theory came in 1905 from a man who was to exert a profound influence on scientific thought in the 20th century. That man was Albert Einstein,[3] then only 26 years old. He applied the quantum theory to the photoelectric effect puzzle, thereby solving it.

The Photoelectric Effect

While Hertz was making the investigations that led to the successful emission and detection of Hertzian (radio) waves, he made the observation that the spark jumped more readily across the metal spheres that served as the electrodes of his receiver if they were well polished. Investigation revealed that radiation of high frequency, such as that in the ultraviolet region, impinging on the polished cathode could expel negative charges (electrons) from it. These expelled charges helped to maintain the current between the electrodes, and thus

---

[3] It is worth noting that Einstein, like Maxwell and Planck, never performed a significant experiment in his life. All were theoretical physicists and mathematicians who worked at desks with paper and pencil. Perhaps Einstein played his violin while he meditated on the results of experiments performed by others. In any event, he analyzed, correlated, synthesized, and drew conclusions from these results after applying his mathematics to their unsolved problems. Such work takes a mind very different from that of great experimenters like Faraday. For several years Einstein was able to work at physics only in his spare time while he earned his living as a patent clerk in Switzerland. In 1905 he published three great papers, one explaining the photoelectric effect, one explaining the Brownian movement, and one on his special theory of relativity. By 1909 the universities took note of him, and later one made him a full professor after previously refusing him a job as instructor. In 1916 he published his general theory of relativity, which made him a public figure. By the time Hitler came to power he was in the United States, where he lived the rest of his life, much of it at the Institute for Advanced Study in Princeton. He died in 1955.

the spark jumped more readily between the spheres.

We conclude that when light of the right kind falls on clean metal, electrons may be ejected. This expulsion of electrons by light is called the photoelectric effect. A negatively charged electroscope to which a metallic plate is attached by a conducting wire will demonstrate the effect (Fig. 22-4). A negatively charged body has an excess of electrons, some of which cause the leaves to diverge. If we remove the excess electrons from the system, the leaves will collapse. We now allow ultraviolet rays from a mercury vapor lamp to shine on the charged plate; the leaves quickly col-

lapse, showing that electrons have been removed from the system. Let us call the removed electrons *photoelectrons* to distinguish them from those not removed.

Further investigation revealed that whereas the ultraviolet and higher frequencies were effective in expelling electrons from practically any metal surface, those of visible light were effective only with the alkali metals and the alkaline earth metals. In fact, not all frequencies of visible light will eject electrons from sodium. Red light, no matter how intense, will not do so; but blue light, no matter how faint, will. These results were explained by Planck's theory: A quantum of blue light carries more

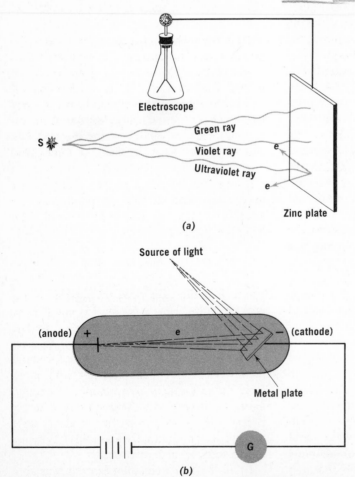

Fig. 22-4. Photoelectric Effect. (*a*) A mercury vapor lamp, *S*, emits visible light of various wavelengths along with considerable ultraviolet. These rays strike a zinc plate. Only the ultraviolet rays have enough energy to eject electrons from zinc. Loss of electrons leaves the plate with an excess of positive charges, as is indicated by the electroscope. No matter how intense the visible light nor how weak the ultraviolet, the former will not eject electrons, the latter will. (*b*) Completion of an electric circuit by a flow of electrons ejected from the cathode in a gas discharge tube (see Fig. 18-2), by light of sufficient frequency shining on it. The ejected electrons are repelled by the cathode and attracted by the anode. The chief function of the electrical source is to keep a negative charge on the cathode, a positive one on the anode. Its voltage is too weak to eject electrons from the cathode.

energy than a quantum of red light. It is the energy per quantum that is important in the photoelectric effect, not the total energy.

Further experiments revealed that *for light of a specific frequency, the number of photoelectrons ejected is directly proportional to the intensity of the light, but that their velocity is independent of the light intensity*. The experiments also showed that an increase in the frequency increased the velocity of the photoelectrons, no matter how low the intensity. In other words, a certain minimum frequency, often referred to as the threshold frequency, is necessary to eject photoelectrons from any one metal. This threshold frequency is different for different metals. Ordinary light will eject photoelectrons from cesium and rubidium but not from zinc or iron. Furthermore, the ejection is instantaneous if the frequency is high enough, showing that no accumulation of energy is necessary.

Infrared light will not eject photoelectrons from any metal; its quanta do not have enough energy to do so. Of still lower frequency are radio waves; their quanta have so little energy that special instruments have to be used to prove that the quantum relation holds for them also. The greater the frequency the greater the energy of ejection. As Eric Rogers of Princeton said,

> Visible light gives electrons a little flip at best, ultraviolet flings them, X rays hurl them out, gamma rays smash them out with the crack of a bullwhip. And very short wavelength gamma rays have such a huge quantum that it can break up a nucleus [Fig. 22-3].

Laws of Photoelectricity

This ejection of electrons in itself might be explained in some manner by the electromagnetic theory, but the previously listed energy-intensity relationships certainly could not. The experimental facts almost shouted "quanta." In 1905 Einstein used the quantum theory and the semiquantitative information we have described to explain the photoelectric effect. What Planck called quanta, he called *photons*.

Einstein's explanation of the photoelectric effect is as follows: The amount of energy received by a photoelectron from a photon equals the total energy of the photon. According to Planck's theory, this energy is given by *hf*. If no work had to be done against forces tending to prevent the electron from leaving the surface of the metal, the photoelectron would be ejected with a kinetic energy given by the equation

$$\tfrac{1}{2}mv^2 = hf$$

That is, the energy of the ejected photoelectron would equal the energy of the photon. This is in accord with the law of conservation of energy. The attraction of the positive charges within the atom, however, constitutes a force that does tend to prevent electrons from escaping from the surface of the metal. Work has to be done to overcome these forces, and energy is needed to do work. Therefore, the photoelectron is ejected with a kinetic energy that is less than that of the photon by the amount of energy needed to do the work. The equation therefore becomes

$$\tfrac{1}{2}mv^2 = hf - W$$

where *W* is the work done (in ergs). If *W* (in ergs or joules) equals *hf*, $\tfrac{1}{2}mv^2$ is equal to 0, and so the electron will not escape from the metal. The amount of work needed to eject an electron varies with the metal, for some metals hold onto their electrons with more force than do others. The amount of energy, *hf*, varies directly with the frequency. Thus, it is easy to see that for a particular metal, light of a particular minimum (threshold) frequency is necessary to eject electrons.

From the above equation Einstein was able

to predict the laws of photoelectricity as follows:

1. Electrons are ejected from metal surfaces by light (photons) of sufficiently high frequency striking (shining on) the metal. The sufficient frequency is called the threshold frequency. One photon ejects one electron only.
2. The *energy* of a particular photoelectron is *independent* of the intensity of light but is dependent upon its frequency.
3. The *number* of photoelectrons ejected is proportional to the *intensity* of the light striking the metal but is independent of its frequency.

These laws were not validated until 11 years later when Robert A. Millikan performed the necessary exact experimental work.

Photoelectric Emission vs. Thermionic Emission

Let us return briefly to the problem of removal of electrons from a metal surface. Suppose we carry our reasoning a bit further and speculate on what may happen if the metal surface is heated strongly enough. Furthermore, let us remember that the phenomenon of electrons escaping from a metal surface for any cause whatsoever is analogous in most respects to the evaporation of a liquid. We may thus speak of the "evaporation" of electrons. As the temperature rises, the electrons gain kinetic energy, some more than others, and the additional energy needed to evaporate them becomes less. We might then assume that photons of lower energy would eject them. It is found that they do. In fact, as the temperature rises higher and higher, we eventually find the electrons evaporating without benefit of photons. This is called *thermal* emission of electrons, or *thermionic* emission (Fig. 18-7). As in liquids, the evaporation is easier and faster with some substances than it is with others.

The Photon Theory of Light

Assumptions of the Theory

Einstein used his laws of photoelectricity to formulate his photon theory of light, as follows:

1. Light is propagated through space in the form of individual packets of energy called photons.
2. The energy of any photon is directly proportional to the frequency of the particular kind of light. For any photon, $E = hf$, where h is Planck's constant.

We might wonder why Planck did not develop the photon or quantum theory of light himself, since it is based on his work. The reason is that Planck could not cut himself loose from the Maxwellian electromagnetic theory, so that he could follow the consequences of his own theory to the bitter end, no matter where that end might be. Planck was convinced that his quantum theory would set the understanding of light back a century or more, that is, to the time of Newton and the corpuscular theory.

Photon Theory vs. Wave Theory

Therefore it was left to Einstein to follow through, and Planck was by no means pleased that he did so. The photon theory as proposed by Einstein did not abandon the wave concept completely, but stated that the energy of light was not distributed over the whole wave front as in Maxwell's theory. Instead he assumed that it is concentrated or localized in discrete small regions in the form of tiny bundles called photons. The intensity of the light is a consequence of the closeness of the spacing of the photons on the wave front. As a light wave spreads out away from its source, the light becomes weaker, not because the photons lose energy, but because the distances between neighboring photons becomes greater, and the energy per unit area becomes less. Ordinarily in experiments dealing with reflection, refraction, interference, diffraction, and polarization we are dealing with enormous numbers of photons on each wave front. They are so closely spaced that the individuality of each photon is masked, and the wave front appears to be continuous and homogeneous, just as any material solid appears to be made of continuous matter rather than of individual atoms. That is why Maxwell's theory is still most useful when dealing with ordinary problems of optics, but when we get down into the finer structure of matter, that is, inside the atom, the finer structure of the light wave becomes important. Therefore, we will use Einstein's photon theory in our attempts to explain the relationship between light and individual atoms. You will recall that this has been our chief problem throughout this section, and that we have not yet solved it.

We must not think that the photon theory is a reversion to Newton's corpuscular theory. Newton's corpuscles were thought of as actual particles of matter, whereas photons represent bundles of energy that have no rest mass. This means that once the photon stops it ceases to exist, its energy being transferred to whatever stopped it.

The photon theory has a set of problems all its own aside from those already mentioned. For example, how large is the "spot" on the wave front where the photon is located? How does an electron absorb a photon? What is the meaning of frequency and wavelength if the photon is only a dot on the wave front? And so on. Our real difficulty is that we want a mechanical model we can visualize pictorially. We can picture either waves or moving particles, but we cannot picture a wave-particle duality, something that acts like a wave under some circumstances and like a particle under others, or possibly acts like both at the same

time. All we can say is that the wave and the photon concepts are both needed to explain the phenomenon of light; we must learn to regard them as complementary ways of viewing one and the same process. We will have more to say on this subject later.

Einstein (1905) not only rescued the quantum theory from indifferent opposition by explaining the photoelectric effect, but also by explaining a puzzle about specific heat changes. We will omit this puzzle from our discussions. Much later (1923) the American physicist A. H. Compton showed that X-ray photons lost some of their energy when they collided with electrons—the frequency of the X rays was less after the collision than before. This could only mean that photons had momentum, *mv*. This was an added trump for the quantum theory.

The Bohr Theory of the Hydrogen Atom

We have seen how the concepts of matter, electricity, and energy slowly evolved in the direction of particulateness and away from the idea that each was a continuum in itself. The evidence that matter comes in the particles we call atoms, molecules, and ions was overwhelming; there was a sizable group of physical laws to support the concept of the particulateness of all kinds of matter. The acceptance of the view that atomic nuclei are composed of protons and neutrons that can be isolated from one another came easily 100 years later. The evidence that electricity is particulate in nature was not so clear-cut, but electrons did have mass and charges that could be measured. Much more difficult to accept was the particulateness of energy. Planck's quanta were far more intangible than any of the other mentioned particles. Although light may come in individual packets called quanta or photons, we must not think of them as physical particles in the same sense that electrons are.

We say the photon behaves as if it had mass but only because it has kinetic energy and momentum that it transfers to an electron in the photoelectric effect; then it ceases to exist. This may stagger our imaginations, but to think of kinetic energy ($\frac{1}{2}mv^2$) and momentum (mv) being transferred with no mass involved would stagger us even more. These photons travel with the speed of light; the relativistic mass formula states that they must therefore have zero rest mass.

The quantum and photon theories still left some unsolved problems concerning light. The emitters of photons were atoms. But what was the mechanism for emitting them? How was light created? The plausibility of Rutherford's model of the atom had been established experimentally (in 1911), but classical electrodynamics and Newtonian laws not only could not explain line spectra but would not even allow atoms to emit light. Yet obviously they do emit light.

In 1913 Niels Bohr (1886–1961), a 27-year-old physicist from Denmark, who was working with Rutherford, came to the conclusion that it was no longer possible to ignore the experimental facts that had accumulated by that time. Bohr was thoroughly familiar with Planck's quantum theory and Einstein's photon theory, theories widely publicized on the Continent, but which had gained little attention in England.[4] Bohr accepted the main assumption of Rutherford's nuclear theory and thought that he might be able to explain line spectra by combining Planck's quantum theory

with it. Thus, he "married" Planck's theory to Rutherford's theory and came up, in 1913, with his theory of the hydrogen atom as the offspring.

Bohr's First Postulate

In formulating his theory Bohr made two startling changes in the electrodynamics of the time. Rutherford had developed his nuclear theory two years previously, and had adopted the suggestion that whatever electrons an atom had revolved about the nucleus. A revolving electron is an accelerated electron—a force is needed to change its direction—and how could it keep from radiating its energy? If its energy is radiated, it would lose its energy and fall into the nucleus within one billionth of a second—and the atom would cease to exist as such. Bohr evaded the conflict simply by stating that *Maxwell's theory did not apply to systems of atomic size; electrons could revolve without radiating.* He made no apologies for being arbitrary. He simply presented the idea on a take it or leave it basis. Adherence to Maxwellian electrodynamics had long led only to wrong answers insofar as line spectra were concerned, so why not abandon them? After all, Einstein had abandoned the Maxwellian theory for Planck's quantum theory in his explanation of the photoelectric effect. Moreover, the assumption is obviously in accord with the facts; electrons do not continuously radiate as they revolve in atoms. The normal unexcited electron revolves without radiating in the orbit closest to the nucleus, an orbit that is often referred to as the ground state.

Bohr's Second Postulate

Bohr then placed a restriction on the orbits in which electrons could revolve without radiating. *Electrons can revolve about a nucleus only in orbits in which their angular momentum,*

[4] A. S. Eddington, an English physicist and astronomer, in 1936 wrote: "Let us go back to 1912. At that time quantum theory was a German invention which had scarcely penetrated to England at all. There were rumors that Jeans had gone to a conference on the Continent and had been converted; Lindemann, I believe, was an expert on it; I cannot think of anyone else."

mvr (Chapter 7), is some integral multiple of *h/2π, where h is Planck's constant.* These orbits are referred to as permitted or stable orbits. The revolving electrons may be called orbital electrons to distinguish them from cathode ray electrons or photoelectrons. We may write the restriction as an equation,

$$mvr = n\left(\frac{h}{2\pi}\right) \qquad [22\text{-}1]$$

where n is an integer (1, 2, 3, . . .). By this relationship we are postulating that the angular momentum of orbiting electrons is always quantized; that is, it comes in particulate units whose value is equal to $h/2\pi$. Suppose we transpose 2π in the above equation to the left side. We then have:

$$mv \times 2\pi r = nh \qquad [22\text{-}2]$$

We may then state the postulate in the following terms: The electrons can travel only in orbits for which the linear momentum multi-plied by the circumference, $2\pi r$, is equal to a whole number multiplied by Planck's constant. This is analogous to stating that a person can walk in a circle 10 yd, 11 yd, 12 yd, and so on, in radius, but that he can never walk in one with a radius of 12.6 yd, and so on. Bohr placed no restriction on the number of permit-ted orbits; n might be any number (Fig. 22-5).

Test of the Second Postulate. One can test the adequacy of Bohr's second postulate, $mvr = n(h/2\pi)$, by applying it to the hydrogen atom in its normal, nonradiating state. Since the hydrogen atom consists of a single electron revolving about a nucleus, the radius of the electron's orbit is obviously also the radius of the nonradiating hydrogen atom. We know that its radius, calculated by entirely different methods, is about 0.5×10^{-8} cm. On the fol-lowing pages we shall show, by simple alge-braic methods, two independent validations of Bohr's model of the hydrogen atom. This mathematical treatment will be set off in

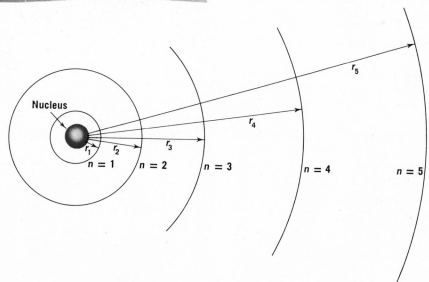

Fig. 22-5 First Five Permitted (Stable) Orbits of Electron in Bohr's Hydrogen Atom. The circles and arcs represent the orbits (not drawn to scale). The radii r_1 to r_5 are in the ratios of 1:4:9:16:25; that is, the radii are proportional to the squares of the values of n.

smaller type so that the student who feels that it is not essential to his understanding of Bohr's work may proceed directly to the conclusions.

Let us see what we get by solving for r in Eq. 22-2. The mathematics involve nothing more than elementary algebra. Transposing, we have

$$r = \frac{nh}{2\pi mv} \qquad [22\text{-}3]$$

There are two unknowns r and v, in this equation. We shall have to get rid of one of them by getting a value for v.

According to Newton's second law, $F = ma$. For motion in a circle $a = v^2/r$. Substituting,

$$F = \frac{mv^2}{r} \qquad [22\text{-}4]$$

But the net force acting at any instant on the revolving electron is also given by Coulomb's law of electrostatic attraction,

$$F = \frac{Ke \times e}{r^2} \qquad [22\text{-}5]$$

where e, the charge on the electron (a known quantity), is equal to e, the charge on the nucleus, and K is a proportionality constant.[5] As things equal to the same thing are equal to each other,

$$\frac{mv^2}{r} = \frac{Ke \times e}{r^2} = \frac{Ke^2}{r^2} \qquad [22\text{-}6]$$

Solving for v^2, we have

$$v^2 = \frac{Ke^2}{rm} \qquad [22\text{-}7]$$

Now if we square Eq. 22-3 and substitute this value of v^2 in it, we get

$$r^2 = \frac{n^2h^2}{2^2\pi^2m^2(Ke^2/rm)}$$

[5] Note carefully what Ke is. Do not confuse it with KE (kinetic energy).

Simplifying,

$$r = \frac{n^2h^2}{4\pi^2mKe^2} \qquad [22\text{-}8]$$

(*Note:* The letter Z, which represents the number of positive charges on the nucleus, is often included in equations 22-5 through 22-8. For hydrogen, $Z = 1$ so we have omitted it from these equations.) Now h, π, m, K, and e are all fixed quantities—that is, they are all constants[6]—and n is an integer (1, 2, 3, . . .). When n equals 1, r has the smallest possible value, which is the value of the radius of the lone electron in the nonradiating hydrogen atom. Substituting these known values in Eq. 22-8 we have

$$r = 0.53 \times 10^{-8} \text{ cm} \qquad [22\text{-}9]$$

Thus we see that the value of the radius of the hydrogen atom calculated from two postulates of the Bohr theory is almost exactly the value calculated for the radius of the hydrogen atom by very different methods. It looks as if Bohr was on the right track.

It should be noted that in Eq. 22-8, n is squared; therefore, the radii of the permitted orbits are in the ratio of 1^2, 2^2, 3^2, 4^2, and so on; the radius of the second is 4 times the first, that of the third is 9 times the first, and so forth (see Fig. 22-5).

The Ground State and Energy Levels

The ground state is one of the permitted orbits, $n = 1$. This is the orbit in which the energy of the electron is the lowest possible. All electrons in hydrogen atoms in this state have the same energy. It follows that an electron having greater energy than that in the ground state must have shifted to an outer

[6] h = Planck's constant, 6.6×10^{-34} joule-sec
   π = 3.1416
   m = mass of electron, 9.1×10^{-31} kg
   K = 9×10^9, coulomb constant (conversion factor from electrostatic units)
   e = charge on electron, 1.6×10^{-19} coulomb

permitted orbit (one with a value of $n = 2$, $n = 3$, $n = 4$, and so on). To shift it must have absorbed energy. The greater the amount of energy absorbed, the greater the shift and hence the greater the radius of the new permitted orbit. Thus, electrons in outer orbits have more energy than electrons in inner orbits. This shift to outer orbits takes place during a period of excitation that may be accomplished by absorption of energy from an outside source, for example, by strong heating, by an electrical discharge, or by absorption of radiation of quanta of higher energy. An electron remains in this state of higher energy for approximately one billionth of a second (10^{-9} sec). It then takes "jumps" to states of lower energy until it reaches the ground state, or it may reach the ground state directly by one big jump, liberating quanta of energy in the form of photons of visible or invisible electromagnetic radiation. The emissions of billions of photons give our eyes the impression of a continuous emission of light.

Such a description of the transition from one orbit to another cannot help but be accompanied by an attempt to visualize the method of the transition. Bohr's warning that the method cannot possibly be visualized does us no good, for the human mind is so constructed that it always tries to visualize its concepts. To help us here—and we will need it in the modern theory anyhow—we are going to introduce the term *energy level* to replace orbit except in those cases when we cannot help ourselves. Thus we will speak of shifts to lower or higher energy levels rather than from inner or outer orbits. Let us restate what we have just said about emission of photons in terms of energy levels.

Bohr's Third Postulate

To radiate a photon, an orbital electron must shift from a higher energy level to a lower one, for example, from an $n = 3$ to an $n = 1$ level

or from an $n = 3$ to an $n = 2$ level, or from an $n = 2$ to an $n = 1$ level, and so on, and in doing so must radiate exactly the amount of energy that corresponds to the difference in the energies of the electrons in the two levels in question. In accord with Planck's quantum theory the energy is absorbed or radiated in units proportional to the frequency, that is,

$$E_2 - E_1 \propto f \quad \text{(proportionality)}$$
$$\text{or} \quad E_2 - E_1 = hf \quad \text{(equation)} \quad [22\text{-}10]$$

Thus the radiated energy is in the form of a single photon of light, light of a single frequency, wavelength, and color. All electrons making the same shifts emit light of the same color. When we see light in the hydrogen discharge tube, we are "seeing" the result of electrons going from higher levels into lower energy levels. The color of the light[7] seen is a composite of all the different frequencies emitted. If, however, the great majority of electrons are making the transition between the same two energy levels, the light we see is essentially monochromatic. When an alpha particle strikes a fluorescent screen, it boosts electrons in some of the atoms of the fluorescent paint into higher levels. The flash of light we see is caused by the electrons in the atoms of the paint returning to lower energy levels.

Summary of the Bohr Postulates

To summarize, Bohr's postulates may be stated as follows:

1. An electron revolving about an atomic nucleus in a permitted orbit does not radiate energy.

[7] The eye can detect color only when extremely large numbers of electrons are emitting photons of the same energy at the same time. If the number is too small, it is possible that no device whatever will detect them. Hence only the first 10 or 12 Balmer lines are obtainable from gas discharge tubes, whereas 33 such lines can be detected in the corona of the sun because of the far greater number of electrons making the bigger jumps.

2. An electron can revolve about a hydrogen nucleus only in certain permitted or stable orbits, orbits in which the angular momentum of the electron is equal to n times a fundamental unit, $h/2\pi$. Symbolically,

$$mvr = \frac{nh}{2\pi} \qquad [22\text{-}11]$$

3. When an electron *absorbs* energy from the outside, it makes a transition to a new stable energy level with greater energy; and on returning to any lower level, the energy difference is radiated as a photon in accordance with the equation $E_2 - E_1 = hf$.

4. In all other ways the electron obeys the classical laws of mechanics and electrodynamics.

Bohr was aware of the difficulties that his theory of the hydrogen atom would meet before his fellow physicists would accept it. Hard to understand was that an electron radiating its energy in packets, that is, in one fell swoop instead of continuously, cannot spiral from one level to a lower one but must make the change by a method that takes place in zero time. Here again we have a departure from classical mechanics, for how can anything move through a finite distance in no time at all? Bohr says that the classical laws were not designed to explain intra-atomic behavior, and that we should simply accept the idea that the electron emits a photon whose frequency is given by Eq. 22-10 during a transition between two energy levels in a manner that cannot be pictured. He says,

> This assumption . . . appears to be necessary to account for the experimental facts. . . . [Also] We stand here almost entirely on virgin ground, and upon introducing new assumptions we need only take care not to get into contradiction with experiment. Time will have to show to what extent this can be avoided but the safest way is, of course, to make as few assumptions as possible.

Explanation of Bright Line Spectra

The greatest achievement of the Bohr theory was its explanation of the line spectra of incandescent hydrogen. Spectral lines are the result of transitions from one energy level to another. All electrons making the same transitions from higher to lower energy levels cause the emission of the same quanta, the same "color" photons with the same frequency and wavelength. Together they form a single bright line in the spectrum of hydrogen. You will remember (Plate I) that there are four bright lines in the visible part of the hydrogen spectrum—red, green, blue, and violet. Jumps from the $n = 3$ to the $n = 2$ level account for the red line, those from the $n = 4$ to the $n = 2$ level account for the green line, those from the $n = 5$ to the $n = 2$ level account for the blue line, and those from the $n = 6$ to the $n = 2$ level account for the violet line. Note that the "size" of the jumps increases from the red to the violet, and that the "size" of the quanta and the frequencies emitted increase the same way.

We know that Balmer had hit upon a formula that allowed him to calculate the wavelengths of those four lines (Chapter 20) by a trial and error method in which he worked backward from the measured wavelengths of Ångström. However, he could offer no theory to explain his success, and no true scientist would be satisfied with that. Moreover, there was no explanation of the peculiar constant R in his formula.

Another Test of the Bohr Theory

Now if Bohr's theory had any validity, he should be able to calculate the energies of the above lines by means of his third postulate, $E_2 - E_1 \propto f$, or to make it an equation by adding a constant, $E_2 - E_1 = hf$.

As stated previously, detailed mathematical validation of the Bohr theory will be set off in a smaller type, and the student who feels that it is not essential to his understanding may proceed directly to the conclusion on p. 390.

E_2 is the energy of the electron in its higher level, E_1 the energy in its lower level, and hf is the difference in energy between these two levels. The total energy of any electron revolving in an orbit is in part kinetic and in part potential. Then the total energy, E, of an electron = KE + PE.

First let us derive an expression for the KE of the revolving electron. From Eq. 22-6 we have

$$\frac{mv^2}{r} = \frac{Ke^2}{r^2}$$

We now multiply both sides by r, getting

$$mv^2 = \frac{Ke^2}{r}$$

Next we divide each side by 2,

$$\frac{mv^2}{2} = \frac{Ke^2}{2r}$$

But

$$\frac{mv^2}{2} = KE$$

therefore

$$KE = \frac{Ke^2}{2r} \qquad [22\text{-}12]$$

and we find that we now have an expression for the kinetic energy of the electron.

The calculation of potential energy is not so easy. It can be shown by mathematical methods that we shall not use here that

$$PE = \frac{-Ke^2}{r} \qquad [22\text{-}13]$$

where the minus sign is a consequence of the point chosen as our level of reference from which we measure the potential energy. As a matter of convenience, we choose for our reference a point infinitely far from the nucleus where the electrostatic attraction between the nucleus and the electron is zero. If the force between the electron and the nucleus were one of repulsion so that work would have to be done to move the electron closer to the nucleus, the potential energy would be positive. As it is one of attraction, the potential energy is negative. This accounts for certain minus signs in some of the equations that follow.

We started out to calculate the total energy, E, which is the sum of the kinetic and the potential energies. That is,

$$E_n = KE + PE = \frac{Ke^2}{2r} + \left(\frac{-Ke^2}{r}\right)$$

$$= \frac{Ke^2}{2r} - \frac{Ke^2}{r}$$

Factoring out the common factor Ke^2/r, we have

$$E_n = \frac{Ke^2}{r}(\tfrac{1}{2} - 1) = \frac{Ke^2}{r}(-\tfrac{1}{2})$$

$$E_n = -\frac{Ke^2}{2r} \qquad [22\text{-}14]$$

We have already found the value of r in Eq. 22-8. Substituting, we get

$$E_n = -\frac{2\pi^2 mK^2 e^4}{n^2 h^2} \qquad [22\text{-}15]$$

Note that n is the only variable on the right side of this equation (the others are all constants; see footnote 5). Therefore the radius r of any permitted orbit depends on the value of n^2.

Our next step in obtaining the principal lines of the hydrogen spectrum is to calculate the difference in energy between two energy levels, that is, between two of the permitted orbits. To do so we solve the equation of Bohr's third postulate,

$$E_2 - E_1 = hf \qquad \text{or} \qquad f = \frac{E_2 - E_1}{h}$$

We now substitute Eq. 22-15 for E_2 and for E_1 (and, of course, n_2 and n_1 for n). We will not burden you with the calculation but will be content to give the result:

$$f = \frac{E_2 - E_1}{h} = \frac{2\pi^2 m K^2 e^4}{h^3}\left(\frac{1}{n_1{}^2} - \frac{1}{n_2{}^2}\right)$$

[22-16]

The value of f will depend upon the values we use for n_1 and n_2. Although we have solved our equation, we are not satisfied because we want to compare Bohr's results with Balmer's revised formula, Eq. 20-4 (p. 357), and this formula is for reciprocals of wavelengths, not for frequencies. Now, for any wave, v (velocity) $= \lambda f$ (p. 156). The velocity of light is a constant (3×10^{10} cm/sec) and is commonly designated by the letter c. Hence $c = \lambda f$. Solving for λ,

$$\lambda = \frac{c}{f}$$

Since we want the reciprocal of λ,

$$\frac{1}{\lambda} = \frac{f}{c}$$

[22-17]

We now substitute Eq. 22-15 for f in Eq. 22-17. In our result there is an array of constants, $2\pi^2$, m, K^2, and e^4, in the numerator and the constants c and h^3 in the denominator. We can combine them into a new constant, R. We then have

$$\frac{1}{\lambda} = R\left(\frac{1}{n_1{}^2} - \frac{1}{n_2{}^2}\right)$$

[22-18]

A Comparison of Bohr's Equation with Balmer's Formula

The mathematical calculations of the preceding few pages have shown that Bohr derived a formula (Eq. 22-18) for the wavelengths of the principal spectral lines of the hydrogen atom from the assumptions of his theory. The constant, R, should have the same value as the Rydberg constant in the Balmer formula. Equation 22-18 has an oddly familiar look so we check back to p. 357 and find the same equation, written in its more general form so as to apply to all series—Balmer, Lyman, Paschen, Brackett, and Pfund—which we will shortly explain.

The Rydberg constant, R, in the Balmer formula now finds an explanation—provided it is the same R as in Eq. 22-18. The value of R in the Balmer formula is 109,677.58 cm^{-1} (the superscript, $^{-1}$, means "reciprocal of"). The value of R in Eq. 22-18 is found by multiplying $2\pi^2$, 9.1×10^{-28}, $(9 \times 10^9)^2$, and $(1.6 \times 10^{-19})^4$ together and dividing by $3 \times 10^{10} \times (6.6 \times 10^{-27})^3$. The result is within a fraction of 1% of the Balmer R. Here, then, was a tremendous triumph for the Bohr theory, for it gave a wondrous explanation of the four spectral lines of hydrogen. But the really wondrous thing about it was this: The Balmer formula constant, R, was not calculated from data derived from experiment, nor was it based on any theory; justification for its use was simply that it worked—but here Bohr deduced it from the assumptions of the Bohr theory. This was a remarkable agreement between theory and experiment, for the probability that all of the constants used in Eq. 22-16 with their large negative and positive powers of 10 should combine to give the correct answers by mere chance is very close to zero.

An inspection of Fig. 22-6 reveals that all four lines of the Balmer (visible) series end on the orbit labeled $n = 2$. The original Balmer formula was designed to apply only to the four visible lines of hydrogen. The value of n_1 is fixed for any one series of lines; thus, when $n_1 = 2$, the wavelengths of the lines obtained are all in the Balmer (visible) series (Fig. 22-6). When $n_1 = 1$, 3, 4, and 5, the lines obtained are in the Lyman, the Paschen, the Brackett, and the Pfund series, respectively. Further-

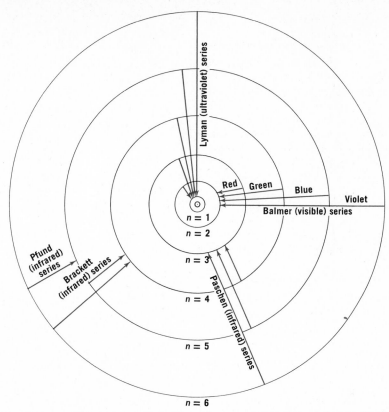

Fig. 22-6. Series of Spectral Lines due to Transitions Between Stable Bohr Orbits in the Hydrogen Atom. Orbits are not drawn to scale; radius of $n = 2$ orbit is four times that of $n = 1$ (Fig. 22-5). Each series belongs to a different final energy level. Thus the final energy level of the Lyman series is the $n = 1$ orbit, that of the Balmer series is the $n = 2$ orbit, and so on. The transition from the $n = 6$ to the $n = 1$ orbit involves a greater energy release than one from the $n = 6$ to $n = 2$, $n = 3$, and so on. Therefore the photons released by transitions to the $n = 1$ orbit are the most energetic; they are in the ultraviolet range. Also, transitions to the $n = 2$ orbit are more energetic than those to the $n = 3$ orbit, and so on. This can be more easily understood from Fig. 22-8.

more, if we compare Eq. 22-18 with the Balmer equation (Eq. 20-4, p. 357), we see that they are of the same general form. The difference in the two formulas is that Balmer's will give the wavelengths of only the principal lines of hydrogen, whereas the Bohr formula is equally good for lines outside the visible range of the spectrum, that is, for the Lyman series in the ultraviolet and the Paschen, Brackett, and Pfund series in the infrared.

Some Successes and Failures of the Bohr Theory

Perhaps we need, at this point, to summarize the initial successes of the Bohr theory. We can do this best by quoting Holton.[8]

Thus we have come to the initial successes of Bohr's model. It predicts the size of the

[8] Gerald Holton, *Introduction to Concepts and Theories in Physical Science*, Addison Wesley, Reading, Mass., 1952, p. 596.

unexcited atom, and the prediction is of the correct order of magnitude. It yields an expression for the wavelengths of all lines that are to be expected from radiating hydrogen atoms, and this expression coincides exactly with one that summarizes the experimental facts of line emission. It accounts for Rydberg's empirical constant in terms of physical quantities. It provides us with a visualizable (although therefore perhaps dangerous) system, and establishes physical order among the events accompanied by emission, whether the particular lines are well-known, or as yet beyond the region of the experimentation. The model introduces quantum theory into the atom and thereby gives on the one hand a physical basis for Planck's induction that the energy in the atom is quantized, and on the other hand removes the problem of the stability of electron orbits from the classical theory which could not provide the solution.

Bohr's theory also dealt successfully with energy levels, ionization potential, and the number of emission lines, all of which are discussed in the next section, and successfully explained absorption spectra (p. 354).

We have previously pointed out that the Bohr theory was originally designed to apply to the hydrogen atom. It accounted both qualitatively and quantitatively for the hydrogen spectrum and was almost equally good for the helium *ion* carrying a single electron (as does hydrogen). It could not account for the spectrum of the helium atom with its two electrons, nor for spectra of other atoms with larger numbers of electrons. This means that Bohr's final equation (22-18) could not be used to calculate the wavelengths of the spectral lines of atoms with more than one electron.

We might hazard a guess that the reason for this is that in the hydrogen atom the single electron moves in the constant electrical field of a nucleus carrying only one positive charge, whereas in an atom with more than one electron and more than one charge on the nucleus, each finds itself in a rapidly fluctuating electric and magnetic field caused by the motions of the other electrons. As a result, the energies of the electrons would not be the same as they would be if they were not under the influence of other electrons and of greater charges on the nucleus. Despite these failures, the Bohr theory stands out as one of the greatest conceptions the human mind has ever devised, for it opened the way for the elucidation of the structures of these more complex atoms. We will shortly show how the theory was altered to account for their spectra.

Energy Levels

Elsewhere we have used the terms stable orbit and energy level interchangeably. As long as we are talking about Bohr's original theory it makes no difference which we use. We have already stated that this theory had to be altered for atoms with multiple electrons. In the "final" revision of the theory the concept of definite orbits had to be given up because it gave us a false mental picture of the atom. On the other hand, the term energy level gives us no definitive picture of an atom and yet serves a necessary purpose.

The concept of energy levels may be likened to a very tall building whose floors represent energy levels, but with the distances between floors becoming less and less as we go upward from the ground floor. In our analogy the atom is the building and its occupants are the electrons. When the hydrogen atom represents the building, its lone electron becomes the sole occupant, which normally occupies only the first floor. The distance between the ground floor and the second floor is much the greatest, as is common in modern office buildings. Thus it takes by far the most energy to climb one floor higher when we are on the ground floor.

We can check our analogy against the observed data from the hydrogen atom in Table 22-1. Note the very rapid decline in the differences between adjacent levels as we go to higher values of n. The basic cause here is that the force between the nucleus and the electron varies as the square of the distance between them. Thus the corresponding lines get closer and closer together as the differences converge toward zero (Figs. 22-7 and 22-8).

This electron can absorb enough energy to go to any of the higher floors. But here our analogy begins to break down. The energy needed to move upward from one floor to another comes in units (photons) of many sizes (Fig. 22-8), and there is no such thing as a fraction of a unit (Planck's quantum theory). To get from the first (ground) floor to the second ($n = 2$) floor, the electron must absorb an amount of energy equivalent to that possessed by an ultraviolet photon. To get from the second ($n = 2$) floor to the third ($n = 3$) floor, it must absorb additional energy, an amount equivalent to that possessed by a photon of red light. Since the distance between the second and the third floors is far less than the distance from the first to the second, it can be seen that a photon of red light has sufficient energy to cause the transition. Thus, in order to get to the $n = 3$ level from the ground floor, our electron has absorbed an amount of energy equivalent to the sum of the energies of

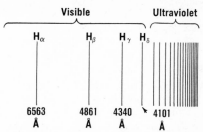

Fig. 22-7. Convergence of Spectral Lines of Hydrogen. The four principal lines of the visible range are individually labeled. Calculations from the Balmer formula show that as the value of n rises the wavelengths of the hydrogen spectral lines should become progressively closer together. This means that the difference between two successive wavelengths approaches zero. A spectrum of hydrogen that shows the ultraviolet range reveals that the calculations are in agreement with observation.

an ultraviolet photon and a red photon. To go from the third to the fourth (the $n = 4$) floor it would have to absorb energy equivalent to that of a high energy infrared photon and so have more energy than before. Its total energy above the ground state is equal to the sum of the energies of an ultraviolet, a red, and an infrared photon. Now our electron can return from the $n = 4$ floor to the ground floor in any one of several ways. It can go down by stopping at each floor in succession, but to do so it has to emit first an infrared photon, then a red photon, and finally a low energy ultraviolet photon. Or it can jump out the window and land on the ground in one fell swoop, giving up a higher energy ultraviolet photon. All transitions from any level to the $n = 1$ level result in the emission of an ultraviolet photon. The lowest energy ultraviolet photon is emitted in the transition from the $n = 2$ level to the ground state, the highest energy ultraviolet photon is emitted in the transition from the level just below $n = \infty$ (Fig. 22-8). This series of lines is called the Lyman series.

Table 22-1
Convergence in the Hydrogen Spectrum

"Jump"	Color of line	Wavelength (Å)	Difference (Å)
$n = 6$ to $n = 2$	violet	4101	
$n = 5$ to $n = 2$	blue	4340	239
$n = 4$ to $n = 2$	green	4861	520
$n = 3$ to $n = 2$	red	6563	1702

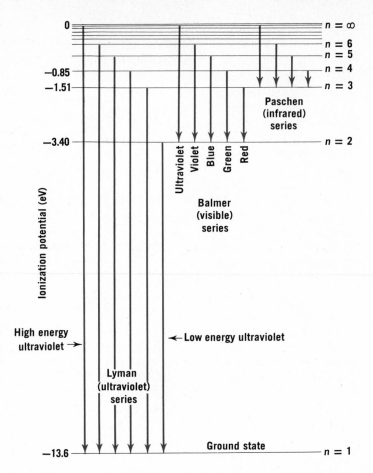

Fig. 22-8. Energy Levels in Transitions Between Stable Bohr Orbits. The ionization energy is the energy, most commonly expressed in electron volts, that must be applied under specified conditions to strip an electron from an atom. For hydrogen it is −13.6 eV if the electron is in the $n = 1$ orbit, −3.40 eV if it is in the $n = 2$ orbit, −1.51 eV if in the $n = 3$ orbit, and so on. The minus sign is the result of our choice of a reference level for the energy of the electron in an orbit, energy that is largely potential. Note the relatively great difference between the energies in the $n = 1$ and the $n = 2$ orbits. In all transitions to the $n = 1$ orbit, the energy released is high; a photon in the ultraviolet range is emitted. Compare with Fig. 22-6.

All stops at the $n = 2$ floor from higher levels result in the emission of visible light photons, red if from the $n = 3$ floor, green if from the $n = 4$ floor, blue if from the $n = 5$ floor, and violet if from the $n = 6$ floor. All stops at the $n = 3, n = 4, n = 5$ floors, and so on, from higher floors result in the emission of infrared photons of varying energies. The general rule is that the longer the jump the higher the energy of the emitted photon. Thus *the emission of energy by vibrating electrons within atoms* in the manner described will account for ultraviolet light, visible light, and infrared light. It will not account for the emission of radio and TV waves. For them the electron must vibrate outside the

atom. Nor will it account for X rays by the same type of electron vibration within atoms. The type of vibration that produces X rays is discussed in the next chapter.

There is room here for a possible misconception. We have used the terms orbit and energy level interchangeably at times, yet when we compare Fig. 22-5 with Figs. 22-8 and 22-9 we see the distances between orbits increase as n increases in the former but that distances between energy levels decrease as n increases. The first diagram and the two latter diagrams are not designed to show the same thing. Figure 22-5 is designed to show the relationship of distance and decreasing Coulomb forces between nucleus and electron, whereas Figs. 22-8 and 22-9 are designed to show the effect on the energy by the same decrease in Coulomb forces.

Ionization Energy and Ionization Potential

The Electron Volt. The energy of an electron in a particular orbit or level may be calculated from $E = hf$; it is expressed most conveniently in electron volts (eV). When an electron traverses an electric field without experiencing any collisions with gas molecules or ions, it gains energy from the field. If it moves from one point to another in that field, and there is a potential difference of 1 volt between those two points, it will gain 1 eV of energy. The electron volt is an extremely small unit,

but the mass of an electron is only 9.1×10^{-28} g, and so, *relatively*, the electron volt is a large quantity of energy (equivalent to 1.6×10^{-19} joule).

Ionization Energy. The minimum energy level is that of the ground state ($n = 1$), the state of the electron in the normal unexcited atom; the electron may be considered to be at the bottom of its energy "well." If sufficient energy is absorbed by an electron at the bottom of its well, it is able to climb completely out the well and wander as a free electron. Its nucleus is left behind as a positive ion. For the electron in a hydrogen atom, this minimum energy required is 13.6 eV. *This is called the ionization energy of hydrogen.* Another way of saying this is that its ionization energy is the energy needed to lift it from the ground state to

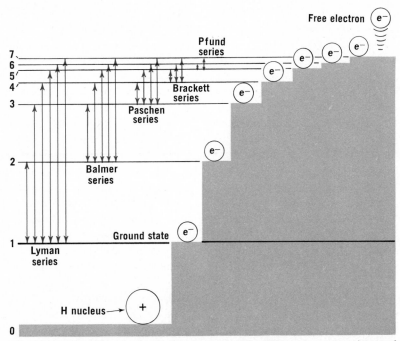

Fig. 22-9. Energy Level Transitions in the Hydrogen Atom. The different quantum jumps that the electron of a hydrogen atom can make are made clearer by considering them as energy steps or levels. Arrows read downward indicate radiation; read upward they indicate the absorption of light quanta.

infinity, where infinity is defined as a distance so far away that the force of attraction between the electron and its nucleus is no longer sufficient to hold the electron in orbit;[9] the electron is completely free to move about, completely independent of the nucleus. Such a free electron can now absorb or emit energy in any quantity; that is, it no longer absorbs or emits energy in units called photons (as it must when in the $n = 1$, $n = 2$, $n = 3$, and so on, orbits). Its energy is all kinetic, the amount depending only on its velocity.

In each of these orbits specified by an integral value of n, the electron has a specified amount of energy that it can emit in units of hf.[10] This amount increases as the value of n increases, but the rate of increase becomes less and less with each shift to a higher value of n, as seen in our floor analogy.

When the difference between two successive energy levels becomes zero, the electron is at infinity, and the minimum energy it then has is equal to the ionization energy, 13.6 eV. This zero difference in energy levels marks the boundary line between the free state and the state in which the electron is *bound* to the hydrogen nucleus.

The energy of an electron in a stable orbit is about two thirds potential and one third kinetic. We must select a level of reference from which to measure the potential energy. Most commonly a value of zero is given to the energy level represented by the ionization state. That of the ground state then becomes -13.6 eV. This simply means that the energy in the ground state is 13.6 eV lower than the ionization energy. From Eq. 22-15, we see that

$$E_n = \frac{-2\pi^2 mK^2 e^4}{h^2}\left(\frac{1}{n^2}\right)$$

[9] Infinity for the electron of hydrogen is of the order of 10^{-5} cm.

[10] Except, of course, when it is in the ground state, where it has energy that it is incapable of emitting.

Now the measured value of E_n for the hydrogen electron in the ground state is -13.6 eV. The factor $2\pi^2 mK^2 e^4/h^2$ must therefore be equal to 13.6 eV. This it turns out to be, and we have another compatibility between theory and experiment. Therefore,

$$E_n = \frac{E_I}{n^2}$$

where E_n is the energy for any value of n, and E_I is the ionization energy, will give us the energy levels of the hydrogen atom (Fig. 22-8). With due regard to our level of reference, the energy in any orbit is given by

$$E_n = \frac{-13.6 \text{ eV}}{n^2} \qquad \text{[22-19]}$$

There may be confusion over the use of the unit of energy, the electron volt, and the unit of potential difference, the volt. They are obviously related since potential difference tells us how much energy can be obtained from an electrical system per unit of charge flowing through the circuit. To create a positive ion we remove an electron from an atom, and this takes energy because we have to do work to overcome the attraction between an electron and its nucleus. The easiest way to do this for a gas, and to measure the energy needed (to create the ion), is to use a three-electrode tube filled with low-pressure hydrogen. The first electrode is a hot cathode (for thermionic emission of electrons), the second is an open-work mesh called a grid, and the third is a metal plate, the anode (Fig. 22-10).

Ionization Potential. Electrons leaving the cathode are accelerated by the potential difference between the grid and the cathode and, if the potential difference is sufficient, the electrons will have enough energy to ionize the hydrogen atoms in this region.

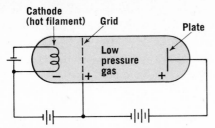

Fig. 22-10. Three-Electrode Tube for Measuring the Ionization Potential of a Gas.

The minimum voltage that must be applied if the gas is hydrogen is 13.6 volts. This is the ionization potential of the hydrogen electron. An electron moving from the cathode to a grid at this potential gains energy equal to 13.6 electron volts. The measurement recorded is that of the voltmeter—which reads volts, not electron volts. This voltage is then a measure of the energy required to remove electrons from atoms of hydrogen in the ground state. To do so from other atoms will require different amounts of energy that are characteristic of the elements in question:

$$E_n = \frac{-13.6 \text{ eV}}{n^2} \qquad \text{(see Eq. 22-19)}$$

If $n = 1$,

$$E_1 = \frac{-13.6 \text{ eV}}{1^2} = -13.6 \text{ eV}$$

If $n = 2$,

$$E_2 = \frac{-13.6 \text{ eV}}{2^2} = -3.4 \text{ eV}$$

If $n = 3$,

$$E_3 = \frac{-13.6}{3^2} = -1.51 \text{ eV}$$

If $n = \infty$,

$$E_\infty = \frac{-13.6}{\infty^2} = 0 \text{ eV}$$

These values tell us that the first excited state ($n = 2$) is only 3.4 eV below the ionization energy, the second only 1.51 eV below it (Fig. 22-8). The differences between E_4, E_5, E_6, and so on, and the ionization energy, E_∞, become successively smaller until, at infinity, the difference is zero. If we translate these converging energy levels to spectral lines, we see the reasons for the convergence of the lines toward a limit (Fig. 22-7).

Compare these values with the corresponding ones in Fig. 22-8. These values derived from theory tell us that the least amount of energy the normal unexcited hydrogen electron can absorb is $13.6 - 3.4 = 10.2$ eV. This is confirmed by experiment by using the tube filled with hydrogen under low pressure and applying a potential difference between the electrodes, as previously described. Suitable spectroscopes or other means are provided to detect the radiation emitted. A hot cathode is used so that electrons (called cathode electrons) are ejected from it (thermionic emission). Some of the cathode electrons will strike the electrons of the hydrogen atoms (called orbital electrons). If the cathode electrons have energy enough they will lift some of the orbital electrons into higher levels; that is, orbital electrons will absorb energy from cathode electrons. Theory tells us that if the energy of the colliding cathode electron is less than 10.2 eV, an orbital electron will not absorb it. The energy of the cathode electrons is controlled by the potential difference.

Not until the potential difference is 10.2 volts is there any evidence of radiation from the tube. At that voltage we detect the first spectrum line. It is in the ultraviolet region (Lyman series). This means that cathode electrons have collided with orbital electrons, transferring 10.2 eV of energy to them and elevating them to the $n = 2$ level, and that these electrons, in returning to the ground state ($n = 1$), have emitted low-energy ultraviolet photons. As the voltage is slowly increased no more lines are seen until it reaches 13.6 − 1.51 or 12.1 volts. Then we detect both a second ultraviolet line of higher energy than the first one and the first Balmer line (the red one) in addition to the ultraviolet line we detected earlier. This means that the cathode electrons now have energy enough to lift orbital electrons up to the $n = 3$ level. Some of these return to the ground state in single transitions, emitting photons that give rise to the second ultraviolet line. Some return to the $n = 1$ level by stopping at the $n = 2$ level emitting photons that give rise to the red line of the Balmer series.

Similarly, another increase in the voltage—a smaller increase than before (13.6 − 0.85, or 12.75 volts)—will allow us to detect a third ultraviolet line, a second Balmer line (green), and the first infrared line, in addition to those seen before. This is because some orbital electrons have been boosted into the $n = 4$ level by cathode electrons of higher energy than before. More ways to return to the ground state are now available. Another still smaller increase in the voltage gives us still more lines, and so forth, until we reach 13.6 volts. No new lines appear, for now the orbital electrons are knocked completely out of the atom; they are now free to move independently of their nuclei. The nucleus now free of its electron is a positive ion. The voltage needed to create this ion is called the ionization potential of hydrogen. It is 13.6 volts.

We might ask—how do we recognize 13.6 volts as the voltage necessary to strip the hydrogen electron from its nucleus? Remember that an electric current is a flow of electrons and that the greater the number of electrons the greater the current. In our experiment we find that when the voltage reaches 13.6, the current suddenly increased (Fig. 22-11). This is what one would expect if a lot of free electrons were released suddenly.

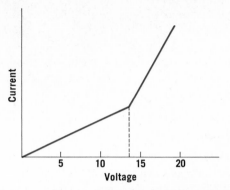

Fig. 22-11. Graph of Current vs. Voltage in Determining Ionization Energy of Hydrogen. Note that the current abruptly increases at 13.6 volts, indicating that there are now more particles (electrons in this case) to carry the current. These electrons have been knocked loose from the hydrogen atoms, which thus are ionized.

Cathode Electrons vs. Orbital Electrons. We must avoid one misconception about this process. The cathode electrons have no potential energy, only kinetic energy, which they can have or can gain and lose in any amount. The orbital electrons have both potential and kinetic energy, which they can increase by absorbing energy in units called photons. They can also lose energy by emitting photons, providing they are not in the ground state. Now when a cathode electron with an energy of less than 10.2 eV, say with 10.1 eV, squarely strikes an orbital electron in the $n = 1$ level, the orbital electron does not rise to the $n = 2$ level. It does not go even part way; in fact, it isn't even budged by the blow. There might just as well as not have been a collision insofar as any detectable effect is concerned. But let the colliding cathode electron have an energy of 10.2 eV and the orbital electron makes the shift to $n = 2$ orbit in no time at all. Why this peculiar behavior? Planck said, as you know, that radiant energy is absorbed or emitted only in units proportional to hf, and Einstein in his explanation of the photoelectric effect said that any photon of ultraviolet light could eject an electron from zinc whereas thousands of photons of violet light would not. Orbital electrons absorb or emit energy in units proportional to the frequency or not at all. Cathode electrons can absorb or emit energy in any amount.

More About the Successes and Failures of the Bohr Theory

The most important criteria of a physical theory are its powers of prediction and interpretation. The Bohr theory had these powers with respect to hydrogen and singly ionized helium. It explained the Balmer series of spectral lines of hydrogen, and it predicted the Lyman series (Fig. 22-6), which were discovered a year after Bohr announced his theory. (The Paschen, Brackett, and Pfund series were already known.) Unfortunately, most experimental data concerning the atoms of heavier elements, that is, elements whose atoms contain many electrons and whose nuclei contain many charges, could not be reconciled with Bohr's predictions. Agreement of the experimental data with theory, in the eyes of Bohr himself, was the ultimate test of the validity of a theory. Just as Bohr made changes in the Rutherford model when he deemed it necessary, so other physicists (and Bohr himself) changed Bohr's model when an abundance of new experimental data made it necessary.

The new data came chiefly from the heavier elements, elements whose atoms had many electrons that interacted with one another. The radii of the innermost electronic orbits are smaller because of increased forces of attraction due to the greater positive charge on the nuclei, which caused the electrons to be held more tightly. This meant that the energy

needed for them to make transitions to higher levels had to be correspondingly greater. The greater the number of electrons in an atom, the greater the number of energy levels needed to explain a spectrum. We remind you that line spectra are emitted by hot glowing atoms in the gaseous or vapor state, that each line corresponds to a different frequency of radiation, and that each line represents a different pair of energy levels. If you will keep in mind that whatever modifications were made in the original theory were essentially attempts to "find" enough energy levels to account for all the observed spectral lines, this account of them should not be too difficult to follow.

Modification due to Motion of the Nucleus

We have been using rough estimates of the ionization potentials against actual measurements in checking our assumptions. They served our purposes very well in the development of the concept of the arrangement of the electrons in shells about the nucleus. However, spectroscopy has developed into a precise science, and even close approximations are not good enough when we attempt to compare wavelengths calculated from the Bohr theory with the actual spectroscopic measurements. As always in science, when theory does not agree with observation, it is the theory that must be modified. One of the first modifications involved motion of the nucleus.

In the original theory, the assumption was made that the nucleus was motionless as the electrons swirled around it. The mutual attractions between the nucleus and the electrons cause the nucleus to have a motion of its own, just as the influence of the moon causes the earth to move somewhat differently than it would if there were no moon. Bohr's correction for this motion of the nucleus changed the value of the Rydberg constant so that the calculated values of the wavelengths of even the hydrogen lines were in better agreement with their observed values.

Electron Orbits, Shells, and Energy Levels

Bohr had postulated circular permitted orbits for the lone electron of hydrogen. These were characterized by the quantum number n, which had the value of 1 for the smallest orbit, the value 2 for the next larger orbit (4 times as large), the value 3 for the next larger (9 times as large), and so on. The electrons in multielectron atoms were assumed by the spectroscopists to be arranged in concentric shells (see Chapter 24), which were labeled by the capital letters K, L, M, N, O, P, and Q before the shells were really understood, because of the need for talking about them. Electron shells are the energy levels of the orbits in which the electrons can move without loss of energy by radiation. Note that energy levels are not orbits. An orbit describes the path of an electron in space; the energy levels are merely a series of numbers that can be plotted as a graph such as that shown in Fig. 22-8. One can easily form a mental image of an orbit whereas an energy level is something of an abstraction. However, energy levels are subject to direct measurements whereas orbits are not.

The chief researchers into the structure of atoms in the decade or two following the publication of Bohr's theory were the spectroscopists. Spectral analysis gradually became a powerful method of scientific research.[11] Thousands of spectral lines were systematically catalogued and made ready for spectral analysis by a relatively small number of theorists, chiefly German.

[11]The extreme sensitivity of spectral analysis may be illustrated by the fact that 1 oz of the metal sodium evenly distributed throughout 300,000 tons of another substance may be detected as an impurity by means of a first class spectroscope.

The Bohr–Sommerfeld Modifications— Quantum Numbers

One of the great German theorists working on the data furnished by the spectroscopists was Arnold Sommerfeld. In the original Bohr theory orbits were circular, with the result that there were not enough energy levels to account for the number of observed lines in the spectra of multielectron atoms, nor were the differences in energy between the levels exactly the right size; the measured wavelengths did not quite agree with those calculated from theory.

Quantum Number n. In 1915 Sommerfeld proposed that electrons could move in elliptical orbits as well as in circular ones. Precision measurements on many elements show that the energy levels have a fine structure that can be partially explained by elliptical orbits (Fig. 22-12). Each circular orbit was assumed to have a set of corresponding elliptical orbits characterized by slightly different energy levels. Ellipses have major and minor axes; the circle, from the mathematical viewpoint, might be considered as a special case of an ellipse

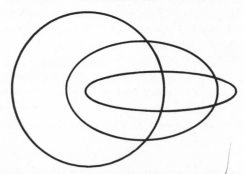

Fig. 22-12. Orbits Corresponding to $n = 3$. The diameter of the circle is equal to the long axes of the ellipses. The quantum number, n, denotes the sizes of the orbits in the modified theory. The period and the angular momentum are the same for all orbits with the same quantum number. (After Sommerfeld.)

with the two axes equal. All other ellipses could then be viewed as flattened circles. The other extreme form the ellipse would be reached when the minor axis became zero. This form would then be a straight line, a rather absurd form for an ellipse and one that seems to make no sense. It does, however, make mathematical sense to say that the shape of an ellipse varies between that of a circle and a straight line. It also allows us to say that the angular momentum of an electron in an elliptical orbit varies from some maximum value when the orbit is a circle to zero when the "orbit" is a straight line. As hereby implied, it is mechanically absurd to think of an electron passing through the nucleus as required, but this was reasonable in the wave mechanical theory (p. 406) that was introduced some time later.

We remember that Bohr's first postulate was that the angular momentum of a revolving electron is an integral multiple, n, of $(h/2\pi)$. If all orbits were circular, then the quantum number,[12] n, could refer either to the orbit or to the number of units of angular momentum $(h/2\pi)$ without confusion. However, in elliptical orbits the distance of the electron from the nucleus is variable (just as the distance of the earth in its elliptical orbit about the sun is variable), and the angular position of it changes from a minimum to a maximum during one revolution. Sommerfeld retained n as the principal quantum number to designate the "size" of the orbit, either the radius of the orbit for circular orbits or the length of the major axes for ellipses.

Quantum Number l. Another quantum number, l, also an integer, was introduced to specify the number of units for angular mo-

[12] The Bohr theory and its modifications were based on Planck's quantum theory. Hence we may speak of quantum orbits, quantum (energy) levels, and quantum numbers to designate those levels.

mentum $(h/2\pi)$ associated with an electron in a given orbit. Since the ellipses differ from one another and from a circle in shape, this second quantum number is said sometimes to describe the shape of an orbit, that is, the degree of flattening of the ellipse. The integer l can have integral values that range from 0 to $n-1$. Thus for $n = 1$, the value of l is 0. When $n = 2$, l is 1. When $n = 3$, l is 2. Thus when the principal quantum number is n, the second quantum number is always one less than the value of n. Note that angular momentum is quantized; it comes in units $(h/2\pi)$.

Quantum Number m. So far the changes in the Bohr theory have involved motion all in one plane. We might now ask: In what directions of space can the possible orbits of the electron exist? Are they all expected to lie in the same plane, or are all spatial directions permitted? As early as 1896 the Dutch physicist Pieter Zeeman had discovered that if the atoms of a radiating element are subjected to the influence of a strong magnetic field, the spectral lines are split into a specific number of lesser lines. This specific number of lines means that the electron orbits can orient

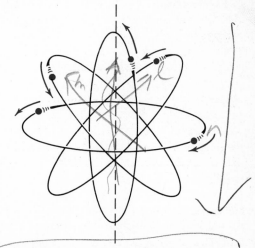

Fig. 22-13. Orientation of Planes of Orbits.

themselves only in certain permitted directions in relation to the direction of the external magnetic field. The permitted orientation of the orbits in space is called *space quantization*. It was experimentally confirmed in 1921 (Fig. 22-13). We offer a brief explanation of this behavior in a magnetic field, as follows:

An electron orbiting a hydrogen nucleus is a moving charge and so is equivalent to an electric current in a loop of wire. We have seen that such a loop behaves like a miniature magnet with north and south poles. A magnetic field is associated with it. Therefore it is not surprising to find that when atoms are in a magnetic field, they behave somewhat differently than they do when no field is present. Evidence of this is seen when the spectral lines of hydrogen, or other atoms, split into several closely spaced lines in the presence of a magnetic field. These lines represent slightly different energy levels with none of them quite the same as the single line observed when the field is absent. Transitions from these levels to levels of lower energies result in the emission of frequencies that are slightly different from those normally emitted. From these observations it was concluded that the field changed the alignment of the atomic orbits so that they were tilted in a limited number of ways with respect to the magnetic field. Only certain definite angles of tilt were possible, the amount being specified by a third quantum number, m. The permitted values of m range from $-l$ through 0 to $+l$. Values of m are always integral. For a given value of l, m cannot have a value greater than that of l. If l is 0, then m must be 0 also. If l is 2, then possible values of m are $-2, -1, 0, 1, 2$.

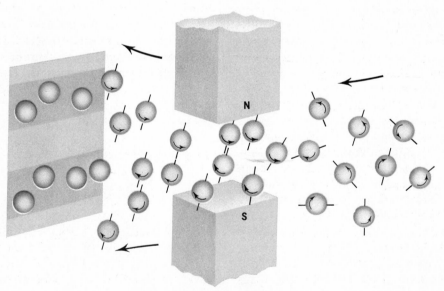

Fig. 22-14. Experiment Demonstrating Electron Spin. A beam of atoms of an element having only one electron in its outermost shell (such as silver) splits into two beams when passed through a strong magnetic field. This is due to the interaction of the electron spin magnetic field with the external magnetic field; the fields may be either added or opposed to each other.

Electron Spin: Quantum Number s (or m_s).
The quantum numbers n, l, and m, with their various values gave a great variety of permitted orbits and so allowed a large number of spectral lines to be explained; yet there were some that were not yet accounted for. The answer came when it was discovered that if a beam of atoms was passed through a magnetic field and observed with a spectroscope, the beam was seen to be split into two parts (Fig. 22-14). (Do not confuse the splitting of a beam of atoms with the splitting of spectral lines.) The splitting was evidently due to different reactions to the field. It could be explained if it was assumed that electrons were spinning on axes in a manner analogous to the earth's rotation on its axis. Such a spinning electron has angular momentum: spin angular momentum. But the electron is moving in an orbit and so has orbital angular momentum, as previously indicated. The spin angular momentum may be in the same direction as the orbital angular momentum or it may be in opposition to it. The spin momentum has a numerical value of $\frac{1}{2}(h/2\pi)$. When the spin angular momentum and the orbital angular momentum are in the same direction (angular momentum is a vector quantity), the orbital part is increased by the spin part, whereas when they are in opposition, the orbital part is decreased by the spin part. The quantum number s (or m_s) can then take on the values $+\frac{1}{2}$ and $-\frac{1}{2}$. Note that the first three quantum numbers, n, l, and m, all have integral values, whereas s has half-integral values. Note also that the orbital angular momentum m arises from an electron revolving in an orbit, whereas s arises from an electron spinning (rotating) on an axis.

The discovery of electron spin greatly improved our understanding of magnetism, for the electron itself is a tiny magnet. If these electronic magnets in an atom are predominantly oriented in the same direction, the atom becomes a magnet. If these atomic magnets are predominantly aligned in the same direction, that aggregate of atoms becomes a magnet. Thus magnetism is explained in terms of the smallest discrete particle that we know. Compare this concept of magnetism with that given on p. 284.

We may summarize the above information on quantum numbers as shown in Table 22-2.

Table 22-2
Possible Quantum Number Values for $n = 1, 2, 3$

Principal quantum number, n	Orbital quantum number, l	Magnetic quantum number, m
1	0	0
2	0	0
2	1	−1
2	1	0
2	1	+1
3	0	0
3	1	−1
3	1	0
3	1	+1
3	2	−2
3	2	−1
3	2	0
3	2	+1
3	2	+2

Waves vs. Particles

The modified Bohr theory was an extraordinarily fruitful theory. By means of the four quantum numbers Bohr (among others) was able to "build" the periodic table (to which Chapter 24 is largely devoted). The theory guided investigators on to the right track, both theoretically and experimentally. There came a time, however, when it failed to bear fruit.

There were a number of difficulties. Despite the fact that the theory was reasonably successful qualitatively, it failed miserably in explaining spectral lines quantitatively. The wavelengths predicted from theory did not agree closely enough with those determined by experiment. It could not predict the intensities of the spectral lines. Its postulates were arbitrary. Bohr had no answer to the question, "Why can the electron only move in a few permitted orbits around an atomic nucleus?" Although he was able to formulate the quantum conditions, that is, the numerical ranges and limits of the quantum numbers, precisely, he could not substantiate them. His postulates did not tie in with other basic principles of physics. Einstein objected to the visualization of an atom as consisting of a nucleus with swarms of electrons revolving in pictured orbits. The model took on too much of an air of reality. Einstein said that a theory should not be decorated with details that could not be checked. The modifications that we have already listed were not fundamental to the theory itself. In retrospect they only seem to have been patches that made the theory better able to fit the facts of spectra. When the fundamental modification of the theory came, it was a sweeping one.

De Broglie's Matter Waves

It was made by the young French physicist Prince Louis de Broglie in 1924. The electron had been regarded for 25 years as the smallest particle known and one that carried a negative electric charge. All phenomena involving light were more explicable in terms of the models, the photon and the wave, than with a single model. Might not that which was true for light also be true for the electron? That is, if light can sometimes act like a wave and sometimes like a particle, might not the electron do so, too?

If photons have a momentum depending upon their wavelength, perhaps electrons had a wavelength depending upon their momentum, mv, that is,

$$\lambda \propto \frac{1}{mv} \quad \text{or} \quad \lambda = \frac{h}{mv}$$

where h is Planck's proportionality constant. This equation is derived by equating Einstein's relativistic mass ($E = mc^2$) of the photon to its energy as given by Planck's equation ($E = hf$). Thus $mc^2 = hf$, where c is the velocity of a photon. Now $f = c/\lambda$. Substituting for f,

$$mc^2 = h\frac{c}{\lambda}$$

Simplifying,

$$\lambda_{\text{photon}} = \frac{h}{mc}$$

Substituting v, the velocity of a particle for c, the velocity of a photon,

$$\lambda_{\text{particle}} = \frac{h}{mv}$$

This is the de Broglie equation. De Broglie pointed out that since light behaved like particles in some phenomena and like waves in others, perhaps electrons also behaved like particles and like waves. This is equivalent to saying that perhaps matter had two aspects, a particle aspect and a wave aspect. Perhaps in macroscopic matter—that is, matter in relatively large chunks—the wave aspect is so overwhelmingly overshadowed by the particle aspect that the former not only cannot possibly be detected, but is probably meaningless. As the size gets smaller, perhaps the wave aspect becomes more important. It might be important in particles of atomic size if we could learn how to detect it. Perhaps in particles the size of electrons, the wave aspect is fully as important, and even possibly more so, than the particle aspect. He suggested that somehow waves accompanied electrons just as waves accompanied photons.

His idea is not very difficult up to this point. Suppose we have an electron moving in an orbit about a nucleus. If a wave accompanies it (Fig. 22-15), going round and round in an orbit whose circumference is a whole number of wavelengths, we have a resemblance to a standing wave (Fig. 9-1). Now a standing wave is stable (remember the rope waves that seemed to stand still). The complete set of loops in a standing wave occupies exactly the distance between the two ends of the rope (Fig. 22-2). If $n = 1$, the matter wave fits into the circumference of the orbit just once. If $n = 2$,

it fits twice, and so on, but never a fractional number of times. If the waves are one-dimensional, they need only a single integer to describe them. Thus $n = 1$, $n = 2$, and so on.

Put in mathematical form, de Broglie's assumption is $2\pi r = n\lambda$. Transposing n,

$$\frac{2\pi r}{n} = \lambda \qquad [22\text{-}20]$$

Bohr's second postulate is

$$mvr = \frac{nh}{2\pi} \qquad [22\text{-}11]$$

Transposing mv and $n/2\pi$, we have

$$\frac{2\pi r}{n} = \frac{h}{mv} \qquad [22\text{-}21]$$

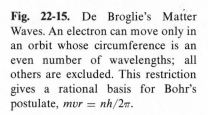

Fig. 22-15. De Broglie's Matter Waves. An electron can move only in an orbit whose circumference is an even number of wavelengths; all others are excluded. This restriction gives a rational basis for Bohr's postulate, $mvr = nh/2\pi$.

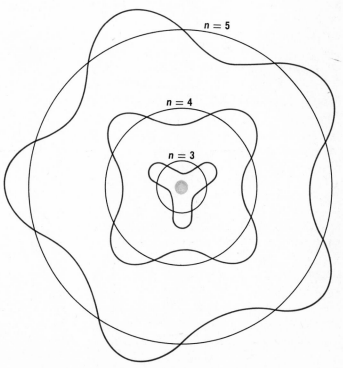

From Eqs. 22-20 and 22-21, it follows that

$$\lambda = \frac{h}{mv}$$

Thus de Broglie found a very plausible answer to the "why" of Bohr's quantized orbits. But plausibility was not enough to cause de Broglie's extraordinary suggestion to be accepted. Direct experimental confirmation was needed, and it was not long in coming. Einstein stated that if de Broglie was right, electrons should show diffraction effects.

Several scientists began the necessary experimenting at once. We have seen that light has both a wave and a particle aspect, and so has two sets of conflicting properties even though they have some properties in common. We need to remember the differences between waves and particles as well as the similarities. A particle can pass through one hole or another in a wall, or a sieve, but it cannot pass through two holes in the same wall or sieve at the same time, whereas a wave can pass through any number of holes side by side. Add particles to particles and you always have more particles. Add waves to waves (from the same source) and you get more waves in some places and no waves in others, as in interference. If we use a coarse sieve, or a coarse-meshed fabric, both photons and electrons pass through in the manner expected. If we use a fine sieve, photons behave differently—as we have seen with a diffraction grating. But we can get much the same result if we look at a distant light source through a fine-meshed fabric in a darkened room. Instead of a single spot of light, we see a pattern of points of light owing to diffraction and interference. Now our eyes cannot detect a stream of electrons in the same way, but a proper photographic plate can. Accordingly we construct the necessary setup, but we get no such pattern on the plate. X rays (Chapter 23) could not be diffracted

or caused to interfere by even the best of ordinary diffraction gratings because the slits were much too wide relative to the wavelength. Eventually certain crystals were successfully used as diffraction gratings. Using similar techniques and electrons in place of X rays, patterns were obtained on photographic plates that resembled those that Laue and his colleagues had gotten with X rays (see Fig. 23-1). Thus the wave nature of electrons was convincingly demonstrated. The wavelengths of the electrons used in the experiments were of the same order of magnitude as those of X rays, that is, about 10^{-10} cm.

Another confirmation came when the electron microscope was successfully developed from the idea that if microscopes using light waves were possible, then microscopes using electron waves should also be possible. The limitation of ordinary microscopes is the magnitude of the wavelengths of visible light. Since the electron wave has a wavelength about $\frac{1}{100,000}$ that of visible light, the electron microscope goes far beyond the magnification of the optical microscope. Recently developed electron microscopes are capable of yielding images of large atoms and molecules.

The Wave Mechanical Theory

We have already stated the general dissatisfaction with the modified Bohr theory. It was considered, at the time of the introduction of de Broglie's wave model of the electron, to have become an arbitrary and somewhat muddled theory that operated according to the rules of the as yet little understood quantum physics, and was no longer esteemed by either theoreticians (including Bohr himself) or by the experimentalists. Then came Erwin Schrödinger with his wave mechanics theory, a theory impossible to visualize but one that "represents a theoretical description of nature which aims at expressing the phenomena of nature in an artificial language, the language of mathematics." His striking wave equation of matter with its differential equations already well-known to physicists had a greater universality than any equation previously formulated in atomic physics.[13] Schrödinger and P. A. M. Dirac of England simultaneously and independently developed this wave equation in 1926. For it they were jointly awarded the Nobel Prize for Physics in 1933, but the equation has come to be associated with Schrödinger rather than with Dirac. This equation can be fully appreciated and understood only by those who have had mathematical training on a very high level.

We will, however, make a sketchy summary, vastly oversimplified, of it here. Schrödinger started out with the assumption that an electron has a wave associated with it. We have seen that it is possible to assign a certain wavelength to every photon according to the color of the light produced. De Broglie assigned a definite wavelength to all moving electrons regardless of whether the electrons were in an orbit about an atomic nucleus or moving in straight lines like cathode rays or beta rays. The wavelength depended on the speed of the moving electrons. Schrödinger believed that waves associated with an atomic nucleus were three-dimensional.

Let us consider simpler waves for a moment. A stretched rope vibrates if there is something at one end to vibrate it. If the length of the rope, the tension in it, and the frequency of vibration are properly adjusted, standing waves are generated in the rope (Fig. 9-1). These loops always occupy exactly the distance between the two ends. The number of loops is always an integral number, never a fractional number. These standing waves are

one-dimensional and may be described by assigning integral numbers to them, say the number n. If $n = 1$, there is only one loop in the rope, if $n = 2$, there are two loops, and so on.

If we sprinkle sand to form a thin layer on a vibrating drumhead, it is possible to observe loops extending in two directions at right angles to each other. Two numbers, n plus a new number, will be needed to describe these two-dimensional standing waves.

It is possible to generate standing wave patterns in a sphere. By the use of the mathematics for vibrating spheres, Schrödinger developed his ideas about atoms. These patterns are three-dimensional and it takes three numbers to describe them. Let us now consider these three-dimensional standing waves in terms of energy. To produce standing waves in a rope, the rope must be stretched. The energy needed to stretch it becomes stored in the rope as potential energy. When we start it vibrating, the rope obviously has kinetic energy. In the atom the potential energy arises from the attraction of the nucleus for the electron. The relationship between the amounts of potential and kinetic energy in each wave pattern—that is, in each value of n—is unique. This relationship increases in complexity as the complexity of the wave increases. It is too complex for this discussion.

In a hydrogen atom the electron wave completely surrounds the nucleus in a three-dimensional pattern. A different set of three numbers is needed for each different pattern and so each pattern corresponds to a certain total energy for the atom. A change in the pattern results in a change of total energy, or vice versa. Since only integral numbers are involved in describing the patterns, only certain total amounts of energy—that is, only certain energy levels—are possible. We will go no further because things get more and more involved in the multielectron atoms. The

[13] There were wave equations applicable to the behavior of waves in classical physics. Maxwell had developed such equations for his electromagnetic wave theory.

mathematics become impossibly high level. In fact, exact mathematical solutions to the equations in the case of multielectron atoms have not yet been obtained. Appropriate assumptions, however, allow useful results to be obtained with the use of modern computers.

Heisenberg's Uncertainty Principle

In Newtonian mechanics, still applicable to the macroscopic world of matter, both the position and velocity (or momentum) of a body are easily calculable; for example, both the position and the velocity of the earth in its orbit can be known precisely at any instant. Inside the atom this is not possible. We have already learned that electrons orbiting within atoms can absorb light energy in units proportional to the frequency, and that in doing so they shift energy levels. Now suppose that we could "see" an electron. You need light to see it, but when you turn on the light to see it, the electron absorbs some of the light energy and instantly moves to another energy level with a different velocity. This is the basis of Werner Heisenberg's uncertainty principle: *It is impossible to obtain accurate values for the position and momentum of an electron simultaneously.* We are therefore reduced to talking

of the region about the nucleus in which the probability of finding the electron is greatest. This principle of uncertainty means that Newtonian mechanics cannot be applied to the atomic world. It sets fundamental limits upon our ability to describe nature.

Electron Clouds vs. Bohr Orbits

The sharp circular and elliptical orbits of the Bohr–Sommerfeld model were replaced by "fuzzy" regions that represent the most probable positions of the electrons. These fuzzy regions are now commonly called electron clouds (Fig. 22-16). More formally defined, an electron cloud is the region of space inside an atom in which there is a high probability (of the order of 95%) of finding a particular electron. It might be viewed as the sum of all of the places that a particular electron is likely to be at one time or another in a neutral atom.

In the electron cloud terminology the electron is considered to be a negatively charged cloud of variable shape and size that is described by the values of n and l. The simplest of the shapes is a sphere, in which the probability of locating the electron decreases outward from the center. In chemical reactions clouds of the reacting atoms may merge (or overlap).

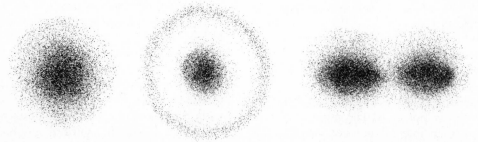

Fig. 22-16. Some Examples of Electron Cloud Diagrams. The relative darkness with which any region of the cloud is drawn represents the relative probability of finding an electron within that region. Thus these drawings are only graphical representations of statistical statements about the probable locations of electrons in atoms and molecules, and our former rather concrete image of an electron shell is replaced by the concept of a less sharply defined region of electron density.

Wave Mechanical Theory vs. Bohr–Sommerfeld Theory

The wave mechanical solution of the hydrogen atom does everything that the Bohr theory does and much more; for example, it gives not only the wavelengths of the lines but their intensity and width as well. It also confirms the existence of energy levels. However, the incorporation of Heisenberg's uncertainty principle into the theory *destroyed completely the concepts of circular and elliptical orbits.* The definite location of electrons within orbits is replaced by probability distributions. The various quantum numbers come out of the theory logically and systematically instead of resulting from special assumptions introduced to account for the observable facts concerning spectra. The theory can account for all the observable properties, both qualitatively and quantitatively, of even the most complex spectra. However, complete analytical solutions of Schrödinger's equations for complex atoms are extremely difficult even with modern digital computers.

Exercises

1. What is Planck's quantum theory?
2. In what way is it different from Maxwell's theory?
3. Why was it not accepted at once?
4. What is the photoelectric effect?
5. Why could it not be explained by Maxwell's theory?
6. (a) Name two metals from which ordinary light will eject electrons.
   (b) What kind of light will eject electrons from zinc?
7. What effect does temperature have on the ease with which electrons will be ejected? (See pp. 311–312.)
8. One ultraviolet photon will eject one electron from zinc but a hundred photons of blue light will not. Why?
9. Will X rays eject electrons from zinc? Justify your answer.
10. What is the present standing of the two theories of light, the photon theory and the electromagnetic theory?
11. State the four postulates of the Bohr theory of the hydrogen atom.
12. Could energy be continuous and quantized?
13. Both photons and particles have or may have kinetic energy and momentum. In what fundamental way does a photon differ from a particle?
14. What reason did Bohr give for making assumptions that were in conflict with the classical physics of the time?
15. What does the quantity $h/2\pi$ represent? How do orbits vary as n increases?
16. How was the adequacy of the first Bohr postulate tested? Was the test successful?
17. The radius of a permitted orbit is given by $r = n^2h^2/4\pi^2mKe^2$. State what each one of the quantities on the right is.
18. If the radius of the first permitted orbit is 0.5×10^{-8} cm, what is the radius of (a) the second permitted orbit, (b) the third, and (c) the fourth?
19. Specifically, what use did Bohr make of Rutherford's nuclear theory; that is, what did he abstract from it and include in his own theory?
20. Specifically what use did he make of Planck's quantum theory?
21. Why did Bohr have n equal only integers?
22. What equation gives you the energy difference between two permitted orbits?
23. What is meant by the excited state of an atom? State two ways in which this excited state may be attained?
24. By what process is electromagnetic radiation produced according to the Bohr theory?

25. Why are there no photons of white light?
26. (a) What transitions in Bohr's hydrogen atom give rise to ultraviolet radiation?
    (b) How may spectral lines in the ultraviolet be detected?
27. What transitions give rise to visible radiation? Compare the color of the line produced by a jump from the $n = 12$ orbit to the $n = 2$ to one produced by a jump from the $n = 3$ to the $n = 2$ orbit, and one produced by a jump from the $n = 11$ to the $n = 2$ orbit. In what part of the spectrum would you expect to find each?
28. Why should the energy that a hydrogen electron absorbs in being lifted from the $n = 1$ to the $n = 2$ orbit be so much greater than that absorbed in being lifted from the $n = 2$ to the $n = 3$ orbit?
29. (a) What is meant by the ionization energy of an atom?
    (b) What is it for hydrogen?
30. Calculate the energy of the fifth hydrogen orbit.
31. Consider Fig. 22-11. To what is the sharp increase in the current at 13.6 volts due?
32. Calculate the energy of an electron volt in joules. (The charge on the electron is 1.6×10^{-19} coulomb. A volt is 1 joule/coulomb.)
33. What is an energy level?

34. In what way does the Bohr theory advance our understanding of the origin of light beyond that of the quantum or photon theories?
35. What is an ion?
36. How may positive gaseous ions be produced?
37. (a) What is meant by ionization potential?
    (b) What is it for the lone electron of hydrogen?
38. A neutral lithium atom has three electrons arranged in two shells. How do we know that all three are not in the same shell?
39. (a) Sodium has 11 electrons arranged in how many shells?
    (b) Which electron is easiest to remove? Why?
40. An atom has a shell designated by the letter N. What other shells *must* it have?
41. Why did the original Bohr theory need revision?
42. (a) What is a quantum number?
    (b) How are quantum numbers designated?
43. Essentially, what was the proposal of de Broglie? Was he shown to be right?
44. What is Heisenberg's uncertainty principle? What fundamental change did it make in the then-prevailing concept of atoms?

X Rays and the Concept of Atomic Number

23

Wilhelm Röntgen[1] of Germany discovered X rays accidentally in 1895 while he was investigating cathode rays by means of a gas discharge tube. At one stage in his investigations he noticed that certain crystals that were on his desk some distance away began to glow. He knew that cathode rays did not have enough energy to penetrate the distance from his tube to the crystals. He investigated to see if the fluorescence was caused by a new radiation with exceptional penetrating ability. This supposition proved correct. However, all efforts to determine whether the radiation was particle-like or wave-like met with defeat. Hence he called the rays X rays.

This discovery seems to have attracted more public attention more quickly than any other ever made by man. The fact that the rays permitted one to see to some extent through opaque objects was sensational, so much so

A striking discovery like that of roentgen rays acts much like the discovery of gold in a sparsely populated country; it attracts workers who come in the first place for gold, but who may find that the country has other products, other charms, perhaps even more valuable than the gold itself.

J. J. THOMSON
Discoverer of the electron

---

[1] Röntgen, the German spelling, is often converted to Roentgen in this country. Thus, X rays are also called roentgen rays in honor of their discoverer.

that they caught the fancy of the public as soon as Röntgen announced his discovery. The possibility of "seeing" through opaque objects provided sensational material for certain newspapers of the day, for then it was easy to believe that X rays could make fully clothed people appear naked. The Pennsylvania legislature passed a law forbidding the use of X rays in opera glasses. In a remarkably short time, however, the potentialities of X rays were correctly understood, and many of the modern uses of them were developed, particularly their use in setting broken bones. The damaging effects of overlong exposure to them were not so quickly understood. It was not until the mid 1940's that their use in the fitting of shoes, particularly the shoes of children, was outlawed.

The discovery was a prime example of the happy accident (Chapter 10). Such accidents can happen to anyone, but they benefit only those deserving few who have the patience, insight, and objectivity to take advantage of the unexpected.

In Chapter 20 we mentioned the discovery of X rays as one of the triumphs of the electromagnetic theory of Maxwell, but postponed their explanation because the proper background for understanding them had not yet been laid. X rays played the star role not only in the development of the concept of atomic number, but also in the opening up of a wholly new field of research into the structure of crystalline solids. It is therefore necessary that we now understand something of their nature.

X Rays—Particles or Waves?

Within a few weeks of the announcement of their discovery by Röntgen, scientists everywhere were investigating X rays. Among the properties discovered were their ability to make certain minerals fluoresce, to pass through most opaque matter, to darken a photographic plate, and to ionize the air through which they passed. The failure to determine conclusively whether they were waves or particles was not for want of trying. Scientists passed beams of X rays through electric and magnetic fields with negative results, proving that they were not charged particles. This left two possibilities, that they were either neutral particles or a form of wave motion. At first glance it might seem that the neutral particles hypothesis could be checked by setting up a nearly frictionless paddle wheel in their path to see if they possessed kinetic energy. The trouble was their great penetrating power; they go through the thin light blades of such a wheel almost as if it were not there. Attempts to produce diffraction and interference patterns failed. Nevertheless, Röntgen and many others believed that they were waves because of the manner in which they were produced—by the deceleration of high energy charged particles (electrons).

The problem was finally settled in 1912, when Laue, a German physicist, acted on the suggestion that they might be electromagnetic waves of such short wavelength that even the finest diffraction gratings had slits too far apart to produce diffraction. To show measurable diffraction, a slit must be small, the degree of smallness being determined by the wavelength. Even in a grating with 10,000 slits per centimeter (25,000 per inch), a slit is wide (10^{-4} cm) compared with the wavelength of X rays—which ranges from 10^{-6} to 10^{-10} cm. Crystals of many minerals have regular shapes; most regular-shaped crystals have plane cleavage surfaces and well-defined edges. This must mean that their molecules, atoms, or ions are regularly arranged, probably in layers. Laue thought that in some kinds of crystals the layers might be far thinner and more closely spaced than were the slits in even the best of diffraction gratings. Perhaps crystals could be used in place of diffraction gratings to produce interference patterns. Some of Laue's students tried and succeeded in combining the rays constructively and destructively. Thus, both of the two unique experimental criteria for wave motion, diffraction and interference, were successfully applied to X rays.

The Fruits of Röntgen's Discovery

Structure of Crystals

Once it was known that crystals could be used to produce interference patterns, patterns that were different for each type of crystal, it became possible to turn the experiment around and use X rays to identify crystals (Fig. 23-1). The mineralogist can now compare the interference patterns made by an unknown crystal specimen with the patterns made by known minerals. Furthermore, the pattern made by a particular kind of crystal depends in part on how the atoms in that crystal are arranged.

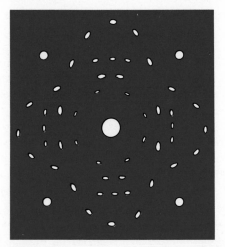

Fig. 23-1. X-Ray Diffraction Pattern of NaCl. (After M. Sienko and R. Plane, *Chemistry,* McGraw-Hill Book Co., Inc., New York, 1957.)

Thus, a whole new field of research into the structure of crystalline substances was opened.

Production of X Rays—Continuous Spectra

As X rays have been conclusively identified as a type of high energy electromagnetic radiation, we can expect them to emit energy in the form of photons of extremely short wavelength and high frequency, for in all cases $f\lambda = v$ (or c), where v (or c) is the velocity of light, 3×10^{10} cm/sec. A few other principles we have already learned will be used in our discussion; you will be reminded of them at appropriate times. We are going to concern ourselves with only two aspects of X rays: (1) a rather thorough account of how they are produced, and (2) a brief account of how Moseley used them to determine atomic number, that is, the number of positive charges on the nucleus.

X rays are produced in low-pressure gas discharge tubes such as those used by the investigators of cathode rays. In modern tubes (Fig. 23-2) the source of the electrons is a heated filament—thermionic emission. The target material forms the anode; it is a metal of high melting point and high atomic number. The target material is mounted with a flat surface at an angle to the direction of travel of the electrons. The thermionic electrons, which we will call cathode electrons, are given a high velocity, a high kinetic energy, by a potential difference between 10,000 and 1 million volts, depending upon the ultimate use of the X rays. To maintain a steady stream of rays either direct current is used, or alternating current is rectified (p. 312). These cathode electrons strike the target, most with glancing blows, so that only a part of their kinetic energy is transformed into electromagnetic energy. Photons must have a frequency of 10^{16} cycles/sec or more to lie in the X-ray range of the electromagnetic spectrum.

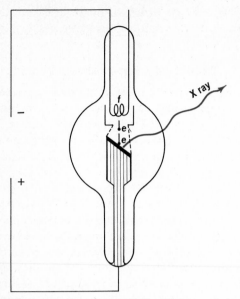

Fig. 23-2. Modern X-Ray Tube. High-speed electrons, *e*, ejected from the filament, *f*, strike a target of tungsten metal where they "lose" most of their energy. This energy is transformed into electromagnetic radiation of extremely short wavelength. High voltage is applied to the tube to give the electrons the necessary speed.

Only a few (relatively) of the electrons that strike glancing blows lose so much of their energy all at once that they can emit X-ray photons. Most of the cathode electrons undergo a series of collisions with particles of matter—target, side of tube, molecules of air, and so on—losing only a small part of their energy with each collision. They radiate photons in the infrared range of the spectrum as they are decelerated. The result is that their energy is frittered away in the form of heat; modern tubes must therefore be made so that cooling water or oil can be circulated through the target material. About 99% of the total energy of the cathode electrons is dissipated in this manner.

Those electrons that lose sufficient energy all at once when they strike glancing blows emit photons of varying energies—all of them

in the X-ray range—for not all of them lose the same amount of energy when striking the target. The result is that photons of a wide range of frequencies are emitted, giving a continuous X-ray spectrum analogous to the continuous spectrum of visible light emitted by glowing liquids and solids (p. 352). The continuous spectra of X rays are much alike regardless of the target material, just as continuous spectra of visible light are all much alike regardless of what solid or liquid is glowing.

Production of X Rays—Line Spectra

A few of the high-energy electrons make more direct hits, hits that strike and eject electrons from atoms of the target material, thus making ions of them. Consider tungsten, a common target material, whose symbol is W and whose atomic number is 74. It has six shells, K, L, M, N, O, and P, and a corresponding electron configuration of 2, 8, 18, 32, 12, 2. It takes only a few electron volts (eV) to remove the outer two electrons in the P shell, and the number of eV to remove electrons in the N shell one at a time increases

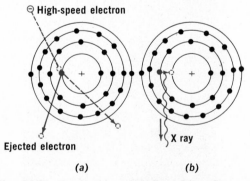

Fig. 23-3. Production of X-Ray Line Spectra. (*a*) High-speed cathode electron ejects orbital electron from K shell of atom, leaving vacancy that may be filled by L-shell electron. (*b*) Energy difference between K and L levels is radiated as K_α line in X-ray spectrum. If M-shell electron fills vacancy, the more energetic K_β line is radiated.

progressively until it takes about 2000 eV to remove the 32nd one. However, the energy required to remove an electron from the K shell (that is, the innermost shell) of tungsten is about 70,000 eV.

As the removal of an electron from an atom in the target material ionizes that atom, a vacancy is left in one of the shells of that atom. This vacancy, or hole if you like, will be filled by an electron that occupied a shell farther out. Let us suppose that the hole is in the N shell and that the electron filling it comes from the O shell. We learned in our study of the Bohr theory that electrons in the outer shells (energy levels) of atoms have more energy than those in inner shells (Fig. 23-3). An electron in the O shell will fall into the hole in the N shell, but since it has more energy than the electron ejected from the N shell had (before ejection), it will radiate a photon whose energy is equal to the difference. This photon will be in the visible range of the electromagnetic spectrum. If the hole is in the M shell, the same sort of thing happens; that is, an electron from a shell farther out falls into the hole, and a photon in the far ultraviolet region

is emitted.[2] But when the hole is in the L shell and it is filled by an electron from either the M shell or from one farther out, the photon emitted will be in the near X-ray region, that is, in the high ultraviolet region. If the hole is in the K shell and is filled by an electron from the L shell or by one from farther out, the photon emitted will be in the X-ray region. Remember that if the cathode electrons are accelerated by a potential difference of 70,000 volts, then all of the cathode electrons strike the target with 70,000 eV of energy. The K electrons are closer to the nucleus than any of the others, and are held tightly by the 74 protons in the tungsten nucleus. When a K vacancy is filled, either from the L shell, M shell, or any shell farther out, photons of varying energy will be emitted, but they will all be in the far-out range of the X-ray spectrum. The important thing here is that these are line spectra (Figs. 23-4 and 23-5), for each photon

[2] You will remember that the energy level differences between the $n = 3$, $n = 4$, $n = 5$, . . . levels—the M, N, O, and so on, shells—are small compared to the differences between the $n = 1$, $n = 2$, and $n = 3$ levels—the K, L, and M shells (see Fig. 22-8).

Fig. 23-4. Positions of X-Ray Line Spectra with Respect to Wavelength. The line spectra (K_α right and K_β left) of all elements are much alike, but they shift toward the shorter wavelengths as the atomic number increases. Note the regularity of the shift. If number 21 were unknown, the unusually large shift from Ca to Ti would indicate a missing element (see p. 417).

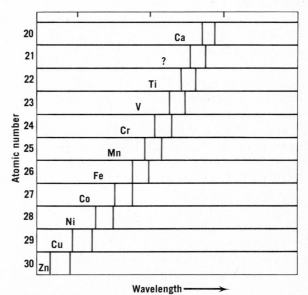

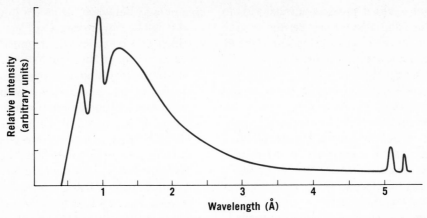

Fig. 23-5. General Form of Graph of X-Ray Spectrum of Metal. The X-ray intensity, in arbitrary units, is plotted against wavelength in Ångströms. The curve minus the spikes is that of the continuous spectrum produced when cathode electrons are stopped abruptly. The wavelength decreases (frequency increases) with the electron speed, which is governed by applied voltage. The spikes represent the line spectra. They are produced only at high voltages because cathode electrons must be given high speeds to penetrate into the K and L shells of atoms with enough energy to dislodge orbital electrons (Fig. 23-3).

emitted has a specific frequency; that is, the photon emitted when an electron moves from the L shell to the K shell of tungsten has a frequency that is different from that emitted when an electron moves from the M shell to the K shell, and so on. Photons with frequencies in between are not emitted and so the spectrum is not continuous; that is, an X-ray line spectrum is produced.

Moreover, if we change the target material from tungsten to another element, say gold (Au), atomic number 79, all of the photons emitted by electrons filling vacancies in the manner described for the K and L shells of tungsten will have their own characteristic frequencies; that is, they are different not only from those of tungsten but from those of any other element.

The Concept of Atomic Number

This was what Moseley, one of Rutherford's assistants, discovered in 1913, that the K radi-

ation of each element was distinct from those of any other element. This provided a unique way of identifying elements. Not only that but it provided a justification for Mendeleev in reversing the positions of tellurium and iodine, and cobalt and nickel, in his periodic table. Moseley arranged the wavelengths of the K_α lines in the order of their atomic weights just as Mendeleev did. There were fewer gaps because many of the elements missing in 1869 had been discovered before 1913. Moseley found a regular progression in the wavelengths of the K_α lines that exactly matched Mendeleev's progression of atomic weights except for the two reversals noted above, and a third one between potassium and argon that had arisen after the discovery of argon in the middle 1890's. Moseley found that his progression put the elements in the proper order, that is, the order after Mendeleev had made his reversals for other reasons. He judged that the order according to his wavelengths was more consistent than that according to atomic weights—that is, that there is a unique correlation between the X-ray line spectra wavelength series and atomic number. The wavelengths decreased in regular steps as the atomic number increased (Fig. 23-4)—or, we could say, the frequency increased as the atomic number increased.

It is interesting to note that Moseley announced his concept of atomic number in the same year that Bohr announced his theory of the hydrogen atom. The fact that the charge on the nucleus (à la Moseley) was more fundamental than the mass (given by the atomic weight) dovetailed nicely with the Bohr model of the hydrogen atom, for the charge was basic to his model and the mass was not. Certain metals were not known to Moseley at the time, for example, scandium, atomic number 21. Nevertheless he predicted the wavelengths of its K lines, which were later found to be almost exactly correct (Fig. 23-4).

The modern concept of the atomic number of any element is, then, the number of charges on the nucleus of an atom of that element. It is also the number of protons in the nucleus, for each proton carries one positive charge. And, since the atom is neutral, it is also equal to the number of electrons surrounding the nucleus.

Exercises

1. In what ways do X-ray photons differ from those of visible or ultraviolet light?
2. Why did the early attempts to obtain interference patterns of X rays fail?
3. How did Laue solve the problem?
4. How are the X rays that give rise to the continuous X-ray spectrum produced?
5. Compare this production of X rays with the photoelectric effect.
6. What gives the high speed to the cathode electrons in an X-ray tube?
7. How are the X rays that form the line spectrum that is superimposed upon the continuous spectrum produced?
8. What is the source of the energy of the K_α line? The K_β line? Which represents the greater amount of energy?
9. If the "hole" left by an orbital electron ejected from the K shell of an atom having several shells is filled by an electron from the next outer (L) shell, then a hole must be left in the L shell, which may be filled by an orbital electron from a shell still farther removed from the nucleus, and so on. Would you expect the radiation produced by an orbital electron from the N shell filling a hole in the M shell to have a higher or a lower frequency than that produced by an electron from the L shell filling a hole in the K shell? Explain.
10. What is the modern concept of atomic number?
11. Describe briefly what Moseley did to arrive at the modern concept of atomic number.
12. How does the arrangement of elements in the periodic table according to atomic number compare with an arrangement according to atomic weights?
13. How did Moseley use prediction to lend support to his concept of atomic number?
14. We learned that radiation from the infrared to the ultraviolet inclusive are produced, according to the Bohr theory, by electron transitions from the $n = 2, n = 3, n = 4$, and so on, energy levels to a lower one. How does their origin differ from the origin of X rays?

PART VI

Atomic Structure and Chemical Combination

The Periodic Table and Electron Configurations of Atoms

Chapter **24**

We are now ready to integrate and correlate a very large number of facts, along with many of the associated laws, theories, and concepts that we have been discussing in the last group of chapters, into a meaningful whole that will permit us a better understanding of the structure of atoms than we would have otherwise.

For the better part of 100 years after Dalton formulated his atomic theory, atoms were believed to be indivisible and so could have no structure. Such a belief left too many unsolved problems. Chief among them were those concerning spectra. The accumulated evidence indicated that spectra originated within atoms by the vibration of a highly complex set of oscillators. How could a simple indivisible particle like an atom give rise to such complicated patterns of bright line spectra? In the relentless search for order, particularly in the post-Copernican world, a search that is based on the conviction that nature does not ever act capriciously, many long-held beliefs have had to be abandoned, or at least greatly modified. Eventually the belief in the atom's in-

Orderly arrangement is the task of the scientist. A science is built out of facts just as a house is built out of bricks. But a mere collection of facts cannot be called a science any more than a pile of bricks can be called a house.
HENRI POINCARÉ

divisibility had to go. The first faint hint came with Faraday's discovery of ions in the 1830's. Ions were of two kinds, one consisted of an atom minus something, the other of an atom plus something. What was that something? J. J. Thomson found out when he discovered the electron 65 years later. About the same time radioactivity was discovered, with its ejection of alpha particles from the nuclei of certain heavy atoms—and the case for divisibility was complete.

Investigations into the nature of atoms now turned to their structure. Our study of these researches followed two lines of development, the wave line and the particle line. These two lines fused to form one line in Bohr's daring and revolutionary theory of the hydrogen atom. His theory immediately furnished an explanation for bright line and other spectra, and after considerable modification, made possible that crowning glory of science, *the explanation of the periodic table by means of the electron configuration of atoms,* and gave us an interpretation of the chemical behavior of atoms. Thus, the regularities in the periodic table are explained in terms of regularities within atoms.

Before we begin a study of these regularities we need to turn our attention to certain topics that we did not find convenient to discuss elsewhere. One of them is the shell structure of atoms, which we mentioned in Chapter 22 without presenting the evidence for it.

The Evidence for the Shell Structure of Atoms

According to modern theory, the electron in an atom of hydrogen moves within a fuzzy region called an electron cloud rather than in the definite orbit of the original Bohr theory, or its modification, the Bohr–Sommerfeld theory. The electron cloud may be regarded as a "distribution of probability" of the electron. The probability of finding the electron is spread over a volume in space that, depending on the energy state of the atom, assumes different shapes. This electron cloud can have different densities at different places (Fig. 22-16). There is greater probability of finding an electron in the dense part of the cloud than in a diffuse part. There is no particular problem involved in the unexcited hydrogen atom, a one-electron atom. However, in multielectron atoms we need to know how the electrons are arranged with respect to one another as well as with respect to the nucleus. What we want is the appearance of the electron shells, visualizable in the Bohr–Sommerfeld theory but utterly impossible in the wave mechanical theory. How can you describe something you cannot visualize? We are left to do the best we can to interpret the statistical wave patterns of Schrödinger's mechanics without giving up entirely the familiar particle model of the electron.

The electrons in an atom can exist only at certain energy levels, levels that we thought of as extremely vague "concentric shells" around the nucleus. You must not think these shells are as nicely concentric as shown in Fig. 24-1; we show them that way because of the impossibility of showing them as they really are. After all, we are trying to get across to you an idea, not a mental image. Each shell describes the *average* distance to the nucleus; the circles shown are meant to represent this average distance in that shell and not the path the electron traveled. Spectroscopists labeled these shells K, L, M, N, O, P, and Q in that order, with the K shell having the smallest radius. They determined the arrangements of the shells by measurements of ionization energies. Electrostatic forces are involved in holding the electrons about the nucleus, one of attraction between the positively charged nucleus and the negatively charged electron, and

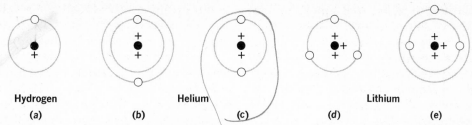

Hydrogen   Helium   Lithium

(a)   (b)   (c)   (d)   (e)

Fig. 24-1. Shell structure of Atoms. Hydrogen (*a*), with its single electron, offers no difficulty. An ionization energy of 13.6 eV is needed to remove the electron, leaving the nucleus as a positive ion. Two arrangements (*b* and *c*) are possible for helium. Assume (*b*) to be correct. If it is, the energy needed to remove the first electron should be less than 13.6 eV because of a greater distance from the nucleus. Experience proves the need for much more energy; we conclude that (*b*) is incorrect. Further experiment and calculation indicate that (*c*) is correct. Two arrangements (*d* and *e*) are possible for lithium with its three electrons. Removal of the first electron takes far less energy than predicted if (*d*) is correct, but is about right if (*e*) is correct. In (*e*) this third electron is farther from the nucleus than the other two and is partially shielded from the attraction of the nucleus by the two inner electrons. Thus we infer that the capacity of the first shell is two electrons and that the third electron starts a second shell.

one of repulsion between the electrons themselves (for multielectron atoms). The magnitudes of these two forces can be closely estimated from Coulomb's law, and the approximate net force calculated by measuring the ionization energies of the electrons.

Consider Fig. 24-1, which shows the possible arrangements of electrons for the atoms of hydrogen, helium, and lithium, atomic numbers 1, 2, and 3, respectively. The caption explains the method of making a choice among the possible arrangements in helium and lithium. Read it before proceeding further. For the elements succeeding lithium in the second period—beryllium (Be), boron (B), carbon (C), nitrogen (N), oxygen (O), fluorine (F), and

Fig. 24-2. Graph of Ionization Energy vs. Atomic Number. Note the drop in ionization energy at the end of each period and the rise in the following period. This is excellent evidence that electrons are arranged in shells. The low points mark the beginnings of periods, the prominent peaks the ends of periods.

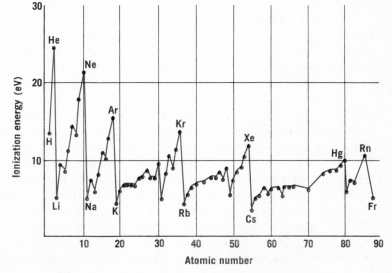

neon (Ne)—the energy needed to remove the first electron increases more or less steadily from left to right (see periodic table, period 2), going from 5.4 eV for lithium to a high of 21.6 eV for neon (atomic number 10). Next we try sodium (atomic number 11), and find the ionization energy needed to remove the first electron drops (from the 21.6 eV of neon) back to 5.1 eV. This is even less than that for lithium, which is exactly what we would predict if this electron was in a different shell farther from the nucleus. This is the third, or the *M*, shell.

Examine Fig. 24-2, which is a graph showing the ionization energy in electron volts plotted against the atomic number. Note the amazing drop in ionization energy after the end of a period. This drop can mean only that the outer shells of an inert gas can hold no more electrons; that is, their outer shells are "closed." If more electrons are added, they must go into a new shell. Thus, each alkali metal starts a new period with one electron in its outer shell. A more striking evidence for the assumption that the electrons are really arranged in shells about the nucleus could scarcely be desired.

Valence

Another topic that we might have discussed earlier (Chapter 16), but did not because we had no real need for it until now, is *valence*. The word was coined by an English chemist in 1850 to acknowledge the fact that elements that combine to form compounds have a specific combining capacity. The term today has a far more complicated meaning than it did originally. Professional chemists used the simple meaning for 75 years and we, for the most part, will follow in their footsteps.

Two elements with the lowest combining capacities were selected and assigned a valence of 1. These elements were hydrogen and chlo-

rine. They themselves combine in a one-to-one ratio to form HCl (hydrogen chloride). One or the other of them will combine with every other naturally occurring element (except for the monatomic gases, which are reluctant to combine with any element). By determining the atomic ratios in a compound containing an element combined with either hydrogen or chlorine, we learn its valence. Thus, the valence of oxygen is 2, for, from the method of determining atomic ratios (see Chapter 16), we see that its combining capacity is twice that of hydrogen. For example, one oxygen atom will combine with two hydrogen atoms to form H_2O. Using the same method we find that three hydrogen atoms will combine with one nitrogen atom to form NH_3 (ammonia). The valence of nitrogen is thus 3 in ammonia. In methane (cooking gas) we find (Table 16-3) that one atom of carbon will combine with four atoms of hydrogen. Thus, carbon has a valence of 4. Higher principal valences are unknown, as we shall see later. Once the atomic ratios (formulas) have been determined experimentally by the methods described previously, the valence can be determined by simple inspection of the formula as long as we use simple compounds. The situation is complicated by a few elements that have multiple valences, for example, iron, phosphorus, nitrogen. Such elements, as a general rule, have one valence that occurs more often than the other (or others); it is called the principal valence.

None of these facts explains chemical affinity. The view that electrical attractions were the cause of the affinity of atoms for one another gained status about 1800 when the newly invented battery was used to decompose water into hydrogen and oxygen. Soon sodium, potassium, barium, calcium, strontium, and chlorine were discovered by the same method. Berzelius, the great Swedish analytical chemist, had strongly advocated a relationship between electric charges and chemical reactions as early as 1807. However, he believed that these attractions existed only between different kinds of atoms. This belief delayed acceptance of Avogadro's hypothesis.[1] Faraday came very close to the concept of a smallest possible electric charge—that on a monovalent atom—from his work on the passage of electricity through ionic solutions in the 1830's. The passage of electricity through gases by Thomson ultimately yielded the information that the electron was the smallest unit of electric charge and that it was a universal constituent of all atoms. The divisibility of atoms into electrons and nuclei, the suggestion of a Japanese physicist that electrons orbited the nuclei like miniature solar systems, and the work of Moseley on atomic numbers all offered possibilities of an adequate explanation of valence.

As both atomic number and valence are related to position in the periodic table, it seemed likely that the chemical behavior of atoms depended on the number of electrons (which is determined by the nuclear charge) around the nucleus of the neutral atom. These nuclei are, in general, well screened from one another by the intervening shells of electrons, so that they are relatively far apart, so far apart that the chemical activity of atoms must depend directly on the electrons, and most probably on the outer electrons only. Bohr's theory gave credence to these concepts by postulating that visible light has its own origin not only in the behavior of electrons in atoms but most probably in the behavior of the outer electrons at that. In hydrogen it was the transitions of its one electron from outer orbits to inner ones that gave us its spectrum. But how about spectra of atoms with four, five, or six shells? The electrons in inner shells of such atoms are far too tightly bound to the nucleus (because of the greater number of protons in the nuclei) for them to participate in the emission of visible light.[2] They are also too tightly bound to be responsible for the valence of an atom. We will have more to say about valence in the next chapter where we will have the opportunity to apply it. Meanwhile we will return to our discussion of the regularities and periodicities of the periodic table.

The Periodic Table

The States of Matter

At the end of Chapter 16 we discussed very briefly some of the problems of classification of the elements as an equally brief introduction to the periodic table. We suggest you return to these pages (259–261) to refresh your memories. The periodic table is a classification scheme of unusual brilliance that was developed just over 100 years ago by the Russian chemist Dmitri Mendeleev. A total of 65 elements had been identified at the time; a few others were still on the doubtful list. Today 88 elements occur in nature, mostly as compounds. There are also about 11 artificially made elements (p. 443), and 4 that are disintegration products of such short half-lives (Chapter 36) that they do not occur naturally. We will not concern ourselves with any of them. Of the known elements that occur in nature, 11 are gases, of which 6 are monatomic[3] and 5 diatomic (hydrogen, oxygen, nitrogen, chlorine, fluorine). Two elements (mercury, a metal, and bromine, a nonmetal) are liquids at STP. The others are all solids.

---

[1] Berzelius believed that there were electrical attractions between hydrogen atoms and oxygen atoms to form water, but he did not believe that there were any between two atoms of hydrogen to form molecules of H_2, or of oxygen to form molecules of O_2.

[2] We have learned (p. 415) that they do participate in the emission of X rays.

[3] See p. 428 for a discussion of them.

These elements are of three kinds: metals, semimetals or metalloids, and nonmetals.

Location in the Periodic Table

The general locations in the periodic table of these three groups of elements—metals, metalloids, and nonmetals—are *not* random. The gases are all on the far right, the six monatomic gases occupy the whole right-hand vertical column; the five diatomic gases are grouped to their left in the upper half of the table, three of them in the second vertical column, one (oxygen) in the third, and one in the fourth column.

The metals occupy the left and lower portions of the periodic table; the nonmetals are on the right and upper sides. They are separated by the zigzag diagonal line of the metalloids, running from boron (B) to polonium (Po) and astatine (At), as indicated on the periodic table inside the front cover of this book.

About 75 of the elements, if we include the artificially made ones, are metals. We hesitate to state a definite number because the distinction between a metal and a metalloid is not always clear-cut. The reason should be evident from what we have already said: Most transitions from metals to metalloids to the solid nonmetals are gradual.

A period represents a stepwise change from elements strongly metallic to weakly metallic to weakly nonmetallic to strongly nonmetallic, and then, at the end, to an abrupt cessation of almost all chemical properties, that is, to the completely nonmetallic monatomic gases. In the next period, the same sequence is repeated all over again, although not exactly in the same way. For example, the boundary line between the metals and the nonmetals, indefinite though it may be, shifts to the right from period to period. This is described by the statement that there is an increase in metallic

properties downward in the main groups IIIA through VIA.

Metals and Nonmetals in the Periodic Table

The division of the elements into metals and nonmetals is the simplest and the oldest of all classifications. It is an obvious one, for metals have a characteristic way of reflecting light, a metallic sheen that we call luster, which makes them look different from the nonmetals. They also conduct both heat and electricity far better than the nonmetals, most have high density, and most can be flattened by hammering without breaking, or can be drawn into wires. Not all have these properties to the same degree; they range from a degree that borders on perfection to almost not at all. Some are semimetallic in character; that is, their properties are, in part at least, nonmetallic.

Nonmetallic elements that are solids lack the luster, the conductivity, and the malleability of metals. Many nonmetals are gases at room temperature. Actually there is a gradation both ways, from the metallic into the nonmetallic and from the nonmetallic to the metallic, not only in physical properties, but also in chemical properties. The result is a number of borderline elements, for example, silicon, arsenic, boron, germanium, that are sometimes called metalloids. In general, metals have no great tendency to combine with other metals to form simple compounds, but show a considerable tendency—sometimes violent— to combine with nonmetals. Nonmetals, on the other hand, show a considerable tendency to combine with one another, although rarely with the readiness with which they combine with metals.

The search for regularities among these two groups continued. Gradation of properties existed no matter what property was considered. For example, among the metals, the melting points ranged from below 0°C (mercury) to more than 3300°C (tungsten). The hardnesses paralleled the melting points; that is, those with the highest melting points had the greatest hardnesses. On the other hand, as the intensities of some properties increased, those of others decreased; for example, the densities of some subgroups increased as the melting points dropped. The most active metals formed the strongest bases when they reacted with water, the least active the weakest (if any at all). These were general trends only; exceptions among them made the task more difficult. More detailed investigation led to the grouping of elements into families, the members of which had for the most part similar properties, or properties that changed systematically. Progress along this line was handicapped at first by too few of the possible members of a family being known, but as time went on, more and more elements were added to the list, and confidence in the family grouping as a valid concept increased.

The Families (Groups)

Each family occupies a vertical row in the periodic table. As stated above, members of the same family have similar properties. In the periodic table of this textbook the main families are labeled IA through VIIIA. (Some-

times the VIIIA column is labeled 0 for zero valence.) Hydrogen is the only element that does not fit into any family. You will note that it is listed in two places, high up on the upper right and on the extreme upper left. It is placed on the right because it is a gas, and so belongs here with all the other gases. It is in the halogen (see Table 24-3) family column but it certainly is not a halogen. It is placed on the left because its chemical properties are much more like those of the metals in the IA family than like those of any other elements. Like the IA metals, hydrogen has only one electron in its outer shell. We will learn more about it later.

The Alkali Metals. Each element of the IA family has one electron in its outermost shell and so has a valence of one. They are all (hydrogen excepted) alkali metals. All these metals are soft and light and have low melting points. They are highly active chemically; all combine with chlorine and other nonmetals, reacting with varying degrees of violence, to form salts of various kinds. Most familiar is the salt formed when sodium is burned in chlorine, NaCl, our common table salt. All alkali metals react more or less violently with water, releasing hydrogen gas and forming strong bases (hydroxides). NaOH (sodium

Table 24-1
The Alkali Metals

	Lithium	Sodium	Potassium	Rubidium	Cesium	Francium
Symbol	Li	Na	K	Rb	Cs	Fr*
Chemical activity	High—increasing →					
Strength of base	Very strong—increasing →					
Density	Low—increasing →					
Melting point	Low—decreasing →					
Atomic weight	Low to moderate—increasing →					
Valence	All are 1					
Formula of chloride	LiCl	NaCl	KCl	RbCl	CsCl	FrCl

*Occurs briefly and in minute amounts as a radioactive decay product of actinium, atomic number 89.

Table 24-2
The Alkaline Earth Metals

	Beryllium	Magnesium	Calcium	Strontium	Barium	Radium
Symbol	Be	Mg	Ca	Sr	Ba	Ra
Chemical activity	Moderately high—increasing →					
Strength of base	Moderately strong—increasing →					
Density	Moderate					
Melting point	Moderately high*					
Atomic weight	Low to high—increasing →					
Valence	All are 2					
Formula of chloride	$BeCl_2$	$MgCl_2$	$CaCl_2$	$SrCl_2$	$BaCl_2$	$RaCl_2$

*The melting points do not grade systematically as do those of the alkali metals.

hydroxide) and KOH (potassium hydroxide) are sold commercially as lye. In the reactions with water much heat is evolved; potassium, rubidium, and cesium evolve so much that the released hydrogen bursts into flame spontaneously, combining with the oxygen of the air to form water. All alkali metals react with oxygen or moisture in the atmosphere, tarnishing so quickly that they have to be kept submerged in a protective liquid such as kerosene. Their properties are summarized in Table 24-1.

The Alkaline Earth Metals.   The alkaline earth metals (family IIA) are beryllium, magnesium, calcium, strontium, barium, and radium. They are all active metals but not so active as the alkali metals. They all react vigorously with chlorine to form salts with similar properties; they all form bases but of more moderate strength than those of the alkali metals. They are also harder, denser, and have higher melting points. Most importantly they all have a valence of 2. Their properties are shown in Table 24-2.

The Halogens.   The *halogens* (meaning "salt-forming")—fluorine, chlorine, bromine, iodine, and astatine (which is not found naturally)—are a familiar family of nonmetals. At STP the first two are gases, bromine is a red-dish brown liquid, and iodine a steel-gray solid. Both bromine and iodine evaporate readily. In the vapor phase they are all diatomic gases. All have unpleasant odors. All react with hydrogen to form strong acids (except fluorine, which forms a weak acid). They are all highly active chemically, fluorine being the most active of all the nonmetals. The trends of their properties are shown in Table 24-3.

Monatomic Gases.   The monatomic gases form a single vertical column on the extreme right of the periodic table. This family was completely unknown before the 1890's, largely because of their inertness and scarcity. Helium was discovered in the spectrum of the sun in 1868 but not here on earth until 1895. It is by far the most abundant of these gases here on earth, most of it coming from wells in Utah and Texas. Radon, a radioactive disintegration product with a short half-life (Chapter 36), does not occur naturally. The other five are minor constituents of the atmosphere, argon being most abundant (nearly 1.0%). See Table 24-4.

The whole group was long thought to be completely unreactive chemically—until 1962, when xenon was found to react with fluorine. Since then it has been found to form compounds with oxygen. Krypton and radon have also been found to react. Under the influence

Table 24-3
The Halogens

	Fluorine	Chlorine	Bromine	Iodine	Astatine*
Symbol	F	Cl	Br	I	At
Chemical activity	Extremely high	Very high	High	Moderately high	?
Strength of acid	Weak	Strong	Strong	Strong	Strong
Melting point (°C)	−223	−103	−7.2	114	High
Valence	1	1	1	1	1
Atomic weight	19	35.5	80	127	210
State	Gas	Gas	Liquid	Solid	Solid
Odor	Strong	Strong	Strong	Strong	Strong
Molecular formula	F_2	Cl_2	Br_2	I_2	At_2

*If astatine occurs at all in nature, it does so in infinitesimal amounts. It is a radioactive decay product of uranium and/or thorium with a half-life of 7.5 hr (Chapter 36). Its properties are partially extrapolated from those of the other halogens.

of electric glow discharge or electron bombardment, helium has formed compounds with tungsten, iodine, sulfur, and phosphorus. Although these gases may react with other elements, they will not pair up with atoms of their own kind to form diatomic molecules like H_2, O_2, N_2, Cl_2, and F_2. Hence the terms *molecules* and *atoms* do not have separate meanings for them.

The Periodic Law

The periods are horizontal rows, seven in number, not all of the same length. A better idea of their relative lengths can be obtained from Fig. 24-9. Mendeleev arranged the elements in the order of their atomic weights in a series of rows in such a manner that elements

with similar physical and chemical properties were in the same column. These formed the families that we have just studied. He knew only 65 elements, and he did not know how many were yet to be discovered. To adhere rigidly to the family concept he had to leave gaps in the rows, gaps that he predicted would be filled some day by newly discovered elements. In making his rows and columns he saw that where there were no gaps, the properties of the elements changed gradually, not abruptly, as one proceeded along the row or down the column. Consequently he was able to predict the properties of an as-yet-undiscovered element by noting the properties of the elements on either side of, and above and below, the gap he had left for that missing element. For example, two gaps appeared be-

Table 24-4
Monatomic Gases

	Helium	Neon	Argon	Krypton	Xenon	Radon
Symbol	He	Ne	Ar	Kr	Xe	Rn
Chemical activity	Extremely weak to zero					
Melting point (°C)	−272	−249	−189	−156	−112	−71
Boiling point (°C)	−269	−246	−186	−152	−107	−62
Valence	?	0?	?	?	4?	?
Atomic weight	4.00	20.18	39.95	83.80	131.30	(222)

Table 24-5
Predicted and Observed Properties of Germanium

Mendeleev's prediction (1871) for the undiscovered element he called eka-silicon (Es)	Observed properties of germanium, discovered in 1885
Atomic weight 72.	Atomic weight 72.60.
Es a dark gray metal, with high melting point and density = 5.5.	Ge is dark gray; melting point = 958°C, density = 5.36.
Es only slightly attacked by acids, resistant to alkalies such as NaOH.	Ge not attacked by HCl, but dissolved by concentrated HNO_3; not attacked by NaOH.
Es will form oxide EsO_2 on heating; EsO_2 will have high melting point and density = 4.7.	Ge forms oxide GeO_2, with melting point 1100°C, density = 4.70.
Es will form a sulfide EsS_2 which is insoluble in water but soluble in ammonium sulfide.	Ge forms sulfide GeS_2, which is insoluble in water but soluble in ammonium sulfide.
Es will form a chloride $EsCl_4$, with boiling point a little less than 100°C and density = 1.9.	Ge forms chloride $GeCl_4$, with boiling point 83°C and density 1.88.
Es will be formed upon reaction of EsO_2 or K_2EsF_6 with sodium metal.	Ge is formed by reaction of K_2GeF_6 with sodium.

tween zinc (Zn) and arsenic (As) in period 4. He predicted that some day elements would be found to fill the gaps, that both would have atomic weights less than that of arsenic but greater than that of zinc, that one would have properties similar to aluminum, the other properties similar to silicon. Not long afterward two such elements were discovered. One of them was named germanium; how close he came in his predictions of its properties is shown in Table 24-5. Such predictions aided his justification of his periodic law: *When the elements are arranged in the order of their atomic weights, elements with similar properties are repeated periodically.* In the words of Mendeleev, "the properties of the elements are a periodic function of their atomic weights."

In his arrangements of the elements according to atomic weights Mendeleev had to make two reversals in order to get certain elements into the right families; for example, not to reverse tellurium (Te) and iodine (I) in the fourth period would have meant taking iodine out of the halogen family—where it obviously belongs. Cobalt (Co) and nickel (Ni) in the fifth period—and, later, argon and potassium—had to be reversed. In 1913, when Moseley (p. 328) had determined the numbers of charges on their nuclei and assigned atomic numbers accordingly, it was found that the reversals were justified. Hence we now substitute the word *numbers* for *weights* in the periodic law.

Acceptance of the Periodic Table

Chemists were slow to accept the table at first, despite the brilliance of Mendeleev's predictions. By 1900, however, the periodic table, greatly improved, was a tool for every chemist in the world. In the modern form, atomic numbers are assigned each element, and serve for easy reference, just as do house numbers on a street.

The table contains a great wealth of information for those who know how to read it. All the elements in the first vertical row on the left have a valence of 1, those in the second vertical row a valence of 2, and so on. The transition series offer complications that we will unravel later in this chapter.

From the atoms are made all of the different kinds of matter that we know. Therefore, if we can completely understand everything the table has to tell us, including, above all, the basic reasons for the periodicity, the gradually changing properties in each period, and in each family, we will have progressed a very long way toward understanding matter.

Using the Periodic Table

We gave the evidences for the shell structure of atoms earlier in this chapter. We now need to correlate this shell structure with the periodic table (see inside front cover), and in doing so we will learn more about how to use it. Chemical symbols are used for identification in this table, but inside the *back* cover of this textbook the various elements are listed by name, alphabetically, along with their symbols. Atomic numbers and atomic weights are given in both the table and the alphabetical list. In the table the atomic number is given in bold-faced type for easy recognition; it gives not only the number of protons in the nucleus but the number of electrons in the neutral atom also. The number of the period is given in the narrow column on the extreme left.

As previously explained, the capital letters $K, L, M, N, O, P,$ and Q are also used to denote periods. The numbers have one advantage in many situations, for they also represent the principal quantum n for all of the elements

in that period. Thus the K shell and the $n = 1$ shell are the same, and so on. A key in the upper left explains what the numbers associated with each symbol mean. The electron configuration refers to the number of electrons in each of the shells of each particular atom. With the exception of hydrogen, all elements have two in the first shell because two is its capacity—two electrons is all that shell can hold. If we look further, we will see that neon, atomic number 10, is the first element that has eight electrons in its second shell, and that all the elements following it have eight in the second shell. We conclude that the capacity of the second shell is eight electrons. A shell that is filled is said to be closed. If we look at the element with atomic number 72 in the sixth column, we see that the capacities of the first two shells are omitted because of lack of space.

Each period begins a new shell because the monatomic gas at the end of the preceding period closed the outer shell of that period. Only monatomic gases can close periods, and they all do it with eight electrons, except helium in the first period, and it does it with two. Why? The first shell has the smallest radius; there is no room for more than two electrons. As more shells are added, the radius of the outer shell increases; there is room for more electrons, and hence the number of elements in a period can increase. The fourth period contains 10 more elements than the second and third periods, so a gap is provided to allow space for them. The sixth and seventh periods have not only these 10 but 14 more. Since our book is not wide enough to accommodate them, we take them out and put them separately at the bottom.

Subshells and Orbitals

We have said that shells may be thought of as energy levels described by the quantum number n that gives the size of the standing electron wave (p. 405). Within these shells are a number of subshells, which have been labeled s, p, d, and f.[4] The K ($n = 1$) shell has only one subshell, the s subshell. The L ($n = 2$) shell has two subshells, an s and a p; the M ($n = 3$) shell has three subshells, s, p, and d; and all other shells have four, an s, a p, a d, and an f. These subshells are energy sublevels described by the quantum number l, which in the wave mechanical theory refers to probability distributions of electrons in electron clouds. Each subshell has one or more orbitals (not orbits); the s has one orbital, the p has three, the d has five, and the f has seven. Each orbital can hold one or two electrons, but never more than two, and when two are present, they must be of opposite spin. The shapes of these three-dimensional orbitals are not arbitrary; they are derived from wave equations that give the probability of finding an electron in a particular place, that is, they outline zones of probability of electron density. Electrons that share a particular value of l in a shell occupy the same subshell.

The Role of the Electron

Most necessary to the attainment of the most important of our objectives in our study of matter and energy is the understanding of the structure of matter and how that understanding was obtained. More specifically, this involves the structure of atoms and the nature of the energy associated with them. Throughout, it has been the electron that has played the star role. This role included the formation of ions, the emission of the many kinds of energy inherent in the electromagnetic spec-

---

[4] Like the designations K, L, M, and so on, for the shells, these came from the spectroscopists: s for sharp, p for principal, d for diffuse, and f for fundamental.

trum from the ultraviolet through visible light, the infrared, radio and TV, the emission of line spectra, the origin of X rays, photoelectricity, and thermionic emission, as well as the common electric current. Through it all the nuclei of atoms have played a necessary but a quiescent subsidiary role. However, as we proceed to investigate the chemical behavior of atoms and the reasons therefor, the role of the nuclei will become somewhat more important, for it is the number of protons in them that distinguishes one kind of atom from another. Nevertheless the electron will continue to play its star role, until we begin to investigate the energy within nuclei, at which time the electron will not only lose its role, but will retire from the stage completely.

It is somewhat amazing to learn that when Mendeleev originated the periodic table, he knew nothing of these things, not even of the existence of electrons. To him—and all of his colleagues—atoms were still indivisible and so without structure. His table was entirely empirical; that is, there was no theory whatever existing at the time that could explain the regularities and periodicities in the table. Moreover, none of the monatomic gases were known until another 25 years had passed, and so he had no elements that could end the periods so convincingly, for these were elements that could not possibly have been predicted.

By this time you should not be at all surprised that the understanding of the periodicity in the periodic table was achieved through the study of electricity and light. It must not be assumed that there was any overall planning of these investigations. The principles that lie behind the periodic table were uncovered by scientists from many countries, mostly during the 1920's, each working on problems of particular interest to himself. It is questionable whether many could have related their immediate work to the periodic table.

As the development and refinement of the concepts of energy levels, ionization potentials, quantum numbers, and an accumulation of a host of facts about line spectra progressed, Bohr and many other workers began to look to these concepts and facts for an explanation of the periods and families in the periodic table. They believed that with them they should be able to "build" the periodic table.

Pauli's Exclusion Principle

For a time they met with failure. The concept that an electron left to itself would seek to occupy the lowest energy level available was firmly established. In the unexcited hydrogen atom the electron always occupies the position of lowest energy, the ground state. A system of particles is stable when its total energy is at a minimum.[5] If all of the electrons in a complex atom were to occupy the orbital of lowest energy, the K shell would be overflowing. Different types of experiment show that this isn't so; there obviously must be some natural exclusion principle that limits the occupancy of an energy level. Eventually Wolfgang Pauli concluded that each electron in an atom must be described by four quantum numbers, and that *no two electrons in the same atom can have the same four quantum numbers.* This is Pauli's exclusion principle. It set definite limitations on the possible states of the electrons as regards their energy, momentum, orientation, and spin. It provided the key by which Bohr and Pauli explained the regularities in the periodic system by setting an upper limit on the number of electrons that can occupy any part of the space within an atom.

[5] A rock on the floor of a valley is more stable than it would be poised on the edge of a cliff above it. Water is more stable in a pond than it would be in a stream flowing into the pond.

The periodic table could now be "built" using the Bohr–Sommerfeld theory of electron orbits—and it was. The wave mechanical theory had not yet been completely developed.

Quantum Numbers in the Wave Mechanical Theory

In our discussion of the wave mechanical theory an electron wave was described as a three-dimensional standing wave whose energy state could be expressed by three numbers. We might have stated that three numbers are needed to describe the three-dimensional standing wave pattern, which can be visualized as having a size, a shape, and an orientation. In the Bohr–Sommerfeld theory we used three empirically derived numbers, n, l, and m, to account for many of the observed spectral lines in multielectron atoms, and to which there had to be added a fourth, m_s (the spin), to account for all such lines. Each of the numbers had a limited range of values that were also derived empirically. Eventually it turned out that the three numbers used to describe the energy states of three-dimensional electron waves could be the first three quantum numbers, n, l, and m, of the Bohr–Sommerfeld theory. The same range of values could also be used. It is therefore possible to use these quantum numbers to build the periodic chart without doing violence to the wave mechanical theory. We should, however, remember that the numbers do not refer to the same thing in the two theories. For example, in the Bohr–Sommerfeld theory the quantum number n refers to the size (radius) of now-discarded circular and elliptical orbits, whereas in the wave mechanical theory it refers to the number of loops in the electron wave. The same is true of the quantum number l, which in the former refers to angular momentum whereas in the latter it refers to probability distributions of charge in electron clouds.

More About Visualizable Models

Lest we be unduly criticized for combining ideas in that which is to follow, some of them from a discarded theory, some from an accepted theory, and some from a visualizable model of concepts that really cannot be visualized, we will present a justification. In the atomic world correct visualizable models are not possible. We stated on p. 350 that a faulty visualizable model of a highly complex process is better than no model provided we know that it is faulty and in what way.

To justify this statement we refer you to another map analogy. Road maps are far less accurate than topographic maps (the most accurate of all maps). Nevertheless, on a cross-country trip we all use road maps. They are a better guide for they are less cumbersome, easier to follow, and contain far fewer irrelevant details than does the topographic map. The Bohr–Sommerfeld theory is like a road map that we may use even though we know a more precise map exists. Despite its shortcomings the Bohr model was a conceptual breakthrough that had to precede the wave mechanical theory; the latter had its birth in the attempts to remedy the faults of the former. Truth is far more likely to come out of error that it is out of chaos. The Bohr–Sommerfeld theory facilitated many empirical observations about the electronic structure of the heavier atoms to which Bohr's original theory did not directly apply. His conceptual scheme was very useful in describing the X-ray spectra of the heavy elements. Although wave mechanics has replaced the Bohr model, wave mechanics confirms and builds upon the energy level concept that Bohr introduced.

The Atomic Orbital Model

We have seen how the shell structure of atoms was determined by their ionization energies. These shells are major energy levels for electrons within atoms, and are designated

Table 24-6
Occupancy of the 2p orbitals, Period 2*

	K shell 1s	L shell 2s	L shell 2p		
Boron	↑↓	↑↓	↑		
Carbon	↑↓	↑↓	↑	↑	
Nitrogen	↑↓	↑↓	↑	↑	↑
Oxygen	↑↓	↑↓	↑↓	↑	↑
Fluorine	↑↓	↑↓	↑↓	↑↓	↑
Neon	↑↓	↑↓	↑↓	↑↓	↑↓

*The squares represent orbitals, the arrows electrons. The arrow pointing up has a + spin, the one pointing down a − spin. Note the order of filling of the p orbitals; no p orbital gets two electrons until each has one.

either by the letters K, L, M, N, O, P, and Q or by the numbers 1, 2, 3, 4, 5, 6, and 7. These numbers are possible values for the quantum number n. The major levels are relatively far apart. Each, except the first, has 2, 3, or 4 closely related sublevels, or subshells. The chemist commonly refers to the subshells by the letters s, p, d, and f. The physicist refers to them by the different values of quantum number l: 0, 1, 2, and 3, respectively (Fig. 24-4). Each subshell has 1, 3, 5, or 7 orbitals.

An electron that obeys a particular wave function is said to occupy a certain orbital (p. 432). Pictorially an orbital is a three-dimensional region in space in a subshell that can be occupied by one, or at most two electrons, or is perhaps unoccupied. If two are present they must have opposite spins. A fully occupied orbital is commonly represented by either a small square or a circle with two arrows on the inside, one pointing up, the other down, to indicate opposite spins for the two electrons (Table 24-6). For some purposes dots are used in place of arrows (Fig. 24-4).

It is convenient at times to refer to the shells by the letters K, L, M, N, and so on, and at other times by the principal quantum numbers, $n = 1$, $n = 2$, and so on. When we wish to refer to a particular subshell of a particular shell, we commonly combine the principal quantum number with the s, p, d, or f designation, for example, $1s$, $2s$, $3s$, $2p$, $3p$, $3d$, $4f$. This makes for precision and brevity. We can also refer to the electrons occupying a particular subshell of a particular shell as $1s$, $2s$, $3d$, $4d$,

$5f$, and so on, electrons. It is imperative that the student be able to handle these designations with ease. It is important that you do not confuse shells with periods. A new shell appears with the beginning of each period, but note that this is an additional shell; all of the elements in any period have all of the shells and subshells that the elements preceding it in the periodic table have. Thus radon, atomic number 86, is in period 6 and its outer shell is the $n = 6$ (or P) shell. It has, however, five inner shells. Every shell and every period begin with an s subshell, and every period except the first closes with a p subshell. All of this will be better understood if we "build" the periodic table in a purely *artificial* manner. Proper use of the four quantum numbers and due regard for Pauli's exclusion principle permit us to do this.

Building the Periodic Table

We will start off with the nucleus of a hydrogen atom, and then add electrons one at a time in the order of atomic numbers to obtain the other elements. We will, of course, have to add whatever protons and neutrons are necessary to keep the atoms electrically neutral and to account for their atomic weights. We will assume that this is done automatically every time we add an electron so that we will not have to repeat it hereafter. We will also have to make proper use of the permitted ranges of values for each of the four quantum numbers as given in Table 24-7. Because add-

Table 24-7

Symbol	Name	Describes	Permitted values
n	Principal quantum number	Energy	$1, 2, 3 \ldots$
l	Angular momentum quantum number	Angular momentum	$0, 1, \ldots, n-1$
m	Magnetic quantum number	Magnetic properties	$-l, \ldots, 0, \ldots, +l$
m_s	Spin quantum number	Direction of spin	$-\frac{1}{2}$ or $+\frac{1}{2}$

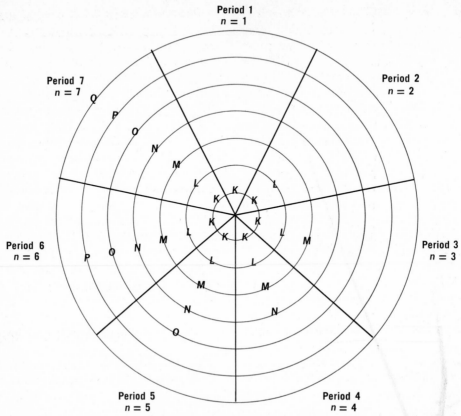

Fig. 24-3. Stadium Analogy: 1. Seating Plan. Each wedge represents a period. The shell letters, *K*, *L*, *M*, and so on, represent sections. Period 1 has only one section (*K*), period 2 has two sections (*K* and *L*), and period 7 has seven (*K–Q*). Each section contains from one (for *K*) to four (for *N*, *O*, *P*, *Q*) rows of seats. The rows are shown in Fig. 24-4. The values of *n* represent the principal quantum numbers of the electrons in the outermost shell only. See Table 22-2.

ing electrons in a definite order to the various kinds of nuclei that are themselves arranged according to a definite plan bears certain similarities to seating people in a circular stadium, we will use an analogy to aid our understanding.

The Stadium Analogy

Imagine a small circular stadium that can be divided into seven wedges (like pieces of pie). See Fig. 24-3. Like any stadium we will

assume that ours contains seats, but they will be occupied by electrons rather than by people. The arrangement of the seats in our stadium is unlike that in any real one, and the order in which they are filled in unique. Therefore, the analogy—like all analogies— should not be pushed too far. The wedges are numbered 1 through 7 (Fig. 24-3), and each *wedge* represents a period in the periodic table. Just as the number of elements within a period in the table varies from 2 to 32, so does the number of seats in a wedge vary from 2 to

32. Each wedge has one or more *sections* (shells) designated by the shell letters K, L, M, and so on, and each section has from one to four *rows* (subshells). For example, the first wedge (period 1) has only one section (K) with only one row in it (Fig. 24-3). The next wedge has two sections (K and L), K with one row, as always, and L with two rows, as always, and so on. The rows are identified by the values of l (0, 1, 2, 3) or by a subshell designation, s, p, d, f (Fig. 24-4). Each row has a number of orbitals, 1, 3, 5, or 7, which are identified by values of the quantum number m. Each orbital contains two seats, each designated by a spin value, which for the sake of simplicity, we will designate by plus or minus signs instead of $+\frac{1}{2}$ and $-\frac{1}{2}$. Just as seats in a real stadium are identified by section, row, and number, so our electron seats are identified by quantum numbers. Just as no two people can buy tickets marked for the same section, row,

and seat number, so no two electrons can have the same set of four quantum numbers. Electrons will be labeled to identify them as belonging in a particular shell and subshell, for example, 1s, 2s, 3s, 2p, 3p, 3d, 4f.

To see how this seating arrangement works in our hypothetical stadium, we will build an atom of the element radon from a bare hydrogen nucleus. To do so we will have to build atoms of all the preceding elements in the order of their atomic numbers in accordance with a few rules which will be stated as they are needed. Radon, a monatomic gas that closes period 6, is chosen for a specific reason. Its atomic number is 86, and no element of smaller atomic number contains all four subshells, s, p, d, f, with all four completely filled with electrons. Pertinent here is the rule that electrons are seated in the order of lowest energy; that is, they are seated in the subshell that takes the least energy to put them there.

Subshell designations (Rows within a section)	The arrangement of seats within the section	Subshell capacities	Subshell capacity increase with increasing value of l
f, or $l = 3$	-3 -2 -1 0 $+1$ $+2$ $+3$	14	4
d, or $l = 2$	-2 -1 0 $+1$ $+2$	10	4
p, or $l = 1$	-1 0 $+1$	6	4
s, or $l = 0$	0	2	—

Fig. 24-4. Stadium Analogy: 2. Detail of the N shell of radon, atomic number 86, period 6, to show relationships between quantum numbers and sections, rows, seats. The squares represent orbitals in the various rows. The dots represent the seats within an orbital or, if filled, electrons. The figures below each orbital represent the values of the quantum number m. Pairs of electrons with opposite spins may occupy each orbital. Note that the subshell capacity increases in steps of four, a consequence of two things: (1) As the value of l increases by one, the number of values of m increases by two, and (2) for each value of m there are two electrons with opposite spins. The above four subshells are not filled in order. For the order see the energy staircase in Fig. 24-5.

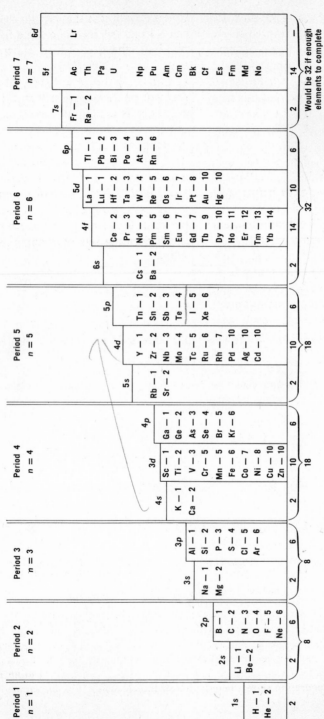

Fig. 24-5. Stadium Analogy: 3. Energy Level Diagram. The energy is that of the indicated electrons. The increase from that of 1s through that of 7s is shown by the staircase running from the lower left to the upper right. The rate of increase is distinctly not uniform. The increase is in potential energy because the electrons get farther and farther from the nucleus as the number of shells increases. In building the periodic table the subshells are filled in the order given at the top of each step. For example, the 4s subshell is filled before the 3d; there are no 3d electrons in the third period. Each period opens with an s electron and closes with six p electrons. The numbers at the bottom indicate the totals, first for the subshells, then for the shell.

The order is shown in the energy-level staircase in Fig. 24-5. Note that this order is predictable for the first three periods only. It is pertinent here to note that a new shell appears at the beginning of each period, that the first subshell in it is always an *s* subshell, and that this new shell is an *additional* shell; already present are all the shells and subshells of all the elements preceding it in the periodic table.

To the bare hydrogen nucleus we add a 1*s* electron. This is the element hydrogen. We add another 1*s* electron and we have helium (remember that we add the necessary protons and neutrons automatically). The four quantum numbers, n, l, m, and m_s (spin), are 1, 0, 0, − and 1, 0, 0, +. If you examine Table 24-7, which shows the ranges of quantum numbers, you will see that as long as $n = 1$, there can be no other nonduplicating sets of quantum numbers, for if $n = 1$, l can only be 0, and if l is 0, m must also be 0. There are two spins, however, for each value of m, and so we have two elements in period 1. Since Pauli's exclu-

sion principle says that no two electrons in the same atom can have the same four quantum numbers, the next added electron must be seated in the *L* shell, which has the principal quantum number $n = 2$ (Fig. 24-6). The first two will be 2*s* electrons; they fill the 2*s* subshell, for its maximum capacity is two. Their quantum numbers are 2, 0, 0, − and 2, 0, 0, +. As long as $l = 0$, there are no more nonduplicating sets of quantum numbers. We do not, however, start a new period, for with $n = 2$, l can have a value of 1, and with $l = 1$, m can have three values, −1, 0, and +1. With two spins for each value of m, we have six new nonduplicating sets of quantum numbers, as follows:

$$
\begin{array}{cccc}
2, & 1, & -1, & - \\
2, & 1, & -1, & + \\
2, & 1, & 0, & - \\
2, & 1, & 0, & + \\
2, & 1, & +1, & - \\
2, & 1, & +1, & + \\
\end{array}
$$

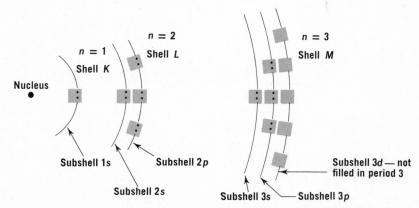

Fig. 24-6. Stadium Analogy: 4. Seating in the First Three Wedges (Periods). The filling of the third period (*M* shell) proceeds normally until row 3*p* is filled with six electrons in three orbitals. Note that this shell now has eight electrons and that this is an outer shell. It is therefore closed despite the fact that the 3*d* row (subshell) is empty, and electrons are barred forever from entering it. Eight electrons, composed of two *s* and six *p* electrons, always close a period. The next added electron must go to an element that starts a new period. The configuration shown here is that of the element argon, the monatomic gas that closes period 3.

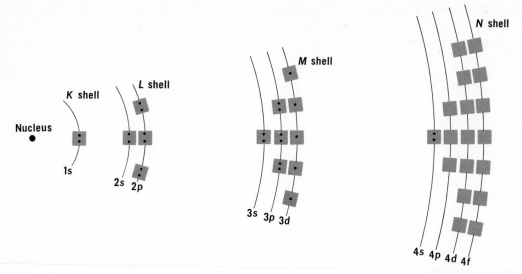

Fig. 24-7. Stadium Analogy: 5. Filling of the Fourth Shell. This figure illustrates the belated filling of *d* subshells. While there are no 3*d* electrons in the *M* shell of elements in the third period, there are 3*d* electrons in the *M* shell of elements in the fourth period. We have seen that argon has eight electrons in its outer shell and that this closes the period. We therefore start a new period. The next two electrons enter the 4*s* subshell of the *N* shell. The next five electrons now become 3*d* electrons in the *M* shells of the five elements following calcium. Each orbital gets one electron before any gets two. This is because the second electron in an orbital has to enter against the repulsion that is already there; more energy is needed. After a second electron has entered each 3*d* orbital, the 4*p* subshell is filled, each orbital getting one electron before any gets two. This closes period 4 even though the 4*d* and 4*f* orbitals are empty. The ten 3*d* elements are the ten that form the transition series of the fourth period.

The elements formed by seating these six electrons, one at a time, are shown under the 2*p* step in the energy level staircase in Fig. 24-5. The distribution of the electrons in shells and subshells is shown in Fig. 24-8. Note that neon (Ne), the last of the six in period 2, has eight electrons in its outer shell. The rule of eight applies here: *There never can be more than eight electrons in the outermost shell of any atom.* Therefore the *L* shell is closed permanently in this period. Added electrons must be seated in a new shell. (Pauli's principle also demands that added electrons be seated in a new shell.) The new shell is the *M* shell with a principal quantum number of 3. Its 3*s* and 3*p* subshells

are filled exactly as the 2*s* and the 2*p* subshells were. Moreover, it becomes closed for the same reason, and by another monatomic gas, argon. This closing of the *M* shell takes place despite the fact that the *M* shell has an empty *d* subshell in the third period (Fig. 24-6). This *d* subshell is filled after the filling of the 4*s* subshell but before the filling of the 4*p* subshell (Fig. 24-7).

From this point on we are going to rely entirely on Figs. 24-3 through 24-9 to present a reasonably adequate picture of the seating of electrons in the remaining periods. Proper study of the figures and their captions should give the student an understanding of the arrangement of the elements in the periodic table. This is something that Mendeleev and a host of his successors never had. This understanding came about during the 1920's; the result was a revolution in theoretical chemistry. This successful unraveling of the reasons behind the periodic table is truly one of the crowning glories of all science.

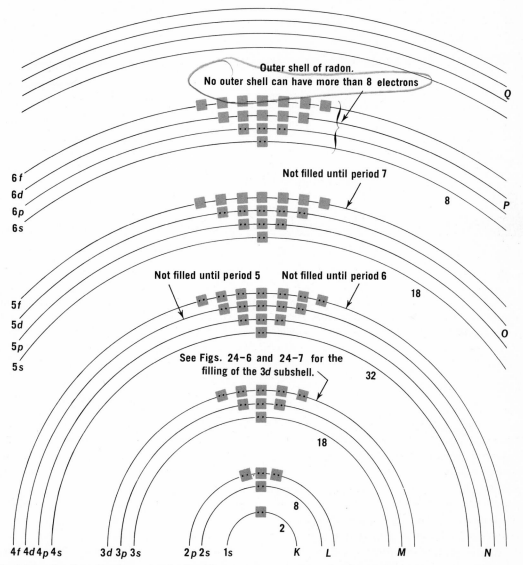

Fig. 24-8. Stadium Analogy: 6. Distribution of electrons in shells and subshells in radon, atomic number 86, period 6. Only the N shell of this sixth period element has a full complement of s, p, d, and f electrons. The $5d$ subshell of group VIIIA is filled but not the $5f$. Note the closing of the P shell. The figures 2, 8, 18, and so on give the total number of electrons in each shell.

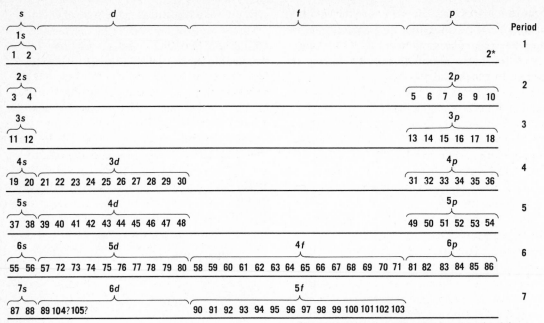

* No. 2 (helium) has no *p* electrons and from that point of view belongs only on the left side of the table — where it is also shown. But it is an inert gas and ends a period just as do the 5 elements below it, and from that point of view belongs here on the right.

Fig. 24-9. Elongated Form of Periodic Table. The elements are identified only by atomic number so that the 4*f* and 5*f* elements can be placed on their proper period lines instead of being removed and placed below the table. This form clarifies certain aspects of the usual table. We can see that the "gaps" within the first five periods are caused by missing subshells: *p*, *d*, and *f* in period 1, *d* and *f* in periods 2 and 3, and *f* in periods 4 and 5. We see the relationships of the two kinds of transition series elements to the rest of the table, one kind with *d* electrons in their next-to-outermost shell (see Figure 24-7) and the other with *f* electrons in their next inner shell (see Figure 24-8).

Examine the periodic table on the inside of the front cover. The period number on the extreme left indicates the number of shells present in the atoms of that period. The vertical rows are the families or groups. The chief families are those marked with a Roman numeral and the letter A. Note that hydrogen is placed in both IA and VIIA (see p. 461 for the special case of hydrogen). Group VIIIA on the right includes all of the monatomic gases. They all have eight electrons in their outermost shells and so close the periods. In some tables group VIIIA is labeled group 0.

Groups IA and IIA have *s* electrons only in their outermost shells. Groups IIIA through VIIIA have both *s* and *p* electrons in their outermost shells. The transition elements in periods 4 and 5 have *d* electrons in their *M* shells but no *f* electrons in their *N* shells. The transition elements in periods 6 and 7 have both *d* electrons in their *M* shells and *f* electrons in their *N* shells. See the key for other information.

Before leaving the building of the elements we should mention that the electrons do not always follow the rules. These anomalies appear in the outer (not outermost) shells beginning in period 4. A glance at the energy level diagram (Fig. 24-5) shows that the energy levels are closer together as more shells are added. In general, as the differences in energy between adjacent shells and subshells become smaller, it becomes more likely that an electron will occupy an orbital out of turn. Thus a $4s$ electron may slip into a $3d$ orbital. Consider copper (Cu), atomic number 29. It lies between nickel and zinc. Compare their electronic configurations. It seems that copper's configuration should be 2, 8, 17, 2. That it isn't is explained by one of the $4s$ electrons slipping into the $3d$ subshell ahead of schedule. The fact that some elements have variable valences is explained in this manner. There are a few other anomalies; we will not consider them here.

You will also note that there are no "holes" in the table. There is no place in it for new elements except at the higher end. The 21 elements at this higher end are all radioactive (which means that they spontaneously change into other elements), and the top 11 do not occur in nature. Consequently, chemists and physicists do not expect to find any new elements here on earth. There is no place to fit new nonradioactive elements into the table. A scientist will not say that discovery of such a new element is impossible. He simply says that the probability of finding such an element is extremely low, say one chance in a hundred trillion. To find one would destroy the foundations of the periodic table; it would make some scientists skeptical about the presence of law and order in the universe. Consider, too, the fact that the spectra of many thousands of stars reveal only elements that we have already identified here on earth, and you should be ready to agree with the scientist that the probability of discovering new naturally occurring elements is about as close to zero as it can get without being zero. Read again "The Role of Probability" in Chapter 10.

Atomic Sizes

Contrary to expectations, the sizes of atoms do not increase as their masses increase. In fact, the mass of the nucleus by itself has no effect on the radii of atoms, for even in the heaviest atoms the nucleus occupies only a minute fraction of the atomic volume. Of greatest importance is the charge on the nucleus, for as the charge increases the electrons are pulled in closer, thus reducing the radius. With the addition of more shells, however, there is some increase in size. Atomic size is a periodic function. It decreases in each period, then increases at the rare gas.

Electron Configurations and Periodicities in the Periodic Table

Before the development of the Bohr-Sommerfeld theory we might have guessed that the reason for the similarity in physical and chemical properties of members of the same family, for example, the alkali metals or the halogens, was their similarities in atomic structure. The experimental evidence for these similarities in atomic structure came from the long and arduous labor of spectroscopists working on atomic spectra. Some of the electronic configurations are shown in Table 24-8.

Hydrogen, although not a member of family IA, is placed at the head of it because its electronic configuration fits here. All members of this family have one electron in the outermost shell, those of IIA have two, those of VIIA have seven, and those of VIIIA have eight (except for helium). This is the only similarity that applies to *all* members of the same family, and at the same time is a way in which the family is different from other main families. It is reasonable to suppose then

Table 24-8
Electronic Configurations of Four Main Families

Alkali metals family IA		Alkaline earth metals family IIA		Halogens family VIIA		Inert gases family VIIIA	
* H	1					He	2
Li	2, 1	Be	2, 2	F	2, 7	Ne	2, 8
Na	2, 8, 1	Mg	2, 8, 2	Cl	2, 8, 7	A	2, 8, 8
K	2, 8, 8, 1	Ca	2, 8, 8, 2	Br	2, 8, 8, 7	Kr	2, 8, 18, 8
Rb	2, 8, 18, 8, 1	Ba	2, 8, 18, 8, 2	I	2, 8, 18, 8, 7	Xe	2, 8, 18, 18, 8
Cs	2, 8, 18, 18, 8, 1	Sr	2, 8, 18, 18, 8, 2	At	2, 8, 18, 18, 8, 7	Rn	2, 8, 18, 32, 18, 8
Fr	2, 8, 18, 32, 18, 8, 1	Ra	2, 8, 18, 32, 18, 8, 2				

* Not an alkali metal.

that the essential character of the elements within a family must be determined by the number of electrons in the outermost shell. The other shells seem to make a difference in degree only, not in kind.

This analysis of the electronic configurations of the various kinds of atoms has several satisfying results. Chief among them is the emergence of certain regularities in electronic arrangements that permit us to demonstrate correlations between these regularities and the periodicities of the periodic chart, and, finally, between these regularities and periodicities on the one hand and the chemical properties of atoms on the other. Once these relationships are understood, the fundamental mysteries of chemical reactions disappear. We should constantly bear in mind that the electronic configurations of the atoms have been determined by experimental evidence, evidence acquired through the study of atomic spectra and by measurement of ionization potentials. By use of the Bohr theory, by use of the knowledge gained from the study of spectra and ionization potentials, and by use of a knowledge of certain chemical properties of the elements, for example, valence, we have been able to deduce the structure of atoms. We shall now turn things around and see if we can use the structure of atoms to explain their chemical and physical properties.

Exercises

1. Mendeleev's periodic law and the periodic table played a role in the research that finally revealed knowledge of the structure of atoms. What was it?
2. What is Pauli's exclusion principle, and why was it necessary?
3. What is (a) an orbital, and (b) a subshell?
4. (a) How many electrons may occupy the same orbital?
   (b) If more than one, how do they differ?
5. Electrons will enter empty orbitals in a particular subshell rather than orbitals containing one electron. Why?
6. (a) Structurally what do all the rare (monatomic) gases have in common?
   (b) The alkali metals?
   (c) The elements in the third family?
7. (a) Structurally how do the elements within a family differ?
   (b) In what was are they similar?
8. The structure of sodium may be indicated as follows: Na (2, 8, 8, 1). Explain.
9. How are atomic numbers related to atomic weights?
10. State Mendeleev's periodic law.
11. In the following statements cross out the incorrect term in each set of parentheses:
    (a) In the periods metallic properties (increase, decrease) from left to right.

(b) In the families they (increase, decrease) (upward, downward).

12. A particular atom has an N shell. What other shells *must* it have?

13. We realize that the wave mechanical model of any atom forbids the shell-like arrangement of electrons that is so commonly used to portray atoms. Why, then, do we portray them that way?

14. (a) The most reactive metals are found in which part of the periodic table?

(b) The most reactive nonmetals?

15. What is a metalloid?

16. What is (are) the difference(s) in atomic structure between a sodium ion and an atom of neon?

17. The first indications worthy of note that atoms had to be divisible came from the study of _____ _____.

18. What role did Faraday's ions play in the recognition of the divisibility of atoms?

The Nature of Chemical Bonds

We have dealt at some length with the arrangement of electrons in atoms because no understanding of chemical reactions is possible without this knowledge. In the 150 years following the laying of the foundations of modern chemistry by Lavoisier an enormous amount of factual data had been accumulated, chiefly by empirical means, for the basic understanding was missing. Chemists from Mendeleev on struggled to correlate the physical and chemical properties of the elements and to tabulate the periodicities in the periodic chart, but without an adequate theory to guide them there could be no understanding of the underlying order. With Rutherford's theory (1911) that atoms consisted of positively charged nuclei having negatively charged electrons circling them, with Bohr's theory (1912) and its later modifications, which described the behavior of electrons in terms of quantum numbers and determinable amounts of energy, and, finally, with the wave mechanical theory, it became possible for the theoreticians to attack the basic problems of chemical affinity with some chance of success.

The theoreticians had to correlate atomic

> Every new theory . . . believes that it is the fortunate theory to achieve the right answer . . . .
> P. W. BRIDGMAN
> (Nobel Prize, Physics, 1946)

446

structures with chemical reactions; they had to explain the nature of the chemical bond, and along with it, valence. The realization that the arrangement of the elements in the periodic table was a consequence of their atomic structures was the greatest possible step forward that could be imagined. Logic indicated that the nature of the chemical bond would naturally follow, and with it the details of chemical reactions. Other phenomena, such as valence, the distinction between metals and nonmetals, and the reasons for other physical properties of masses of atoms should also be correlated with atomic structure. The success or failure of any theory of atomic structure would necessarily stand on its ability satisfactorily to explain these phenomena.

These phenomena were fairly well explained in the period between the two world wars, after the essential data concerning electronic configuration had been accumulated and the interpretations had been made. Atoms obviously combine to form molecules because of some kind of affinity for one another, but this is in no sense an explanation, any more than is the statement that objects fall to the earth when dropped because of gravitational affinity.

The first step toward basic understanding came when the great American chemist G. N. Lewis (1875–1946) suggested that atoms of elements other than those of the monatomic gases would be more stable if they could somehow acquire eight electrons in their outer shells. This hypothesis obviously assumes that it is the presence of eight electrons (two for helium)[1] in the outer shells of the inert gases that accounts for their chemical stability.

The Chemical Bond

What the chemists once referred to as the chemical affinity of one atom for another, we now call the *chemical bond. The chemical bond is formally defined as the attractions between two atoms within a molecule,* attractions in part electrical, in part magnetic. Note carefully that only two atoms are involved and those atoms must be in a molecule.

What Is a Molecule?

To define a molecule is easier said than done. The word (L., little mass) refers, in general, to the individual (discrete) particles characteristic of any type of matter. Most scientists, and the chemists in particular, prefer a more precise definition. We will define it here as the *smallest discrete unit of any compound or of any elemental gas that can exist in nature and still retain the properties of the compound or elemental gas.* There are five elemental diatomic gases—hydrogen, oxygen, nitrogen, fluorine, and chlorine—and six elemental monatomic gases—helium, neon, argon, krypton, xenon, and radon. The smallest discrete particle of carbon dioxide consists of three atoms, that of solid sulfur consists of an aggregate of eight sulfur atoms, and that of aspirin consists of an aggregate of 21 atoms. Each of the above units is called a *molecule.*

In the case of ionic compounds such as NaCl, there are no simple aggregates consisting of a few atoms each. In any single crystal all the atoms of both sodium and chlorine are bound into one giant aggregate. Each chlorine atom is surrounded by six sodium atoms and each sodium atom is surrounded by six chlorine atoms. The consequence is that the attractions between sodium and chlorine atoms are not localized; each chlorine atom has some attraction for each of the six sodium atoms around it, and each sodium atom has some attraction for each of the six chlorine atoms around it. Only in the discrete vapor state is a chlorine atom bonded to one sodium atom; only then can the term molecule be used to apply to them. Strictly speaking, the term

[1] From now on we are going to include helium as an atom with a stable "octet," although its octet is actually a duet. This will save us needless repetition.

molecule cannot apply to any of these aggregates in which there is no pair or other small group of ions that can be called a molecule. The chemical formulas of salts and of a great many minerals that compose many rocks of the earth's crust do not indicate molecules but simply indicate the atomic ratios in the aggregates, for example, SiO_2. Thus it is seen that a precise definition of a molecule is somewhat difficult (see footnote 6, p. 514).

Electrons in Molecules

There are two general approaches to the difficult problem of describing electrons in molecules. One recognizes that each electron belongs to the molecule as a whole. The other assumes that atoms in a molecule are much like single atoms outside the molecule except that one or more electrons from the outer shell of one atom are accommodated in the outer shell of the other atom. This latter view is much simpler to use than the former and can be justified at any level; it has been, and still is, a very useful concept. Therefore we shall assume that molecules can be described in terms of individual atoms whose outer electron shells have reacted. We have defined *valence* as a measure of the combining capacity of atoms. In general, valence is the number of bonds that an atom can form with other atoms. We will rarely use the word valence by itself, but will speak of valence electrons or valence shell.

Some Rules of Chemical Bonding

We will present only one theory in anything like a formal form. No one theory can unify all the facts, observations, and concepts for all chemical reactions. However, most chemists can agree on the following:

1. The only electrons involved in common chemical reactions are those in the outermost shell. These are called the valence electrons.
2. The chemical properties of an element are determined by the number and arrangement of its electrons.
3. Electronic structures of monatomic gases are, in general, the most stable structures.
4. The above rules have occasional exceptions.

Types of Bonding

Electronic theories of chemical bonding have not been itemized assumption by assumption in the manner of many theories heretofore presented. Therefore we will not attempt to present them that way. In general, there are three types of bonding that are believed to exist: ionic, covalent, and metallic. The metallic type applies to metallic bonding in metallic crystals; we will discuss it in the appropriate place in the chapter on the solid state (Chapter 26, p. 473). You should know what a theory is by this time; you should realize that an electronic theory of chemical bonding is an explanation of the observed behavior of electrons in atoms in terms of a simple model that has familiar properties. The observations are "explained" but only in terms of simpler or more familiar phenomena that make them more plausible than they would be otherwise. In any case theories that are valid must be able to answer many broad questions: for example, Why do atoms react with one another? What causes the reactions? Why is a particular result obtained? Valid theories should explain the physical and chemical properties of various groups of elements, and, in some cases, of individual elements, for example, hydrogen.

Before proceeding to find the answer to these questions, and to others, in the theories that have been formulated to answer them, we will need to do a little preparatory work.

H·							·He·
Li·	·Be·	·Ḃ·	·Ċ·	·N̈:	·Ö:	·F̈:	:N̈e:
Na·	·Mg·	·Äl·	·Ṡi·	·P̈:	S̈:	·C̈l:	:Är:

Fig. 25-1. Dot Formulas of Atoms of First Three Periods. The dots represent the number of electrons in the outer shell only. Note that in atoms with 5, 6, 7, or 8 electrons in the outer shell, pairs of electrons appear except in the case of oxygen. Oxygen has two unpaired electrons—which means that these two have the same spin and give oxygen magnetic properties.

Dot System of Notation

We find it desirable to make a brief digression here in order to introduce a useful method of picturing electron transfer and electron sharing before and after a chemical reaction. This system was made possible by the realization that it was only the electrons in the outer shells of atoms that played a role in chemical reactions. The nucleus of the atom together with whatever inner shells there may be is conveniently called the *kernel;* it is represented by the symbol of the element. Dots, arranged singly or in pairs, represent the electrons, lone or paired, in the outermost shell; that is, they represent the valence electrons. The atoms of the first three periods are represented below by the dot system. Note that all members of the same family have the same number of dots. This follows from the fact that the number of dots represents the number of *s* and *p* (if any) electrons in the valence shell. Some examples of molecules written in this system are shown in Fig. 25-1.

Ionization Energy, Electron Affinity, and Electronegativity

These three concepts—ionization energy, electron affinity, and electronegativity—are useful, in varying degrees, in discussing the underlying principles of chemical reactions by electron transfer, as in electrovalent compounds (p. 451), and by electron sharing, as in covalent compounds (p. 453).

Some aspects of *ionization energy* have already been considered on pp. 395–396. In chemical reactions we are concerned with its use as an aid to the understanding of the creation of positive ions. The equations for the formation of positive sodium and magnesium ions from neutral atoms are as follows:

$$Na· \quad - \quad e^- \quad \rightarrow \quad Na^+$$

$$·Mg· \quad - \quad 2e^- \quad \rightarrow \quad Mg^{2+}$$

The ionization energy is the energy required to remove the most loosely bound electron from an atom in the vapor phase. If the removal is made by electrical means, the required voltage is called the ionization potential, and the ionization energy is expressed in electron volts. We may also speak of the ionization potential or energy of the second electron, or of the third electron, and so on. The ionization energy of the electrons in the outer shells of elements that lose electrons in chemical reactions is a measure of the readiness of these elements to react. Some nonmetals gain electrons to form negative ions. Equations for the process are as follows:

$$:Cl· \quad + \quad e^- \quad \rightarrow \quad :Cl:^-$$

$$:O: \quad + \quad 2e^- \quad \rightarrow \quad :O:^{2-}$$

It can be seen that these atoms have a tendency to gain electrons rather than to lose them, so their ionization energies are not as pertinent as their ability to attract electrons to themselves. The term *electron affinity* is applied to atoms that have a high tendency to pick up additional electrons. It is defined as the energy released when an electron is added to a "gaseous" neutral atom to form an ion. It is a measure of an atom's electron-attracting ability. To know the readiness of two atoms to react and the type of bond they would form, it would be advantageous to know both the ionization potential and the electron affinity. The ionization potential is easily measured (pp. 396 and 398), but unfortunately the electron affinities of only a very few elements have been measured.

By measuring various properties of atoms it is possible to arrange atoms in the order of their tendency to attract electrons. A table to show this order is called a scale of *electronegativity* (Table 25-1). The concept of electronegativity applies to all atoms, even to those with a greater tendency to lose than to gain electrons. It is reasonable to expect that atoms that hold their electrons most firmly should have the greatest tendency to gain another one,

Table 25-1
Electronegativities of Some Elements*

IA	IIA	IIIB	IVB		IIB	IIIA	IVA	VA	VIA	VIIA	VIIIA
1											2
H											He
2.1											
3	4					5	6	7	8	9	10
Li	Be					B	C	N	O	F	Ne
1.0	1.5					2.0	2.5	3.0	3.5	4.0	
11	12					13	14	15	16	17	18
Na	Mg					Al	Si	P	S	Cl	Ar
0.9	1.2					1.5	1.8	2.1	2.5	3.0	
19	20	21	22		30	31	32	33	34	35	36
K	Ca	Sc	Ti		Zn	Ga	Ge	As	Se	Br	Kr
0.8	1.0	1.3	1.5		1.6	1.6	1.8	2.0	2.4	2.8	
37	38	39	40		48	49	50	51	52	53	54
Rb	Sr	Y	Zr		Cd	In	Sn	Sb	Te	I	Xe
0.8	1.0	1.2	1.4		1.7	1.7	1.8	1.9	2.1	2.5	
55	56	57	72		80	81	82	83	84	85	86
Cs	Ba	La	Hf		Hg	Tl	Pb	Bi	Po	At	Rn
0.7	0.9	1.1	1.3		1.9	1.8	1.8	1.9	2.0	2.2	
87	88	89									
Fr	Ra	Ac									
0.7	0.9	1.1									

*The number above the element symbol is the atomic number; the number below it is electronegativity on the Pauling scale.

and those that lose electrons most easily should have the least tendency. It should also be apparent that those elements with the highest ionization energies have the highest electronegativity.

The element with the greatest tendency to gain electrons is assigned a value of 4.0 on the electronegativity scale. Cesium, the least electronegative of the naturally occurring elements, is assigned a value of 0.7 (Table 25-1).

The electronegativity scale is useful for predicting which bonds are ionic (electrovalent) and which are covalent. Atoms with many shells have valence electrons relatively far from their nuclei, and so are expected to have lower electronegativities than elements in the same family that have fewer shells. Therefore, electronegativities decrease downward in a family. Increasing charge on the nuclei of atoms with the same number of shells increases the electronegativities. Therefore, electronegativities increase within a period—except for the rare gases. We can predict that the elements cesium and fluorine with the greatest disparity in their electronegativities of all reactive elements ($4.0 - 0.7 = 3.3$) should form strongly ionic bonds. Conversely, we can predict that elements with a small disparity in their electronegativities will form covalent bonds. The polarity of covalent bonds can also be predicted, for the greater the disparity, the more polar the bond. We will find ample use for the concept later.[2]

Ionic Bonds

Once one accepts the existence of ions as atoms that have lost or gained one, two, or three electrons and so are electrically charged, it is not difficult to apply the laws of elec-

trostatics to them. The positive and negative ions are easily visualized as being held together in pairs or groups because of the electrostatic attractions between unlike charges.

Ionic valence[3] is the number of electrons that a neutral atom in the IA through VIIA families (groups) gains or loses in attaining a rare gas configuration. The metals lose electrons, yielding positive ions; the nonmetals gain electrons, yielding negative ions. Thus, atoms with configurations of 2, 8, 1 and 2, 8, 8, 2 can attain the 2, 8 and 2, 8, 8 configurations of neon and argon, respectively, by the loss of one and two electrons, respectively. Also, fluorine, 2, 7, must gain one electron to attain the configuration of neon, 2, 8, and oxygen, with a configuration of 2, 6, must gain two. Experiments show that elements that are close together in the periodic table have little or no tendency to form ions[4] when they combine.

Chemical Reactions by Electron Transfer

As we have already seen, the alkali metals (group IA) react readily with the halogens (group VIIA). Each atom of the alkali metals has one electron in its outermost shell. If each were to transfer this lone electron to another element, thereby becoming a positive ion, it would have the electronic configuration of the rare gas just preceding it in the periodic table. Thus the sodium *ion* would have the configuration of the neon *atom,* the potassium *ion* would have that of the argon *atom,* and so on. All members of the family have a valence of +1 because each transfers one electron per atom.

[2] Yet electronegativity by itself is not always an adequate criterion for predicting the bond type and the properties of compounds. There are a few exceptions.

[3] The word *electrovalence* is sometimes used in place of ionic valence.

[4] How ionic a compound is can often be tested by passing an electric current through it in solution. Pure acids are nonionic, but their water solutions are ionic. Only ionic solutions conduct electric currents, and the more strongly ionic they are the better they conduct it.

The halogens each have seven electrons in their outermost shells, one short of the stable octet, and so have a valence of -1. If an atom of a halogen acquires another electron, thereby becoming a negative ion, it would have the electronic configuration of the monatomic gas nearest it in the periodic table. Thus, the fluoride *ion* would have the configuration of the neon *atom,* and the chloride *ion* would have that of the argon *atom,* etc.

A typical reaction can be written as follows:

$$\text{Na·} + \text{·Cl:} \rightarrow \text{Na}^+ \text{:Cl:}^-$$

Note that all of the valence electrons are around the chlorine ion; the lone sodium electron has joined the seven electrons of chlorine

to make a stable octet. The sodium ion is also surrounded by eight electrons (as in neon, the preceding element), but the dot system does not show this because these electrons are not in the valence shell of the sodium atom.

If magnesium, with two electrons in its valence shell, combines with chlorine to form $MgCl_2$, one atom of it combines with two atoms of chlorine. In order to attain the configuration of the nearest inert gas (neon), magnesium must transfer two electrons per atom. Since a chlorine atom has seven electrons in its valence shell, it can accept only one more in attaining the stable octet, and so each of two chlorine atoms takes one electron from magnesium. Magnesium and all other members of its family have two valence elec-

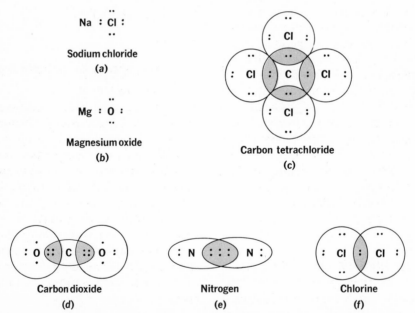

Sodium chloride
(a)

Magnesium oxide
(b)

Carbon tetrachloride
(c)

Carbon dioxide
(d)

Nitrogen
(e)

Chlorine
(f)

Fig. 25-2. Attainment of Stable Octets. (*a* and *b*) By transfer of electrons from a metal to a nonmetal. Only the electrons in the outer shell are transferred. Sodium has transferred one to chlorine; magnesium, two to oxygen. Both metals are left with the configuration of neon, the monatomic gas at the end of the preceding period. The octet about them is not shown because in the dot system of notation only the outermost electrons are shown. (*c* and *d*) By electron sharing in a compound. Within each circle or ellipse there is an octet. (*e* and *f*) Electron sharing is diatomic gases.

trons. In the dot notation we write the reaction as follows:

$$\cdot Mg \cdot \;+\; \overset{\cdots}{:}\!\overset{\cdots}{Cl}\!:\!\overset{\cdots}{Cl}\!: \;\rightarrow\; :\!\overset{\cdots}{Cl}\!:^{-} \; Mg^{2+} \; :\!\overset{\cdots}{Cl}\!:^{-}$$

See also Fig. 25-2a and b.

Certain questions are in order here, chief among them one concerning the underlying reason for the transfer of electrons from a metallic atom to a nonmetallic one. We have stated that the stable octet configuration is attained for both atoms, but this is no reason at all, for neither atom can "know" that the transfer will result in a stable octet. Electrical and magnetic forces must be involved in one way or another. We are sure that in those reactions in which the net result is a liberation of energy, the energy state of the system is lower than before the reaction. That ions are formed in electron transfer reactions is easily confirmed by passing an electric current through either a water solution of the compound, or the molten compound. Such compounds form one class of ionic compounds. All chemical reactions between members of families IA and IIA on the one hand and the halogens on the other result in the formation of ionic compounds. There are many other examples.

In order to form an ionic compound from two atoms, the electron-attracting ability of one must be sufficiently greater than that of the other. This is equivalent to saying that the disparity in their electronegativities must be relatively large.

The energy needed to remove one, two, three or more electrons from the outer shell of metallic atoms can be measured. For members of the first two families this amount is not prohibitively high, so these elements almost always form compounds by electron transfer. For the third family the energy needed to remove three electrons so as to form ions approaches this prohibitive value, so that

many of their compounds are not ionic. Members of the fourth family with four electrons to be removed in order to ionize them almost never form ions by electron transfer.

Let us look at the last two reactions from the electronegativity standpoint. Sodium has an electronegativity of 0.9 and chlorine one of 3.0. The disparity between them is rather large so that we might expect from what has been said about electronegativity that they would react vigorously and form ionic bonds. Hot melted sodium brought into contact with concentrated chlorine bursts into flame to form common table salt. Magnesium has an electronegativity of 1.2. The disparity between it and chlorine is a bit less than between sodium and chlorine but is still considerable. We would predict that ionic bonds would form and that the reaction would be somewhat less vigorous. Experiments show that the prediction is correct.

Covalent Bonding

It is reasonable to expect that two atoms of oxygen, or of any other diatomic elemental gas, cannot be held together by ionic attractions, for any two atoms of the same element have the same electron-holding ability. They have the same electronegativities. Neither can take an electron away from the other. Yet two atoms of oxygen *do* unite to form molecules, and this tendency is so strong that the elemental gases (other than the monatomic gases) do not exist free as discrete atoms but are paired up to form molecules. Clearly there is more to bonding than ionic bonding.

G. N. Lewis, therefore, introduced the concept of the covalent bond. This bond is an electron-pair bond; it involves the sharing of pairs of electrons rather than their transfer, and it applies particularly (but by no means exclusively) to the elements that are close together in the periodic table. The number of covalent bonds formed is equal to the number of shared electron pairs. The ability to form covalent bonds is spread throughout the whole of the periodic table; it is especially characteristic of elements forming organic compounds. Each of the atoms involved in the sharing usually contributes one electron to each pair; *each pair constitutes a single bond.* In each pair, the two electrons have opposite spins.

For example, the carbon atom, with four valence electrons, may share them with the single valence electrons of four chlorine atoms to form carbon tetrachloride, CCl_4:

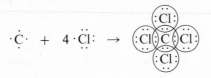

Note that there are eight electrons inside each circle. Thus, each kernel is surrounded by eight electrons. The shared pairs are shown in the overlapping areas of the circles. None of the atoms has an exclusive right to eight electrons; in fact, the carbon atom has an exclusive right to none. Instead it has a half interest in eight electrons. See also Fig. 25-2d, e, and f.

It might seem that a half interest in eight electrons is equivalent to a full interest in four, and so it also might seem that the carbon atom has not gained anything. Yet the chemical reaction has taken place, and therefore it seems that a closer approximation to the stable octet has been attained.

Diatomic Elemental Gases: A Case of Electron Sharing

We remember how the problem of the common chemically active elemental gases (hydrogen, oxygen, nitrogen, chlorine, and fluo-rine) bothered the chemists for decades. The problem had been solved by Avogadro (but his explanation was not accepted for more than 40 years) when he suggested that these gases probably existed as double atoms (molecules) instead of single atoms and that these double atoms broke up on entering chemical combination. How can we explain these facts by the present theory of atomic structure?

They are easily explained if we consider the joining together of two atoms of these gases as a simple case of chemical union by the sharing of electrons. The details of this union are best illustrated by use of the dot system:

$$H:H \qquad :\overset{..}{F}:\overset{..}{F}: \qquad :\overset{..}{Cl}:\overset{..}{Cl}: \qquad :N:::N:$$

Note that the two atoms in both fluorine and chlorine molecules share one pair of electrons, whereas in the nitrogen molecule three pairs are shared. The sharing in these gases is exactly equal (see Fig. 25-2e and f) for the electronegativity of each atom is the same, so that the disparity is zero. Thus, the bond is completely nonpolar. That energy is released when any two of these atoms combine to form a molecule, just as when different kinds of atoms combine, is proved by the fact that energy is needed to separate them.

Polar and Nonpolar Bonds and Molecules

In our discussion of ionic and covalent bonds in the last few pages we limited our discussion to those cases that are essentially (but not necessarily wholly) one or the other, and avoided those that grade one into the other. In other words, we treated those cases in which there is a relatively great disparity in the electronegativities of the atoms involved, and those in which the disparity is zero. We will now deal with those cases in which there is a small to moderate disparity in electro-negativities. If we examine the electronega-tivities of carbon and chlorine (Table 25-1), we see that the disparity between them is rela-tively small (0.5). From this fact we are able to reach the conclusion that there is little tend-ency to transfer electrons. The bonds between carbon and chlorine will, however, be polar because chlorine, with its higher electronega-tivity, will hold the shared pair of electrons a bit more closely than will the carbon atom. The molecule of CCl_4 will, however, be non-polar because the centers of positive and neg-ative charge are both at the same point; that is, the distribution of charge is symmetrical. Carbon tetrachloride is then a case in which *a nonpolar molecule has polar bonds.*

The bond in a molecule of an elemental diatomic gas is nonpolar, for each atom has the same electron-attracting ability. Perfect sharing results in such nonpolar molecules. Molecules of the elemental diatomic gases, along with Br_2 and I_2, are the only nonpolar molecules with nonpolar bonds. If a molecule consists of only *two* atoms and these are of different elements, the bond between them is always polar to some extent, and the resulting molecule must be polar. An example is HCl in which the bond is covalent. The disparity in electronegativities is 0.9, with the chlorine having the higher one. The chlorine atom therefore holds the pair of shared electrons more forcefully than does the hydrogen atom. (This is related to the fact that chlorine has 17 positive charges on its nucleus, hydrogen only 1.) This closer holding of the shared pair of electrons makes the chlorine "end" of the molecule somewhat negative and leaves the hydrogen end somewhat positive, making the molecule polar. Thus we have a polar molecule with polar bonds. This type of molecule may be called a *dipole*. It may be represented on occasion as $(+ \quad -)$. Nevertheless, the mole-cule as a whole is electrically neutral. The

wave mechanical theory would express this closer holding by saying that the probability of finding the electrons close to the chlorine nucleus is greater than that of finding them close to the hydrogen nucleus.

Consider two three-atom molecules with two of the atoms the same, CO_2 and H_2O. The differences in the electronegativities of C and O on the one hand and H and O on the other suggest that the bonds are polar. Symmetry of distribution of charge is possible in three-atom molecules if two of the atoms are the same. Using the dot system of notation, we can write

$$:\overset{..}{O}::C::\overset{..}{O}: \quad\text{and}\quad H:\overset{..}{\underset{..}{O}}:H$$

The properties of CO_2 indicate that the mole-cule is indeed nonpolar; but the properties of water indicate that it is polar—the charge can-not be symmetrically distributed as shown. It is therefore said to be polar covalent. We indi-cate this by writing the formula of water by the dot system as shown in Fig. 25-3a (see also p. 469).

Nonpolar molecules will neither conduct an electric current when in the liquid phase or in an aqueous solution nor orient themselves in an electric field. Polar molecules in similar states will not conduct an electric current, but they will orient themselves in an electric field.

Our examples have all been taken from the nonmetals. Now let us take one in which at least one of the atoms in the "molecule" is a metal, say cesium fluoride (CsF). The disparity in electronegativities is 3.3, the largest possible between any two naturally occurring atoms. We expect the Cs—F bond to be the most polar of all bonds—and it is. The bond, then, must be an ionic bond. But is it 100% ionic? That depends on the state CsF is in. If it is in the vapor state—the discrete gaseous state— then each atom of cesium is paired up with an atom of fluorine. This means that the cesium atom has not transferred its valence electron completely to the fluorine atom; it still maintains an interest in it, so that it is only about 60% ionic. Contrast this with a dilute water solution of CsF, where the Cs and F atoms completely dissociate into Cs$^+$ and F$^-$ ions that move about independently of each other.

Hydrogen Bonding

Hydrogen "bonding" is peculiar to a very few elements, occurring chiefly between hydrogen and oxygen, fluorine, nitrogen, and sometimes chlorine.

The structure of the water molecule is responsible for the remarkable properties of water. Its structure is asymmetrical, geometrically and electrically (Fig. 25-3). The two shared electron pairs make use of the *p* orbitals of the oxygen atom. These orbitals are normally at right angles to each other. In water,

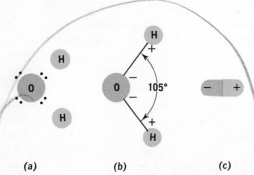

(a)   **(b)**   **(c)**

Fig. 25-3. The Polar Water Molecule. (*a*) The two hydrogen atoms are not symmetric about the oxygen atom. This lack of symmetry leaves the left side (*b*) with a slight residue of negative charge; the right side with a slight residue of positive charge; hence its polarity. (*c*) A simple way of portraying the water molecule—as a dipole. The angular shape of water molecules, plus the fact that the forces are strongest at certain angles, results in ice occupying a greater volume than the same number of molecules of water.

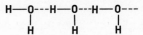

Fig. 25-4. Hydrogen Bonding. The dashed lines represent the hydrogen bonds. Note that the hydrogen bond does not take the place of the two chemical bonds. Although a very weak bond, comparatively, it is present in addition to the normal two bonds with oxygen.

however, the angle is about 105° instead of 90° because the two hydrogen atoms repel each other. Thus the geometrical asymmetry is explained. The electronegativity of oxygen is so much higher than that of hydrogen that each hydrogen gets scarcely more than a quarter of a share in each shared electron pair. Oxygen therefore has about a half-interest in the two shared pairs and each hydrogen has about a quarter interest. This explains the electrical asymmetry; the molecule is highly polar.

For many purposes it is sufficient to describe the water molecule as an electrical dipole, (+ —), as it would be in a linear molecule. However, the angularity of the molecule is such that it has two positive corners (formed by the two hydrogens) and two negative corners (formed by the two unshared pairs of electrons). One result of this geometrical and electrical asymmetry is *hydrogen bonding;* a positive corner of this angular molecule is strongly attracted to a negative corner of another water molecule (Fig. 25-4). Another result is that during freezing the angular molecules cannot be as closely packed in the rigid ice crystal as when they are in the more fluid state. This explains why water expands slightly as it is cooled from 4°C down to 0°C. The lower density of ice compared to water means that ice will float (with important consequences to aquatic life in lakes, rivers, and ponds).

Besides the presence of an H atom, a requisite for hydrogen bonds is a highly electronegative small atom. The hydrogen nucleus is very small, a lone proton, with only one electron. Therefore it can approach far closer to another atom than can any other kind of atom. Hydrogen bonds are not chemical bonds in the same sense as ionic or covalent bonds. Their strength is far less that that of the chemical bond. Nevertheless these "bonds" are important, for they give a substance containing them a considerably higher boiling point than it would have otherwise, and they account for the discordance in properties in comparison with substances in the same family with oxygen, H_2O vs. H_2S, H_2Se, H_2Te. If the boiling point of water followed the trend from He_2Te to H_2S, it would be far nearer $-100°C$ than $100°C$. There would be no water in the liquid state here on earth, and we would not be here to contemplate these phenomena. Hydrogen bonding is important biologically, for it is crucial in determining the structures of nucleic acids (Chapter 29).

Redox (Oxidation-Reduction) Electron Transfer Reactions

Redox, or oxidation-reduction, electron transfer reactions are not any different from other electron transfer reactions as might be implied by our giving them separate treatment. We are merely yielding to historical precedent. There is a certain advantage in doing so, for we now can treat such topics as displacement reactions, the activity (electromotive) series, reactions in current-producing cells, and metallurgy without encumbering our general discussion of chemical reactions by electron transfer and electron-sharing.

Before the electronic theory of chemical bonding was developed, oxidation was defined as the chemical combination of oxygen with other elements. All the common "burning"

processes, whether they involved ordinary combustion, spontaneous combustion, the instantaneous combustion that constitutes one type of explosion, the slower combustion of foods in living animals, or the slow decay of many substances, organic or inorganic, when exposed to the weather, were called *oxidation* if oxides were produced. It became customary to treat reactions of this and the reverse type under the heading of oxidation-reduction.

Many burning processes, however, do not involve oxygen. Sodium will burn brightly in chlorine, powdered zinc will do so with sulfur, and potassium will "burn" in water. There is no significant difference between these cases and the burning of magnesium and steel in oxygen. In all cases there has been a transfer of one or two electrons from the metal to the nonmetal. *Oxidation* is defined as loss of electrons and *reduction* as a gain of electrons.

Oxidation cannot occur without reduction, nor reduction without oxidation. They not only occur simultaneously but always to the same extent. The element that is oxidized is the reducing agent. The metals are oxidized and so they are the reducing agents. Similarly, the nonmetals are reduced and so they are the oxidizing agents. We can say, in general, that metals are reducing agents and nonmetals oxidizing agents.

Consider the reaction

$$Na \ + \ Cl \ \rightarrow \ NaCl$$

This equation is not incorrectly written; it is merely unconventionally written. It is easier to explain when written this way. The conventional way is

$$2Na \ + \ Cl_2 \ \rightarrow \ 2NaCl$$

The sodium atom transfers (loses) an electron and so is oxidized; at the same time the chlorine gains the electron that sodium loses, and so is reduced. The reaction, broken down into half reactions, is as follows:

Oxidation:

$$Na \rightarrow Na^+ + e^-$$

sodium atom   sodium ion   electron

Reduction:

$$Cl + e^- \rightarrow Cl^-$$

chlorine atom   electron   chlorine ion

Adding the two together we get the whole reaction,

$$Na + Cl + e^- \rightarrow Na^+ + Cl^- + e^-$$

Eliminating e^- from both sides,[5]

$$Na + Cl \rightarrow Na^+ + Cl^-$$

Displacement Reactions

The displacement of one metal by another in a solution is a redox reaction. If we place an iron nail in a copper sulfate ($CuSO_4$) solution, we will find that the nail will become coated with copper. Copper sulfate dissolves in water to form ions, a fact that can be checked by passing an electric current through the solution. The valence of the sulfate ion is always -2. Hence the copper ions in the solution have a valence of $+2$. To become an atom a copper ion must gain two electrons. These it obtains from an atom of iron. In the process,

---

[5] The chemist would say that the oxidation number of Na has been increased by one, and that of Cl reduced by one. The concept of oxidation number was developed to deal with the balancing of equations in complex redox reactions. Balanced equations are a necessity for every chemist no matter how complex they are. As nonchemists we will be content to balance simple equations by inspection—as we have already learned in Chapter 16.

the latter becomes a doubly charged positive ion and passes into solution. The copper has taken the place of the iron in the nail. The equation for the reaction is

$$Fe + Cu^{2+} + SO_4^{2-} \rightarrow$$
$$Fe^{2+} + SO_4^{2-} + Cu$$

or more simply,

$$Fe + Cu^{2+} \rightarrow Fe^{2+} + Cu$$

Activity Series. If we wish to find out whether metal A is more or less active than metal B, all we have to do is to place metal A in an ionic solution of a compound of metal B and see if A replaces B. If it does, it is more active than B because it has yielded electrons to B. This method allows us to list metals in a series in the order of activity. Such a series is called an activity series. Hydrogen is also placed in the series (Table 25-2) because it will displace many metals in solution.

Any element in the series will displace any of the others below it in an electrolytic (ionic) solution of the latter. The sequence is in the order of decreasing ability to lose electrons.

Table 25-2
Activity Series for Some of the More
Common Metals (and Hydrogen)

K
Na
Mg
Al
Zn
Fe
Pb
H
Cu
Hg
Ag
Au

Such a series is extremely useful to a chemist because he can tell at a glance the likelihood of many chemical reactions taking place. Redox reactions furnish a precise experimental method of measuring the degree of activity of each of the metals. A similar series may be constructed by the same methods for the non-metals. The degree of activity of the metals is measured by their reducing ability, that of the nonmetals by their oxidizing ability.

Redox Reactions in Current-Producing Cells

Any chemical change that takes place spontaneously liberates energy, which, in theory at least, is capable of being transformed into work. If such changes take place in solutions that are capable of carrying an electric current—that is, if the solutions are electrolytes—then it is possible to obtain the liberated energy in the form of electrical energy. A device that does this is called a voltaic cell. Flashlight batteries are voltaic cells. Solutions of at least two substances, one that can lose electrons and another that can gain them,

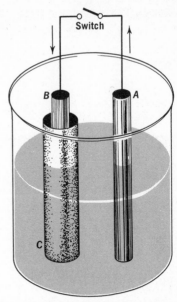

Fig. 25-6. A Liquid Cell. A is a zinc electrode immersed in a Zn^{2+} solution. B is a copper electrode immersed in a porous cup, C, containing Cu^{2+} solution. Electrons are transferred through the wire.

must participate in a redox reaction, and the two substances must not be in contact with each other (Figs. 25-5 and 25-6).

Redox Reactions in Metallurgy

Redox reactions are of great importance in the smelting of ores. An ore is any naturally occurring mineral aggregate from which one or more metals can be extracted *at a profit*. A few metals, for example, gold and platinum, commonly occur in the free, or native, state. The pure metals may be recovered by mechanical methods such as panning, but in almost all ores the metal is in chemical combination in the form of oxides, sulfides, carbonates, and the like. The common ores of iron are Fe_2O_3 (hematite), Fe_3O_4 (magnetite),

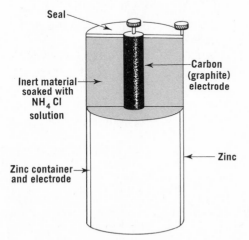

Fig. 25-5. A Common Dry Cell. The upper part is sliced away to show the construction.

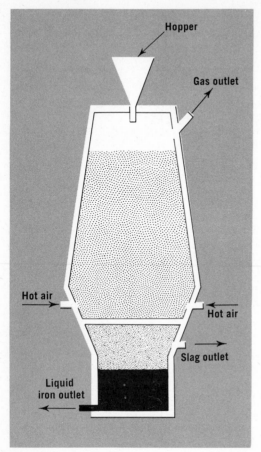

Fig. 25-7. Diagram of a Blast Furnace, Used in the Smelting of Iron. A mixture of iron ore, coke, and limestone is continuously introduced into the furnace via the hopper. A continuous blast of hot air is fed in near the bottom to burn the coke and so reduce the ore. Liquid slag and iron are periodically removed from the bottom.

and $Fe_2O_3 \cdot nH_2O$ (limonite, or hydrated oxide of iron). Other ore minerals are CuO, ZnS, PbS, Ag_2S, CuS, $PbCO_3$, $MnCO_3$. The valuable minerals (do not confuse a mineral with a metal) are commonly associated with more or less (mostly more) worthless minerals, called the gangue minerals, from which they can be separated by mechanical means. However, the separation of the metal from the oxygen, sul-

fur, or carbonate ions, or from other elements, must be done by chemical processes that are grouped under the term *smelting* (Fig. 25-7).

Some metals are very easy to smelt, some very difficult. The first metals known to primitive man were those that occur native, either usually, like gold, or under certain circumstances, like silver and copper. Next came those that were easy to smelt, for example, copper, tin, lead, and much later, iron. The more difficult the smelting process, the later, in general, was the discovery of the metal, and thus the bronze age preceded the iron age.

Many metals may be obtained from their ores by electrolysis. To obtain them the ore must either be in the molten state or in an aqueous solution so that free ions of the metal are present. In the process of electrolysis reduction takes place at the cathode, oxidation at the anode. The most active metals, as we might suspect, are those that are the most difficult and expensive to smelt. Electrolysis can reduce even the most active metals.[6] The process has been described in Chapter 18.

Redox Reactions by Electron Sharing

The commonest of burning processes involve the combining of carbon with oxygen to form CO and CO_2 (preferably CO_2 to reduce the amount of poisonous CO), and the combining of hydrogen with oxygen to form water. Whether we burn wood, coal, paper, gasoline, or oil, all of which contain compounds of hy-

[6] Aluminum, the most abundant metallic element in the earth's crust, used to be prohibitively expensive for most purposes because it resisted all attempts to free it from the oxygen with which it was combined. Molten aluminum oxide does not ionize enough for one to use electrolysis. Adding molten cryolite, a mineral from Greenland, makes it ionize. Electrolysis does the rest. It is still expensive compared to an equal weight of iron, however, as can be seen by the current price of aluminum scrap ($200 per ton vs. about $10 per ton for iron). This is because of the great amount of electrical power needed to produce the aluminum. Thus it is important to recycle aluminum scrap. Return your aluminum beer and soda cans!

drogen and carbon, the following reactions, in which covalent bonds are formed, take place:

$$C \;+\; \underset{\substack{\text{nonpolar}\\\text{covalent}\\\text{molecule}}}{O_2} \;\rightarrow\; \underset{\substack{\text{nonpolar}\\\text{covalent}\\\text{molecule}}}{CO_2}$$

$$\underset{\substack{\text{nonpolar}\\\text{covalent}\\\text{molecules}}}{2H_2} \;+\; \underset{\substack{\text{nonpolar}\\\text{covalent}\\\text{molecule}}}{O_2} \;\rightarrow\; \underset{\substack{\text{polar}\\\text{covalent}\\\text{molecules}}}{2H_2O}$$

The Special Case of Hydrogen

In the first period hydrogen seems to occupy the place of a metal. In fact, it has the electronic configuration of a metal, one electron in its one and only shell. It is unique among the elements in that it is the only one with no neutrons in the nucleus. Furthermore, its chief combining ability is with the nonmetals. On the other hand, it has a higher ionization energy than any of the metals; it does not conduct electricity as they do, even when it is liquefied; it does not generally give up an electron when it enters into chemical combination, but, instead, it shares electrons; it reacts with many metals to form hydrides as do the nonmetals to form chlorides and so forth; its compounds with the nonmetals are not salts as are most simple compounds of metals and nonmetals; its physical properties are wholly nonmetallic.

Hydrogen has, then, a curious mixture of metallic and nonmetallic properties. It appears to be a one-element family for which there is no proper place in the periodic chart; different charts show it in different places. Let us look again at its electronic configuration. Take away its lone electron and a bare proton is left. It is then a positive ion (H^+) like the metallic ions. However, unlike the metals, it does not then have the configuration of a monatomic gas, but when it combines with a nonmetal such as chlorine, it has the configuration of the monatomic gas helium, thus; $H\!:\!\overset{\cdot\cdot}{\underset{\cdot\cdot}{Cl}}\!:$. The positive ion (proton) does not exist in a true chemical sense. It can, however, attach itself to a water molecule forming the hydronium ion, H_3O^+ (Chapter 27). It can also form a negative ion by gaining another electron through reacting with metals, forming compounds known as *hydrides*. Hydrides are easily broken up because hydrogen does not have much ability to retain the electron that the metal gave up. Thus H^- does not exist as a separate ion as do Cl^-, F^-, and so on. Hydrogen has a high ionization energy, nearly three times that of some of the alkali metals, and so does not easily give up its valence electron. Having little ability to attract other electrons and a relatively high ability to retain the one it has, it reacts chemically by sharing electrons. Thus, the unusual properties of hydrogen are explained by its electronic structure.

Monatomic Gases

The monatomic gases all have eight electrons in their outer shells, except helium, which has only two. They were once considered to be completely inert but recently xenon, krypton, and radon were found to combine with fluorine (the most active nonmetal) and oxygen to form compounds that were not all unstable. Their general antisocial behavior causes them to be the only monatomic gases,[7] even down to very low temperatures. All atoms that do not have eight (two for helium) electrons in their outer shells are chemically active to a greater degree than those that do. All this seems to mean that the atoms of the monatomic gases have the most perfect stability possible for atoms of any kind.

[7] Mercury vapor consists of monatomic molecules.

Bonding in Metals and Nonmetals

The distinctions between metals and nonmetals present a number of problems that any fruitful theory of chemical bonding must be able to explain. In the periodic table why does the line of division between the metals and nonmetals slant downward to the right? We might reason as follows: Metals lose their valence electrons far more easily than nonmetals. Atoms with many shells hold their valence electrons less tightly than do atoms with fewer shells because of greater distance from the nucleus. The same line of reasoning explains why metallicity increases downward in a family. Consider group IV. A nonmetal, carbon, has 2 shells. Below it is silicon, a metalloid, with 3 shells; below it is germanium, more of a metal, with 4 shells; and below it two undoubted metals, tin and lead, with 5 and 6 shells, respectively. All have 4 electrons in their outermost energy levels. Stable octets could be acquired if each transferred 4 electrons to other atoms, or the octets could be acquired if each shared its 4 electrons with other atoms. Actually carbon and silicon atoms share their 4 to form covalent bonds, and lead and tin transfer theirs to form ionic bonds. Germanium, in the middle, favors covalent bonds. The difference in bonding is reflected in their melting points, ranging downward from 3500°C for carbon to 1420°C for Si, 959°C for Ge, 232°C for Sn, and 327°C for Pb.

Metals have almost no tendency to combine with one another[8] but combine readily with most nonmetals. The reason in the case of metals is that stable octets cannot be formed by electron transfer. No metal has sufficiently high electronegativity to take electrons away from any other metal. Ionization energies of

metals are, in general, low because they hold their valence electrons loosely, some of them so loosely that low energy photons can remove them in the photoelectric effect. Others take high energy photons in the ultraviolet range, but the nonmetals hold their electrons so tightly that it takes X rays or gamma rays to remove electrons from them (p. 378). A parallel situation exists in thermionic emission, except that it is heat (kinetic) energy that ejects the loosely held electrons. If we remember that an electric current consists of a flow of electrons in a conductor, and that a potential difference between the two ends of a conductor causes a current to flow, it is apparent that the current will flow most easily in conductors where the electrons are held most loosely. Thus, conductivity decreases as we proceed from metals with one outer or valence electron to those with more. The valence electrons in the nonmetals are held so tightly that it takes a potential difference of many thousands or even tens of thousands of volts to make them move appreciably in a linear direction. Thus, most nonmetals make good insulators.

The Molecular Orbital Theory of Covalent Bonding

Important to the understanding of the wave mechanical theory is the molecular orbital theory.[9] This theory considers the molecule as a whole. It uses the idea of orbitals characteristic of the molecule, not of the individual atoms. It adopts the view that chemical bonds can form if two one-electron clouds can overlap to form a single electron cloud with a greater density of charge. In other words, when two atoms combine to form a molecule, each atom introduces electrons into the orbitals of the other. This process is referred to as the

---

[8] We exempt from our discussion certain alloys.

[9] Robert S. Mulliken of the United States won the 1966 Nobel Prize for Chemistry for his work on this theory.

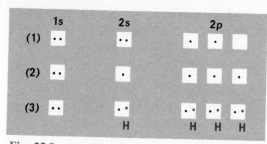

Fig. 25-8. Hybridized Molecular Orbitals in the Methane Molecule. In (1) we show the ground state distribution of the orbitals in carbon. A problem arises: How can the combining of four hydrogen atoms with carbon be explained by the molecular orbital theory when there are only two half-filled orbitals to overlap? Carbon and hydrogen must be well heated before they will combine. This heat raises carbon atoms to the excited state; that is, in terms of the Bohr theory, some electrons enter higher energy states. This is shown in (2), where a 2s electron has absorbed enough energy to transfer to a 2p orbital. We now have four half-filled orbitals. These can now overlap the four half-filled orbitals of four hydrogen atoms, forming sp^3 hybrid bonds (3). They are called that because one s and three p bonds are involved. These overlapping electron clouds supplied by the carbon atom and the hydrogen atoms are called molecular orbitals. They bind the hydrogen atoms and the carbon atom into the methane (CH_4) molecule. The four molecular orbitals are directed toward the four corners of a regular tetrahedron.

overlapping of electron clouds. The formation of a hydrogen molecule from two hydrogen atoms can be used to illustrate the process. The two one-electron clouds, one from each hydrogen atom, approach each other closely so that the two clouds overlap.

We used hydrogen as our example because it is the simplest case possible. Each atom has only one electron in the K shell whose only orbital[10] is a 1s orbital, and that is only half-

---

[10]We need to remember that orbitals are of four types (s, p, d, and f), that the first shell (K) has only one s orbital, the second shell (L) and the third shell (M) each have one s and three p orbitals, and so on, and that an orbital is filled when occupied by two electrons.

filled. In a sense, the overlapping and sharing fills them both, and so it is easy to see why hydrogen is diatomic.

Now consider helium, a monatomic gas. Its K shell has two electrons; that is, the single 1s orbital in the K shell has two electrons in it and so is filled. In a collision between two helium atoms there can be no interaction, no transfer or sharing of electrons, because there are no empty or partially filled K shell orbitals to overlap. So, helium is a monatomic gas. We will explore this theory no further except for the case of hybridized molecular orbitals shown in Fig. 25-8.

Exercises

1. What is meant by a chemical bond?
2. Distinguish between ionic valence and covalence.
3. Distinguish between polar and nonpolar covalence.
4. What is a stable octet?
5. Define electronegativity.
6. How is electronegativity related to ionization potential?
7. For what is the electronegativity scale used?
8. From the electronegativity scale predict the character of the bonds between the atoms in the following compounds: CH_4, K_2O, $SnCl_4$, CCl_4, H_2S, and $AlCl_3$.
9. Which is the more highly polar compound in each pair?
   (a) H_2S and H_2O.
   (b) CO_2 and H_2O.
10. How are ionic bonds formed?
11. What is an oxidation-reduction reaction? In such a reaction, which gives up the electrons, the less active or the more active?
12. What is the activity (electromotive) series?
13. Define covalence.
14. What is a polar bond?

15. CCl_4 has polar bonds, but its molecules are nonpolar. Explain.

16. What *ultimately* determines whether a chemical reaction will take place by electron transfer or by electron sharing?

17. How can you tell whether carbon tetrachloride is ionic or covalent?

18. Explain why nitrogen (in the air) exists as diatomic molecules.

19. The molecules of diatomic gases are completely nonpolar. Would you expect these gases to be easily liquefied? Explain.

20. Why is it possible to ignore the electrons of the inner shells in an electronic theory of chemical bonding?

21. (a) What is hydrogen bonding?
    (b) Why is it considered important?

22. In what ways do hydrogen atoms resemble those of other diatomic elemental gases?

23. In what ways do they resemble metallic atoms?

24. In the reaction $2K + O_2 \rightarrow 2K_2O$ what is oxidized and what is reduced? Justify your answer.

25. (a) Metallic potassium (K) is placed in water. Predict, from your knowledge of the activity series what would happen chemically.
    (b) Would you expect the same thing to happen if copper were placed in water? Explain.

26. What is it that determines the position of an element in the activity series?

27. If you were to add cesium, calcium, and beryllium to Table 25-2, where would you put each of them, and why?

28. Which elements are (a) most easily reduced, (b) most easily oxidized?

29. In a region where the color of the soil is commonly reddish brown (owing to

Fe_2O_3) the color in the marshes, where vegetation is exceptionally abundant and the soil constantly moist, is black. Explain.

30. What led G. N. Lewis to the conclusion that the elements fluorine, chlorine, sodium, and potassium, among others, would be more stable if they had eight electrons in their outer shells?

31. What is a displacement reaction?

32. Consider family IVA in the periodic chart from carbon downward through lead. Note the electronic configurations of each. In carbon the 4 valence electrons are close to the nucleus with its 6 positive charges. The valence electrons are "shielded" from these charges by only 2 electrons, whereas in Si they are shielded by 10, in Ge by 28, in Sn by 46, and in Pb by 78. What effect do you think the differences in shielding should have on the tendencies of these atoms to form covalent and ionic bonds?

33. Why do metals in general make good conductors, nonmetals good insulators?

34. We normally think of gases at STP as being light substances of low density. This is true of the diatomic gases, but the atomic weight of one of the monatomic gases, radon, is greater than that of platinum, gold, and lead. How is this possible; that is, why should radon be a gas?

35. (a) According to the molecular orbital theory of covalent bonding, helium, neon, and so on, are monatomic gases. Why?
    (b) How does this theory explain the fact that some of these gases react occasionally to form compounds?
    (c) Why are such compounds relatively unstable?

The Nature of Solids

Only in the gases do substances exist as discrete particles, that is, as either atoms (in the monatomic gases) or as molecules, largely independent of the others about them at ordinary temperatures and pressures. It is only when this independence becomes greatly restricted that attractive forces of one kind or another cause the discrete particles to form aggregates that we call liquids. This restriction can be brought about by reduction of temperature alone in all cases except that of helium, which ultimately requires an increase in pressure also. In all other cases, pressure is an aid but it is not necessary. Still further restriction of the movements of the ions, atoms, or molecules results in the formation of solids. As the term is used in everyday life, there are two kinds, the crystalline and the noncrystalline. In crystalline solids there is an orderly arrangement of the ions, atoms, or molecules, forming characteristic patterns that are repeated over and over indefinitely in the crystal. Most solid inorganic and many organic substances are crystalline.

The noncrystalline substances are not so

Nature is pleased with simplicity.
SIR ISAAC NEWTON

465

easily defined. A few, like glass, are considered to be supercooled liquids because, as in a liquid, there is no arrangement of the atoms or molecules into patterns that are regularly repeated.[1] Instead, they are randomly distributed throughout. Other examples are sealing wax, asphalt, and certain substances that have been rapidly cooled from the molten state. Another group that cannot be considered crystalline contains the tissues of organisms, such as the woody tissue of plants, the skin and flesh of animals. In them there are orderly arrangements of molecules, chiefly to form fibers, but these patterns are not repeated over and over again with anything like the precision of the patterns of crystals. We will concern ourselves here only with the crystalline state.

An individual discrete atom or molecule cannot be considered a liquid, a solid, or a gas. These terms apply only to relatively large aggregates of atoms, ions, or molecules. We have already learned that the same aggregate can

exist in any one of the three states, depending on the temperature and the pressure. It is reasonable to assume that forces are necessary to hold the particles together, and that the state in which they exist at the moment will depend upon the magnitude of these forces existing between the particles, forces that tend either to keep them apart or to keep them together. It is also reasonable to assume that many of the physical and chemical properties of these aggregates of matter such as melting points, boiling points, heats of fusion and vaporization, solubilities, and even physical properties such as the hardness of crystalline solids, will also depend upon the magnitude of the forces between the particles. As we have already intimated, none of these properties has any meaning when applied to individual atoms.

Crystals

Perfect crystals are solids with smooth plane surfaces called faces. These faces give to a crystal a visible geometric form such as a cube, a prism, a doubly terminated pyramid, and the like. (Fig. 26-1). In nature they vary in size from microscopic to several feet long. The faces themselves may be square, rectangular, triangular, hexagonal, rhombic, and so on. The angles between corresponding faces on all crystals of the same species are always the same, but similar faces on the same specimen may vary in size. All crystals start as individual discrete atoms, ions, or molecules and grow by accretion of more of the same kinds of atoms, ions, or molecules. If crystals have been broken, and they usually have been, many kinds will have smooth shiny surfaces that are not crystal faces; they are cleavage surfaces (planes). There is no limit to the size of the crystal as long as the supply of the same kind of atoms, ions, and molecules holds out, and as long as there is space to grow. Crystallization may start from innumerable centers and grow outward

[1] Another reason is that they have no definite melting points; that is to say, as they are heated, they gradually soften until they become molten.

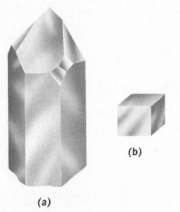

(b)

(a)

Fig. 26-1. (*a*) Half a crystal of quartz. If complete, the other end would look the same. Perfect crystals, which are rare, are six-sided, with pyramids of six main faces on each end. (*b*) A cubic crystal. Halite, the mineral name for table salt, and pyrite have this form.

until crystals crowd against other growing crystals. Perfect crystals of most substances occurring naturally in the earth do not exist because of (1) crowding during growth, (2) defects in the space lattice, or (3) breakage in collecting them. Because of this, the term crystal alone never implies perfection; it is applied to any aggregate that has the crystalline structure.

Space Lattices in Crystals

It should be apparent that the regularities in the same species of crystal present proof of the orderly arrangement of the atoms, ions, or molecules making up the crystal. Although these regularities yield some information about the internal structure, a great deal more is obtained from a study of X ray diffraction patterns. Figure 23-1 shows such a pattern. A detailed mathematical analysis of a spot pattern enables the expert to calculate the distances between the nuclei of adjacent atoms, and the positions that the atoms, ions, or molecules should occupy in order to produce such a pattern. The process is an indirect one and so must be carefully checked by experiment. The pattern of points that describes this internal arrangement is known as a space lattice. Compare the lattice in Fig. 23-1, which shows only the positions occupied by a few of the centers of the ions, with the model in Fig. 26-2, which attempts to portray the actual ions. The

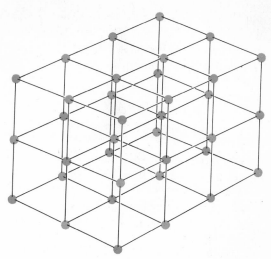

Fig. 26-2. A crystal lattice of sodium chloride. Note that ions of sodium and chlorine alternate in three directions.

space lattice consists of an enormous number of points arranged in one of a limited number of patterns. Like the orbital (p. 435), a lattice point is a region of space that may or may not be occupied by any kind of matter. The mineralogist classifies crystals according to the symmetry of the arrangement of the crystal faces. The physicists and chemists find it more useful to classify them by the atoms, ions, or molecules of which they are constituted and the forces that bond them together. Their classification scheme divides lattices into four groups—molecular, atomic, ionic, and metallic (Table 26-1)—based on the type of bonding

Table 26-1
Types of Space Lattices

Type of lattice	Type of bonding	Example
Molecular	dipole-dipole van der Waals	water (ice) solid CO_2 (dry ice)
Covalent	covalent	diamond
Ionic	ionic	NaCl
Metallic	metallic	iron

holding the particles together in the space lattice. The first-named type can be further subdivided into polar molecular (often called dipole-dipole) and nonpolar molecular (van der Waals).

Bonding in Crystals

We need to clarify the use of terms. The discussion of bonds in the previous two chapters was about the chemical bond between two atoms that form a "molecule." We were not much concerned about the bonds that held these molecules together to form visible large chunks of matter. For example, we were interested in the chemical bond between an atom of hydrogen and an atom of oxygen (interatomic) in a molecule of water, but not the bonding between molecules of water in the substance we call ice. The bonds between the molecules may be called intermolecular bonds. The bonds between the ions Na^+ and Cl^- that are responsible for crystals of salt are interionic bonds. Unfortunately for the sake of clarity, the distinction between chemical bonds and intermolecular or interionic bonds is not always clear-cut. In the discrete vapor state, the molecules of NaCl exist, and the bond between the sodium atom and the chlorine atom is an ionic chemical bond in which one electron has been transferred from the sodium atom to the chlorine atom by "burning" sodium in chlorine. In such a state the molecules are so far apart that they exert no forces on one another; there are no intermolecular bonds present, but only bonds between ion pairs. But the vapor soon cools and "freezes"; ions of sodium and chlorine form crystals like those in our salt-shakers. The ions are then close enough together to exert forces on one another. In the crystal of sodium chloride thus formed, each Na ion is surrounded by six equally distant Cl ions and, in turn, each Cl ion is surrounded

by six equally distant Na ions. Thus each Na ion is attracted to six Cl ions and vice versa. The point is that in ionic crystals there is no single bond between two ions and therefore one cannot talk of NaCl molecules in a sodium chloride crystal. There are no discrete pairs or units in the crystal. A comparable situation prevails in metals. Like most other solids, metals have a crystalline structure. These metallic crystals, although composed of atoms, have no *groups* of atoms within them that could properly be called molecules. However, by considering the properties of an iron bar, we realize that the bonds within the crystal must be very strong. This is in contrast to the situation in a sugar crystal, a solid that is composed of true molecules, each molecule having the formula $C_{12}H_{22}O_{11}$. The bonds between the atoms within each molecule of sugar are chemical bonds (polar covalent), whereas the bonds between the molecules within each sugar crystal are intermolecular.

The properties of macroscopic matter that we can visually investigate are not those of the individual atoms, ions, or molecules composing the substance, and they are not necessarily dependent upon the nature of the chemical bond. They are dependent on whatever does bond enormous numbers of atoms, ions, or molecules into these macroscopic aggregates. Thus we will investigate the forces responsible for the bonding of matter to form crystals, the arrangement of the particles within the crystals, the shapes of some of the crystals, what the limits are, if any, to the size of individual crystals, and how the physical properties are related to the type of bonding. That the melting point of crystals is a measure of the strength of the bonds holding the particles together is evident from a consideration of the differences between the liquid and the solid states. In the latter the molecules cannot move away from one another despite the fact that they have kinetic energy. They can only vibrate. If their kinetic energy is increased by heating, they vibrate faster and faster until they break the bonds; that is, until they melt.

Molecular Crystals

In molecular crystals true molecules occupy the lattice points. The molecules may be polar or nonpolar.

The Polar Molecular Crystal

In the polar molecular crystal, polar molecules occupy the lattice points in the crystal lattice. Polar covalent bonds hold the atoms together *within* the molecules (p. 455). In such molecules, one side of the molecule tends to be slightly more negative and the other slightly more positive. This polar molecule is called a *dipole*. As shown in Fig. 26-3, dipoles are bound into a lattice structure by the electrostatic attractive forces between the oppositely charged ends of the various molecules (dipole-dipole attractions). However, since the charge separation in polar covalent molecules is not complete, the net charge at the end of

Table 26-2
Melting Points of Polar
Molecular Crystals (°C)

H_2O	0*
HCl	-112
HBr	-89
HI	-51

*The exceptionally high melting point of water is discussed under hydrogen bonding in Chapter 25.

the molecule is not very large and the attraction between the molecules is not very great. The greater the disparity in electronegativities of the atoms involved, the greater the degree of polarity of the molecule and the greater the dipole-dipole forces. The melting points of polar molecular crystals are usually low because dipole-dipole bonds are rather weak; water is an exception (Table 26-2).

The Nonpolar Molecular Crystal

The chemical bond in the molecules of the nonpolar molecular crystal is covalent. On the average, these molecules show no external

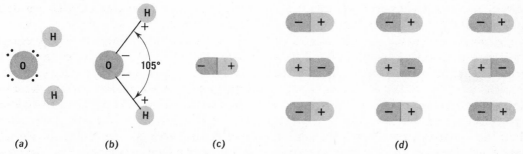

(a)   *(b)*   *(c)*   *(d)*

Fig. 26-3. Water (Ice) as a Polar Molecular Crystal. (*a*) The oxygen atom and the two hydrogen atoms are bound together within the water molecule by covalent bonds. (*b*) Because of the asymmetry (polarity) of positive and negative charges, the water molecule is slightly negative on one side and slightly positive on the other. A molecule with this asymmetry of charge is called a *dipole* and is *conventionally* represented as shown in (*c*). (*d*) The oppositely charged ends of these dipole molecules attract each other. These electrostatic attractive forces bind polar molecules into a lattice structure. Thus, in this case, crystals of solid water (ice) are formed that are fairly rigid and hard. This is an electrical diagram, not a diagram of atomic structure.

polarity; that is, no dipoles are present. It should therefore be difficult, if not impossible, to bind them into a crystal lattice. Yet experimental evidence shows that there are solid crystalline substances whose lattice points are occupied by nonpolar molecules. What are the forces that hold these molecules together? How do they originate? Solid neon or solid xenon offers a good answer. In each, the atoms are about as inert as atoms can be, yet at low temperatures they form a fragile, low-melting solid. The fact that the atoms cohere at all means that they are bonded to some extent. This bonding force is almost always present in other types of lattices as well, but it is so weak that it is masked by the far stronger lattice bonds of the other types.

The neon atom consists of a positively charged nucleus at the center of a spherical cloud of negative charge formed by its 8 electrons. The electrons are moving about rapidly so that the cloud is a bit off center with respect to the nucleus, first in one direction and then in another. When we say that the cloud is centered on the nucleus we mean this only on the average. This constant shifting of the electron cloud produces a dipole. The electric dipoles belonging to any pair of neon atoms

are fluctuating in time, but on the average they will attract each other more of the time than they will repel each other because their energy is lower when they attract. All atoms, ions, or molecules when bonded to form a solid have such fluctuating dipoles, and when they come close, a little attractive force is present that bonds the particles to one another. This is a van der Waals force. The van der Waals forces are named after the Dutch scientist who first investigated them.

As a result of the very weak molecular attractions, nonpolar substances have low boiling points and are usually gases. Their melting points should be the lowest of all crystals (see Table 26-3). However, the larger nonpolar molecules have electron clouds that fluctuate more readily because of greater distance from the nucleus. Therefore their van der Waals forces are larger, their melting points are higher, and they may be either volatile liquids or solids, for example, group VIIA: F, Cl, Br, I.

Molecular crystals (polar and nonpolar molecular lattices) have lattice bonds that cannot possibly be confused with chemical bonds. These bonds can be broken at the expenditure of little energy as can be seen by their low melting points, so low that most cannot exist

Table 26-3
Melting Points of Nonpolar Molecular Crystals*

MONATOMIC ELEMENTAL GASES			DIATOMIC ELEMENTAL GASES			COMPOUNDS		
	Mol. wt.	M.p. (°C)		Mol. wt.	M.p. (°C)		Mol. wt.	M.p. (°C)
He**	4	−272	F_2	38	−223	Carbon dioxide	44	−79
Ne	20	−249	Cl_2	71	−102	(CO_2)		
A	40	−189	Br_2	160	−7	Naphthalene	128	80
Kr	84	−157	I_2	254	113	($C_{10}H_8$)		
Xe	131	−112						
Rn	222	−71	H_2	2	−259			
			O_2	32	−218			
			N_2	28	−210			

*Note that within any one group the melting point rises as the molecular weight rises.
**Helium cannot be solidified at any temperature unless the pressure is at least 25 atm.

as solids outside the laboratory here on earth. Some may exist as solids on the colder planets of our solar system.

Covalent Crystals

The lattice points are occupied by atoms that share electrons with all their immediate neighbors. These covalent bonds are viewed as extending in fixed directions in space. For example, in the diamond crystal each carbon atom is at the center of a regular tetrahedron[2] and is bonded to four other carbon atoms that are at the vertices of the tetrahedron (Fig. 26-4). At the same time the carbon atom at each vertex is also at the center of another tetrahedron. Thus the atoms are completely linked in all directions by covalent electron pair bonds forming an interlocking structure of high rigidity and high bond strength. No individual molecule exists in such a crystal. Instead, the whole crystal, no matter how big, is properly termed a single molecule. The best example is the diamond, in which carbon

[2] A solid figure enclosed by four equilateral triangles.

atoms occupy the lattice points. Since each carbon atom shares four electrons with four other carbon atoms, and all four of these strong bonds must be broken to melt the crystal, the diamond has an extremely high melting point.

Graphite is another form of carbon with visible properties completely different from the diamond, yet the individual atoms are exactly the same. The difference is in the arrangement of the atoms into a sheet-like structure instead of into a tetrahedral structure. Each atom in each sheet is tied to three others by a single bond (Fig. 26-5). The fourth bond in a sense forms a double bond, but since all three other atoms are exactly alike, this fourth bond shows no preference; it is viewed as belonging to all three; that is, it shifts from one atom to another of the three in an endless succession. That the bonding within the sheets is very strong is shown by the melting point of graphite; it is about the same as that of the diamond.

Only the weak van der Waals forces hold the sheets together. They are so weak that the sheets slide over one another giving graphite an easy cleavage that is responsible for its

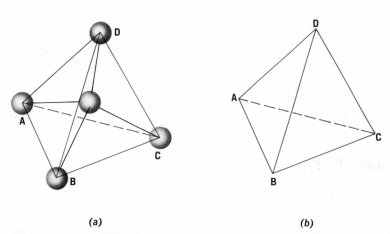

(a)   *(b)*

Fig. 26-4. Tetrahedral Structure of Carbon in Diamond. Carbon atoms are at the four corners, *A*, *B*, *C*, and *D*, and a fifth is at the center, bonded to each of the other four. Each atom at a corner is also the center atom of an adjoining tetrahedron.

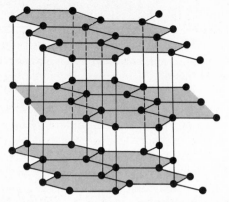

Fig. 26-5. Space Lattice of Graphite. Note that each carbon atom is shown bonded to only three others in the same layer. The fourth bond may be considered a floating one; that is, one electron of each atom temporarily forms a double bond first with one of its neighbors and then with another. This floating bond is not shown in the diagram. The layers are held together by the weak van der Waals forces (colored lines).

greasy feel and for the use of graphite as a lubricant.

Other covalent crystals are SiC (silicon carbide), WC (tungsten carbide), and SiO_2 (silicon dioxide, or silica).[3] The first two can be thought of as analogous to a diamond in which half of the carbon atoms have been replaced by silicon or tungsten molecules. The same general arrangement prevails, the covalent bonding continuing indefinitely. These crystals have very high melting points, 2600°C for SiC and 2900°C for WC. They are high because, as in the diamond, strong covalent bonds must be broken in the melting process.

Ionic Crystals

In the ionic crystal positive and negative ions occupy the lattice points. It is the elec-

[3] The chemistry of silicon will be further treated in Chapter 30.

trostatic attraction between these oppositely charged atoms that holds them together. These positive and negative ions are arranged alternately in the three cardinal directions of space forming a continuous array. One cannot pair up these charges, since each ion is surrounded by six others of opposite charge, one in front and one behind, one above and one below, and one on each side. The whole crystal acts like one gigantic molecule just as the diamond does. The lattice bond strength is not so high as in the covalent lattice. These attractions are large, giving ionic crystals moderately high melting points. To melt the crystal the attractions of these ions for one another must be overcome. Under ordinary conditions the stable state for practically all ionic compounds is the crystalline solid state.

The amount of energy needed to separate the ions depends on two factors: (1) the distances between the ions, that is, ionic sizes, and (2) the magnitude of the charges. Table 26-4 shows the effect of the first factor. The ions of all the compounds in the table have a charge of $+1$ or -1. For the effect of the second factor, consider the melting point of a compound in which both ions have a charge of 2, MgO (Mg^{2+} and O^{2-}); it is 2800°C. The melting points of ionic crystals are, in general,

Table 26-4
Effect of Ionic Size on
Melting Points of Ionic Crystals

	Compound	M.p. (°C)
Increasing size of metallic ion (same nonmetallic ion)	NaCl	804
	KCl	776
	RbCl	715
	CsCl	646
Increasing size of nonmetallic ions (same metallic ion)	NaF	1980
	NaCl	804
	NaBr	755
	NaI	651

much lower than those of crystals with covalent lattices, for the energy needed to pull the ions apart is less than that needed to break strong covalent bonds.

Metallic Crystals

Ions of metals occupy the lattice points in metallic crystals. Neither ionic nor covalent bonds can account for the binding of metals into the large, generally strong aggregates that we use in everyday life. Consider a bar of iron, or of any other metal. What forces hold the atoms together? We can eliminate those in either type of molecular crystal on the basis of strength alone. And they are not due to the attractions of oppositely charged ions, as in ionic crystals, for the metal ions all have the same sign. The bonds cannot be covalent because metals cannot achieve the inert gas electronic configurations by sharing as do such nonmetals as carbon, sulfur, hydrogen, and the halogens. The van der Waals forces that hold discrete molecules together into a crystal lattice are much too weak, even if present, to account for the great strength of most metals.

In the molecular, covalent, and ionic types of crystals, the valence electrons are fixed in certain quantum states and are not free to move. In metals there are a number of available quantum states, thus the valence electrons have freedom to move from atom to atom. *In metallic crystals the valence electrons are shared communally by all of the metallic atoms.* Each atom contributes its valence electrons to an "electron cloud, or sea" that belongs to the whole crystal. This contribution to the cloud leaves the rest of the crystal a mass of positive ions. The valence electrons of this cloud form floating, nonrigid bonds between positive ions. This random wandering of the electron cloud throughout the crystal accounts for the high electrical conductivity of metals and their de-

Table 26-5
Melting Points of Metallic Crystals (°C)

Effect of atomic size		Effect of number of electrons	
Li	179	Na	98
Na	98	Mg	651
K	64	Al	660
Rb	39		
Cs	26		

formability without breaking. However, it is difficult to account for the hardnesses and melting points in terms of the lattice.

Cesium (and the rest of the alkali metals) can be cut with a knife. It has a melting point only slightly above room temperature, whereas tungsten is very hard and has a melting point (3370°C) only a little less than that of carbon. In general, the melting points of metals depend (1) upon the size of the atom, thus decreasing downward within a family (Table 26-5), and (2) upon the number of valence electrons, thus increasing across a period. The decrease downward in the family cannot be due to number of charges, since all have the same number; it is due to the increase in average distance between neighboring atoms because of increasing atomic size, thus bringing Coulomb's law into the picture. There are some exceptions to this general rule.

Chemical Bonds as Lattice Bonds

Three of the types of lattice bonds described—covalent, ionic, and metallic—are basically interatomic bonds, none of them distinct from chemical bonds. We should, when dealing with them in crystals, think of them as lattice bonds. As a result, crystals having these types of lattice bonds are really giant molecules composed of interlocking atoms, or ions.

Conductors and Nonconductors

In any crystalline solid, the valence electrons of the atoms interact with one another so that their energy levels are not sharply defined as in an individual atom but are spread over a small but definite range called an *energy band*. The exclusion principle applies to levels within these energy bands and an electron in a crys-

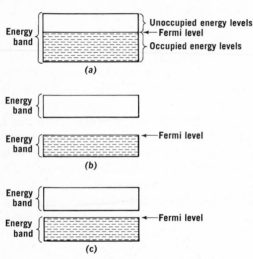

(a)

(b)

(c)

Fig. 26-6. Energy Bands. (*a*) Valence shell energy band of a conductor. The energy band of this conductor is only partially filled and so electrons of adjacent atoms need little additional energy to be raised into and pass through this band. (*b*) Energy bands of a nonconductor (insulator). Since a large energy gap separates the filled band from the empty band, a large amount of energy would be required to raise electrons from the filled band of an adjacent atom to the empty band of this atom thus effectively preventing any substantial flow of electrons from atom to atom. (*c*) Energy bands of a semiconductor. Here only a small energy gap separates the filled band from the empty band. At ordinary temperatures a few electrons will have sufficient thermal energy to jump the gap and there can be a small flow of electrons.

talline solid can have only those energy levels that fall within the energy bands of the particular solid. Energy bands may be completely filled, partially filled, or empty. There is an *energy level* below which all *energy states* are filled and above which all energy states are empty. This is called the *Fermi level*. If the Fermi level falls within an energy band, the substance is a conductor. If it falls between energy bands, the substance is an insulator or nonconductor (Fig. 26-6).

Semiconductors have a conductivity that is intermediate between that of conductors and insulators. This conductivity is easily changed by small amounts of certain "impurities." If a trace of some element having one more valence electron per atom than the semiconductor atoms is introduced, then all the valence electrons in the vicinity of the "impurity" atom are somewhat displaced and can move more freely. Thus the overall conductivity is increased. If, instead, an impurity with one less valence electron is added, then there is a vacancy (called a "hole"). Again there is a distortion in valence electron distribution. An electron from an adjacent atom can move into this hole, but it leaves another hole behind it. This in turn is filled by another electron, which leaves another hole, and so on. Thus the holes can "migrate" in one direction and the electrons in the opposite direction, and an electron current is formed.

This effect of trace impurities on the electrical properties of semiconductors is the basis for the operation of the transistor and other "solid state" devices that have largely displaced thermionic tubes in modern electronic communication.

Exercises

1. Distinguish between crystalline and noncrystalline substances.
2. What is meant by (a) crystal form, (b)

crystal face, (c) lattice point, and (d) crystal lattice?

3. In a general way state how the positions that atoms, ions, or molecules occupy within a crystal are determined.

4. What sorts of particles (atoms, ions, or molecules) make up each of the four types of crystals?

5. What types of forces hold the particles in each of the four types of crystals?

6. What properties of a crystal are determined by the strength of the bonds holding the particles together?

7. What is the size or range of sizes of a "molecule" in the diamond? Explain.

8. Graphite and the diamond both have extremely high melting points but extremely different hardnesses. Explain.

9. (a) What two factors control the melting points in ionic crystals?
   (b) Relate each to the periodic table.

10. Which have the higher melting points, polar or nonpolar molecular crystals? Explain.

11. Solid HCl has a melting point of $-112\,°C$.
    (a) What crystal lattice would you expect it to have? Why?
    (b) Would you expect its molecules to be more or less polar than those of water?

(c) Would you have reached the same conclusion from the electronegativity scale?

12. What type of crystal lattice do you have the most trouble in understanding? Why?

13. See the discussion of molecules on p. 447. Relate the problem reviewed there with the discussion of molecules in this chapter.

14. A piece of ice melts. Compare the volume of the ice with that of the melted water. Explain.

15. Fundamentally, why do some substances exist as gases, some as liquids, and some as solids at normal temperatures and pressures?

16. Essentially how do crystalline and noncrystalline pure substances differ?

17. What is a space lattice?

18. The diamond and graphite are both pure carbon. Why is the diamond the hardest substance known, whereas graphite is among the softest?

19. In the context of this chapter why do the rare gases have such low liquefying temperatures?

20. Helium at ordinary temperatures is the only gas that cannot be liquefied no matter what the pressure. Explain.

Solutions and Related Phenomena

Much of our knowledge of the behavior of matter has come from the study of solutions. We find solutions everywhere. Formally defined, a solution is a homogeneous mixture in which two or more species of pure substances are uniformly distributed on a molecular or ionic scale. It is uniform in color, taste, odor, and other chemical and physical properties. The waters of the oceans, the lakes, the rivers, and even the water we drink are solutions. So are tea, soda pop, beer, wine, hard liquors, and most of the liquid medicines that we take. The air we breathe is a solution composed of a number of gases dissolved in nitrogen, its most abundant constituent. Almost all metals as we see them in everyday life are solutions of solids in solids. Notable examples are brass, bronze, pewter, and coins of all kinds. Our concern here will be almost exclusively with solutions of solids in liquids. It should be clearly understood that in all cases we are dealing with such solutions unless otherwise specified.

The process of the solution of crystalline solids is analogous to the process of melting— but it is very definitely not melting. The two

> **Almost all the chemical processes which occur in nature, whether in animal or vegetable organisms, or in the nonliving surface of the earth, take place between substances in solution.**
> W. OSTWALD, 1890

476

processes are similar in that in both the forces bonding the atoms, ions, or molecules together in the crystals are overcome. In melting, this is done by increasing their kinetic energy with the application of heat. In solutions, the bonding forces of the atoms, ions, or molecules are overcome by an interaction between the particles of the solvent and those of the solute. No solvent is involved in melting.

Solutions vs. Suspensions and Colloids

Three types of systems in which solid particles are dispersed throughout a liquid are recognized, namely, suspensions, colloidal dispersions, and solutions. They are differentiated from one another by the size of the dispersed particles. In suspensions the solid particles are easily visible, either by the naked eye or by a low-power microscope. For some time after a rain the water in a brook or a river is muddy because of the suspended material in it. The size ranges from the size of pebbles (sometimes boulders) down through sand and clay. If the stream flows into a lake where there are no currents of water, most of the material will settle, given time enough. If, after a week or ten days with no further rain, the water still is not clear, the probability is that a colloidal dispersion is present. Colloidal dispersions are also present in all living systems, for example, in blood and protoplasm, and in a high percentage of nonliving systems. The sizes of the particles in colloidal dispersions lie between those of a suspension and those of a true solution. If sand is ground very fine, so fine that the particles are invisible under a good microscope, these particles will not settle out upon standing. The reason is that they are in constant random motion because of collisions with water molecules. This motion is called Brownian movement. Examples of colloidal dispersions are gelatin, protoplasm, rubber latex, "liquid" starch, blood plasma, smoke, soaps, dyes, inks of many kinds, milk, colored glass, and opal. Some of these examples are cases of solids dispersed in liquids, some solids dispersed in solids, liquids dispersed in liquids, and solids dispersed in gases.

Solutions are intimate homogeneous mixtures of particles of atomic or molecular size. Whereas colloids will disperse light, solutions will not; the particles are too small. Hence, colloidal dispersions can be distinguished from solutions by passing a beam of light through them; the path of the light through the colloid is clearly visible, whereas through the solution it is not. Colloidally dispersed matter cannot be removed from the solvent by filtering, frequently to the annoyance of the chemist.

Solvents and Solutes

In every solution there are both a solvent and a solute. (There may, of course, be several solutes in the same solution.) With solids or gases dissolved in liquids, the liquid is the solvent and the solid or gas the solute. With solutions of gases in gases, liquids in liquids, and solids in solids, it is not always clear which is the solvent and which the solute. In these cases we assign the role of solvent to that substance present in greatest quantity. Water is by far the best general liquid solvent.

Systems at Equilibrium

In the mechanical world we recognize the equilibrium state as one of balance, that is, one in which no visible change is taking place. In the chemical world equilibrium has much the same meaning except that it is always a dynamic equilibrium, never a static one. In a dynamic equilibrium changes are continually

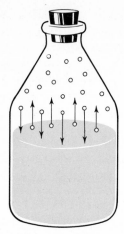

Fig. 27-1. Equilibrium in a Stoppered Container of Water. The number of molecules of water returning to the liquid is the same as the number escaping from it.

taking place, some in one direction, some in the opposite direction, with the balance always being maintained. Chemical equilibrium can exist only in a closed system, that is, one in which both the total amount of matter and the temperature are constant. In other words, the macroscopic properties are constant. Microscopic properties may continue to change but always in a balance that produces no macroscopic changes (Fig. 27-1). It must be remembered that any change in the temperature destroys any existing equilibrium state. A change in pressure will also destroy it if one of the substances involved is a gas. After a while, however, a new equilibrium will be established.

Saturation

Solutions differ from compounds in that they do not have fixed compositions. A solution may be varied continuously without causing any abrupt changes in its properties. Thus you can have a cup of coffee or tea of almost any strength you wish, and you can add a little sugar or a lot. If you add too much, there will be a residue of sugar left in the bottom of the cup. The liquid is then saturated with sugar. There is no such thing as saturation for solutes and solvents that are miscible in all proportions, for example, alcohol and water. Natural petroleum consists of a number of liquids (gasoline, kerosene, motor oils) and gases (natural gas) and various semisolids (for example, grease), and so on, all in mutual solution with one another.

The amount of a solid solute that can be dissolved in a liquid solvent varies with the temperature of the solvent. For most the amount increases with the temperature; for a few it decreases. For gases dissolved in liquid solvents the amount always decreases with an increase in temperature if the system is an open one, that is, not under pressure. We all know that an open bottle of soda will go flat a lot more quickly out of the refrigerator than in. The flat taste of boiled water is due to the fact that the air originally in it has been driven out by boiling it.

It must not be assumed that conditions are static in a *saturated* liquid solution. If there is excess solute in the bottom of the container and the temperature is kept constant, there is an equilibrium between the molecules in solution and those of the undissolved solute. Molecules, atoms, or ions are constantly dissolving while others are constantly being precipitated, always in equal numbers so that the concentration does not change.

Molar Concentrations

Solubilities refer to the *maximum* concentration of a solute in a given quantity of solvent at a given temperature. Chemists are much more likely to be interested in the concentration of the solute in the solvent expressed in moles per liter, that is, in its molar concentration. A mole is 6×10^{23} molecules, atoms, or ions (p. 253). A one molar (1 M) solution of compound X is made by weighing the number of grams of X equal to its molecular weight and adding enough water to make one liter of solution. A two molar (2 M) solution would contain two moles of X per liter of solution. The advantage of using this method is that in a 1 M solution the chemist knows that there are 6×10^{23} atoms, ions, or molecules of any solute. He must remember, however, that if the solute is ionic, as is NaCl, there are 6×10^{23} ions of Na^+ and 6×10^{23} ions of Cl^- in his 1 M solution. It is not possible to have a 1 M (or any other concentration) of Na^+ ions all by themselves without an equal number of Cl^- ions (or some other negative ions).

Solution vs. Chemical Reaction

It is advisable at this point to clarify what we mean by a solution, again restricting ourselves to solid solutes in liquid solvents. Such clarification is necessary because many chemists, as well as most laymen, have fallen into the habit of using the term "dissolve" for any process in which a solid placed in a liquid disappears. Zinc, for example, will disappear if placed in sulfuric acid, but not by the process of solution. It is not soluble in the acid to any appreciable extent. The zinc reacts with the acid forming zinc sulfate and releasing hydrogen, which escapes into the air. The zinc sulfate is soluble in water and so a true solution exists after the zinc has disappeared. The solute is, however, zinc sulfate and not zinc. If we evaporate the water, it is zinc sulfate that is recovered. In a true solution the solid solute can be recovered, unchanged chemically, by evaporation of the solvent. We will restrict our use

of the term solution to true solutions as thus defined.

Still, not all processes of solution are alike. No clear-cut boundary can be drawn between purely mechanical (or physical) processes and processes that are, in part at least, chemical. That some are chemical is attested to by the fact that heat can be given off, for example, 18,000 cal/mole for sulfuric acid dissolved in water; with most solid substances, however, heat is absorbed when they are dissolved. Conversely, heat is given off when these solids crystallize out of solution. This is analogous to the heat of fusion, in which heat is given off as a liquid freezes (crystallizes), and is absorbed as the crystals melt. Melting is analogous to the dissolving process, for in both it takes energy to pull the molecules, or ions, away from the crystal, energy that can come only from the kinetic (thermal) energy of the solvent in the process of solution or from an outside source in the process of melting.

The solution of many gases in water represents instances in which no clear-cut boundary between solution and chemical reaction can be drawn. Carbon dioxide dissolves in water to form H_2CO_3; hydrogen chloride dissolves in water to form hydrochloric acid (H^+ and Cl^-), and so on. Heating these gaseous solutions in an open receptacle will, however, drive off the gases unchanged in composition.

We might logically ask the whereabouts of the ions, atoms, or molecules of solute in a solution, for a glass of colorless solute dissolved in water looks no different from pure water. At this stage of our study of science we should be able to guess that the atoms or ions or molecules must occupy spaces between the molecules (rarely atoms) of the solvent. That there are spaces is attested by the fact that the volume of a solution is commonly less than the sum of the two volumes involved. Thus, if we dissolve a quart of pure alcohol in a quart of pure water, we find that we have a bit less than two quarts of solution. That there are *nearly* two quarts of solution makes it clear that these spaces between the water molecules are not nearly large enough to accommodate the alcohol molecules without moving them somewhat apart. There are cases where the volume of solution is greater than the sum of the volumes of solvent and solute.

Polar vs. Nonpolar Solvents and Solutes

It is common knowledge that water will not dissolve grease but that carbon tetrachloride, benzene, gasoline, or kerosene will. Conversely, water will dissolve sugar, salt, and a host of other things that the other solvents will not. Can we explain these phenomena by our electronic theory?

We have already discussed the question of polarity in Chapter 25. All ionic solutes are polar; a pair of oppositely charged ions constitute the ultimate in polarity. Most, but not all, ionic solids will dissolve in water; one exception is silver chloride (AgCl). Mix water solutions of NaCl and $AgNO_3$ and the following reaction takes place:

$$Na^+ + Cl^- + Ag^+ + NO_3^- \rightarrow$$
$$Na^+ + NO_3^- + AgCl\downarrow \quad [27\text{-}1]$$

Silver chloride is precipitated because it is insoluble in water. Why? Almost all other metallic chlorides are soluble. In AgCl the attraction between the solute particle Ag^+ and the solute particle Cl^- is greater than the attraction of either for water molecules, and so an almost insoluble precipitate (of tiny crystals) is formed. A few ions have enough kinetic

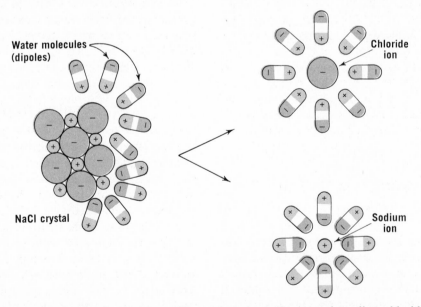

Fig. 27-2. Process of solution of an ionic crystal in a polar solvent (for example, sodium chloride in water). The negative parts of some water molecules are attracted to the positive sodium ions, and the positive parts of other water molecules to the negative chloride ions. There are very many more water molecules than sodium ions and chlorine ions. The end result is that the ions are pulled loose from the crystal and floated away.

energy to escape from the crystals; this explains silver chloride's slight solubility. How an ionic substance goes into solution is shown in Fig. 27-2.

Many nonionic substances are polar, for example, water and grain alcohol. This means that the charge distribution is asymmetric so that one end of a molecule has a residue of positive charge, the other end a residue of negative charge; that is, the molecules are dipoles (see p. 455 and Fig. 25-3). From this discussion one might conclude that sugar is polar, that everything that will dissolve in water is polar. Conversely, substances that will not dissolve in water are nonpolar. Fats, oils, and greases form one big category of the latter. They will "dissolve" in nonpolar solvents like carbon tetrachloride, gasoline, benzene, or kerosene. The process is different, however, than that of polar solvents dissolving polar solutes. In the latter the dipole-dipole attractions "bodily" remove the solute particles; they literally pull the particles away. In the former the process is merely one of dilution, a process of mixing enough solvent with the solute and removing both together. The above explanations show why it is useless to try to remove a sugar stain with a patented spot remover, or to try to remove a grease stain with water.

Dissociation in Ionic Solutions

We learned that solutions containing ions are electrolytic solutions (Chapter 18) when we studied Faraday's discovery of the smallest electric charge that can exist, that which is on a monovalent ion. Salts and bases are ionic and have electrovalent bonds in the solid state, and water solutions of them are both ionic and electrolytic. Acids are covalent substances that are not ionic in the pure state, but their water

solutions are ionic and electrolytic because their molecules react with water to form ions. In ionic solutions there are always two kinds of ions, positive and negative. If a compound is dissolved in water and the solution becomes ionic, then some "molecules" of the compound must have separated into two parts, one part having a positive charge, the other a negative charge. This separation of the "molecules" of a compound into ions in the presence of a solvent is called *dissociation*. Since electrolytes vary in their ability to transmit an electric current, so much so that we call some strong electrolytes and others weak electrolytes, we feel justified in believing that the difference is in the extent of the dissociation. If the dissociation is complete or nearly so, a strong electrolyte is formed, for there is an abundance of ions to transmit the current. A weak electrolyte must therefore contain more undissociated molecules than ions. More than 50 years elapsed after Faraday's discovery of ions (ca. 1834) before any attempt was made to explain these facts, that is, to develop a coherent ionic theory.

Arrhenius Dissociation Theory

Faraday, in his experimental work by which he established his laws of electrolysis (p. 301), assumed that the electric current created the ions in his electrolytic solutions; that is, he assumed that it was electricity that caused the molecules in his electrolytic solutions (in the case of NaCl) to dissociate into Na^+ ions and Cl^- ions. He found that sugar solutions, alcohol solutions, and others, would not conduct an electric current; he called them nonelectrolytes. Some 50 years later, a Swedish graduate student, Svante Arrhenius, decided to examine the differences between electrolytes and nonelectrolytes. He studied Faraday's work carefully, made some new interpretations of it in light of some new knowledge that had developed in the interim, added the results of experiments of his own, and proposed a new theory. His theory did not require an electric current to break up molecules in solution into ions. Instead the water did that. In some way that he could not explain neutral molecules were each separated into two parts by the water, one positively charged, the other negatively charged. He wrote this all up in the form of a dissertation that, he hoped, would earn him a doctorate. He bolstered it with experimental evidence of his own. In one experiment he "froze" electrolytes in gelatin to make the solution semirigid. In the solution were positively charged copper ions—which are always blue regardless of the composition of the negative ion. He could then, after turning on an electric current, watch the blue ions migrate towards the cathode. He described other experiments, but his doctorate committee of professors rejected his thesis with one simple argument against it. A solution of NaCl is an electrolyte. In the solid state salt is harmless; cooks use it often by adding it to the cooking water. Free chlorine is a deadly poison, and here was Arrhenius saying that when molecules of NaCl were added to water, the chlorine separated from the sodium so that there was poisonous chlorine in the food. Arrhenius suggested that the properties of chlorine ions were different from those of chlorine atoms. Their reply was that atoms were indivisible and so when salt was added to water there were either salt molecules or free chlorine and sodium atoms in the water. Therefore there are no ions in the water, not until—as Faraday had first done—an electric current was transmitted through it. Arrhenius sought further evidence.

When a solution of a silver salt, $AgNO_3$, and a solution of sodium chloride, NaCl, are mixed, the precipitate silver chloride, AgCl, forms instantaneously. Yet if you grind solid NaCl and solid $AgNO_3$ together to a fine powder, no reaction will take place. There will be a reaction between potassium iodide and mercuric chloride ground together, but only after much effort. If solutions of each are mixed, the reaction is instantaneous because the positive ions are already separated from the negative ions, and so are ready to react on contact. On the other hand, the reactions between two nonelectrolytes are not instantaneous; time is consumed in the breaking up of the molecules into component parts. Arrhenius also cited the fact that white copper sulfate, black copper bromide, and green copper chloride each yield the same shade of blue when dissolved in water, easily explained if all copper ions are blue, but unexplainable otherwise. He presented evidence that acid solutions owe their properties to H ions, bases to OH ions, yet his thesis was rejected again. Finally, a prominent German chemist learned of his work, studied it, and wrote the Swedish professors an enthusiastic letter congratulating them on the brilliance of Arrhenius' work. Reluctantly, they granted him the doctorate. A few years later (1903) he received the Nobel prize for chemistry for these discoveries. His professors were invited to attend the ceremonies.

Arrhenius believed that the water created the ions. He also believed that dissociation was never complete. Atoms were still indivisible, so how could he believe that the ions were present in the solid state? It was not until the electronic concept of chemical bonding was advanced, well along in the present century, that it was realized that the ions of salts and bases are present in the solid state. X-ray studies of crystals also show that the particles that form the crystals of salts and bases are ions, not molecules. The Debye–Hückel theory of electrolytes (1923) extends the quantitative treatment beyond that of Arrhenius but in no way negates his essential argument.

Freezing Point Depression

Another evidence that Arrhenius used to support his concept of ions was that all electrolytic water solutions have abnormally low freezing points. This is common knowledge to those who drive automobiles in freezing weather. Molar solutions of nonelectrolytes of the same strength ($1\ M$, $2\ M$, $3\ M$, and so on) all depress the freezing temperature of water by almost the same amount. This is not the case with electrolytes. A $1\ M$ solution of NaCl will lower it nearly twice that of a $1\ M$ solution of a nonelectrolyte, a $1\ M$ solution of $CaCl_2$ will lower it nearly three times as much, and a $1\ M$ solution of $FeCl_3$ will lower it nearly four times as much. The above phenomena are easily explained if one assumes that in solution each "molecule" of NaCl forms 2 particles, each "molecule" of $CaCl_2$ forms 3 particles, and each "molecule" of $FeCl_3$ forms 4 particles. To put it in a simpler way we will use a concentration made by adding a gram atomic weight (Chapter 16) of each to separate liters of water. In a nonelectrolyte solution prepared in this way there will be 6×10^{23} molecules (which we will call particles). There are 6×10^{23} sodium ions and 6×10^{23} chloride ions in our NaCl solution, a total of 12×10^{23} particles. In our $CaCl_2$ there are 6×10^{23} calcium ions and 12×10^{23} chloride ions, a total of 18×10^{23} particles. In our $FeCl_3$ solution there is a total of 24×10^{23} particles. The particle ratios are 1 (for the nonelectrolyte), 2, 3, 4, respectively. The reason for the differing amounts of depression of the freezing point of water stands out startlingly clearly. It is the number of particles of solute per unit volume of solvent that determines the amount of lowering. If ions were not present in the water but only molecules, then there would be the same number of particles in each solution and the amount of lowering of the freezing point would be the same for each.

But you ask (or if you don't, you should) what is the fundamental reason for the lowering in any case? When water freezes, crystals of ice form. The polar water molecules must occupy the lattice points in the growing crystal. The solute particles in the solution get in the way of—interfere with—the necessary movements of the water molecules. In fact, their interference is so successful that the crystal of ice does not begin to form until the kinetic energy of the solute particles has been reduced, that is, until the temperature has been reduced.

Boiling points and vapor pressures of electrolytic solutions are also abnormal when compared with those of nonelectrolytes. Interference with the normal processes by the particles of solute in much the same way are responsible.

Properties of Ions vs. Atoms

Let us return to the principal argument advanced by the professors of Arrhenius. They would not agree that chloride atoms had properties different from those of chloride ions. They disagreed by refusing to recognize the existence of either in a water solution of NaCl. What existed were molecules of NaCl. Today we know that there are no molecules of NaCl (see definition of molecule, p. 447). Although we can never isolate a group of chloride ions for study as we can a group of chlorine molecules, we can list some of their differences. Chlorine gas is greenish yellow in color with a suffocating irritating odor and taste; it was used as a poison gas in World War I. Chloride ion is colorless. It can never be tasted except in combination with some other element. It is largely inactive chemically for it has eight electrons in its outer shell. It carries a single negative charge. Chlorine atoms are very active chemically and will react with all metals, and with hydrogen.

Ionic Equations

If positive and negative ions exist as more or less independent particles in an aqueous solution, then it should follow that a negative ion ought to be able to enter into chemical combination without regard to what happens to a corresponding positive ion. Consider a tiny crystal of NaCl. Put it in water and the two ions of each molecule separate, moving about independently. The Cl ions have a set of properties that are quite distinct from those of molecules (or atoms) of chlorine, as we have already seen.

The independence of the chloride ion can be demonstrated by adding a solution of a silver salt—any one will do—to a solution of any chloride, for example, NaCl, KCl, $MgCl_2$, $CaCl_2$, $BaCl_2$. In every case the silver ion combines with the chloride instantly to form an insoluble precipitate of AgCl. Suppose we add NaCl solution to a $AgNO_3$ solution. This reaction used to be written as follows:

$$NaCl + AgNO_3 \rightarrow NaNO_3 + AgCl\downarrow \qquad [27\text{-}1]$$

The electronic way of writing it is

$$Na^+ + Cl^- + Ag^+ + NO_3^- \rightarrow$$
$$Na^+ + NO_3^- + AgCl\downarrow \qquad [27\text{-}2]$$

Since the Na^+ and the NO_3^- ions occur on both sides we can cancel them, and write

$$Ag^+ + Cl^- \rightarrow AgCl\downarrow \qquad [27\text{-}3]$$

This tells us that whenever we bring silver ion

and chlorine ion together in the same solution, *regardless of the source,* AgCl will be precipitated (because it is insoluble in water). See p. 480 for the cause of its insolubility. Since a chemical equation should be a summary of the actual chemical change, we see that Eq. 27-3 is entirely satisfactory. The other ions are merely "spectator" ions, for they take no part in the reaction.

Suppose, however, we mix molar solutions of $NaNO_3$ and Ag_2SO_4 in equal amounts. The ionic equation is

$$Na^+ + NO_3^- + 2Ag^+ + SO_4^{2-} \rightarrow$$
$$Na^+ + NO_3^- + 2Ag^+ + SO_4^{2-} \qquad [27\text{-}4]$$

The same substances appear on both sides, so no reaction has taken place; all four kinds of ions remain in solution. Suppose, however, we evaporate the $NaNO_3$–Ag_2SO_4 mixture to dryness. Presumably we might get crystals of four compounds—$NaNO_3$, Na_2SO_4, $AgNO_3$, and Ag_2SO_4. If all were equally soluble and we had two moles of $NaNO_3$ to one of Ag_2SO_4, we would get equal numbers of "molecules" of each of the four. They are not equally soluble and so we would get a larger proportion of the least soluble of the four compounds.

Acids and Bases

Most commonly acid-base reactions are between covalent and ionic electrolytes. Most bases are ionic electrolytes. Acids are covalent electrolytes. All contain hydrogen, which, we have also learned, forms covalent bonds. The *pure* acids are therefore nonionic and nonelectrolytes, no matter whether they are gases, liquids, or solids.[1] In water solutions all acids

[1] Pure HCl is a gas at room temperature; pure H_2SO_4 is a liquid; many pure organic acids, for example, oxalic, benzoic, salicylic, are solids.

ionize to some extent by reacting with water. Arrhenius defined an acid as a substance whose water solution contains hydrogen ions and a base as one whose water solution contains hydroxide ions. Water solutions of acids react with metals *that are above hydrogen in the activity series* (Table 25-2), with liberation of free hydrogen. For example,

$$Zn + 2HCl \rightarrow ZnCl_2 + H_2 \uparrow$$
$$[27\text{-}5]$$

Written ionically,

$$Zn + 2H^+ + 2Cl^- \rightarrow$$
$$Zn^{2+} + 2Cl^- + H_2 \uparrow$$

Summarizing,

$$Zn + 2H^+ \rightarrow Zn^{2+} + H_2 \uparrow$$

The Arrhenius concept of acids and bases was eventually found to be inadequate, so Brønsted, a Danish chemist, and Lowry, an English chemist, independently proposed a new one in 1923. They defined *an acid as a substance that can donate protons, and a base as a substance that can accept protons during a chemical change.* Pertinent to these definitions is the knowledge that the protons referred to are *always* derived from hydrogen atoms by the loss of an electron; these protons never come from other atoms. The hydrogen ion is but a bare nucleus and is extremely small— about $\frac{1}{10,000}$ the diameter of the chloride ion. In the reaction between acids and bases there is a transfer of protons.[2] This gives a new type of chemical reaction to add to those already studied, namely, to electron transfer and electron sharing.

[2] Another concept of acids and bases considers that a base shares one of its pairs of electrons with acids. The base is an electron-pair donor, an acid an electron-pair acceptor. This is a broader concept than either that of Arrhenius or that of Brønsted. It was advanced by G. N. Lewis the same year that Brønsted advanced his.

The Hydronium Ion

The extremely small size of the hydrogen ion and its lack of any screening shell of electrons allows it to make a closer approach to the nucleus of another atom than is possible with any other nucleus. HCl was known to ionize in water long before the discovery that water had anything to do with the reaction. The equation was written

$$HCl \rightarrow H^+ + Cl^- \qquad [27\text{-}6]$$

In time it was realized that H^+ was far too small to maintain an independent existence; it is a naked positive charge with no screening shell of electrons about it. Therefore the charge density is so high that it *always* attaches itself to an electron pair. This is done practically instantaneously when HCl is put into water because the proton H^+ merely shifts from one electron pair to another; there are no octets of electrons to be changed or disturbed. Thus

$$H\text{:}\overset{..}{\underset{..}{O}}\text{:} + H\text{:}\overset{..}{\underset{..}{Cl}}\text{:} \rightarrow H\text{:}\overset{..}{\underset{H}{O}}\text{:}H^+ + \text{:}\overset{..}{\underset{..}{Cl}}\text{:}^-$$
$$[27\text{-}7]$$

As you see, water has two free electron pairs and hydrogen chloride has three. But oxygen has an electronegativity of 3.5 and chlorine one of 3.0. Therefore the proton, H^+, is more strongly attracted to the oxygen and leaves the chlorine ion to attach itself to the water molecule, turning it into the *hydronium* ion (H_3O^+). Let us look at Eq. 27-7 again. We can see that the HCl molecule has donated a proton to a water molecule. According to the Brønsted–Lowry definition, HCl, the donor, is an acid, and H_2O, the acceptor, is a base.

The Ionization of Water

We have differentiated electrolytes and nonelectrolytes on the basis of their ability or nonability to conduct an electric current. Conductance in water solutions is taken as evidence for the presence of ions to carry the current. The conductance of pure water is very feeble, but it can be measured by sensitive instruments even though only one water molecule in 555 million dissociates into ions. This is so insignificant that it could be entirely neglected if it were not for the fact that it turns out to be responsible for some of the important properties of water. Many metabolic reactions in living organisms depend upon the hydrogen ion and hydroxide ion concentrations in the blood and other body liquids. Acids and bases, as we will have occasion to note later, can be defined on the basis of how they affect these concentrations, as follows: *An acid is a substance that increases the hydrogen ion concentration.*[3]

One of the unusual properties of water is that it can act as either a base (as in Eq. 27-7) or as an acid as follows:[4]

$$H_2O \;+\; H_2O \;\rightleftharpoons\; H_3O^+ \;+\; OH^-$$

acid$_1$ base$_2$ acid$_2$ base$_1$
(weak)   (weak)   (strong)   (strong)

[27-8]

The process is the same as in acids, the transfer of a proton from one molecule to another. One water molecule acts as a proton donor and the other as a proton acceptor. (The difference in the length of the arrows in Eq. 27-8 shows that water has only a slight tendency to ionize.) Thus we see another way in which the Brønsted concept differs from the Arrhenius concept, for here water acts as both a base and an acid.

---

[3] This was the Arrhenius concept, a concept that is still useful to biologists today. We will use it later.
[4] The unequal size of the arrows in Eq. 27-8 is a symbolic way of saying that water has a far greater tendency to remain in the molecular form (H_2O) rather than in the ionic form (H_3O^+ and OH^-). In general, the longer arrow shows the direction in which the reaction tends to proceed.

Other acids react with water similarly to HCl (Eq. 27-7):

$$H_2SO_4 \;+\; 2H_2O \;\rightleftharpoons\; 2H_3O^+ \;+\; SO_4^{2-}$$

acid$_1$ base$_2$ acid$_2$ base$_1$
(sulfuric)   (sulfate ion)

[27-9]

$$HNO_3 \;+\; H_2O \;\rightleftharpoons\; H_3O^+ \;+\; NO_3^-$$

acid$_1$ base$_2$ acid$_2$ base$_1$
(nitric)   (nitrate ion)

[27-10]

$$HC_2H_3O_2 \;+\; H_2O \;\rightleftharpoons\; H_3O^+ \;+\; C_2H_3O_2^-$$

acid$_1$ base$_2$ acid$_2$ base$_1$
(acetic)   (acetate ion)
(weak)   (weak)   (strong)   (strong)

[27-11]

Bases that have metals for their positive ions are ionic compounds and so dissociate in water just as do the salts. The ions are freed from their lattices by the water molecules in the manner previously described (Fig. 27-2). In the process a great deal of heat is given off. The strongest bases commonly available are metallic hydroxides in aqueous media. Simple bases with positive ions that are not metals are rare; NH_3 (ammonia) is the *only common* one.

$$H_2O \;+\; NH_3 \;\rightleftharpoons\; NH_4^+ \;+\; OH^-$$

acid$_1$ base$_2$ acid$_2$ base$_1$

[27-12]

Generalizing with respect to both acids and bases, we can say that (according to Brønsted) those substances that form H_3O^+ ions in water are acids, and those that form OH^- ions are bases.

Conjugate Acids and Bases

Acid-base reactions are proton transfer reactions. After an acid transfers a proton, the residual molecule that is left can accept a proton; it is therefore a base. An acid always becomes a base after the transfer. This base is called the *conjugate base* of the acid. It follows, then, that when a base accepts the proton, it becomes an acid. This acid is the *conjugate* acid of the base. We see then that proton transfer reactions always creates new acids and bases. Consider the reaction

$$HCl \quad + \quad H_2O \;\rightleftharpoons\; H_3O^+ + \quad Cl^-$$

acid$_1$	base$_2$	acid$_2$	base$_1$
(very strong)	(weak)	(strong)	(very weak)

[27-13]

The subscripts indicate the conjugate acid-base pairs. Examine the acid-base reactions in Eqs. 27-8 through 27-11 and test them against the following generalizations:

1. Strong acids generate weak conjugate bases.
2. Strong bases generate weak conjugate acids.

From the Brønsted–Lowry definitions it follows that the better the donor, the stronger the acid. Also, the better the acceptor, the stronger the base.

Leveling Effect

All strong acids—including $HClO_4$ (perchloric acid), HI, HBr, HNO_3, and HCl—when dissolved in water, appear to have exactly equal strengths, although in solvents less basic than water, their strengths decrease in the order listed. A glance at Eqs. 27-9 through 27-11 shows why; all react with water to form hydronium ion. The apparent acidity of all has been reduced to that of the hydronium ion. This is called the leveling effect. Hydronium ion is therefore the strongest acid that can exist in appreciable concentration in a water solution.

Neutralization

Equation 27-8 indicates that the H_3O^+ and OH^- have a considerable tendency to unite to form water, so much so that water is only slightly dissociated into ions. We should not be surprised, therefore, that if these two ions from separate sources are brought into contact with each other, they should combine to form water molecules. Thus, when the strong base, OH^- ion, is added to the strong acid, H_3O^+ ion, water is formed.

$$H_3O^+ \quad + \quad OH^- \;\rightleftharpoons\; H_2O \quad + \quad H_2O$$

acid$_1$	base$_2$	acid$_2$	base$_1$

[27-14]

This process is called neutralization, for by the disappearance of the two kinds of ions, the effects of one kind appear to neutralize the effects of the other kind. We cannot, of course, simply add these two ions together, for each always occurs with at least one other ion. Thus, if we add a water solution of HCl to a water solution of NaOH, we may write ionically.

$$H_3O^+ \quad + \quad Cl^- \quad + \quad Na^+ \quad + \quad OH^- \;\rightarrow\;$$

acid$_1$ base$_2$

$$H_2O \quad + \quad H_2O \quad + \quad Na^+ \quad + \quad Cl^-$$

acid$_2$ base$_1$

[27-15]

Eliminating the ions that occur on both sides (the so-called spectator ions), we have Eq. 27-14. Note that this equation is the same as Eq. 27-8, except that it is written in reverse. Thus, the reaction between an acid and a base tends toward the production of the weakest possible acid and the weakest possible base.

Note that in Eq. 27-15 we have Na^+ and Cl^- on both sides of the equation. The Arrhenius concept of the neutralization of an acid by a base was the production of water and a salt. His concept was developed before anything was known about the structure of atoms, before it was known how ions were produced. He thought that it was the water that created them. Now that we know that the Na^+ was present in the solid NaOH and that Cl^- ions are present in a water solution of hydrogen chloride, we see that it can hardly be said that it was the neutralization that produced the salt. All that really happens when water solutions of NaOH and HCl are mixed is that H_3O^+ ion and OH^- ion combine to form water. The Na^+ and Cl^- ions do nothing except remain Na^+ and Cl^- ions. Thus our neutralization equation is simply Eq. 27-14. It tells us that whenever H_3O^+ (or H^+) ions are brought in contact with each other, the product is water. It matters not what the sources of the ions are.

Which Theory Is True?

We have presented the Arrhenius concept and the Brønsted–Lowry concept of acids and bases in some detail. We mentioned in a footnote another concept that was formulated by the great American chemist G. N. Lewis. There is still a fourth that is in use today, which we will not consider here. This may be confusing to many students but it should not be to you, because you should by this time understand the purpose of theories. No chemist would ever attempt to answer the question, "Which one is true?" These theories are not mutually contradictory. The Arrhenius theory was found to be too narrow in scope to be useful in some situations. The Brønsted–Lowry theory is more extensive and so includes some substances as acids and bases that the Arrhenius theory excluded. The theory of G. N. Lewis is still broader. It includes all of the acids and bases of the other two and more. No one of these theories denies the other. The situation

is similar to that of a carpenter who wishes to reduce the size of a board. He may use a saw, a plane, a knife, a chisel, or a rasp. All can reduce the board in size, but the carpenter uses the tool that is best suited for the particular purpose he has in mind.

Exercises

1. A glass of "water" is clear but red in color. Another is cloudy and red in color. Explain the differences.
2. How does a colloidal particle differ from one in suspension and one in solution?
3. Distinguish between the solution process and the melting process.
4. Distinguish between a material in suspension and one in solution.
5. What is meant by the solubility of a substance?
6. (a) In general, are solids more or less soluble in hot water than in cold?
   (b) Is the case the same with gases?
7. How is the solubility of a substance commonly expressed?
8. Cite from your own experience an example that shows that gases are less soluble in warm solutions than in cold.
9. What is meant by "miscible in all proportions"?
10. A lump of common salt and a lump of sugar look almost exactly alike. Before the invention of the battery, was it possible to know that one was ionic and one was not? Explain.
11. What solvent or solvents would you use to remove (a) a sugar stain, (b) a grease spot, (c) a stain made by spilling soda pop on a rug, and (d) a stain made by heavily sugared coffee containing heavy cream? Give reasons for your answers.
12. Knowing that CCl_4 is nonpolar, would you use it to remove a sugar stain? Explain.

13. Name the three groups of substances that conduct a current when dissolved in water.
14. Molten salts and bases conduct electric currents, but solid salts and bases do not. Explain.
15. What is meant by dissociation?
16. Common table salt is dissolved in water.
    (a) Does the salt dissociate?
    (b) Is it an electrolyte? Explain.
17. Define (a) an acid and (b) a base. Name three of each.
18. What element is commonly (but not always) found in both acids and bases?
19. What is meant by neutralization?
20. What is the hydronium ion?

21. What is always formed whenever hydronium ion and hydroxide ion are brought together?
22. What makes a strong acid fundamentally different from a weak acid?
23. In a $1\,M$ water solution of acetic acid most of the acid molecules remain as acid molecules, whereas in a $1\,M$ water solution of hydrochloric acid, almost none of the acid molecules remain as such. Explain.
24. Suppose you add one liter of a $1\,M$ solution of NaOH to one liter of each of the acid solutions mentioned in exercise 23. Explain what happens in each case in terms of neutralization.

Chemical Energy, Reaction Rates, Equilibrium

That energy is released in many chemical reactions is apparent every time we burn a substance. This energy is observable because it has been transformed, in most cases, to heat, light, kinetic energy, or electrical energy. Chemical energy remained a mystery for a long time. Not until modern theories of atomic structure had arisen did the chemist realize that chemical energy is electron potential energy.

Exothermic Reactions

If we mix solutions of concentrated HCl and NaOH, there will be a violent boiling with much heat released. The chemical union of the molecules of gasoline with those of oxygen in the cylinders of our cars generates so much heat that we must equip them with a competent cooling system. Most burning processes generate light as well as heat; in a few—for example, the burning of the metal magnesium in a flash bulb—the light is more important than the heat. All of the above reactions are said to be exothermic because energy is released when they take place. In most exo-

Imagination is more powerful than knowledge.
ALBERT EINSTEIN

490

thermic reactions almost all of the radiant energy is emitted in the frequencies that lie in the infrared part of the spectrum, although frequencies in the visible range are common.

Carefully controlled experiments reveal that if equal numbers of molecules are involved in a particular reaction, the amount of energy given off is the same every time that reaction takes place. Thus, every time two moles of sodium react with one mole of chlorine, 196,800 cal of heat is liberated. We may write

$$2Na + Cl_2 \rightarrow$$
$$\text{2 moles} \quad \text{1 mole}$$

$$2Na^+ + 2Cl^- + 196,800 \text{ cal}$$
$$\text{2 moles} \quad \text{2 moles}$$
$$[28\text{-}1]$$

Endothermic Reactions

We learned in Chapter 18 that Faraday in his electrolysis experiments broke down NaCl into its component elements, sodium and chlorine, by the use of electrical energy. Energy was consumed—absorbed—in the process instead of being liberated. Thus it was an endothermic process. In the plant world the chemical reactions responsible for the growth of the various parts (leaves, stems, flowers, fruit, bark, wood, and so on) are all endothermic reactions, powered, so to speak, by the energy of the sun aided by chlorophyll as a catalyst. The physiological processes that build the bodies of animal life are all endothermic, although the digestive processes are exothermic.

The formation of NO from N_2 and O_2 is moderately endothermic. (If it were exothermic, there would be no oxygen left in the atmosphere. Why not?) The reaction may be written

$$N_2 + O_2 + 44,000 \text{ cal} \rightarrow 2NO$$
$$\text{1 mole} \quad \text{1 mole} \qquad\qquad \text{2 moles}$$
$$[28\text{-}2]$$

This absorbed heat does not raise the temperature of the NO formed above that of the N_2 and the O_2. Instead, a cooling results, for the absorbed heat must come from the surroundings. It follows that, once the source of the added heat energy is removed, the reaction stops.

Many salts when dissolved in water absorb energy from their surroundings, chiefly from the water itself, thus cooling it. This process is therefore an endothermic one. An example is potassium nitrate, KNO_3 (in aqueous solution).

$$K^+NO_3^- + 8500 \text{ cal} \rightarrow K^+ + NO_3^-$$
$$\text{1 mole} \qquad\qquad\qquad \text{1 mole} \quad \text{1 mole}$$
$$[28\text{-}3]$$

Let us return briefly to Eq. 28-1. This is an exothermic reaction that liberates 196,800 cal per mole of Cl_2. From the law of conservation of energy we might predict that the opposite reaction is endothermic, and that 196,800 cal will be needed to break up two moles of NaCl into Na and Cl_2.

$$2Na^+ Cl^- + 196,800 \text{ cal} \rightarrow 2Na + Cl_2$$
$$\text{2 moles} \qquad\qquad\qquad \text{2 moles} \quad \text{1 mole}$$
$$[28\text{-}4]$$

We can also apply the law of conservation of energy to the reaction described by Eq. 28-3. If this solution is evaporated to regain the dry KNO_3 in crystal form again, 8500 cal will be released per mole of KNO_3 crystals.

Electron Potential Energy

We stated that chemical energy is electron potential energy, a conclusion that can be reached after a study of the original Bohr theory. None of its modifications, not even its replacement by the wave mechanical theory, can negate the general principle involved. We learned that when electrons of hydrogen atoms absorbed energy in quantum amounts they moved to energy levels farther removed from the nucleus, and that when they returned to lower levels they emitted energy. During the time that the electrons remained at the higher levels, the absorbed energy was stored in the electrons as potential energy.

When endothermic reactions take place, new arrangements of the valence electrons in the products formed involve higher energy levels than the old, energy that must be supplied from the outside. In terms of the Bohr theory, the electrons must be supplied with energy to enable them to attain higher energy levels, levels that they must occupy if the particles (atoms, ions, molecules) are to exist in this new state. These transitions to higher levels increase the potential energy of the valence electrons because work must be done *against* the attractive forces of the nuclei to shift them into these more distant orbits. Their potential energy is higher because they are farther from the oppositely charged nuclei.

Conversely, we reason that when exothermic reactions take place, the valence electrons occupy lower energy levels, and at the same time radiate the differences in energy in much the same form as they absorbed it, that is, chiefly as electromagnetic energy—heat and light.

Activation Energy

If 22.4 liters (one gram molecular volume) of O_2 and 22.4 liters of N_2 are mixed and are kept at standard temperature and pressure, the number of collisions between the molecules will be greater than 10^{30} per second. Yet the two gases will not unite to form any of the oxides of nitrogen (Table 15-1) under those conditions. Neither will the paper forming the pages of this book unite with oxygen under normal conditions, despite the innumerable impacts of the oxygen molecules against the pages. These facts prove that more than mere collision is necessary to initiate many reactions. Again we call on our electronic theory of chemical reactions for an answer.

Each atom, ion, or molecule has an electron cloud (Fig. 22-16) surrounding it. These electron clouds, being similarly charged, repel one another. As a result, the reactant particles do not normally get close enough together to react in the collisions that take place under average conditions. To react, at least one of two colliding particles must exist in an activated state; that is, it must possess sufficient energy to penetrate the electron cloud of the other particle.

Ions may be regarded as activated particles, for if both reactants are in the ionic state before mixing, the reaction is instantaneous. Mixing solutions of NaCl and $AgNO_3$, both ionic, produce an instantaneous precipitate. Mixing equivalent quantities of strong acids and bases in water solution, both ionic, produces an instantaneous neutralization. Electrically neutral atoms and molecules must, on the other hand, be activated in most cases before they will react. To become activated such neutral particles must receive kinetic energy from some outside source, such as by collisions with swifter moving particles or, most commonly from the application of heat. Oxygen molecules in the atmosphere are not activated until the covalent bonds that hold the pairs of atoms together are broken. A slight increase, say 10%, in the temperature will sometimes increase the number of activated molecules so greatly that the reaction rate may be increased several hundred or even several thousand per cent.

If all particles that are capable of reacting with one another were in an activated state at normal temperatures, pressures, concentrations, and so on, our world would be so different that we would not be here to contemplate it. Everything that is combustible in oxygen would long since have been burned up. Substances with low activation energies are highly flammable. Some with extremely low activation energies are used as explosives, and are dangerous to handle, for example, nitroglycerine, which may need only a slight jar to activate it.

Factors Affecting Reaction Rates

An electronic theory of chemical bonding, if it is to be considered valid, should be able to explain how certain factors affect the rates at which chemical reactions take place. Observation and experiment have shown these factors to be five in number, as follows:

1. Nature of the reactants.
2. Temperature.
3. Concentration.
4. State of subdivision (in the case of solids).
5. Catalysts.

For any particular pair of reactants the rate depends on 2 through 5.

Nature of Reactants

As the fundamental change that takes place in a chemical reaction is the breaking of chemical bonds and the formation of new ones—that is, a reshuffling of the chemical bonds—it is reasonable to expect that the rate of change would depend on the specific kinds of bonds involved. We have already seen that if a substance is ionic in the solid state, it will be completely ionic in solution. In general, salts and metallic bases are ionic in the solid state. We have also seen that strong acids are completely ionic in water solution. All these substances are ready to react instantly with a proper reactant.

Consider the mixing of two completely ionic solutions, one of them KCl, the other $AgNO_3$. Instantly a white precipitate of AgCl forms. AgCl is only slightly soluble in water (see p. 480). Before the mixing, the silver ions in one solution, the chloride ions in the other, are ready to react. All that is necessary is to bring them together. Dump one solution into the other and the deed is accomplished.

Let us add ferrous ion, Fe^{2+}, to permanganate ion, MnO_4^-. The reduction of the latter to manganous ion, Mn^{2+}, is instantaneous in a well-mixed solution, as is readily observed by the disappearance of the deep purple color.

Oxalic acid, $H_2C_2O_4$, will also reduce permanganate ion, but not instantaneously. Oxalic acid is a nonionic solid whose bonds are covalent. In water solution it ionizes only slightly, for it is a weak acid. Mix it with a solution of permanganate ions and the relatively few acid ions react to reduce an equal number of permanganate ions. Immediately more acid molecules ionize, these in turn are used up, and more acid molecules ionize, and so on, until all the permanganate ions are reduced. This takes time, not very much, but it is far from instantaneous because two reactions are involved, one of ionization, followed by one of reduction.

On the other hand, many of the important reactions in organic chemistry, including those involved in the digestion of food, are so slow that they take hours. Others, as in certain reactions that take place in solids—for example, those that accompany certain geological processes such as weathering and metamorphism (Chapter 34) may take years, thousands of years, or even millions of years to accomplish. Eventually, all reactions either become practically complete, or they reach a condition of equilibrium in which the rate of the reverse reaction is exactly equal to the rate of the forward reaction. Our information is gained chiefly from those reactions in which the rate is moderate.

Temperature

It is reasonable to expect that if there is to be a reshuffling of the bonds, particles—be they atoms, ions, or molecules—must collide. Electrons can neither be transferred nor shared except on close contact. Thus, any factor that increases the probability of collision will *tend* to increase the reaction rate. Chief among these factors is increased temperatures. When substances are heated, the average kinetic energies of their molecules are increased. This means not only more collisions per second but more energetic collisions. The magnitude of the increase in the reaction rate with a given rise in temperature varies widely, not only from one reaction to another but also from one temperature range to another. No simple generalization is possible.

Concentration

If the collision concept is valid, it is apparent why an increase in concentration of one or both[1] of the reactants increases the rate of reaction. The greater the number of particles, the greater the likelihood of collisions.

State of Subdivision

The state of subdivision is important, for reactions can take place only at the surfaces at which particles come in contact. The more finely divided a solid is, the greater the total

area of contact per unit mass. The rate of reaction is proportional to the area of contact between a solid and a liquid or gas. This means that the smaller the solid particles, the faster the rate. A wet mass of steel wool will completely rust away far faster than will a wet cubical bar of iron of equal mass. Coal in the form of chunks burns quietly, but in the form of a fine dust suspended in the air may burn so rapidly that it literally explodes.

Some potential reactants, even if ground as finely as flour, may remain in contact for years without reacting as long as they are kept perfectly dry. An example is ordinary baking powder, which is a mixture of solids. When water is added, there is a moderately violent reaction in which CO_2 is liberated. The role of the water with respect to potential solid reactants is to dissolve the solids; this brings the state of subdivision down to that of discrete particles (atoms, ions, molecules). This increases the surface area to the maximum possible. Thus, most reactions take place in water (or other solvent).

Catalysts

Some substances have been found to speed up chemical reactions even though they themselves remain unchanged. These are called catalysts. Small amounts of catalysts are able to influence the reaction of enormously large amounts of reactants. This is not surprising if the catalyst undergoes no net change. Catalysts are equally effective in the forward and reverse directions of reversible (equilibrium) reactions. Thus, the only effect that a catalyst can have in an equilibrium reaction is to speed up the attainment of the equilibrium. Important as catalysts in biochemical reactions are the enzymes (p. 516).

A catalyst provides a new reaction path calling for lower activation energies. Some catalysts dissolve in a reaction mixture where

---

[1] We are and have been assuming, and will continue to assume, that only two reactants are involved. This is commonly the case, but there may be three, four, or even more in rare cases.

the catalyst quickly reacts with one component to form a compound which in turn reacts quickly with another component. In this second reaction the catalyst is released in its original state, ready to start a new reaction cycle. In photosynthesis (p. 513) the radiant energy supplied by sunlight is absorbed by chlorophyll, a catalyst, which then transfers this energy to the reacting molecules without itself entering into the reaction.

Stability vs. Instability

Substances with high activation energies are chemically stable; that is, they are capable of existing appreciably unchanged for long periods of time and in a variety of environments. Even those compounds whose reactions are highly exothermic are stable if their activation energies are sufficiently high. Substances used as explosives are very unstable. They have abnormally low activation energies. Compounds whose reactions are strongly endothermic are almost always stable, for it takes considerable energy to change their composition. For example, H_2 and O_2 will react with each other with explosive violence, given sufficient activation energy, liberating 116,800 cal per mole of O_2. The resulting water is highly stable. Similarly, the carbon and hydrogen of wood, coal, oil, paper, and such, unite with oxygen with the evolution of much heat to form the more stable CO_2 and H_2O. All of them require some elevation of temperature to start them burning. That is what matches are for.

Stability is, however, a relative concept. A substance that is stable in one environment may be unstable in another. Carbonic acid, H_2CO_3, is stable under high pressures but not at low ones. Milk is more stable in the refrigerator than out of it. All compounds become unstable at the temperatures found in some stars. Minerals formed at considerable depths in the crust of the earth become unstable when exposed to the atmosphere by the erosion of the overlying rocks.

The concept of stability also involves time. Many substances that appear to remain unchanged during a person's lifetime eventually decay and crumble as they slowly react with the water, carbon dioxide, and oxygen of the earth's atmosphere. Man can prolong or permanently forestall such changes by creating an artificial environment in which little or no chemical reaction is possible.[2] In nature, though, given time enough, all matter is reduced to the lowest energy state possible in the environment in which it finds itself. Once in that state it will remain stable as long as the environment does not change in such a way that the electrons of the molecules are forced into a higher energy level. In substances that are completely inert the electrons are in the lowest energy state possible, and the energy needed to move them to higher levels is impossibly high—here on earth at any rate.

Chemical Equilibrium

Actual experiments show that most chemical reactions do not reach completion no matter how long the reaction is allowed to continue. In other words, the reactants are rarely completely changed to products. As the reaction proceeds the concentrations of the reactants decrease and that of the products increase. Sooner or later all concentrations level off and remain constant as long as temperature and pressure do not change. Chemical equilibrium has been reached.

Chemical equilibrium implies that the reactions involved are reversible; that is, there is

[2] In refrigerators, in air-tight receptacles, in a vacuum, and so on.

a forward reaction between two reactants, A and B, to form products C and D, and a reverse reaction in which C and D are reacting to form A and B. The reaction

$$A + B \rightleftharpoons C + D \quad [28\text{-}5]$$

does not simply proceed to a certain point and then stop. At first the reaction consists entirely of A and B reacting to form C and D, but as the concentrations of C and D become appreciable, they begin to react to form A and B although at first more slowly than the forward reaction. The result is that the concentrations of C and D are increasing, and with this increase, the rate of the reaction between C and D increases. Meanwhile the concentrations of both A and B are decreasing, so that the rate of the forward reaction decreases.

A point in time is finally reached when the decreasing rate of the reaction between A and B is equaled by the increasing rate of the reaction between C and D. When this point is reached, both reactions continue at the same rate as long as the temperature does not change. The system is now at equilibrium.

Summarizing, we may say that the concentrations of A and B decrease relatively rapidly at first while those of C and D increase just as rapidly. When equilibrium is reached, the concentrations of all four remain constant as long as the temperature does not change. How long it takes to reach this equilibrium state varies from almost instantaneously to an indefinitely long time. Once established it persists forever if left undisturbed.

We see, therefore, that the concept of chemical equilibrium is analogous to mechanical equilibrium; it is a state of balance between two opposing actions. No *net* change is produced because the two opposing actions cancel each other. We have encountered equilibria in mechanical situations before, one being in Millikan's oil drop experiment (Chapter 18),

where the electrical force, *Eq*, was balanced by the gravitational force, *mg*. We also encountered an equilibrium situation in saturated solutions, where, with an excess of the solute, the number of molecules going into solution equaled the number passing out of solution.

Le Châtelier, a French chemist, announced an important principle concerning chemical equilibrium in 1888. It is now known as Le Châtelier's principle: *If one factor in an equilibrium system is changed, the system will adjust in such a way as to reduce the factor causing the change and thereby reach a new equilibrium.* Remember that this principle applies only to systems that are already in equilibrium.

Factors in Adjusting Chemical Equilibria

The chemist has three methods of adjusting a chemical equilibrium: (1) by changing the temperature, (2) by changing the concentration of one or more of the reactants, (3) by changing the pressure (if one or more of the reactants and/or products is a gas).

The practical use of the concept of equilibrium may be illustrated by the synthesis of ammonia gas (NH_3) from N_2 and H_2. The reaction may be written

$$3H_2 + N_2 \underset{100 \text{ atm}}{\overset{400°C,}{\rightleftharpoons}} 2NH_3 + 26{,}740 \text{ cal}$$

$$[28\text{-}6]$$

This reaction is still of great industrial importance, but in World War I it was crucial because at that time ammonia was absolutely essential in the manufacture of certain explosives and fertilizers. Without the development of a method of synthesizing ammonia by Haber in 1913, Germany could scarcely have survived a year of war, for her supply of nitrates from Chile were effectively cut off by the British blockade. Moreover, when the

United States entered the war, our supply of Chilean nitrates was greatly diminished by the German submarine blockade. The Haber method now makes us independent of the Chilean deposits.

Ammonia, nitrogen, and hydrogen are all gases, and in gaseous reactions pressure is important, for it determines the concentration of the gas by controlling the number of molecules per unit volume at fixed temperatures. This in turn determines the collision rates. The reaction between N_2 and H_2 is almost nil at ordinary temperatures, for the activation energy is high. If the temperature is raised to 500 to 700°C, the rate of conversion to ammonia is increased, for reaction rates are always increased by an increase in temperature.

However, since this is a reversible reaction, the rates of both the forward and the reverse reactions are increased. As predicted by Le Châtelier's principle, the rate of the *reverse* reaction is increased more than the rate of the forward reaction so that the equilibrium is shifted toward the left side of Eq. 28-6, thus actually decreasing the yield of ammonia. The reason for this can be seen by examining the equation. The reactants (left side) are $3H_2$ and N_2. The products (right side) are $2NH_3$ and 26,740 cal of heat energy. Raising the temperature to increase the reaction rate means that heat energy is being added. But heat energy is part of this reaction; it is on the right side of the equation. Therefore, according to Le Châtelier's principle, the equilibrium must shift to the left in order to remove this added factor, and thus more nitrogen and hydrogen will be formed at the expense of any ammonia that has been produced. Catalysts can be used (and were used in this process) to increase the yield, but catalysts increase the reaction rates in both directions. With catalysts the percentage yield at 500°C and a pressure of 1 atm was only 0.13%. At 800°C (and the same pressure) it was reduced to 0.01%. Changes in the concentrations were of no avail. Some other stress had to be applied. The problem here is to increase the reaction rate to the right more than the rate to the left.

Now, if one or more of the reactants or products are gases, then pressure can be a factor in Le Châtelier's principle. Increase in pressure forces the molecules of gases closer together and so increases the probability of collision. Application of Avogadro's law (equal volumes of gases under the same conditions of temperature and pressure contain the same number of molecules) to Eq. 28-6 shows us that if one volume of N_2 were to combine *completely* with three volumes of H_2, there would result two volumes of NH_3. That is, if Eq. 28-6 represented a reaction that goes to completion, we would start with four volumes of gases (one of N_2 and three of H_2) and end with two volumes. This is our way out of the impasse. An increase in pressure (on a gaseous reaction) tends to reduce the volume and therefore moves the equilibrium to the side having the lower volume. The Haber process succeeds by use of very high pressures: the reaction shifts appreciably to the right because the formation of NH_3 reduces the pressure (by conversion of four volumes of gas into two volumes). The result is that at a pressure of 200 atm and 500°C, the yield rises from 0.13% (at 1 atm) to 17.6%, over 135 times as great.

You might well ask how this NH_3 is separated from the uncombined H_2 and N_2. Ammonia gas is highly soluble in water, far more so than either N_2 or H_2. Hence water sprayed from the top of the tank dissolves the ammonia, leaving most of the H_2 and N_2 behind to be used again. The reaction between N_2 and H_2 is a classical example of the use of Le Châtelier's principle to obtain conditions favoring a desired chemical reaction. There are hundreds of similar examples. Knowledge of the principle saves untold time and money over the only alternative, trial and error.

One must not conclude that every reaction that involves gases is favored in the manner of the N_2 and H_2 reaction by an increase in pressure. Consider a reaction in which all components are gases (I_2 is a diatomic gas at 490°C):

$$H_2 \ + \ I_2 \ \rightleftharpoons \ 2HI \qquad [28\text{-}7]$$

Increase of pressure is ineffective in pushing the reaction either way, for there are the same number of molecules in the container regardless of whether the hydrogen and iodine exist as molecules of H_2 and I_2 or as molecules of HI. It is only when the number of volumes of gaseous products is less than the number of volumes of gaseous reactants that pressure drives the reaction to the right.

Some Further Applications of the Equilibrium Concept

The equilibrium concept is of the utmost importance to the understanding of many rather common chemical phenomena. A few of them are worth our attention.

Common Ion Effect. Le Châtelier's principle may also be used to explain the common ion effect. The ionization of acetic acid may be written as follows:

$$\underset{\text{acetic acid molecule}}{HC_2H_3O_2} \ \rightleftharpoons \ H^+ \ + \ \underset{\text{acetate ion}}{C_2H_3O_2^-}$$

The different arrow lengths show that acetic acid is a weak acid and so ionizes sparingly in water. Suppose we add to the above a little of an ionic solution containing acetate ion but not H^+. A test will show that acidity of the acetic acid solution has been greatly reduced. According to Le Châtelier's principle, the addition of acetate ion from any source will drive the reaction to the left so as to reduce the

number of acetate ions present. This reduction can only be done by H^+ and $C_2H_3O_2^-$ recombining to form acetic acid molecules, thus removing H^+ ions from the solution and thereby making the solution less acid.

Likewise, the solubility of one partially soluble salt may be decreased by adding another salt with which it has an ion in common. Consider a saturated solution of $PbCl_2$:

$$Pb^{2+} \ + \ 2Cl^- \ \rightleftharpoons \ PbCl_2$$

Add chloride ions from any source and the reaction will be driven to the right to counteract the addition of Cl^-. This can only be done by precipitation of $PbCl_2$. Add enough chloride ions from the other source and nearly all Pb^{2+} ions will be forced out of solution. This is part of one of the processes used in the production of metallic lead from lead ore.

Extremely Weak Acids and Bases; Neutral Solutions. No adequate discussion of these acids and bases was possible until some of the principles of the previous sections of this chapter had been developed. The pertinent concepts are those of reversibility, equilibrium, and the common ion effect. These may be used to help explain water as an extremely weak acid or an extremely weak base. In our discussion of acids (Chapter 27) we have considered the acidic ion present in water solutions to be the hydronium ion, H_3O^+. It makes little difference whether we use this Brønsted concept or the Arrhenius concept. We have seen that pure water may act either as an acid or a base; it dissociates very slightly, forming H^+ ions (the characteristic ion of acids), and OH^- ions (the characteristic ion of bases), so that it is easy to see why it can be considered either as an extremely weak acid or an extremely weak base. The extent of dissociation is of the order of one pair of ions (H^+ and OH^-) in 555 million molecules of water when the temperature is 25°C. This is to say that at 25°C there is one ten-millionth of a mole of hydrogen ions in one liter of water. An equivalent method[3] of expressing this concentration is to say that it is 1×10^{-7} mole/liter at 25°C. The concentration of OH^- ions in pure water at the same temperature must be the same.

What, then, constitutes a neutral solution? Consider the equation for the ionization of water, which can be written either

$$H_2O \rightleftharpoons H^+ + OH^-$$

or

$$H_2O + H_2O \rightleftharpoons H_3O^+ + OH^-$$

It is seen that the numbers of H^+ and OH^- ions must be equal. We may then define a neutral solution as one in which the $[H^+]$ (to be read "the concentration of H^+ ion") and the $[OH^-]$ (to be read "the concentration of OH ion") are the same. As long as we have pure water, and as long as the temperature is 25°C, each concentration will be 1×10^{-7} mole/liter.

An aqueous *acid* solution is one in which the $[H^+]$ is greater than 1×10^{-7} mole/liter, and an aqueous *alkaline* solution is one in which the $[OH^-]$ is greater than 1×10^{-7} mole/liter at 25°C. The product of these two concentrations, 1×10^{-7} and 1×10^{-7}, is

---

[3]We arrive at this result as follows: A liter of water weighs 1000 g. Its molecular weight is 18. Therefore in a liter of water there are $1000/18 = 55.5$ moles. The concentration of pure water may therefore be said to be 55.5 moles per liter. One H^+ ion in 555 million molecules of water is equivalent to one mole of H^+ ions in 555 million moles of water. The number of moles of H^+ ion in 55.5 moles of water (one liter) at 25°C is thus,

$$55.5 \times \frac{1}{555,000,000} = \frac{55.5}{55.5 \times 10^7} = \frac{1}{10^7}$$

$$= 1 \times 10^{-7} \text{ mole/liter}$$

As concentrations are commonly expressed in moles per liter, it follows that the concentration of H^+ in pure water is 1×10^{-7} mole/liter (at 25°C).

1×10^{-14}. This is known as the equilibrium constant of a neutral solution at 25°C.

It follows that alkaline (basic) solutions always have a few H^+ ions present and that acidic solutions always have a few OH^- ions present. The number may be very small, but it is never zero for the H^+ ion in strong *basic* solutions or for the OH^- ion in strong *acidic* solutions. As $[H^+]$ goes up, $[OH^-]$ must go down a corresponding amount. Thus, if $[H^+]$ is increased to 1×10^{-6} mole/liter (at 25°C), the $[OH^-]$ is decreased to 1×10^{-8} mole/liter. Note that the product of these two concentrations is also 1×10^{-14}.

pH[4]. In the fields of analytical chemistry and biochemistry minute changes in the $[H^+]$ and $[OH^-]$ may have significant consequences. The chemist and the biologist both find it awkward to express the $[H^+]$ and $[OH^-]$ in the negative powers of 10. To simplify matters a scale called the pH scale has been devised. It simply takes the negative power of 10, changes the sign, and uses it all alone. Thus, instead of saying that the $[H^+]$ in a solution containing 0.0000001 mole/liter is 1×10^{-7}, we simply say its pH is 7. This is, by definition, a neutral solution because pure water contains 1×10^{-7} moles/liter of H^+ ion, and 1×10^{-7} moles/liter of OH^- ion. Numbers higher than 7 indicate alkaline solutions, and those lower than 7 indicate acidic solutions.

Indicators. Accurate measurement of the pH of a solution involves considerable difficulty, in part experimental, in part theoretical. The approximate pH may be determined by the use of certain indicators, the colors of which change as the $[H^+]$ changes. These indicators are always either slightly acidic or slightly basic (alkaline) themselves. Since the color of

---

[4]Pronounced pee aitch.

an indicator changes with the concentration of the H$^+$ ion, the addition of acid to a neutral solution containing the indicator will give one color, the addition of a base will give another color. Various indicators have different sensitivity ranges, some changing color while still faintly acid, others while still faintly basic. Any indicator whose color change falls in the pH range of 4 to 10 may be used to determine the neutralization point of a strong base and a strong acid.

Buffer[5] Solutions. The H$^+$ ion and OH$^-$ ion concentrations of the solutions we have been dealing with are astonishingly small. A solution with a pH of 5.0 corresponds to the degree of acidity produced by adding a single drop of concentrated HCl to 20 gal of water. A pH of 9.0 corresponds to the degree of alkalinity produced by adding one drop of concentrated NaOH to the same quantity of water. Such faintly acid or faintly alkaline solutions are difficult to preserve with a definite pH. Faintly acid solutions may be neutralized in time by alkali dissolved from the glass of the container. Faintly alkaline solutions may be neutralized or even made faintly acid by H$_2$CO$_3$ derived from the atmosphere

$$H_2O \quad + \quad CO_2 \quad \rightleftharpoons \quad H_2CO_3$$

Thus, the pH of distilled water on exposure to the atmosphere changes from 7.0 to 6.0 or even to 5.0.

The remedy, if a constant pH is desired, is to add to the faintly acid or faintly alkaline solution a salt or a mixture of salts that have been derived from *weak acids and strong bases,* or from *strong acids and weak bases.* The re-

[5] The concept here is much the same as that of a buffer state in international politics. Just as a series of small states surrounding a major state may protect the latter to some extent from direct aggression, so a buffer solution is protected from the effects of small additional quantities of acid or base.

sulting solution will maintain a nearly constant pH even if moderate amounts of additional acid or alkali are added. Consider a solution of acetic acid in water:

$$\underset{\substack{\text{acetic acid}\\\text{molecules}}}{HC_2H_3O_2} + H_2O \quad \rightleftharpoons \quad H_3O^+ + \underset{\substack{\text{acetate}\\\text{ions}}}{C_2H_3O_2^-}$$

Now let us add an acetate salt to this solution, say sodium acetate (NaC$_2$H$_3$O$_2$). This salt is composed of Na and C$_2$H$_3$O$_2$ ions. Adding the sodium acetate greatly increases the number of acetate ions present in the solution, constituting a reserve supply, with no corresponding increase of hydronium ions. Since acetic acid ionizes so sparingly in water, there is also a reserve supply of acetic acid molecules. We will suppose that this water solution of acetic acid and sodium acetate is in equilibrium.

If we now add a little alkali, say NaOH, to it, the OH ions will neutralize an equivalent number of H$_3$O ions, thus tending to reduce the acidity. However, the loss of acid ions is immediately made good by the dissociation of more acetic acid molecules from the reserve supply into H$_3$O and C$_2$H$_3$O$_2$ ions. That is, in accordance with Le Châtelier's principle, upsetting the equilibrium by addition of alkali pushes the reaction to the right to create more H$_3$O ions to restore the equilibrium. Thus, the pH remains constant—provided not too much alkali is added.

If, instead, a small amount of acid is added to the solution, the equilibrium is again upset, pushing the reaction to the left. The H$_3$O ions from the added acid and C$_2$H$_3$O$_2$ ions from the reserve supply recombine to reduce the H$_3$O population, thus preserving the pH of the solution. Thus the pH of a weak acid solution is buffered with an acetate salt against the addition of moderate amounts of either acid or alkali. Similarly, a weak basic solution may be buffered against an acid by adding the salt of a strong acid and a weak base, for example, NH_4Cl.

Buffer salts play an important role both in nature and industry. Our blood is buffered to maintain a faint alkalinity (pH of 7.33) that cannot vary except within very narrow limits if we are to maintain our health. Milk stays sweet longer than it would if it were not naturally buffered to a faint alkalinity. Juices of fruits and vegetables are naturally buffered to maintain a slight acidity. In fact, all of the processes of life take place in solutions that are buffered to the hydrogen ion concentration that is most effective for the particular chemical changes that constitute each process. Soils are or can be buffered by certain salts so as to maintain the proper pH for efficient production of different types of crops.

Exercises

1. Which of the following reactions are exothermic? Which endothermic? Justify your answer for each.
   (a) The union of carbon with oxygen.
   (b) Your digestive processes.
   (c) The rusting of iron.
   (d) The electrolysis of water
2. Are the valence electrons of the products of an exothermic chemical reaction at higher or lower energy levels than those of the reactants before the reaction? Explain.
3. Suppose it were an endothermic reaction?
4. In the process of photosynthesis in plants, CO_2 and H_2O are combined to make a sugar. Is this an exothermic or an endothermic process? Make your reasoning clear.
5. Explain the role of temperature, concentration, and state of subdivision in governing the rate at which chemical reactions take place.

6. What is meant by activation energy? Describe its role (a) in exothermic reactions and (b) in endothermic reactions.
7. (a) What is an activated particle?
   (b) How does it differ from an unactivated particle?
8. Which take place more rapidly, reactions between ionic substances or those between nonionic substances? Explain in terms of activation energies.
9. Which are more stable, compounds formed by exothermic reactions or those formed by endothermic reactions? Explain.
10. What general class of substances have low activation energies?
11. How would you explain the fact that coal dust densely suspended in the atmosphere may be highly explosive even though coal itself burns slowly?
12. (a) Which are more active chemically, oxygen atoms or oxygen molecules? Explain.
    (b) Relate your answer to the activation energy needed to start normal combustion.
13. Define a saturated solution in terms of chemical equilibrium.
14. Would the concept of chemical equilibrium apply to a wholly nonreversible reaction? Explain.
15. Name some reactions that you, for all practical purposes, would consider nonreversible.
16. What is meant by the equilibrium constant of a particular reaction?
17. State Le Châtelier's principle.
18. Consider Eq. 28-7. What effect would pressure have on the equilibrium point, and why?
19. The gases H_2, O_2, and H_2O are all in equilibrium at about 2000°C.
    (a) Write the equations to indicate this.
    (b) What effect would increasing the

pressure have on the equilibrium point? Why?

20. Consider the equilibrium equation $H_2O + CO_2 \rightleftharpoons H_2CO_3$. The materials are in a closed container. What effect would adding more CO_2 have on the equilibrium point? What effect would leaving the container open have? Explain.

21. Consider the equilibrium reaction, $NH_3 + H_2O \rightleftharpoons NH_4^+ + OH^-$. What effect would adding NaOH solution have on the equilibrium point? Explain.

22. What is a neutral solution? (Merely to state that it is one which is neither acidic or basic is insufficient.)

23. Define pH. Of what use is the concept?

24. (a) What are buffer solutions?
    (b) Of what use are they?

25. What one principle is used to explain the common ion effect, pH, buffer solutions, indicators, neutral solutions?

The Chemistry of Carbon

Chapter 29

The Occurrence of Carbon

Carbon is one of the minor constituents of the earth, forming not much more than 0.03% of the outer few miles of the earth and, presumably, none of its deep interior. Yet there is an inexhaustible supply of carbon in the carbonate rocks, chiefly limestones and marbles, found on all continents. The coal, peat, graphite, and petroleum deposits of the world all contain large amounts of carbon. All organic matter, from wood to bones and shells and even flesh, contains large amounts. The atmosphere contains billions of tons of it, and still greater quantities are dissolved in the waters of the oceans.

Carbon passes through a definite cycle in nature. Carbon dioxide is extracted from the atmosphere by plants to form living matter, part of which in times past has gone to form peat, coal, and petroleum. The burning of these fuels returns carbon dioxide to the atmosphere. Living matter dies and decays; again the carbon dioxide is returned to the atmosphere.

Great ideas emerge from the common cauldron of intellectual activity, and are rarely cooked up in private kettles from original recipes.
JAMES R. NEWMAN

503

The very large number of carbon compounds is justification enough for treating the chemistry of carbon in a separate chapter. The fact that carbon is the key element in organic matter is additional justification, and is responsible for the division of chemistry into organic and inorganic by the early chemists. The basis of the division was the belief that, except for the oxides, the carbonates, the sulfides, and a few others, the compounds of carbon could be produced only by plants and animals through the action of some "vital living force." The nature of this force was presumably similar to those other "imponderables" phlogiston, caloric, and the ether. This concept was blasted about 1830 when the first organic compounds were synthesized in the laboratory. Others quickly followed, until today the number of organic compounds runs into the hundreds of thousands, perhaps a million or more, with hundreds of new ones being added to the list every year. With a few exceptions, most of the compounds in living matter have been synthesized. In recent years a few proteins have been made in the laboratory. A great many synthetic compounds have been created in the laboratory that have no counterparts in nature. Most of the modern chemical industry is based on the chemistry of carbon.

Forms of Carbon

Carbon occurs in nature in two forms that are about as different from each other as two substances could in their physical properties. Graphite, by far the most common, is a soft, black, flaky, slippery compound that is a good conductor of electricity. The diamond is the hardest substance known, colorless and transparent, and a nonconductor of electricity. Yet both are composed solely of carbon atoms, and there is not one bit of difference between the carbon atom in graphite and the carbon atom

in the diamond. The difference must lie in the arrangement of the carbon atoms, that is, in the crystalline structure of graphite and the diamond; X-ray diffraction patterns confirm this.

We have already learned that carbon forms covalent bonds not only with other elements but with itself. Carbon has a valence of four, so each atom can share four pairs of electrons with four neighboring carbon atoms. If these four neighbors are symmetrically arranged about a fifth atom, they form a tetrahedral pattern. Each carbon atom is at the center of a tetrahedron (Fig. 26-4) and forms the corner of some other tetrahedron. The four covalent bonds might be pictured as radiating from the kernel of the atom in the directions of the corners of the tetrahedron where they meet the bonds of other carbon atoms similarly arranged. This arrangement, repeated indefinitely, makes each diamond crystal one giant molecule. As the valence of carbon is four, each carbon atom is held to four other atoms by nonpolar covalent bonds. This accounts for the hardness of the diamond, its high melting point (3500°C), and its nonconductance.

In graphite the carbon atoms are arranged in the form of hexagonal rings, as in Fig. 26-5. Each carbon atom is bonded to three others that lie in the same plane, so each forms a part of three hexagons. These hexagons, extended in all directions within a plane, are responsible for the flaky property of graphite. The fourth bond of each carbon atom is a "floating" bond, that is, one that doubles up first with one of the other bonds and then with another, as described on page 471. Thus one fourth of the valence electrons are free to move, much as are the valence electrons of metals. This explains the electrical conductivity of graphite. The relative weakness of the van der Waals forces, which are the only forces holding the plates together, allows the plates to slide easily over one another, and so the slippery feel of graphite is accounted for. The hexagonal platy arrangement of the atoms is reflected in the six-sided tabular crystals that occur in some deposits of graphite.

Forms of carbon that are apparently non-crystalline occur in coal, charcoal, and coke. We say apparently, for X rays reveal that these materials consist of submicroscopic crystals of graphite mingled with more or less of other materials. Boneblack, lampblack, and carbonblack are other forms of pure carbon composed of the tiny crystals of graphite.

The Unique Nature of the Carbon Atom

The astounding ability of the carbon atoms to form compounds is due to a combination of three familiar properties, electronegativity, covalence, and size. The electronegativity is moderately high so that the carbon atom is able to form strong covalent bonds by means of its four valence electrons. The carbon atom has a small radius and a relatively high nuclear charge. Carbon can form very stable single, double, and triple covalent bonds with other carbon atoms, thus enabling carbon atoms to link together in enormously long chains, some straight, some branching, some in rings, and some forming three-dimensional networks to produce extremely large numbers of complicated molecules. No other atom can do anything like this to the extent that the carbon atom can. The bonds between the carbon atoms are so strong that the chains and rings can go through many chemical reactions without breaking.

Saturated Hydrocarbons

Hydrocarbons are compounds of carbon and hydrogen only. They are simple in composition, but nevertheless exist in astonishing variety. Petroleum and natural gas are mixtures of large numbers of the hydrocarbons of the paraffin (or methane) series, all in mutual solution with one another. The members of this series have a composition that conforms to the formula C_nH_{2n+2}. This means that the number of hydrogen atoms is always two more than twice the number of carbon atoms.

The simplest and lightest member of the series is methane, CH_4 (the chief constituent of common cooking gas). A methane molecule has its atoms arranged in the form of a tetrahedron with the carbon atom at the center and the four hydrogen atoms at the four corners. The next simplest are C_2H_6 (ethane), C_3H_8 (propane), C_4H_{10} (butane), and so on. The first four are gases. The next twelve are liquids whose volatility decreases with increasing numbers of carbon atoms (and increasing molecular weight). Included in these liquids are such fuels as gasoline and kerosene. Still higher members of the series are the semisolids that form the heavy lubricating oils, greases, and petroleum jelly (Vaseline). The rest are solids like paraffin, which is a mixture of hydrocarbons ranging from $C_{23}H_{48}$ to $C_{29}H_{60}$.

methane

Separating these mixtures of hydrocarbons from one another to obtain the pure compounds is difficult and expensive. Fortunately, for ordinary commercial purposes a complete separation is neither necessary nor particularly desirable. Natural gas is a mixture of the first four members of the series, methane through butane. Since the boiling points increase from 1°C for butane to above 200°C for some of the hydrocarbons in kerosene, the boiling point of a mixture will rise as the hydrocarbons with the lower boiling points are boiled off. Thus, by collecting different fractions of the vapors, the separation into groups of compounds is attained. The first fraction derived from crude petroleum is a mixture of the lighter liquids, largely C_5H_{12} and C_6H_{14}, which is sold (in the United States) as naphtha. The next fraction is gasoline, which is a mixture of liquids with a composition ranging from C_6H_{14} to about

$C_{10}H_{22}$. A third fraction is kerosene, and so forth. The whole process of separation is called *fractional distillation,* or *fractionation.*

In this age of motor cars and airplanes the most valuable of the fractions is gasoline. Unfortunately, the size of the gasoline fraction is small, so small that to provide us with enough gasoline would not only use up our supplies of petroleum at a prodigious rate, but would also swamp us with the other fractions. Petroleum chemists have learned how to increase the gasoline fraction in two ways. One is to *crack* the larger molecules into the smaller ones of gasoline by heating under pressure in the presence of a catalyst. The yield of gasoline per barrel of crude oil has been increased enormously by this process of cracking. The second method is to combine the smaller molecules into the larger ones of gasoline. Not all crude oils are alike; some have a much larger proportion of the light hydrocarbons than others.

Molecules of hydrocarbons are only slightly polar, as is shown by the symmetrical arrangement of their atoms, and so are, in general, insoluble in water. They are generally rather unreactive at room temperature. They will react more or less violently with oxygen at temperatures of a few hundred degrees and are valuable as fuels. They are not affected by prolonged boiling in concentrated NaOH or H_2SO_4, and are only slightly affected by vigorous oxidizing agents. Chlorine and bromine are almost the only substances that will react with them at room temperatures.

Structural Formulas

The formulas that we have dealt with so far are called molecular formulas since they simply indicate the number of each kind of atoms in the compound, H_2O, H_2SO_4, $CaCO_3$. There is nothing in these formulas that tells us directly how the atoms are arranged, and for most purposes it has not greatly mattered. The compounds of carbon present us with another problem. If you were to ask a chemist for some C_2H_6O, he might ask you, "Which C_2H_6O?" for there are two compounds with very different properties that have this composition. One is common grain alcohol, the other is an ether. The difference is made apparent by their structural formulas:

ethyl alcohol   dimethyl ether

Note that the difference is in the way the oxygen atom is connected. In the alcohol (and this is true of all alcohols) the oxygen lies between a carbon and a hydrogen atom, whereas in the ether (and this is true of all ethers) it lies between two carbon atoms. We might have used the dot system, as many chemists do.

The dash system is quicker and easier, and serves our purposes better, but one must *never fail* to count the number of dashes (which we will call bonds) about each atom. This number *must always* be equal to the valence. A dash represents a single shared pair of electrons, that is, a bond between two atoms. There are therefore four bonds about each carbon atom, two about each oxygen atom, and one about each hydrogen atom. Count them in the two structural formulas given above.

Isomerism

Compounds with the same molecular formula but with different structural formulas are called isomers.[1] Thus, dimethyl ether is an isomer of ethyl alcohol, or vice versa. These two examples were chosen because alcohol and ether are familiar compounds, but isomerism is of great importance in the paraffin series itself. Consider the following structural formulas:

methane   ethane   propane

butane   pentane

These all form straight chains of carbon atoms. No matter how you arrange the atoms of the first three, remembering to count the bonds, you will come up with the same essential arrangement. There are therefore no isomers of these three hydrocarbons. When the number of carbon atoms rises to four, two arrangements are possible, the one given above and the following:

isobutane

Note that one carbon atom is now attached to the middle one of the other three. Thus, we do not have a straight chain of carbon atoms but a branching one (or at least the

beginning of a branch).[2] The properties of isobutane are similar to, but not identical with, those of butane.

When the number of carbons rises to five, as in pentane, three isomers are possible. One has been given. The other two are as follows:

isopentane   neopentane

Isopentane is similar in structure to isobutane except that there is another CH_2 unit. Shifting the branching carbon to the carbon atom to its left would not make any significant change in the structure. In neopentane we have omitted writing in the hydrogen atoms in order to make the pattern of the carbon atoms a bit clearer. One must always count the bonds. Note that there are three carbon atoms in each chain. Shifting the carbon atom from a position below the horizontal chain to one above would not create a new isomer.

As the number of carbon atoms increases, the number of possible isomers increases fantastically. For example, 35 different isomers of C_9H_{20} are known, and the theoretical number for $C_{40}H_{82}$ is 69,491,178,805,831. You should now understand why we use structural formulas rather than molecular formulas for so many carbon compounds.

The question might fairly be asked about isomers, "How do we know which formula belongs to which isomer?" To answer this question let us return to the examples of ethyl alcohol and dimethyl ether. Sodium will not react with the ether but it will with alcohol. In the reaction hydrogen is liberated. This

---

[1]One cannot speak of a single isomer any more than one can speak of a single twin. We may refer to one of two or more isomers just as we refer to one of a pair of twins.

[2]Shifting this branching carbon to either end carbon in the chain does not make it a branching chain but merely a bent chain. Hence we would have no isomer.

suggests that in alcohol one hydrogen must be bonded differently than the others. Furthermore, sodium will liberate only one sixth the total amount of hydrogen present. Alcohol will also react with other compounds in a similar manner. With HCl water is a product, the H of the HCl combining with an OH. This practically demands that the OH be present in the alcohol. We scarcely need more evidence.

Unsaturated Hydrocarbons

The hydrocarbons so far discussed have all had single bonds between the carbon atoms; that is, each carbon atom shares not more than one pair of valence electrons with any other carbon atom. Such valences are said to be saturated. If more than one bond exists between two carbon atoms—that is, if the two atoms share two or three pairs of valence electrons—the valences are said to be unsaturated. There are two such unsaturated series, one of which is called the ethylene series, the other the acetylene series.

Ethylene Series

The general formula for this series is C_nH_{2n}. Since the valence of carbon is four, no such compound as CH_2 can exist. The simplest of the series is C_2H_4, known as ethylene. Its structural formula is

$$\begin{array}{cc} H & H \\ | & | \\ C & = C \\ | & | \\ H & H \end{array}$$

Other members of the series are

$$\begin{array}{ccc} & | & | & | \\ -C & = C & -C- \\ | & | & | \end{array} \qquad \begin{array}{cccc} | & & & | \\ -C & -C & = C & -C- \\ | & | & | & | \end{array}$$

propylene   butylene

The first two have no isomers; butylene and higher members do. The double bonds may occupy positions between pairs of carbon atoms other than those shown. Members of the ethylene series are produced in quantities during the cracking of petroleum hydrocarbons.

The members of the ethylene series are more reactive than those of the saturated series. The reason is that the double bonds are rather easily broken and converted into single bonds by the addition of other molecules. Thus,

$$\begin{array}{cc} H & H \\ | & | \\ C & = C \\ | & | \\ H & H \end{array} + Br_2 \rightarrow \begin{array}{cc} H & H \\ | & | \\ Br-C & -C-Br \\ | & | \\ H & H \end{array}$$

ethylene   ethylene bromide

and

$$\begin{array}{cc} H & H \\ | & | \\ C & = C \\ | & | \\ H & H \end{array} + H_2O \rightarrow \begin{array}{cc} H & H \\ | & | \\ H-C & -C-OH \\ | & | \\ H & H \end{array}$$

ethylene   ethyl alcohol

There are other hydrocarbons with several, sometimes scores, of double bonds in the same molecule. Some of their derivatives are abundant in food; for example, one forms the red coloring matter of tomatoes, another the yellow coloring matter of carrots and butter, and so on. Vitamin A ($C_{20}H_{29}OH$) has double bonds between five pairs of carbon atoms.

Acetylene Series —an alkyne

The acetylene series has three bonds between two carbon atoms, and so the general formula is C_nH_{2n-2}. The simplest is acetylene, C_2H_2 or $H-C\equiv C-H$. It burns with a very hot flame (up to 2800°C in pure oxygen) and is used in welding and cutting metals. It is produced from calcium carbide and water, or by the dehydrogenation of natural gas.

Hydrocarbon Ring Structures

The hydrocarbons discussed so far have been those with either straight or branching chains or combinations thereof. Another somewhat different class of hydrocarbons has all or many of the carbon atoms arranged in rings, six carbon atoms to a ring with one hydrogen atom attached to each carbon atom in the ring. The simplest of these compounds is benzene, discovered by Michael Faraday. Its composition is C_6H_6. When it became customary to write structural formulas for hydrocarbons, chemists at first found it impossible to write one for benzene that would have four bonds about each carbon atom. Eventually Kekulé, a German chemist, had the inspiration to try writing the formula as a ring in which every other bond was a double one:

Benzene and others of the group have long been derived from coal tar, a by-product of the heating of bituminous coal in the absence of air to produce coke. From the coal tar, which is an ugly, black, evil-smelling residue, the chemist produces choice perfumes and flavors, dyes of delicate shades, solvents, lacquers, drugs, insecticides, powerful explosives, and a host of other products.

Some Derivatives of the Hydrocarbons

Every organic compound may be considered to have been derived from a simple saturated or unsaturated hydrocarbon by substituting another atom or a group of atoms for one or more of the hydrogen atoms, that is, by substituting certain *reactive functional atoms or groups* for the hydrogen atoms. The compounds derived in this way are called derivatives of the hydrocarbons.

The study of organic chemistry is primarily a study of the hydrocarbons and their derivatives. The study may be best started by first considering a few of the alkyl groups of the saturated hydrocarbons:[3]

1. The methyl group, CH_3—.
2. The ethyl group, C_2H_5—, which may also be written $CH_3 \cdot CH_2$—.
3. The propyl group, C_3H_7—, which may also be written $CH_3 \cdot CH_2 \cdot CH_2$—.
4. The butyl group, C_4H_9—, which may also be written $CH_3 \cdot CH_2 \cdot CH_2 \cdot CH_2$—.

Note that each has been formed by the subtraction of one hydrogen atom. Each therefore has one "unattached" bond, and so does not exist by itself.

Consider the methyl group. If we add a chlorine atom, we have, in effect, substituted a chlorine atom for a hydrogen atom to give us CH_3Cl (methyl chloride). If we substitute another chlorine atom for a second hydrogen atom, we have CH_2Cl_2 (dichloromethane). Substitution of a third chlorine atom will give us $CHCl_3$ (chloroform), and of a fourth, CCl_4 (carbon tetrachloride). The same substitutions may be made in the other groups, and other atoms may be used in place of chlorine.

Alcohols

Of much more interest is the substitution of the various functional groups listed in Table

---

[3] The members of the methane series—methyl (CH_3—), ethyl (C_2H_5—), butyl (C_3H_7—), and so on—are called alkyls.

29-1. If we add an —OH to any of the alkyl groups we get an alcohol.

$$H-\underset{\underset{\displaystyle H}{|}}{\overset{\overset{\displaystyle H}{|}}{C}}-OH \qquad H-\underset{\underset{\displaystyle H}{|}}{\overset{\overset{\displaystyle H}{|}}{C}}-\underset{\underset{\displaystyle H}{|}}{\overset{\overset{\displaystyle H}{|}}{C}}-OH$$

methyl alcohol   ethyl alcohol
(methanol)   (ethanol)

$$H-\underset{\underset{\displaystyle H}{|}}{\overset{\overset{\displaystyle H}{|}}{C}}-\underset{\underset{\displaystyle H}{|}}{\overset{\overset{\displaystyle H}{|}}{C}}-\underset{\underset{\displaystyle H}{|}}{\overset{\overset{\displaystyle H}{|}}{C}}-OH \qquad H-\underset{\underset{\displaystyle H}{|}}{\overset{\overset{\displaystyle H}{|}}{C}}-\underset{\underset{\displaystyle H}{|}}{\overset{\overset{\displaystyle H}{|}}{C}}-\underset{\underset{\displaystyle H}{|}}{\overset{\overset{\displaystyle H}{|}}{C}}-\underset{\underset{\displaystyle H}{|}}{\overset{\overset{\displaystyle H}{|}}{C}}-OH$$

propyl alcohol   butyl alcohol

If we let R stand for an alkyl group, then the general formula of these monohydric alcohols is R—OH. If we substitute another —OH for a second hydrogen atom that is attached to some *other* carbon atom, we get a dihydric alcohol. The simplest and best known is ethylene glycol, which is used extensively as an antifreeze. Its structural formula is

$$HO-\underset{\underset{\displaystyle H}{|}}{\overset{\overset{\displaystyle H}{|}}{C}}-\underset{\underset{\displaystyle H}{|}}{\overset{\overset{\displaystyle H}{|}}{C}}-OH$$

If a third hydrogen atom from still another carbon atom is replaced by —OH, we have glycerol (glycerine). Its structural formula is

$$HO-\underset{\underset{\displaystyle H}{|}}{\overset{\overset{\displaystyle H}{|}}{C}}-\underset{\underset{\displaystyle H}{|}}{\overset{\overset{\displaystyle OH}{|}}{C}}-\underset{\underset{\displaystyle H}{|}}{\overset{\overset{\displaystyle H}{|}}{C}}-OH$$

Organic (Fatty) Acids

The characteristic group of the organic acids is —COOH, called the carboxyl group. Note in Table 29-1 that the first oxygen is double-bonded to the carbon atom.

The general formula for organic acids is RCOOH, where R is hydrogen in the simplest of this large group, and an alkyl group in any of the others. Structurally they are written

$$R-\overset{\overset{\displaystyle O}{\|}}{C}-OH$$

The simplest is formic acid, HCOOH. Next simplest is acetic acid, which we have heretofore written as $HC_2H_3O_2$, but which we will write here as CH_3COOH. Others are butyric

Table 29-1
Some Common Active Groups

Characteristic group	Type formula	Class of compound	Example formula	Name
—OH	R—OH	Alcohol	C_2H_5OH	Ethyl alcohol (ethanol)
$-\overset{\overset{\displaystyle O}{\|}}{C}-OH$	$R-\overset{\overset{\displaystyle O}{\|}}{C}-OH$	Acid	$CH_3-\overset{\overset{\displaystyle O}{\|}}{C}-OH$	Acetic acid
$-\overset{\overset{\displaystyle O}{\|}}{C}-OR'$	$R-\overset{\overset{\displaystyle O}{\|}}{C}-OR'$	Ester	$CH_3-\overset{\overset{\displaystyle O}{\|}}{C}-OC_2H_5$	Ethyl acetate
$-NH_2$	$R-NH_2$	Primary amine	CH_3-NH_2	Methylamine
$-\overset{\overset{\displaystyle O}{\|}}{C}-NH_2$	$R-\overset{\overset{\displaystyle O}{\|}}{C}-NH_2$	Amide	$CH_3-\overset{\overset{\displaystyle O}{\|}}{C}-NH_2$	Acetamide

acid, C_3H_7COOH (found in rancid butter and limburger cheese), palmitic acid, $CH_3 \cdot (CH_2)_{14}COOH$ (derived from vegetable oils) and stearic acid, $CH_3 \cdot (CH_2)_{16}COOH$ (derived from animal fats). Palmitic and stearic acids, when chemically combined with glycerol, are the common vegetable oils and animal fats. These two acids find their chief use in soap-making.

Esters

Organic acids and alcohols slowly react to form esters. In the process a molecule of water is eliminated.

$$CH_3COOH \quad + \quad C_2H_5OH \quad \rightarrow$$
$$\text{acetic acid} \qquad \text{ethyl alcohol}$$

$$CH_3COOC_2H_5 \quad + \quad H_2O$$
$$\text{ethyl acetate}$$

Esters have pleasant flower- and fruit-like odors; in fact, the natural odors of fruits and flowers are due to esters. They are therefore used as artificial flavors and in perfumes.

Amines

Amines may be considered either as alkyl groups to which the amino group, $—NH_2$, is attached, or as derived from ammonia by substituting an alkyl group for one or more hydrogen atoms.

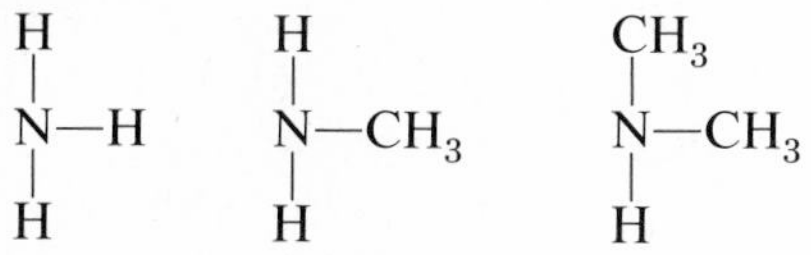

$$\begin{array}{ccc}
H & H & CH_3 \\
| & | & | \\
N—H & N—CH_3 & N—CH_3 \\
| & | & | \\
H & H & H \\
\text{ammonia} & \text{methylamine} & \text{dimethylamine}
\end{array}$$

Amides

The amides are similar to the fatty acids whose general formula is

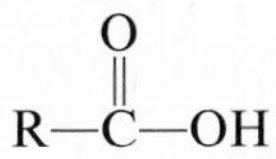

$$\begin{array}{c}
O \\
\| \\
R—C—OH
\end{array}$$

If we substitute an $—NH_2$ (amino) group for the $—OH$, we have the general formula for an amide,

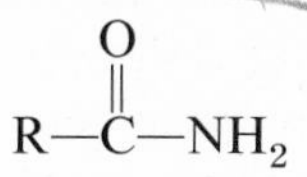

$$\begin{array}{c}
O \\
\| \\
R—C—NH_2
\end{array}$$

Nylon and silk are complex polyamides.

Amino Acids

Amino acids contain both the carboxyl ($—COOH$) and the amino ($—NH_2$) groups. The simplest is

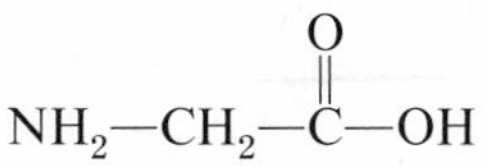

$$\begin{array}{c}
O \\
\| \\
NH_2—CH_2—C—OH
\end{array}$$
$$\text{glycine}$$

Amino acids combine with one another to form proteins. They are discussed further under that heading.

Benzene Rings

The benzene ring can also act as the basic structure in which other atoms or groups of atoms may be substituted for one or more of the hydrogens. One example is

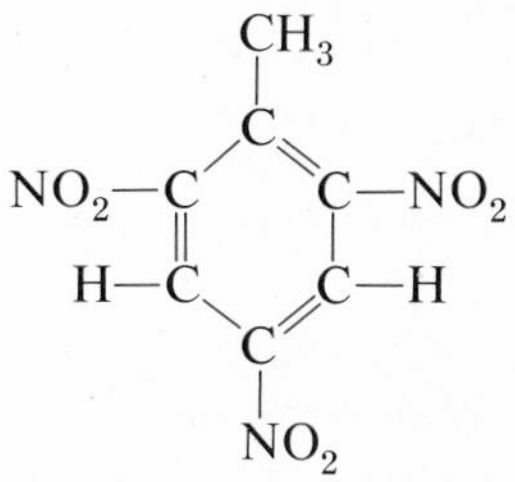

$$\begin{array}{c}
CH_3 \\
| \\
C \\
NO_2—C \qquad C—NO_2 \\
H—C \qquad C—H \\
C \\
| \\
NO_2
\end{array}$$
$$\text{trinitrotoluene (TNT)}$$

Giant Molecules—Polymers

All the organic materials that possess the properties of elasticity, resiliency, high tensile strength, and pliability are made of "giant" molecules, molecules whose atomic weights run up into the thousands, tens of thousands, hundreds of thousands, or even millions. Such organic materials include cotton, wool, silk, wood, rubber, and resins among the natural products, and the plastics and synthetic fibers and rubbers among the artificially made products. These giant molecules are made up of groups of atoms that are repeated over and over in a regular order, sometimes thousands of times to form single huge molecules. The process of joining them together is called *polymerization;* the products are called *polymers,* and the atom groups are called *monomers.* The architecture of these giant molecules has been worked out largely since 1925, much of it since World War II.

An excellent example of a polymer in which the monomers are simply "added" together is polyethylene. Such polymers are called addition polymers; they can form only from the unsaturated hydrocarbons. The monomer of polyethylene is ethylene,

$$
\begin{array}{c}
\text{H}\quad\text{H}\\
|\qquad|\\
\text{C}=\text{C}\\
|\qquad|\\
\text{H}\quad\text{H}
\end{array}
$$

If we break the double bond we can write it:

$$
\begin{array}{c}
\text{H}\quad\text{H}\\
|\qquad|\\
-\text{C}-\text{C}-\\
|\qquad|\\
\text{H}\quad\text{H}
\end{array}
$$

We can now break the double bond of other ethylene molecules, and add one on the right and one on the left.

$$
\begin{array}{c}
\text{H}\ \ \text{H}\ \ \text{H}\ \ \text{H}\ \ \text{H}\ \ \text{H}\\
|\quad|\quad|\quad|\quad|\quad|\\
-\text{C}-\text{C}-\text{C}-\text{C}-\text{C}-\text{C}-\\
|\quad|\quad|\quad|\quad|\quad|\\
\text{H}\ \ \text{H}\ \ \text{H}\ \ \text{H}\ \ \text{H}\ \ \text{H}
\end{array}
$$

Since we still have a vacant bond at each end,

we can add other monomers, and so on indefinitely.

Natural rubber is made of giant molecules in the form of long coiled chains. The coils unroll when the rubber is stretched and roll up again when it is released. The monomer of natural rubber is isoprene.

$$
\begin{array}{c}
\text{H}\quad\text{CH}_3\ \ \text{H}\ \ \text{H}\\
|\qquad\ \ |\qquad|\quad|\\
\text{C}=\text{C}\ \ -\text{C}=\text{C}\\
|\qquad\qquad\quad|\\
\text{H}\qquad\qquad\text{H}
\end{array}
$$

During polymerization one or both of the double bonds is broken so that monomeric unit after monomeric unit can join together.

$$
\begin{array}{c}
\text{H}\ \ \text{CH}_3\ \ \text{H}\ \ \text{H}\ \ \text{H}\ \ \text{CH}_3\ \ \text{H}\ \ \text{H}\\
|\qquad|\qquad|\quad|\quad|\qquad|\qquad|\quad|\\
-\text{C}-\text{C}=\text{C}-\text{C}-\text{C}-\text{C}=\text{C}-\text{C}-\\
|\qquad\qquad|\quad|\quad|\qquad\qquad|\\
\text{H}\qquad\qquad\text{H}\ \ \text{H}\ \ \text{H}\qquad\qquad\text{H}\\
\uparrow\\
\text{connecting bond}
\end{array}
$$

Many rubber substitutes (popularly known as synthetic rubbers) with compositions quite different from that of natural rubber have been made. Man has never been able to synthesize natural rubber. One of the substitutes may be superior to natural rubber for one purpose, some other one for another purpose.

Some polymers are made of alternately repeating units of two monomers. They are known as copolymers. Some are condensation polymers, in which a water molecule is "condensed out" when two monomeric units combine. Proteins are condensation polymers.

Although polyethylene is probably the simplest of the addition polymers, as many as 200,000 carbons may be present in one of its long chains. By choosing appropriate components and controlling their arrangements, the polymer chemist can get the desired qualities of strength, durability, elasticity, insolubility, and so on. He is a designer and a builder of giant molecules; he can outline in advance the properties of the product he wants, and with his knowledge and understanding of the structure and properties of small molecules and how to manipulate them, he can combine them into giant molecules more or less to order. It was not always that way, however, for the first true plastic was celluloid, made in 1868 by accident. Other "accidents" followed, some of them in the worst sense of the word, in which men were maimed and even killed. If you will think back about the development of our knowledge of how atoms are constructed, you will readily see that the techniques of how to manipulate atoms could not possibly have begun much before 1930. Cellulose (p. 514) is nature's own giant molecule, and rayon, made from cellulose, was the first man-made fiber. For decades it was believed that man-made fibers had to be synthesized from raw materials that nature had already made fibrous. In the late 1920's and throughout the 1930's a Du Pont chemist believed that synthetic fibers could be made from coal, air, and water. He worked 10 years and spent $27 million of the Du Pont Company's money before he succeeded in making polyhexamethylene-adipamide, otherwise known as nylon. In the first year, 1940, nylon was a sensation, chiefly as the material that went into the manufacture of women's stockings. Nylon went to World War II in the form of military parachutes, tents, and cord for airplane tires. After the war 90% of the nylon produced went to hosiery manufacturers but it took two years and 700 million pairs of stockings before supply equaled the demand.

Since World War II there has been a spectacular chemical revolution that has resulted in the large-scale synthesis of rubbers, plastics, and a host of other products from hydrocarbon compounds found in petroleum. These same compounds can be obtained from coal, wood, and grain, but petroleum is cheaper to obtain and process than they are. By far the most useful of the hydrocarbons obtained from petroleum and natural gas are the gases methane, ethylene, propylene, and butylene and the liquid benzene. With these as starting points, more than half the plastics and fibers, two thirds of the synthetic rubber, two thirds of the detergents, and so on, are made; they appear in almost all cosmetics, pharmaceuticals, and insecticides, and yet tens of thousands of new molecules remain to be made from these five basic hydrocarbons.

Chemistry of Food

The diet of a healthy person must include carbohydrates, fats, proteins, vitamins, and certain so-called minerals.[4] All but the last are organic, and all living matter contains them in varying proportions.

Carbohydrates

In plants the carbohydrates are most important, for from them are derived the other foods. Plants, using the energy of sunlight, and with chlorophyll as a catalyst, synthesize carbohydrates from CO_2 abstracted from the atmosphere and H_2O from the soil. The general reaction[5] is as follows:

$$6CO_2 \;+\; 6H_2O \;\rightarrow\; \underset{\text{glucose}}{C_6H_{12}O_6} \;+\; 6O_2$$

This is a reaction in which the valence electrons in the products are at higher energy levels than they were in the reactants; energy is absorbed in the process. The energy needed

---

[4] They are not minerals in the geological sense. They are simply compounds containing metals that are essential to health.

[5] This is a highly simplified statement of the process of photosynthesis, for the products formed vary in different plant species. The biochemists are uncertain about the details of the chemical processes involved.

is one photon for each molecule of reacting substance. Photons, each with energy equal to *hf*, can be absorbed only by some colored substance (there are no photons of white light, but only photons of red, orange, yellow, green, blue, and violet); in the process of absorption molecules of H_2O and CO_2 become activated. Thus, the radiant energy of the sun is stored in plants as chemical energy.

The simplest carbohydrates are the sugars; more complex ones include starch, glycogen, and cellulose, which consist of very large molecules. The general formula is $C_x(H_2O)_y$, from which it may be seen that the process of photosynthesis consists essentially of combining carbon with water. Also it is seen that the ratio of hydrogen to oxygen is $2:1$.

Sugars. Glucose and fructose are isomers; they are the most important simple sugars. Glucose (sometimes called dextrose, grape sugar, corn sugar) is found uncombined in leaves, sap, flowers, honey, and fruits. As noted in the preceding equation, it is glucose, or its isomer fructose, that is made during photosynthesis. Fructose is the sweetest of all the sugars.

Cane sugar ($C_{12}H_{22}O_{11}$) may be considered to have been formed by the union of a molecule of glucose with one of fructose, with the elimination of a molecule of water:

$$C_6H_{12}O_6 \ + \ C_6H_{12}O_6 \ \rightarrow$$
$$C_{12}H_{22}O_{11} \ + \ H_2O$$

Two isomers of cane sugar (sucrose) are malt sugar (maltose) and lactose (milk sugar). In the digestive process all of these sugars combine with water again to form the original simpler sugars; they are said to have been hydrolyzed. The glucose so formed is absorbed directly through the intestinal walls to serve as a source of energy.

Starch. Starch is a noncrystalline insoluble substance that forms the reserve supply of food in tubers and seeds of plants. Its empirical[6] formula is $(C_6H_{10}O_5)_x \cdot H_2O$, where x may have varying values up to 3000. It consists of long branching chains of glucose units as monomers, any pair of which are linked together with the loss of a molecule of water. Starch is therefore a condensation polymer of glucose. During digestion, which for starch begins with the saliva in the mouth, the monomeric units are separated and recombined with water (hydrolyzed) to form glucose. Glycogen, a smaller, more highly branched polymer of glucose, is stored in the liver of animals as a reserve supply of readily available food; whenever the concentration of glucose in the blood falls below a certain level, glycogen is rapidly hydrolyzed into glucose.

Cellulose. Cellulose has a molecular formula like that of starch in that it is made up of large numbers of monomeric units of glucose, but structurally it is sufficiently different to be indigestible to man. It is the most abundant of the carbohydrates, since it constitutes the skeletal material in all kinds of plants. Some animals have digestive systems that can hydrolyze it to glucose.

Fats and Oils

We have already stated that fats and organic oils are esters of the large-molecule fatty

---

[6] Every chemical substance can be described by an *empirical* formula that merely indicates the simplest ratio of the atoms present in the substance. It does not necessarily describe the true composition of the molecule. Sometimes it can be used to describe a substance incapable of existing in the form of independent molecules. For example, the empirical formula of sulfur is S, that of benzene is CH, and that of sodium chloride is NaCl. Their respective molecular formulas are S_8, C_6H_6, and *none* (see "What Is a Molecule?" in Chapter 25).

acids—palmitic acid, stearic acid, oleic acid, and others—and the trihydric alcohol glycerol. Fats and oils are easily decomposed by boiling them with strong alkali, usually NaOH. The products are glycerol and the sodium salts of the fatty acids—sodium palmitate, sodium stearate, and sodium oleate—otherwise known as soap. If KOH is used, the resulting salts constitute soft soap.

The vegetable oils are generally liquid at normal temperatures. They are composed of chains with double bonds between some of the carbon atoms; that is, they are unsaturated. Because of the double bonds they are more reactive than the saturated fats and so spoil more quickly. They may, however, be converted to solid fats by breaking the double bonds and adding hydrogen. Many commercial vegetable shortenings used in the home are produced in this way. Fats are, of course, a source of energy for the body. They also serve other purposes, which we will not discuss here.

Proteins

Proteins are constituents of all living cells, and so are essential to life processes. In part they serve as the structural materials for animals except for their bones and shells. Skin, tendons, muscle fibers, hair, wool, feathers, nails, and hoofs are largely made of proteins. The blood contains many kinds of protein molecules. In all, the human body contains several hundreds, possibly thousands of them, each having special structures that allow them to carry out specific tasks. In the human diet proteins are obtained chiefly from lean meat, eggs, fish, cheese, milk, and cereals. The function of proteins is to build body tissues and to repair them.

All proteins contain approximately 16% nitrogen, combined with carbon, hydrogen, oxygen, and sometimes iron, phosphorus, sulfur, and copper. The digestive juices of man hydrolyze them, breaking them down into a number of amino acids. Actually proteins are condensation polymers in which the monomers are amino acids. There are more than 25 amino acids known, most of them found in the human body. It is difficult to tell which are essential to life. By varying the combinations of amino acids and with the elimination of a water molecule from each pair, tens of thousands of different proteins are made possible. The number of monomeric units in proteins is sufficiently large to give their molecules a molecular weight of about 40,000 (for egg albumin) to 2 billion (for vaccinia virus).

Consider the simplest amino acid, glycine, which can be written as follows:

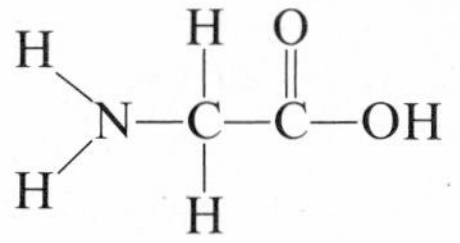

Let us suppose that two molecules of it combine. The —COOH end of one molecule combines with the —NH$_2$ end of the other, eliminating a water molecule. Thus,

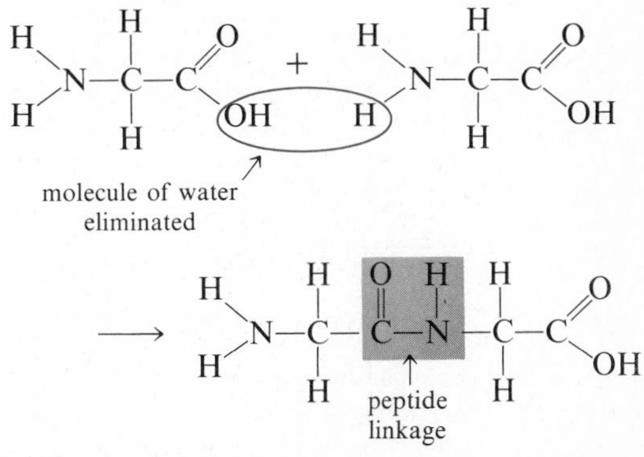

molecule of water
eliminated

peptide
linkage

The other four atoms from —COOH and —NH$_2$ (C, O, N, and H) are bonded together as shown in the colored box. Together they form a link between what is left of each of the two glycine molecules. This link is called a *peptide linkage*. A third glycine molecule can be linked in the same manner to the right end and a fourth to the left end of the product in the equation above, and so on almost ad infinitum. Different amino acids, all of them more complex than glycine, may appear as monomers in the same protein. They are all linked together by the peptide linkage.

Amino acids are water soluble, so that they can be carried by the blood to the cells of the body, where the acids are synthesized by the cells into the particular kind or kinds of protein the cell needs. This is a remarkable feat, considering the fact that in the laboratory man has been able to synthesize only a very few of the simpler proteins, such as insulin. Proteins are also a source of energy for the body.

Enzymes. Most of the chemical reactions of the human body (as well as those of all other animals) take place at a slow rate. The surprising thing is that they take place fast enough to furnish the energy needed, for at body temperatures outside the body the rate is far slower than in the body. The answer is found in enzymes, themselves proteins, which act as catalysts to speed up the various physiological reactions. The importance of enzymes is beyond estimation. The human body contains thousands of them, each specific in its action.

Nucleic Acids

The two nucleic acids deoxyribonucleic acid (DNA) and ribonucleic acid (RNA) have been much in the news in recent years. Both have played an important role in the development of molecular biology. DNA consists of enormous numbers of atoms arranged in a very long thin double chain, the two strands being twined together and connected in places. RNA is a single chain. Both are present in the nuclei of cells of all kinds of life. They are the controllers of the processes of heredity by which cells reproduce themselves. Thus they are the carriers of the genetic code.

Genetics, the science of heredity and variation, was born about 1900. Not much later genetics and cytology—the study of cell structure—joined hands to solve common problems concerning the mechanics of heredity. In time genetics also joined hands with chemistry to seek to explain not only how genes control the fundamental chemistry of life but what the exact chemical nature of the gene is. Analysis of chromosomes, the genes' parent bodies, revealed the presence of proteins and nucleic acids. The nucleic acids were deoxyribonucleic acid and ribonucleic acid. Scientists jumped to the conclusion that proteins were the important ingredients of the genes. Experimentation continued into the early 1940's in an attempt to solve a 13-year-old mystery—which we will not elucidate here. When the mystery was solved, the important ingredient of genes had been proved to be the nucleic acid DNA. In fact, DNA and genes were one and the same thing. Some of the protein advocates wanted more proof. By 1952 this proof was produced, and it was then certain that DNA is the genetic material.

Even before the final proof was at hand, attempts were made by chemists to analyze and synthesize DNA. Success crowned these efforts when an enzyme was discovered that could cause the synthesis of DNA molecules from other DNA molecules of exactly the same type. This showed that the DNA molecules could reproduce themselves, an absolute necessity if DNA was the genetic material. Chemical analysis also showed that there were just three types of ingredients in DNA: (1) simple sugars of a kind known as deoxyribose, (2) phosphate units, and (3) nitrogen compounds (called bases) known as adenine, thymine, cytosine, and guanine (A, T, C, and G for short).

Fig. 29-1. Formulas of Deoxyribose (*a*) and Ribose (*b*) Sugars. Ribose, the five-carbon sugar of RNA, differs from the sugar of DNA only in the presence of one more oxygen atom at the location indicated by the arrows.

(a)   *(b)*

Structure of DNA

Before proceding further we will present a few chemical formulas to see how these ingredients differ in chemical composition. Deoxyribose and ribose, the two five-carbon sugars of DNA and RNA, respectively, are shown in Fig. 29-1. The compositions of the four nitrogen bases in DNA are shown in Fig. 29-2. The RNA molecule possesses three of these bases, A, C, and G, along with the base uracil (U for short), which is closely related to thymine. We need not concern ourselves with the structure of the phosphate units.

The next big problem was to learn how these groups of atoms fitted together because the investigators could not hope to discover how

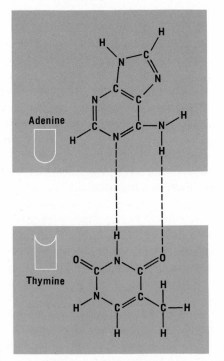

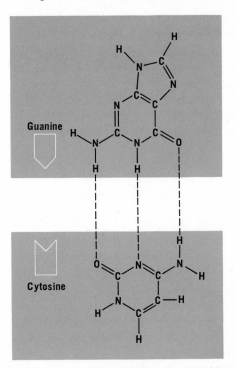

Fig. 29-2. The Four Nitrogen Bases in DNA. They are shown as two pairs, each pair connected by weak hydrogen bonds (dashed lines), because this is the way they occur in the DNA molecule. The shapes beside the formulas are used to represent the nucleotides in subsequent figures.

DNA might transmit genetic information and reproduce itself until they knew how a molecule of it was constructed. A physicist, turned biologist, who was a specialist in X-ray crystallography (p. 413) was called in to help solve the problem. With the information furnished by him, the team of J. D. Watson and F. H. C. Crick was able to construct a model of the DNA molecule and explain how it could faithfully reproduce itself.

We have already seen that proteins are condensation polymers (p. 515) whose monomers are amino acids. Nucleic acids are also polymers—their monomers are called nucleotides. A single nucleotide is composed of a phosphate unit (labeled P in Fig. 29-3), a five-carbon sugar (labeled S), and a nitrogen base (A, T, C, or G). These nucleotides are joined together to form long single chains. Two such chains, connected through the bases, form a DNA molecule. Not all such double DNA chains are the same length; that is, they do not all have the same number of nucleotides.

We have also learned that amino acids are water soluble, and so they can be carried by the blood to the many different kinds of cells in the body where they can be synthesized into the specific kind (or kinds) of proteins the cells need. Now the remarkable thing about this synthesis is that a cell "knows" what amino acids to use to synthesize a specific protein. How does it "know"? (There are 23 amino acids in the human body.) And how does a cell "know" what proteins it needs? This is all the more remarkable when one learns that protein molecules are composed of hundreds or thousands of amino acid monomers, joined together in long chains, so many that the molecules have molecular weights that are incredibly large (p. 515). Before we can answer these questions we need to know how the chromosomes and the genes replicate themselves. Living organisms grow only by their cells being able to reproduce themselves by

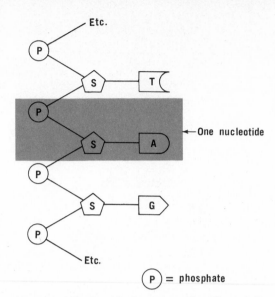

Fig. 29-3. Nucleotide Structure. The P's and S's together form one upright of the DNA molecule and each nitrogen base forms half of a step (see Figs. 29-4 and 29-5).

mitosis. This is the process by which the cell divides to form two new cells. During mitosis the chromosomes replicate themselves, one set going to one of the new cells formed by the splitting, the second set going to the other new cell. Since the genes are carried by the chromosomes, the genes are replicated too, and divided in the same way. We need to know how this replication occurs.

The Watson–Crick Model of DNA

The Watson–Crick model of DNA attempts to explain the replication. It consists of two long thin chains of nucleotides loosely twisted together in a helix, with the two chains connected together at selected points. In some respects the helix resembles a twisted ladder (Fig. 29-4) in which alternate phosphates and sugars form the uprights and the bases (adenine, thymine, cytosine, and guanine) form the steps (Fig. 29-5). Each step is made

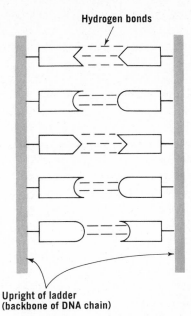

Hydrogen bonds

Upright of ladder
(backbone of DNA chain)

Fig. 29-5. A Fragment of the Untwisted Ladder of a DNA Molecule. The uprights consist of alternating phosphate and sugar (Fig. 29-3) and the steps are pairs of bases connected by weak hydrogen bonds.

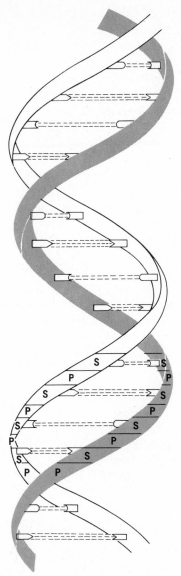

Fig. 29-4. Twisted-Ladder Model of Part of a DNA Molecule. The pairs of bases may be in any order as long as adenine is paired with thymine and cytosine with guanine.

up of two bases, one connected to each upright, that are joined together in the middle by weak hydrogen bonds (Figs. 29-4 and 29-5). This joining is not random; adenine (A) always joins with thymine (T), and cytosine (C) always joins with guanine (G). The steps can follow each other in any order—for example, AT, GC, AT, CG, GC, AT, TA, and so on—almost endlessly. However, the sequence does make a difference, for substitution of GC and AT anywhere in the chain means a different gene. Thus a particular sequence gives every gene its special character. It is the particular sequence of the steps and the length of the nucleotide chain (number of steps) in a DNA molecule that make a dog give birth to a dog instead of a cat.

We can picture the twisted ladder (Fig. 29-4) as untwisted and separated into two parts by breaking the weak hydrogen bonds (Fig. 29-5). During mitosis the chromosomes reproduce themselves to produce two daughter cells, and the two DNA strands that form the chain split along the line of hydrogen bonding (Fig. 29-5), in a sort of unzipping process. We see now why the DNA chain must have two strands. But we should still wonder how the two new double-stranded molecules become identical.

First, however, we need the answer to another question, Where do the basic parts that build the complementary chains come from? To answer this question we need to learn a bit about cell structures. All living matter, plant and animal, is composed of widely different organizations of cells. Individual cells are of every imaginable shape, texture, and appearance. They vary in size from $1/100,000$ in. long to nearly 5 in. (an ostrich egg). Fundamentally they are all much alike. A typical cell consists of a protective wall surrounding a mass of living matter called *protoplasm,* which is differentiated into a nucleus and cytoplasm. The nucleus is separated from the cytoplasm by a membrane perforated with pores to allow passage of matter in and out. The nucleus is the control center for the hereditary material of the cell—chromosomes and genes (DNA). The cytoplasm is a semifluid material in which the life activities of the cell are carried on. The amino acids are synthesized into proteins in an assembly-line fashion in the ribosomes, spherical bodies less than a micron in diameter, lying within the cytoplasm. However, the component parts of the nucleotides are manufactured as separate entities and joined together to form individual nucleotides. There are always free-floating nucleotides in the nucleus. How a portion of a DNA chain is replicated during mitosis is shown in Figs. 29-6 and 29-7.

Thus the Watson–Crick model (theory) admirably explains how DNA self-replicates. Formulated in 1953, it has never been successfully challenged. In 1962 James Watson (an American biologist), Francis Crick (a British physicist), and Maurice Wilkins (a British biophysicist) all received Nobel prizes for this brilliant work in molecular biology.

We can now explain how cells assemble proteins from amino acids. Our digestive juices break down the proteins in our food to amino acids, which our blood carried to the cells. Different kinds of cells need different proteins; for example, a muscle cell needs proteins that are different from those a brain cell needs. We repeat our questions: How does the cell "know" what proteins it needs? How does the

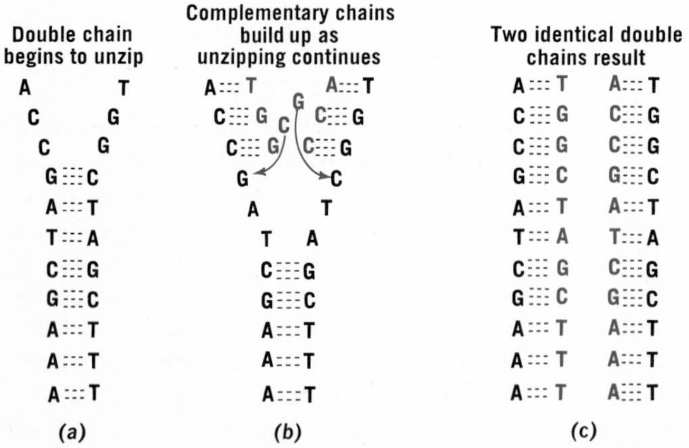

Fig. 29-6. Replication of a Portion of a DNA Chain. Note the unzipping process and how the complementary chains begin to build even before the unzipping is complete. Note also the two identical chains when the replication is completed.

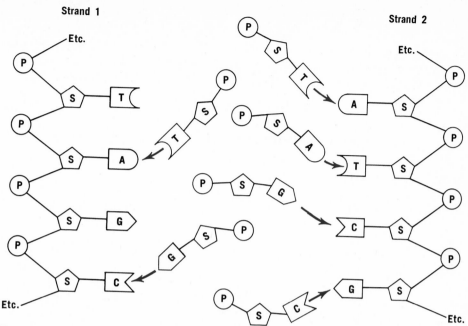

Fig. 29-7. The Pairing Up of Bases, A and T, G and C. A two-strand chain of DNA has just been unzipped by mitosis into two strands. A number of nucleotides with various bases are floating around in the nucleus. To form two new double-strand chains the floating nucleotides will attach themselves to the bases on the strands shown as each finds a base that it fits. Note that only a T will fit an A, only a C will fit a G. As there is no dearth of floating nucleotides, each of the two single strands shown quickly becomes a double-strand chain of DNA with the bases in exactly the same order as in the original chain before mitosis.

cell "know" what amino acids will form a specific protein? The genes (DNA molecules) must send instructions to the cells in some kind of code. Our problem is to discover and decipher that code.

Ribonucleic Acid (RNA)

So far we have said almost nothing about ribonucleic acid because it played no part in the replication of DNA. DNA stays in the chromosomes within the nucleus, yet it directs the synthesis of proteins in the ribosomes in the cytoplasm. This it does by messenger-RNA, which it manufactures by a process that is

much like the replication of DNA. The two-strand DNA ladder (Figs. 29-4 and 29-5) partially unzips itself, and compatible nucleotides floating free in the nucleus attach themselves to one strand in the manner shown in Fig. 29-8a. Thus a new strand that is similar to part of a DNA molecule is produced. However, this new strand differs from DNA in two important ways: it is a single strand instead of a double strand—that is, there is only one upright with half a step—and the nitrogen bases are adenine, guanine, cytosine, and uracil (instead of thymine). Uracil (U) is a compound closely related to thymine. Once formed, this new single strand breaks away from the DNA and

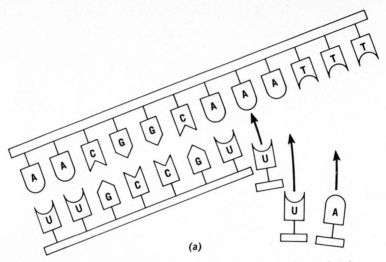

(a)

Fig. 29-8. Building a Protein. Actual proteins are too large and complex to be shown, so we illustrate the building of a hypothetical protein fragment consisting of the amino acids leucine (Leu), proline (Pro), phenylalanine (Phe), and lysine (Lys). (a) Within the nucleus of a cell, a DNA molecule, which carries the "blueprint" for our hypothetical protein fragment, Leu—Pro—Phe—Lys, temporarily unzips and a molecule of messenger-RNA (m-RNA) builds up against the DNA model. Note that a uracil nucleotide lines up opposite each adenine nucleotide in the DNA chain, a guanine opposite each cytosine, a cytosine opposite each guanine, and an adenine opposite each thymine. When complete, the m-RNA separates from the DNA (which re-forms a double chain) and moves out of the nucleus into the cytoplasm where it is picked up by a ribosome. (b) Within the ribosome various transfer-RNA's approach, each t-RNA carrying its own kind of amino acid. Those that fit (for example, the ones carrying Phe and Lys) are attracted to specific sites on the m-RNA. The t-RNA carrying Arg does not fit and so will not be used by this m-RNA. (c) Matching t-RNA's, each carrying its amino acid, line up along the m-RNA, and the amino acids are joined together by peptide linkages (p. 515). (d) The protein fragment Leu—Pro—Phe—Lys separates from the t-RNA's and the t-RNA's are released to pick up other molecules of their appropriate amino acids for assembly of other proteins.

moves through the pores of the nucleus into the cytoplasm; the DNA ladder zips itself back up again. Such single strands are called messenger-RNA, abbreviated m-RNA. A different and smaller form of RNA, known as transfer-RNA (t-RNA), is also found in the cell outside the nucleus. Transfer-RNA is different from m-RNA, for the former bonds to an amino acid whereas the latter cannot. The t-RNA acts as a sort of intermediary between m-RNA and the specific protein being assembled. Thus these two types of RNA work together to assemble specific amino acids to form specific proteins (Fig. 29-8).

The Manufacture of Proteins

At this point we should expect that the assembling process would have considerable resemblance to the process of DNA replication. The chief difference is that in the synthesis of proteins it is the amino acids that are assembled, whereas in DNA replication it is the bases A, T, C, and G that are assembled. We will make two assumptions: (1) that each amino acid molecule has a specific "chemical shape" that clearly differentiates it from every other amino acid molecule and (2) that there are as many different kinds of transfer-RNA's

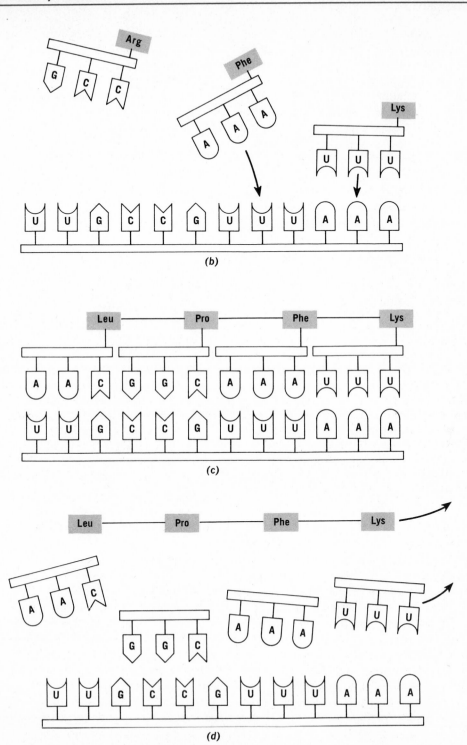

(b)

(c)

(d)

as there are different kinds of amino acids, say 23. Each transfer-RNA has its own "chemical shape" by means of which it is chemically attracted to a particular amino acid molecule that has a compatible chemical shape. These t-RNA molecules pick up their compatible amino acid molecules and carry them to the m-RNA assembly line. When a t-RNA finds a matching unit on the m-RNA chain, its amino acid becomes a part of the developing protein, as shown in Fig. 29-8. Thus the amino acids are variously linked together to form some 100,000 different kinds of proteins in the human body. The structure of each is specified by the DNA in the forty-six chromosomes found in man.

Exercises

1. Name three different forms of pure carbon.
2. What are the "big four" among the elements involved in organic chemistry?
3. Using the general formulas, C_nH_{2n+2}, C_nH_{2n}, C_nH_{2n-2}, write specific formulas, molecular and structural, for the first three members of the first two groups, and for the first one of the third group.
4. Write the structural formulas for three of the isomers of C_7H_{16}.
5. We rarely use structural formulas in inorganic chemistry. Why not?
6. (a) How do saturated carbon compounds differ from unsaturated?
   (b) Which of the compounds that you listed in your answer to exercise 3 are saturated and which unsaturated?
7. (a) Which of the hydrocarbons occur as such in nature?
   (b) How do we obtain the others?
8. In the plant and animal world there is a vast host of compounds containing carbon. Are these hydrocarbons, derivatives of the hydrocarbons, or both?

9. Would you expect any difference in the polarity of CCl_4 and $CHCl_3$ (chloroform)? Explain.
10. Name four different kinds of hydrocarbon derivatives.
11. Classify the following compounds as completely as you can:

    C_4H_9OH C_4H_9Cl
    C_4H_9COOH $C_{15}H_{32}$
    C_6H_6 $C_3H_7(OH)_3$
    NH_2CH_2COOH $C_4H_9NH_2$
    $C_4H_9COOCH_3$ $C_{12}H_{24}$
                         $C_{16}H_{33}COONa$

12. You should be able to supply the names (common or otherwise) of at least four of the above compounds. Do so.
13. Try to write the hydrocarbon C_6H_6 as a chain, either straight or branching, remembering to count to four for the bonds of each carbon atom. You should then be able to appreciate the problem of Kekulé. How did he solve it?
14. (a) How can you distinguish most easily between CH_3COOH and CH_3OH?
    (b) Between $CH_3COOC_2H_5$ and C_2H_5OH?
15. (a) What is coal tar?
    (b) Of what use is it?
16. Wine, if left exposed to the atmosphere for a time will go sour (turn to vinegar) by oxidation of the alcohol. Explain why this is possible.
17. Distinguish between polymers, copolymers, and monomers.
18. Distinguish between addition polymers and condensation polymers.
19. What sorts of hydrocarbons form addition polymers?
20. Show by structural formulas how C_3H_6 can act as a monomer to form a simple addition polymer.
21. Explain the process of photosynthesis as far as you can. (See footnote 5.)

22. (a) What are amino acids?
    (b) Name the simplest one.
    (c) About how many are known?
23. The next simplest amino acid is valine. It contains one more carbon atom than glycine, and the amino group is attached to the middle carbon. Write the structural formula for it.
24. What do amino acids form when they polymerize?
25. What is the peptide linkage?
26. (a) Are proteins addition or condensation polymers?
    (b) What is a "simple" protein?
27. A third amino acid is phenylalanine. Its structural formula is

    (a) Show, by a structural diagram, how two such molecules may polymerize.
    (b) Is the resulting product a protein? Explain.
28. Distinguish as simply yet as meaningfully as you can between fats, carbohydrates, and proteins. What one property do they have in common?
29. What are fatty acids of high molecular weight used for?
30. (a) What happens to proteins during the digestive process?
    (b) Could you use amino acids for food directly?

(c) What does your body do with amino acids once they are formed?
31. In man's fight against pollution of our environment, which types of compounds does he find most difficult to cope with, organic or inorganic? Why?
32. What is the difference between ribose and deoxyribose?
33. What holds the nitrogen bases in pairs in DNA?
34. What is the invariable arrangement of pairing of nitrogen bases in DNA?
35. What are the differences in composition between DNA and RNA?
36. What investigational tool was used to determine the molecular structure of DNA?
37. Nucleic acids are polymers.
    (a) What are their monomers called?
    (b) What are the monomers composed of?
    (c) How are they linked together to form chains?
38. What characteristics of a DNA molecule determine the particular genetic characteristics it transmits?
39. During mitosis the two sides of the DNA molecule split apart. Each part then replicates the original opposite side. What is the source of the necessary materials and how is this replication accomplished?
40. (a) Where—in the cell—are proteins "assembled"?
    (b) What substance in this part of the cell picks up the appropriate amino acids for assembly into proteins?
    (c) What substance carries protein assembly information from the gene to "assembly line"?

PART VII

Matter and Energy in the Study of the Earth

Matter of the Earth: Rocks and Minerals

30

The Chemistry of Silicon

Silicon, a member of the same family as carbon, occupies the same relative position in the inorganic world that carbon occupies in the organic world. All of us are familiar with carbon: We have seen it in the pure state (diamond, graphite, lampblack) and in the impure state (in charcoal, coal), but few, if any, of you have ever seen silicon. Yet in the outer part of the earth there are about 10,000 atoms of silicon for every 27 atoms of carbon; if we include the whole earth, the ratio is even larger.

Silicon is much more active chemically than carbon, which is why we never see it in the free (native) state in nature. Silicon constitutes about 25% of the crust of the earth. Oxygen constitutes about 50% of the average rock, so that together they make up nearly 75% of the earth's crust. The two combine to form crystals of the mineral quartz (SiO_2). Most of the SiO_2 is, however, combined with various metals to form a group of minerals called silicates. From the abundance of SiO_2 in the crust of the earth, it inevitably follows that the chief rock-forming

Nature is more intimately organized and cross-linked than our theories, so that each model or likeness that we try scores some striking successes, and then falls short. All that we can do, at any state of our factual knowledge, is to prefer that code which makes what we know most orderly.
J. BROWNOWSKI (1955)

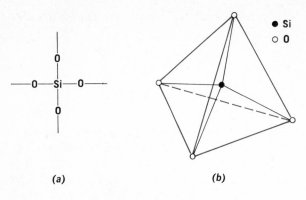

Si
O

Fig. 30-1. Silicon-Oxygen Tetrahedron. (a) Two-dimensional representation of SiO_4^{4-} tetrahedron; (b) three-dimensional representation.

(a)   (b)

minerals are silicates.[1] Quantitatively, they make up about 98% of the crust of the earth.

Silicon-Carbon Similarities and Differences

Silicon, atomic number 14, is directly beneath carbon in the periodic table. We should therefore expect it to have properties similar to those of carbon. Chief among them are its valence of 4 and the ability to combine with other atoms chiefly by sharing its four outer electrons. Silicon has little tendency to form chains of silicon atoms in the manner of carbon, but it will form chains of alternating silicon and oxygen atoms. These are commonly arranged in tetrahedral structures as in the diamond; the silicon atom is at the center of the tetrahedron with an oxygen atom at each of the corners.

The mineral quartz is composed of nothing but SiO_4^{4-} tetrahedra (Fig. 30-1). Since each silicon atom is tetrahedrally surrounded by four oxygen atoms and each oxygen atom serves as a neighbor to two silicon atoms, the atomic ratio of silicon to oxygen is 1:2. The empirical formula of a crystal of quartz is

therefore SiO_2, but it should be understood that there is only one molecule per crystal even though some such natural crystals weigh a ton or more. The formula merely expresses the ratio of silicon atoms to oxygen atoms. A two-dimensional representation of the way these two elements are linked together in quartz is shown in Fig. 30-2. The Si—O bonds are covalent, as in the diamond, and to break or melt a quartz crystal (which is one giant molecule) many of these bonds must be broken. The crystal is therefore very hard and has a high melting point (1600°C), but it is not as hard as the diamond.

The differences between CO_2 and SiO_2 are much more striking than one would predict from the similarities of the silicon and carbon atoms. Carbon dioxide is a gas that can be liquefied at a temperature below 31°C only if a pressure of 73 atm is applied. Its freezing (or melting) point is −56.6°C. SiO_2 melts at a temperature of about 1700°C. In the solid state the molecules of CO_2 are held together by weak van der Waals forces, whereas the "molecules"[2] of SiO_2 are covalently bonded together in a network of continuous crystal lattices to form a solid mass of silicon-oxygen

[1] Quartz should also be considered a silicate, even though no metal appears in its composition, for the structure of quartz is fundamental to the structure of the silicates. Silicon dioxide is better known as silica. The chief crystalline form of silica is quartz, but the two words are not interchangeable; for example, molten SiO_2 is silica but not quartz.

[2] The word *molecule* is in quotes because neither silicon dioxide nor the tetrahedral units exist in nature as separate structures but as continuous crystal lattices in the manner of giant molecules. The formula SiO_2 merely expresses the ratio of Si atoms to O atoms, 1:2.

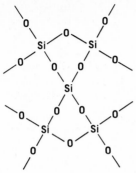

Fig. 30-2. A Continuous Lattice Network of SiO_4^{4-} Tetrahedra. Two-dimensional representation of a continuous lattice network of SiO_4^{4-} tetrahedra such as that present in the mineral quartz. Note that between each Si and O is an electron pair bond; that is, each atom of silicon shares one pair of electrons with each of four oxygen atoms.

tetrahedra. The bonding between the silicon and oxygen atoms extends in all directions within the crystal, giving it a rigid structure without cleavage and a hardness greater than that of steel. These latter two properties are usually sufficient to identify a mineral possessing them as quartz.

The reason for the differences in bonding in carbon dioxide and quartz presumably lies largely, perhaps entirely, in the differences in the sizes of the carbon and silicon atoms. Not more than three oxygen atoms can fit around the small carbon atom (as in the carbonate ion, CO_3^{2-}), whereas four oxygen atoms can easily cluster around the larger silicon atom. Silicon is more metallic than carbon, enough so that one form of it has some of the lustrous sheen of a metal, but it is not metallic enough to form the positive ions so characteristic of a metal.

Silicate Minerals

The tetrahedral units, SiO_4^{4-}, do not have enough valence electrons to complete the octets of all the atoms in them (as the dot

$$: \overset{\displaystyle ..}{\underset{\displaystyle ..}{O}} :$$
$$\cdot \overset{..}{O} : \overset{..}{Si} : \overset{..}{O} \cdot$$
$$: \overset{..}{\underset{\displaystyle .}{O}} :$$

representation makes clear), hence the negative charge of 4. Positive metal ions, particularly Ca^{2+}, Mg^{2+}, Fe^{2+}, Na^+, K^+, and Al^{3+}, may attach themselves to the tetrahedral units and so neutralize them. The resulting silicate minerals are relatively simple in structure; for example, Fe^{2+} and Mg^{2+} may form $(Fe,Mg)SiO_4$, which is one variety of a ferromagnesian mineral called olivine (Fig. 30-3).

Linking of SiO_4^{4-} Tetrahedra

Most silicate minerals have an excess of silicon atoms so that some of the oxygen atoms have to be shared by two tetrahedra. The simplest example is the $Si_2O_7^{6-}$ ion (Fig. 30-4), which is formed by the two silicons in two SiO_4^{4-} tetrahedra sharing one oxygen atom, thus releasing one oxygen atom for "duty" elsewhere. In the simplest compound (mineral) the net negative charge of -6 is neutralized by two metallic ions, each with a valence of $+3$. In some other minerals three metallic ions, each with a valence of $+2$, may neutralize the negative charge of -6. The metallic ions may be of the same or different species.

In the $Si_2O_7^{6-}$ ion one oxygen forms a bridge between two silicons, as shown in Fig. 30-4. Not only one but two, three, or even four

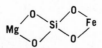

Fig. 30-3. The Bonding Within a Simple Silicate Mineral, Olivine. The ratio of magnesium (Mg) to iron (Fe) atoms need not be 1:1. Thus there are a number of different olivines.

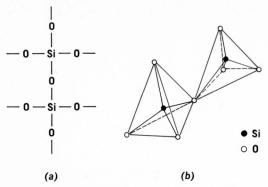

Fig. 30-4. Linking of Tetrahedra. (a) A simple linking to form the $Si_2O_7^{6-}$ ion in two dimensions. (b) Three-dimensional representation of the $Si_2O_7^{6-}$ ion. Note that the central oxygen forms a bridge between two silicon atoms. Two metallic ions, each with a valence of $+3$, may neutralize the $Si_2O_7^{6-}$ ion to form a silicate mineral. Si atoms in black.

oxygens can bridge to other silicons to form more complex silicate ions such as $Si_4O_{12}^{8-}$, $Si_3O_9^{6-}$, and $Si_6O_{18}^{12-}$. Note that by combining tetrahedra the ratio of the number of positive charges needed to neutralize the ion to the number of Si atoms has been reduced from the ratio in SiO_4^{4-}.

The Feldspar Minerals

We have already described the tetrahedral structure of quartz, with a silicon atom at the center of each tetrahedron and oxygen atoms at the corners, where each is joined to another silicon atom at the center of another tetrahedron. These tetrahedra, repeated almost endlessly, give a tetrahedral framework structure. Aluminum atoms can substitute for silicon in some tetrahedra, most commonly in the ratio of $1:3$; that is, in the framework lattice every fourth tetrahedron will have an aluminum atom at the center; these are AlO_4^{3-} tetrahedra. Aluminum adjoins silicon in the

periodic chart; it is slightly larger, but not enough to alter the structure of the tetrahedra significantly. However, aluminum has a valence of only 3, and so a singly charged positive ion must be present to preserve electrical neutrality in the tetrahedron.

The common singly charged positive ions are potassium (K^+) and sodium (Na^+). The resulting minerals are the light-colored feldspars, chiefly orthoclase ($KAlSi_3O_8$) and albite ($NaAlSi_3O_8$). If every second tetrahedron is an AlO_4 tetrahedron, then a doubly charged positive ion, commonly Ca^{2+}, must be present to preserve electrical neutrality. The resulting mineral is a very dark-colored lime feldspar, anorthite ($CaAl_2Si_2O_8$). This dark feldspar and the light-colored soda feldspar albite may have their tetrahedra mixed in all proportions; they (the atoms of sodium and calcium) are almost the same size. When they are mixed about half and half, the resulting feldspar is the common dark lime-soda feldspar called labradorite.

The potassium atoms are considerably bigger than either the sodium or the calcium atoms so that the tetrahedra to which they are attached do not fit into the same framework as those of sodium and calcium; instead they form the potash feldspars, orthoclase and microcline. Note that AlO_4 tetrahedra are present in all feldspars. There are many other framework minerals, but these, together with quartz, form the great bulk of the rocks of the earth's crust. The feldspars alone outbulk all of the other minerals of all kinds in the crust of the earth. Ground-up feldspar, together with a white clay mineral and quartz, forms the porcelain of our kitchens and bathrooms, and the glaze on our dishes.

Ferromagnesian Minerals

We have already mentioned the neutralization of a silicate tetrahedron by Fe^{2+} and

Mg^{2+} to yield the ferromagnesian mineral olivine. More complicated silicate structures may be formed to yield parallel single and/or double chains that are tied together and neutralized chiefly by Ca^{2+}, Fe^{2+}, and Mg^{2+}. The resulting minerals are the pyroxenes and the amphiboles, common constituents of many rocks. The chain-like structure of these minerals causes them to have a fibrous character that is readily apparent in some mineral species but obscure in others.[3]

The Layer Minerals

The layer minerals include such well-known minerals as the micas and talc. Others, less well known but more important, are the clay minerals that are abundant constituents of all good soils.

Structurally, the layer minerals are composed of SiO_4 and/or AlO_4 tetrahedra arranged in the form of continuous layers. In the micas the metallic (positive) ions lie between the layers. Their attraction for the negative ions forming the layers binds the layers together. These attractions are not nearly so great as those between the Si and O ions in the layers. Thus, the layers can be cleaved (split apart) readily. In talc and the clay minerals the layers are electrically neutral and are loosely superimposed on one another. They slip over one another easily; this accounts for their softness, ready cleavage, and soapy feel.

Note that the metallic ions in all of the silicate minerals (feldspars and ferromagnesian and layer minerals) are almost exclusively those of aluminum, potassium, sodium, iron, calcium, and magnesium. These six elements, along with silicon and oxygen, make up more

than 98% of the earth's crust, leaving less than 2% for all of the other 80-odd elements.

Definition of a Mineral

So far we have been using the term *mineral* without formally defining it. Minerals are naturally occurring inorganic substances having a characteristic range of physical and chemical properties and a characteristic crystal structure. A careful inspection of this definition will show that many things called minerals are not true minerals. Thus, coal is not a mineral; neither are most metals. The significance of the characteristic crystal structure requirement is easily seen by comparing the diamond with graphite.

Nonsilicate Minerals

There are some 2000 known minerals, most of which are rare and of little consequence either as constituents of the earth or to man. Not many of the chief rock-forming minerals are of great direct importance to man. None has equaled the role played in the development of our civilization by a few of the nonsilicate minerals, such as magnetite (Fe_3O_4), hematite (Fe_2O_3), and limonite ($Fe_2O_3 \cdot xH_2O$). The first two are oxides; the third is a hydrated oxide (of which common iron rust is an example). Other minerals that occur as oxides and are essential to man are those of copper, tin, aluminum, and manganese. Another major group is the sulfides; of greatest importance to man are those of lead, zinc, copper, silver, mercury, nickel, and the like. Among the chlorides are those of sodium and potassium; among the carbonates are those of calcium, magnesium, zinc, lead, and copper. Only gold and platinum are prominent as native metals, although there have been (and are) some ex-

---

[3] The mineral known commercially as *asbestos* is extremely fibrous in appearance, but it is actually a "layer" mineral in which the layers are rolled up, thereby giving the fibrous appearance.

tensive deposits of copper and silver in the native state. There are a score or two groups of lesser significance.

These nonsilicate minerals occur as ores; that is, they occur as parts of mineral aggregates from which one or more metals may be extracted at a profit. There are many low-grade deposits of mineral aggregates that contain enormous quantities of the metals but not in sufficiently high concentrations to make them minable at a profit. Mineral aggregates that are not ores at one time may become ores at another time if the price of the metal goes up or if a cheaper process of smelting is discovered. Whatever concentrations there are in nature that are profitable were made by one or more of a variety of natural processes. The study of ore deposits is therefore largely a study of the various natural methods of concentration. We will not discuss them here, except to say that if no such natural methods existed, man would still be in the Stone Age.

Rocks

A rock is a very difficult thing to define in satisfying terms. To say that it is anything that naturally forms a significant portion of the earth's crust is scarcely satisfying, yet it is the only all-inclusive definition that we can give. Most rocks are aggregates of minerals, but there are a few with no minerals, for example, the volcanic glasses (obsidian, pumice, scoria) and the coals (which are commonly called minerals). To the geologist minerals are not rocks. To think they are is somewhat analogous to calling a piece of cloth a dress.

We might suspect from the definition of a rock that rocks would be difficult to classify. Basing a system on definite substances like elements and minerals has its problems in any classification scheme. Any scheme based on chemical composition breaks down so completely that it is entirely unusable, because

rocks of very different origins, even different mineralogical compositions, may have closely similar chemical compositions. Systems based on mineralogical compositions run into similar difficulties that are nearly as great. A usable one is based on origin, although there are some rocks whose origin is in dispute. The major rocks, however, have origins agreed on by all geologists.

On this basis rocks are classified as igneous, sedimentary, or metamorphic. The igneous rocks are those that have solidified from a once molten state. While deep in the crust of the earth, this molten material is called magma. If the magma works its way upward without reaching the surface, it is called an intrusive. When poured out on the surface, it is called lava. The rocks formed from either magmas or lavas are sometimes referred to as the primary rocks, for if we go back far enough in time, all rocks were igneous (since the whole earth was once molten). From the products of destruction of these original igneous rocks, through the processes of weathering and erosion, the first sedimentary rocks were formed. In the course of vast periods of time other processes (volcanism and diastrophism) caused these sedimentary and igneous rocks to be changed in various ways, sometimes in chemical composition, sometimes in mineralogical composition, sometimes in the way the crystals were arranged, or even all three. If these changes are great enough, we call the resulting product a metamorphic rock. Obviously, there are all sorts of gradations between sedimentary and metamorphic rocks on the one hand, and between igneous and metamorphic rocks on the other. There are even metamorphic rocks that have a mixed origin, and some whose ancestry is uncertain.

Igneous Rocks and Their Minerals

Magmas and molten lavas are heterogeneous liquids that have high freezing points—1000°C or higher in most cases. However, granite, the most common igneous rock in the crust of the earth, can crystallize below 700°C. Magmas and molten lavas might be considered to consist almost wholly of various silicate ions, such as SiO_4^{4-}, SiO_3^{2-}, $Si_2O_7^{6-}$, $Si_3O_9^{6-}$, and $Si_6O_{18}^{12-}$, all negatively charged, and the positively charged metallic ions Al^{3+}, Fe^{2+}, Ca^{2+}, K^+, Na^+, and Mg^{2+}, all in mutual solution with one another. As long as the temperature is high enough, the kinetic energy of the ions is great enough to prevent the attractive forces between negative and positive ions from forming bonds. Thus, no minerals are formed; the whole mass remains a liquid. If the temperature drops far enough and slowly enough, the whole mass becomes solid by the process of crystallization of various minerals. The reason is as follows:

Minerals are solid substances in which the ions are arranged in characteristic patterns, more commonly called crystal lattices (p. 467). To form these lattices, the temperature must slowly drop to the point where the attractive forces between the ions begin to overcome the kinetic forces. Until this point is reached the ions will not occupy the lattice points. Furthermore, if crystals large enough to be visible to the naked eye are to form, the melt must remain at the crystallizing temperature for a long time. This allows the ions to still have some freedom of movement, enough freedom to find and occupy lattice points, but once in the lattice, not enough freedom to move out against the attractive forces. If these conditions prevail, ion after ion occupies the lattice points, slowly building up solid mineral crystals or grains, neutral with respect to electric charge. The temperature at which the ions *begin* to form the crystal lattice of any particular mineral is highly variable. For olivine it is about 1500°C; for quartz it is less than 800°C.

The sizes of the individual crystals (also called grains) in the resulting rock clearly depend upon the length of time that the tem-

perature of the magma remains within the range where the ions can occupy the lattice points and *stay there*. The greater the number of ions in a particular lattice the larger the size of the crystal. Slow cooling promotes large grain size, easily seen with the naked eye. Thus, the coarse-grained igneous rocks, such as granite, are formed. Conversely, rapid cooling promotes small grain size, sizes too small to be seen with the naked eye. Thus the fine-grained igneous rocks, such as basalt, are formed. In some cases the cooling may be so rapid—as when lava is poured out on the surface to form a thin sheet—that few or no ions manage to occupy lattice points. The result is a rock with no grains, a rock we call a volcanic glass because, like glass, it has a noncrystalline structure. Such rocks either have a glassy appearance like obsidian or are full of holes formed by bubbles of expanding gases as the pressure on the lava is relieved by escape to the surface; scoria and pumice are examples of this type.

The rate of cooling of a molten mass varies enormously with depth and with thickness. For example, it has been estimated that a 3 ft layer of lava on the surface at a temperature of 1100°C (2000°F) would cool to 750°C (1400°F) in about 12 days, whereas the deep interior of a mass 30,000 ft thick (about 6 mi) would take about 3 million yr to cool from 1100 to 750°C. Of course, no layer of lava is ever anything like that thick. It follows that an intrusive 30,000 ft thick whose top is several *miles* below the surface would take far more than 3 million yr to cool from 1100 to 750°C. This is in part because rocks are notoriously poor conductors of heat.

The minerals that form from lavas and magmas are obviously dependent upon the kinds and proportions of ions that compose the molten matter. Most magmas are high silica magmas, composed largely of silicate ions, up to 75% or even more. Metallic ions, chiefly Al^{3+}, Na^+, and K^+, make up the remaining

25%. The lattices that form are those that use large amounts of silica. The resulting minerals are chiefly the light-colored soda and/or potassium feldspars already discussed. What little Fe^{2+} or Mg^{2+} there is usually goes into the biotite (black mica) lattice. If Ca^{2+} ions are present in significant amounts, amphibole may form in place of biotite. Any excess iron may crystallize as tiny crystals of magnetite.

In these high silica magmas there is always an excess of silicate ions after all of the metallic ions have entered into the lattices. These excess silicate ions break up into SiO_4^{4-} ions, which then arrange themselves in the quartz crystal lattice in the ratio of two oxygen ions to one silicate ion. That quartz is in an igneous rock is an indication that the magma from which it formed was a high-silica magma. Furthermore, since the great bulk of the minerals formed are the light-colored feldspars and quartz, the resulting rock will be light-colored. Most commonly the rock formed, if coarse-grained, is *granite*.

In low silica magmas silicate ions compose about 50% of the mass; metallic ions form the other 50%. Thus, the proportion of the latter is doubled, the increase being chiefly in Fe^{2+}, Mg^{2+}, and Ca^{2+} ions. Hence, crystal lattices form that use more of these ions and fewer silicate ions. Minerals with such lattices as these are the ferromagnesians, olivine, pyroxene, and amphibole and the dark-colored lime feldspar (or lime-soda feldspar). Obviously there are no silicate ions left over to form quartz. The resulting rocks are therefore dark-colored with *no* quartz. The feldspar will always be the one that is most sparing in the use of silica, dark-colored lime feldspar. The most common fine-grained low-silica rock is *basalt*.

It is well worth noting that color is an extremely useful property in igneous rock identification. One should no more think of hunting for quartz and light-colored feldspars in a dark-colored rock than one should think of hunting lions in Greenland. There are, of course, exceptions to every rule, but let us not concern ourselves here with them.

Sedimentary Rocks and Their Minerals

The chief sedimentary rocks are conglomerate, sandstone, shale, and limestone. They are formed chiefly by the consolidation of the products of weathering and erosion of previously existing rocks. Some are formed from accumulations of organic debris. The coals are examples of the latter; we will omit them from the following discussion because they are not typical sedimentary rocks.

The products of weathering and erosion are for the most part sediments—gravels, sands, clay muds, and lime muds. In time these sediments usually become consolidated into solid rock either by compaction (of the muds) or by cementation (of the gravels and sands). Compaction is accomplished by sheer weight of the sediments as layer is piled upon layer. Compaction is effective only in fine-grained sediments, for it is obvious that coarse sands and gravels cannot be made to stick together by pressure alone.

Cementation involves the introduction of cements between the pebbles or sand grains by percolating ground waters. The chief cements are silica, calcium carbonate, and the iron oxides, limonite and hematite. Cementation is not effective in the muds because the pore spaces are too small for the cement-carrying waters to freely pass through them. The color of the cement commonly determines the color of the rock. Thus, sandstones cemented with either silica or calcium carbonate are commonly white or gray, those cemented with hematite are red or reddish brown, and those cemented with limonite are yellow or yellow brown.

On consolidation by compaction or cementation the gravels become conglomerates, the sands become sandstones, clay muds become shales, and the lime muds become limestones. The first three—conglomerates, sandstones, shales—are called the clastic rocks because they are formed from fragments of minerals. These fragments are *either* original minerals, such as quartz, that were not affected by chemical weathering or they are the insoluble products of chemical weathering, for example, the clay minerals. They are transported by one or the other of the agents of erosion—of which streams are by far the most important—and eventually deposited mechanically in some low place to form the clastic rocks.

The lime muds that eventually form limestones are called *precipitates* because they were precipitated from solution. During the chemical weathering of the minerals in igneous rocks, some of the minerals are changed into new minerals by chemical reactions with moisture and air. A small fraction of these new minerals are water soluble and so are dissolved out of the weathered material by rainwater. Much of this water finds its way to seas or lakes where the dissolved material is precipitated if conditions are right. Limestone, made of calcium carbonate (calcite), is by far the most common precipitate. Two others are halite (NaCl) and gypsum ($CaSO_4 \cdot 2H_2O$).

Most sedimentary rocks are chiefly accumulations of clay, quartz, and calcite, either alone or in various combinations. Most sandstones are made essentially of quartz because quartz, an original constituent of most igneous rocks, is not only immune to change by chemical weathering but is also almost completely insoluble in water. Sandstones may sometimes contain feldspar and mica grains as well as many other resistant minerals in small quantities. A few sandstones with little or no quartz do exist, but none extensively.

The clay minerals form a group we will refer to as *kaolin*. The chief source of clay is the feldspars, from which it is derived by the processes of chemical weathering, as follows:

$$2K(AlSi_3O_8) \ + \ CO_2 \ + \ 2H_2O \ \rightarrow$$
potash feldspar

$$Al_2Si_2O_5(OH)_4 \ + \ K_2CO_3 \ + \ 4SiO_2$$
clay mineral   potassium   silica
carbonate

From this reaction it is readily seen that if most of the mass of an igneous rock is feldspar (which it is), far more clay than anything else is produced when that rock is chemically weathered. It follows that the rock that forms from this clay, that is, shale, should be the most abundant of the sedimentary rocks.

The clastic sediments, gravels, sands, and clay muds, are washed into the streams by rain or they creep or slide down the slopes into the streams under the force of gravity. The streams carry them in suspension to their more or less "final" resting place. Loss of velocity causes the stream to deposit them, the coarsest first, the finer later. The result is a succession of layers or strata. This *stratification* is the most characteristic feature of sedimentary rocks.

Metamorphic Rocks and Their Minerals

Rocks, like living things, adjust themselves to changes in their environment. When rocks are subjected to greatly increased pressure or temperature, or a combination of them, metamorphism may result. The degree or "grade" of metamorphism depends on the intensity of these factors and the duration of their action. The heat is in part derived from igneous activity and the pressure is derived chiefly from diastrophic activity (Chapter 32). This heat and pressure, if great enough, impose a new set of characteristics—minerals, structures, textures—on the original rocks, metamorphosing them.

Pressures of 40,000 to 60,000 lb/in.^{2} are

great enough to cause rocks to flow plastically. These pressures combined with the horizontal pressures that cause rocks in *some* areas to bend and fold are capable of bringing about metamorphism. It should be obvious from this that rocks at or near the surface can never be metamorphosed. Where metamorphic rocks are exposed at the surface today, it is because erosion to considerable depths has exposed them.

Heat is a necessary agent of metamorphism because it increases the average kinetic energy of the atoms in the minerals, and so weakens the bonds between them. This accelerates the rate at which chemical reactions take place. Obviously, the higher the temperature, the faster the rate. As previously stated, part of the heat is derived from igneous activity (in those areas where such activity exists), and in part it is derived from friction in areas where folding and/or faulting on a large scale have taken place. Both igneous activity and folding are associated with mountain building. Therefore, metamorphic rocks are confined to those regions where complex mountains, past or present, have been formed. The rocks of New York City and at shallow depths in adjoining regions on Long Island are highly metamorphosed rocks. Therefore, the geologist infers that part of a great complex mountain range once occupied these areas; only the roots remain.

Because igneous rocks were formed under conditions of high temperature, and, in the case of intrusive igneous rocks, under high pressure, it follows that such rocks are difficult to metamorphose. Sedimentary rocks, on the other hand, were formed at the surface of the earth under conditions of low temperature and low pressure. It is to be expected that they would metamorphose most easily. It also follows that metamorphic rocks would resemble igneous rocks more than they would sedimentary rocks, because the conditions under which they formed resemble those under which igneous rocks formed. In fact, the most abundant minerals in metamorphic rocks formed from either igneous rocks or the *clastic* sedimentary rocks are those most abundant in igneous rocks—feldspars, micas, amphibole, quartz. Much of the quartz is reconstituted quartz of the sedimentary rocks. Thus, a quartz sandstone becomes a quartzite by recrystallization of the grains so that their rounded discrete character is lost. The result is a tougher rock, one that breaks right through the grains rather than around them, as in sandstones. If the sedimentary rock is a limestone, the calcium carbonate is recrystallized into larger grains, forming a marble. The size of the grains depends upon the intensity of the metamorphism and its duration; they vary from those barely visible to those a quarter of an inch or more across.

The density of metamorphic rocks is, on the average, greater than that of their sedimentary antecedents. In part their greater density is due to reduction of pore spaces, and in part to the application of Le Châtelier's principle: When a system is in equilibrium and one of the factors that determine the equilibrium is altered, the system always reacts in such a way as *to tend* to counteract the original alteration. The factor in question here is pressure. At the start of metamorphism the pressure is increased. New minerals that are denser than the original ones may form, or many small grains may unite to form fewer larger ones. In either case space is saved as the system reacts to counteract the increase in pressure.

Some metamorphic rocks are foliated, for example, slate, schist, and gneiss; and some are nonfoliated or massive, for example, quartzite, marble, and hornfels. In the foliated rocks pressure has been an important factor. If the composition of the original rock allows platy minerals like mica or elongate minerals like amphibole to form, these minerals form with a parallelism that to the uninitiated looks like stratification but which is called *foliation* by geologists. The trend of the parallelism is at right angles to the pressure causing the folding. Marbles and quartzites show little or no parallelism because their minerals, calcite and quartz, respectively, are neither platy nor elongate but equidimensional. There is nothing to line up. Hornfels is not foliated because it does not form where there is any orienting stress; it is the product of heat (thermal) metamorphism only.

Exercises

1. (a) Name the eight most abundant elements forming the crust of the earth.
   (b) Name the first four in order of abundance.
2. (a) Which of these eight elements occur as element(s) in the outer part of the earth?
   (b) Why it, or them, and not the others?
3. What is the importance of silicon in the mineral kingdom?
4. Define *mineral*.
5. (a) What is a feldspar?
   (b) What is the importance of feldspars in the mineral kingdom?
   (c) In our own lives?
6. (a) What is an ore?
   (b) Distinguish among a rock, a mineral, and an ore.
7. What is a magma composed of? (Make your answer significant.)
8. Which can crowd around a carbon atom more easily, four oxygen atoms or four other carbon atoms? Explain.
9. (a) It is incorrect to speak of a molecule of SiO_2. Why?
   (b) Would it be incorrect to speak of a molecule of quartz? Explain.
10. Some fibrous minerals are amazingly fi-

brous, whereas others are not at all obviously fibrous. Why the difference?
11. Why is coal not considered a mineral in the scientific sense?
12. Define each of the three great classes of rocks.
13. (a) What is grain in a rock?
    (b) Where is the boundary line between fine-grained and coarse-grained rocks drawn?
    (c) What factors determine grain size in igneous rocks?
14. (a) What is a glassy rock?
    (b) What conditions produce glassy rocks?
15. What is the most abundant mineral group in most igneous rocks?
16. Under what conditions will quartz form in an igneous rock?
17. Why should rocks from low-silica magmas be darker in color than those formed from high-silica magmas?
18. (a) What is by far the most common coarse-grained igneous rock?
    (b) The most common fine-grained igneous rock?
19. What, considering your answers to the above questions, would you expect to be the most abundant constituents of lavas and magmas?
20. Distinguish between the essential minerals of a granite and those of a basalt.
21. (a) How do sediments differ from sedimentary rocks?
    (b) What processes can convert the former into the latter?
22. What are the chief cements in sedimentary rocks?
23. Cementation is far more important in sandstones than in shales. Why?
24. What is the role of weathering in the formation of sediments?
25. Why should any rock undergo metamorphosis?
26. Which would you expect to undergo

metamorphosis most easily, a sedimentary or an igneous rock? Explain.

27. Name the common metamorphic rocks and state the kind they may have been before metamorphism.

28. Name the essential minerals in each of the following: a sandstone, a shale, a limestone, a quartzite, a slate, and a marble.

A General View
of the Earth

Before continuing our discussion of matter and energy in and on the earth, it is highly desirable to take a general look at the earth as a whole. If we do, the later discussions will be much more meaningful. We will start with the surface of the earth.

There exists a passion for comprehension. That passion is rather common in children, but gets lost in most people later on.
ALBERT EINSTEIN, 1950

Continents and Ocean Basins

The outstanding feature of the earth's surface is its division into continents and ocean basins. The latter are much the larger; they occupy about 70% of the earth's surface, leaving only 30% for the land areas. The average depth of the oceans is a little over 2 mi below sea level and the average height of the continents is about $\frac{1}{2}$ mi above. The greatest depth in the oceans is about 37,000 ft below sea level, the greatest height above is a bit over 29,000 ft. This makes the difference between the highest mountain top and the greatest depth of the sea over 65,000 ft (12.5 mi).[1]

[1] This is called the relief of the earth. *Relief* is defined as the difference in elevation between the highest and the lowest points *in the area under consideration.*

541

More fundamental than the differences in elevation with respect to sea level are the differences in composition of the crustal materials of continents and ocean basins. Moreover, to view sea level as the boundary line between continents and ocean bases is a highly untenable viewpoint, for the continental shelves are unquestionably parts of the continents rather than parts of the ocean basins.

How did the earth's surface get that way? The origin of continents and ocean basins is never asked about by the average person; he takes them for granted, perhaps because he believes the earth was created that way. If we all believed that, there would be no science of geology, for the answers to all our questions would be the same: Things are as they are because they were created that way.

Our basic question is this, "Why is the earth not covered with a universal ocean two miles deep?" This is the way it would be if we removed the water, shoveled the continents into the basins to make a uniform surface, and then let the water return. No direct evidence of any sort has been found that would indicate how the land and water became divided, and no widely accepted theory has ever been formulated. An associated problem that may be solved, if and when that one is, is that of the origin of fold and complex mountains, to be discussed in the next chapter.

The evidence indicates that there have always been continents and ocean basins as far back in geologic history as we can probe, even though they may not always have been located where they are today. Radioactive age deter-

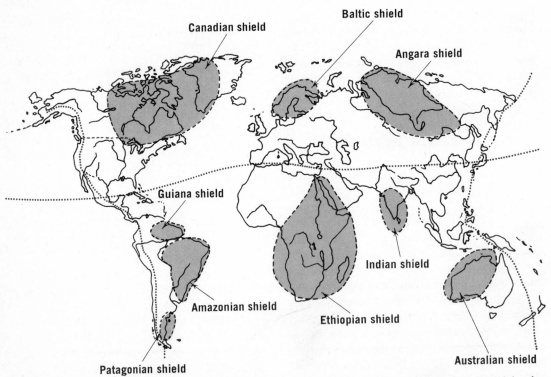

Fig. 31-1. Shield Areas of the World. The oldest exposed rocks of each continent are found in the colored areas. Very largely they are igneous and metamorphic rocks. The dotted lines indicate the approximate positions of the earth's two chief mobile belts.

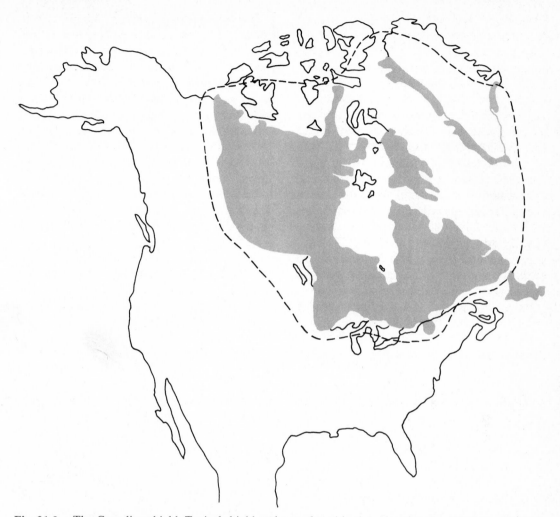

Fig. 31-2. The Canadian shield. Typical shield rocks are found in the colored region. White areas within the dashed line are covered with water or ice, or are areas where typical shield rocks are interspersed with sedimentary rocks. Typical shield rocks are igneous (largely granitic) and highly metamorphosed rocks, such as gneisses and schists.

minations seem to indicate that, in general, the central parts of shield areas (Figs. 31-1 and 31-2) of each continent are made of the oldest rocks of that continent, and that as we go outward from these centers the rocks become younger. Perhaps the formation of continents is related to the fact that mountain-building has always been concentrated in narrow strips called mobile belts, that is, belts in which the earth's crust has been subject to movements of one sort or another. Two such belts exist today. One extends from Antarctica up the west coasts of South and North America to the Aleutians, where it swings westward and then southward along the Kuriles, Japan, Philippines, and Indonesia. The other includes the Atlas, Alpine, Turkish, Persian, Himalayan, and Burmese mountains and the island chains of Indonesia, New Guinea, the Solomons, New Hebrides, and New Zealand.

Along these belts are all of the world's youngest mountains, most of its active and recently extinct volcanoes, and most earthquake epicenters. Chief among the features of these mobile belts are the island arcs and the associated deep sea trenches. Island arcs are chains of submarine volcanic mountains with only the highest peaks protruding above sea level. The Aleutian island chain, which extends from the mainland of Alaska westward toward Japan, forms one example. Adjacent to it on the convex side is an arcuate (bowed) trench, called the Aleutian Trench. The Philippine–Japanese–Kurile island system is another island arc, with the Japanese trench a relatively short distance offshore. These trenches include the deepest parts of the oceans; the deepest part of the Japanese trench is 37,000 ft, about 25,000 ft more than the average depth of the ocean basins. The Antilles in the Caribbean form another island arc, with the Puerto Rican Trench on its convex side.

Perhaps the earth was covered by a universal ocean early in its history. Then vulcanism started as a consequence of fracturing of certain parts of the solid crust beneath the waters; great volumes of molten materials were poured out. If the fractures were arcuate, then the piles of volcanic materials eventually built up above the ocean levels would be arcuate also. Thus, the first island arcs would have been formed somewhat more than 3 billion years ago. In time other island arcs might have developed more or less parallel to the first ones and adjacent to them.

According to J. Tuzo Wilson of the University of Toronto these arcs went through a series of stages, much too complicated to be presented here. When the final stages were completed, an embryonic continent had come into existence. The final stages of the adjacent island arcs allowed them and their associated features to be added to the first. Thus, the continents grew by accretion, that is, by the addition of more island arcs. The process may not yet be ended. This process of accretion would explain why the rocks get younger outward from the centers of the shield areas. The ejection of volcanic materials in such enormous amounts would have made it necessary for other areas to sink as material (at relatively shallow depth in the crust) moved inward toward the arc to replace the ejected material. Thus, the continents and the ocean basins may have come into being. This is, of course, only a sketch of the hypothesis, and a greatly oversimplified one at that.[2]

Structure of Continents

The structure of a continent—that is, the arrangement of its major relief features—is not haphazard. Each continent has a shield area (Figs. 31-1 and 31-2). These are vast areas (about 2 million mi^2 for the Canadian shield) of ancient igneous and intensely metamorphosed (for the most part) sedimentary rocks that form the "cores" of their respective continents. Their rocks represent the roots of complexly folded (Fig. 31-3) mountain ranges that have been deeply eroded, re-elevated, and eroded again and again. The shield areas stand an average of a few hundred feet above sea level at present. They are the most stable areas of the continents and have been so for the last half billion years. If we could remove from each of the continents all rocks younger than about one-half billion years, then the rocks exposed would be the ones like those in the shield areas. The younger rocks are chiefly sedimentary, with interbedded lava flows in some areas, but others have been metamorphosed and igneous material has been forcibly injected into some of them.

[2] For more details, see Russell, Jacobs, and Wilson, *Physics and Geology*, New York, McGraw-Hill, 1959, Chaps. 14 and 15.

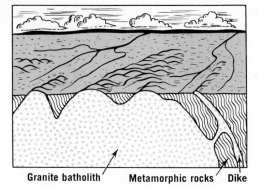

Fig. 31-3. Roots of a Complexly Folded Mountain Range. Previously existing rocks were complexly folded, metamorphosed, and intruded by molten magma to form a great mountain range. The processes of weathering, masswasting, and erosion through countless millions of years have removed several miles of rock so that only the mountain roots remain.

Each continent has a number of mountain systems that more or less parallel the continental borders. In the United States the Appalachians parallel the east coast, while the Rockies, the Sierra Nevada, the Cascades, and the coast ranges parallel the west coast. None is more than a quarter of a billion years old. In general, igneous and metamorphic rocks form the cores of at least the older of these mountains, and folded sedimentary rocks are exposed on the flanks (Fig. 31-4). In the northern Appalachians erosion has not yet cut deep enough to expose the core, even though they have been nearly leveled by erosion and re-elevated at least three times.

In contrast to the folded character of most mountain ranges, the plains and plateaus are composed of essentially flat-lying, sedimentary rocks, or, exceptionally, of flat-lying lava flows (Fig. 31-4). These rocks may be a few hundred or at most a few thousand feet thick (in contrast to the tens of thousands of feet of origi-

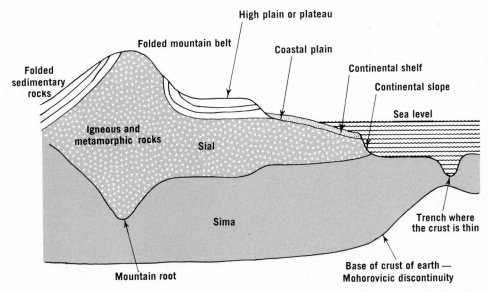

Fig. 31-4. Generalized Section Across a Continent. The vertical scale is greatly exaggerated with respect to the horizontal. The continental block, composed of sialic rocks, rests on simatic rocks. Note that sialic rocks are thickest beneath the mountain ranges, and generally absent from the ocean basins. Note also that the crust is thinnest in the deep sea trenches that always lie relatively close to the continents.

nally sedimentary rocks in folded mountain chains). Below the horizontal rocks there are always deformed (tilted or folded) sedimentary, metamorphic, or igneous rocks (Fig. 31-4), or all three. These plains or plateaus typically lie between the mountain ranges. Thus, the Appalachian plateaus (Cumberland, Allegheny, Catskill), the Interior Lowlands (plains), and the Great Plains lie between the Appalachians and the Rockies; the Colorado Plateau lies between the southern Rockies and the Sierras; and the Columbia Plateau (a lava plateau) lies between the northern Rockies and the Cascades.

The coastal plains represent an exception to what we have just said. When present, they typically lie on the ocean sides of mountain ranges, for example, the Atlantic Coastal Plain. The rocks are always sedimentary and have a significantly broad slight seaward dip. There is no significantly broad Pacific coastal plain; the coast ranges there come right down to the sea in most places.

Continental Shelves

Every continent is surrounded by a continental shelf that extends outward beneath the ocean waters for at least a mile or two, and in some places as much as 100 mi or more. The shelf is over 100 mi wide off New England but narrows to less than 60 mi off Florida (Fig. 31-3). Shelves are narrowest on the sides of continents having the youngest mountains. Hence, on the Pacific Coast of the United States they are less than 10 mi wide. The slope of the shelves may be as little as 5 or 6 ft/mi (0.071°). Southeastward from Long Island the 300 ft depth contour is not reached until in the neighborhood of 85 mi seaward, and the 600 ft contour is reached at about 100 mi. At the edge of the shelf the water deepens rapidly, for the 6000 ft contour is reached at about 125 mi.

From the geologic viewpoint these shelves are best considered as parts of the continents rather than as parts of the ocean basins. The ocean basins are a bit overfull at the present time, so that the sea waters spill over the edges of the continent, forming the shelves. In past geologic time the ocean basins have been a bit more overfull, thus flooding large parts of the continents. At times the ocean basins have been a bit less than full, thus allowing the shelves to be exposed. The Hudson Canyon, now an underwater feature, which extends from New York Bay out to the edge of the shelf, was cut at a time when the shelf was exposed.

If the ocean basins were a bit more overfull, Long Island and other large parts of the Atlantic and Gulf Coastal plains would be under water. These submerged regions would, however, still be parts of the continents. In fact, if we go back far enough in geologic history, we would find that at one time or another the waters of the sea have covered every part of the continents (but never all at once). We have positive evidence for about 75% of the land surface. For many reasons, geologists infer that the sea has covered the other 25% at one time or another. There is no place on earth about which the geologist can definitely say, "The sea was never here." Yet, as we have said before, so far as we know, the ocean basins have always been ocean basins and the continents have always been continents.

Despite all we have said, neither the Alps nor any other great mountain range, even though they are largely made of marine-deposited strata containing marine fossils, were ever beneath the sea. *When the sea covered the areas where the mountains now stand, the mountains had not yet been formed.* The mountains were made essentially by compression and uplift of a few tens of thousands of feet of sediments, much of which was deposited in shallow seas covering the area. The water in these seas was probably never more than a few hundred feet deep. How such great thicknesses could accumulate in such shallow water will be explained later.

The continental shelves are the great repositories of the sediments eroded from the lands. There are thousands of feet of sediments below the surface of the Atlantic continental shelf. The sedimentary rocks of the coastal plains form a part of these sediments as they dip beneath the waters of the oceans.

Structure of Ocean Basins

At the seaward edge of the shelf the slope of the bottom increases with some abruptness to 300 to 400 ft/mi (about 4°). Generally, this change in slope takes place at a depth of about 600 ft. The continental slopes may be thought of as forming the sides of the ocean basins, whose average depth is about 12,000 ft. The ocean basins were once thought to be more or less featureless topographically. This view has been entirely changed through use of sonic methods of mapping the sea floor—methods hundreds of times faster than the old "lead and line" method. These new sonic methods have made oceanography a rapidly developing earth science, even rivaling space exploration. Geologists have long tried to unravel the history of the earth from a study of only 30% of its surface, the other 70% being hidden by

the waters of the oceans. A vast amount of information has been obtained since World War II, information that is already causing earth scientists not only to develope new theories but to re-examine the present ones and to resurrect some theories that had been discarded for lack of supporting facts.

Rifts and Oceanic Ridges

This new information shows that the Mid-Atlantic Ridge is not just a narrow ridge that extends from the Arctic to the Antarctic, but is a part of a world-encircling submarine mountain and rift system some 64,000 km long, which in some places is nearly 1600 km wide, with some peaks rising more than 3 km above the ocean floor. Most astonishing is a great rift valley (Fig. 31-5) about 15 km wide running along the central zone of the ridge. Along this rift are many active or recently active volcanoes that erupt basaltic lava. In many places the ridge is offset by cross fractures (faults) perpendicular to its trend. As might be expected, the crest is also the locus of many earthquakes.

At the northern end the Mid-Atlantic Ridge (Fig. 31-6) passes through Iceland, which is one of the most active volcanic regions in the world, and continues onward into the Arctic Ocean. The southern end of the Mid-Atlantic

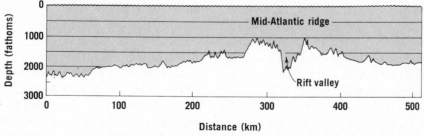

Fig. 31-5. Profile of the Mid-Atlantic Ridge. See Fig. 31-6 for the extent of the ridge. In general, it occupies the center third of the Atlantic Ocean. The deep cleft in the crest is a rift valley. The mountains on either side are exceptionally rugged. Some of these mountains project above the level of the sea to form island groups such as the Azores. (Courtesy of Bruce C. Heezen, Lamont-Doherty Geological Observatory.)

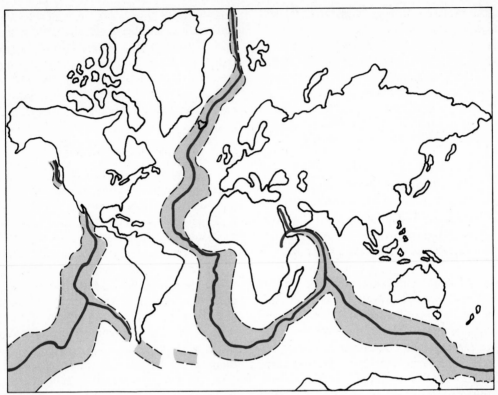

Fig. 31-6.   World-Girdling Oceanic Ridge-Rift System. The location of the ridge is given by the grey shaded area. The more or less central rift is indicated by the colored line. The numerous cross faults are not shown here. Any profile across the Mid-Atlantic Ridge (Fig. 31-5) closely resembles any other. (Modified from the Bruce C. Heezen, *Journal of Tectonophysics,* vol. 8, 1969, p. 270.)

Ridge bends around the southern tip of Africa into the Indian Ocean, where it bifurcates. One branch of this ridge-rift system extends into the Antarctic Ocean and then bends northerly into the eastern Pacific Ocean up to the Gulf of California, where it joins the San Andreas fault zone.[3] The other branch runs north and west into East Africa and through the Red Sea.

Near the southern end of the Red Sea it jogs and contacts the East African rift valleys, which are now occupied in part by a chain of deep lakes (of which Lake Victoria is one). Our knowledge of this ridge-rift system is still incomplete. Note the branch originating in the eastern Pacific Ocean and running toward the southern tip of South America. This branch may continue eastward and join the Mid-Atlantic Ridge in the South Atlantic. Accompanying the rift are numerous cross faults (p. 564), fractures in the ridge more or less at right angles to the rift. These are associated with sidewise displacements and give the rift

[3] This fault zone extends through San Francisco, the scene of a disastrous earthquake early in this century. Northwestward the zone disappears in the Pacific Ocean. Southeastward it passes east of Los Angeles, the site of a disastrous earthquake in 1971, eventually disappearing in the Gulf of California. See Fig. 31-6.

system a somewhat zigzag appearance. Some faults are large enough to displace the entire ridge.

Trenches (or Deeps)

Trenches, or deeps, are areas that are greater than about 23,000 ft deep. They are never found out in the middle of the basins far from land but always relatively near the continents where active mountain-making is still going on or is very recent. Most of the great trenches are in the Pacific where the most active mountain-making of the present is going on. Most are on the convex side of island arcs (archipelagoes), for example, the Aleutians, the Japanese Islands, and the Philippine Islands in the Pacific, and the Antillean Arc in the Atlantic. The greatest deep is in the Japanese Trench; its depth is about 37,000 ft. The greatest depth in the Atlantic is off the coast of Puerto Rico, where it is a bit over 27,000 ft. There is evidence that the Japanese Trench has recently been deepened by a further dropping down of this part of the ocean floor.

The Concept of Isostasy

Consideration of these observations can lead to a number of questions. We will not attempt to ask all of them, let alone answer them. Here we will concern ourselves with the differences between the elevations of the continents and the ocean basins. "Why are the continental masses able to stand so high above the ocean floors?"

We can probably understand this question better if we first take only one phase of it, namely, "How can the earth's crust support a great mountain range like the Himalayas?" Is it because the rocks at the base of the range are strong enough to do so? Now we know rather accurately the crushing strength of rocks under various conditions, and we also know

with reasonable accuracy the weight per unit area the rocks beneath the Himalayas have to support. These figures show that the rocks are not anywhere near strong enough; they should spread out underneath their own weight, thus lowering the height of the mountains to a point where the strength of the rocks is sufficient to support the mountains. Now it is perfectly apparent that the rocks do not spread out in this way, the mountains *are supported,* and so there must be some way to support them. What other way is possible? There are two.

The first is by the compressional forces that originally formed the mountains, and which may still be operating to hold them up. However, although in some areas there is evidence of this, in many there is none. This leaves us the other possibility, one that seems to tie in well with all of the evidence. This is that the mountains are supported by roots that penetrate deeply into underlying *denser* rocks (Fig. 31-4) so that they are literally supported (buoyed up) by them. These denser rocks are at such depths that they are under tremendous pressures and at high temperatures. Under these conditions the rocks are plastic, and have the property of liquids that enables them to buoy up bodies of lesser density, just as water buoys up an iceberg.[4] The mountains are thus in balance with the rocks into which their roots are submerged. The condition of balance is called *isostasy*. Just as the higher an iceberg is above water, the deeper the bottom of it is in the water, so the higher the mountain, the deeper its roots.

The inevitable conclusion is that the continents stand higher than the ocean basins be-

[4]If you stood on a scale to weigh yourself while both you and the scale were completely submerged in water, you would find that you weighed only a few pounds. This weight would represent the difference in your weight outside the water and the weight of the water you displace. If your density were exactly that of water, the scale would register zero. Your body would be entirely supported (buoyed up) by the water.

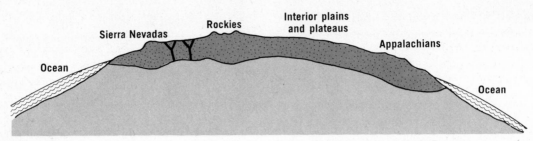

Fig. 31-7. Profile of a Continent. The sialic rocks (colored area) average 10% lower density than the simatic rocks below the ocean basins. The continents therefore stand higher than the ocean basins. (The base of the sima is not shown.)

cause they are composed of lighter rock (Fig. 31-7). It is an established fact that they are composed essentially of granite, whereas the ocean basins are composed essentially of basalt, a rock about 10% denser than granite.

Suppose the earth divided into a number of huge blocks, each of the mountain ranges representing a block, each of the great plateaus, plains, coastal plains, and so on, representing other blocks. The continental rocks everywhere have much the same density, except for local variations. The difference is in the *vertical* lengths of the blocks. Thus, the short blocks—the coastal plains and the low interior plains—neither rise high nor sink low in the substratum. The high plateaus and the various mountain systems, being longer, rise higher and sink lower than the low blocks. Each block, according to the concept of isostasy, stands at an elevation that places it in equilibrium with the other blocks. Gravity determinations and plumb-bob deflections do show a lesser average density for higher blocks. The behavior of earthquake waves (not explained here) suggests that the higher blocks also extend deeper than the lower blocks into the denser plastic substratum.

Like any other theory, this one must not be pushed too far. It does not explain how the continents came to be continents. It does not explain how mountains came into being. It does not apply to small blocks of the earth's crust. Neither is isostatic adjustment perfect, because the rocks do have considerable strength and can stand a very considerable imbalance (caused by erosion and deposition) before adjustment (by diastrophism) takes place.

This adjustment explains the re-elevation of mountain areas after they have been reduced by gradational processes. Erosion of material from the high blocks lightens them and deposition on a low block (for example, the continental shelves) makes them heavier. Eventually the lighter block rises and the heavier one sinks as the plastic substratum flows out from beneath the subsiding block to the region beneath the rising block.

Two additional facts support the concept: (1) Lavas from oceanic volcanoes (volcanoes that rise from the true ocean floors) have a higher specific gravity than most lavas from continental volcanoes. (2) The acceleration due to gravity, that is, the value of g, averages slightly greater over the oceans than over the continents even after corrections for decreased distance from the center of gravity. If the continents did *not* stand considerably higher than the ocean basins, then we really would be puzzled.

Interior of the Earth

The solid part of the earth is easily divided into three parts, crust, mantle, and core. The core has a diameter of about 2100 mi and is surrounded by a mantle, which is about 1800 mi thick. The mantle is, in turn covered by a crust, which varies from a few miles (beneath the ocean basins) to as much as 50 mi in thickness (beneath the great continental mountain ranges).

At the present time ideas about the interior of the earth are changing. A few years ago we could not have written so confidently, and a few years hence the newer concepts will probably have been sorted out and tested. For the present we will choose those concepts that appear to be soundest and in best accord with the facts, and we will use them as a framework for describing that part of the crust not visible in any way to man and for describing the mantle and the core.

The evidence for the properties of the material forming the deeper parts of the crust, the whole of the mantle, and the core, comes from the behavior of earthquake waves as they pass through the earth. Earthquakes are caused by vibrations (mechanical waves) that are propagated within the earth and travel through it. There are several types of waves, but we will be concerned with only the primary (longitudinal) and the secondary (transverse) waves (Fig. 31-8).

The primary (*P*) waves travel about one and two thirds times as fast as the secondary (*S*) waves. The speeds of these waves increase as the rigidity of the rocks through which they pass increases, and decrease as the density increases. Both the rigidity and the density increase with depth, but the effect due to increase of rigidity is greater than the effect due to increase of density; therefore the speeds of both types of waves increase with depth. This rate of increase should be constant, other things being equal. *If at any particular depth there should be an abrupt increase or decrease, then some other factor, such as composition, should play a part.*

Crust and Mantle

The first concrete evidence that the earth's crust had a natural lower boundary came in 1909 when Mohorovicic, a Yugoslav seismologist, attempted to explain a peculiarity in certain seismograms.[5] At depths that ranged from 25 to 50 mi beneath the great mountain systems, and from 18 to 25 mi elsewhere beneath the continents, and as little as 2 to 3 mi beneath the ocean basins proper, these seismograms showed an abrupt increase in wave velocities. This zone of abrupt increase is now called the Mohorovicic Discontinuity, usually abbreviated to Moho, and the crust is now defined as that part of the earth that lies above this discontinuity.

Further seismographic research has indicated that the crust itself can be divided into

[5] Seismograms are the records of the vibrations made by an earthquake on a seismograph.

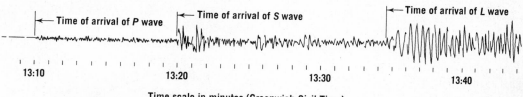

Fig. 31-8. Seismogram of an Earthquake Recorded at Victoria, B.C., on May 24, 1944. The dashes along the lower margin give the time in minutes at the recording station. The epicenter of this quake was located at 2.5° South Latitude, 152° East Longitude, near New Ireland (northeast of Australia). The time of the shock was fixed at 12:58 Greenwich Civil Time. (Courtesy of James T. Wilson, University of Michigan.)

two parts. The upper part, where the wave speeds are slower, consists of rocks whose chemical composition averages that of granite, and is, in fact, largely granite. It is called the *sial,* a mnemonic term coined from the chemical symbols for silicon and aluminum. The density of the sialic rocks averages about 2.7. The lower part, where the wave speeds are faster, consists of rocks whose composition is that of an olivine basalt. It is called the *sima,* coined from silica and magnesium. Its density averages about 3.0 or a bit higher. The sima forms the lower part of the crust of the conti-

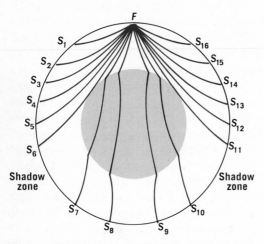

Fig. 31-9. Cross Section Through the Earth. The core is shown surrounded by the mantle. F is the focus of an earthquake. Primary and secondary waves from it are received at seismographic stations S_1 through S_6 and S_{11} through S_{16}. Note that none of these waves strikes the core. No waves of any kind are received at stations in the shadow zone, between S_6 and S_7 and between S_{10} and S_{11}, because of refraction. Secondary waves are of a kind that cannot pass through liquids; the core is therefore inferred to be liquid. Primary waves travel faster through solids than through liquids. The time interval between a quake at F and the arrival of waves at S_7, S_8, S_9, or S_{10} is too great for us to assume that the core is entirely solid, but too small for us to assume that it is entirely liquid. Therefore a liquid core with an inner solid core (not shown) is postulated.

nents, and essentially the whole of the crust of the ocean basins proper (Fig. 31-3). Thus, we have the evidence to support the statement made previously (under isostasy) that the continents stand higher than the ocean basins because they are composed of less dense rock.

That part of the earth between the crust and the core is called the mantle. Since the wave speeds increase abruptly (from 7.0 and 3.8 km/sec to 8.15 and 4.7 km/sec, respectively, for the P and S waves) at the Mohorovicic Discontinuity, a compositional change in the rock is postulated. The change is from a feldspar-pyroxene basalt with some olivine to a rock composed chiefly of pyroxene and olivine. The latter would satisfy the density and rigidity requirements. At about the 275 mi depth there occurs another discontinuity in wave speeds. This minor discontinuity may be accounted for by an increase in the amount of iron in the olivine. (Olivine is an iron-magnesium silicate in which the ratio of Mg to Fe may vary from 16:1 to 2:1; p. 531.)

At a depth of about 1800 mi the greatest change of all takes place, not only in amount but also in kind. For here the speeds of the P waves *decrease abruptly* from 13.6 to 8.1 km/sec, and the S waves *disappear,* never to be heard from again.

Core

Long before these changes in speeds had been worked out, it was known that the earth had a core. Whenever an earthquake was sufficiently strong to be recorded on seismographs on the opposite side of the earth, it was noted that there was a belt about 40° wide encircling the earth in which seismograph stations received no record. This belt lies between 102° and 145°, approximately, from the epicenter. Stations at a greater distance from 145° received the P waves strongly but no S waves. This belt has been termed the shadow zone (Fig. 31-9).

The explanation of the shadow zone is as follows: Waves are refracted as they pass through media of differing rigidities. Therefore their paths are curved. Those that penetrate the crust and the mantle only, that is, penetrate no deeper than 1800 mi, follow normal curved paths, eventually reaching all stations not more than 102° (7000 mi, since 1° = 70 mi) distant from the epicenter. Waves that penetrate more deeply enter a different material with a greatly different rigidity, and so are strongly refracted towards the medium of lesser rigidity. This means that the *P* waves are bent so that they penetrate deeper into the earth. Eventually they re-enter the mantle and emerge at stations 143° to 180° (10,000 to 12,500 mi) distant from the epicenter.

This great ball of material with a rigidity less than that at the base of the mantle is called the core. Another piece of evidence for the core consists of the difference between the predicted arrival time of the *P* waves at stations near 180° from the epicenter and their actual arrival time. Enough information had been obtained so that the arrival time at stations up to 102° distant could be predicted within a few seconds if the time the quake took place was known. Assuming that there was no core and that the mantle extended clear to the center, then a *P* wave that went straight through should arrive at a station directly opposite the epicenter in 16 min. Actually it arrived in 20 min, *4 min late*. This meant that it had been slowed down by passing either through less rigid material, or material of greater density, or both.

For a time the state of the matter in the core was uncertain. If it were liquid, then *S* waves could not pass through it. (Mechanical transverse waves can traverse solids only.) The uncertainty arose from the fact that the wave record is much more complex than we have led you to believe. At every boundary surface new waves are set up, some reflected, some refracted, and all with less energy than the original wave. Therefore the seismogram recorded a complex of waves that took long study to sort out. Some observers thought that the *S* waves came through feebly. If they did, the core was solid. Eventually better seismographs and more knowledge solved the problem in favor of a liquid core—or at least part liquid. Assumption of a completely liquid core raised problems with wave speeds also, but we will not analyze them here. These were resolved by assuming the presence of an inner solid core over 3000 mi in diameter surrounded by a layer of liquid over 250 mi thick.

The range of choice for the material of the mantle and core is limited, in part for seismic velocity reasons, in part for density reasons, and in part for other reasons. The possibilities for the mantle are peridotite (chiefly pyroxene and olivine), dunite (chiefly olivine), and eclogite (a garnet-pyroxene rock). The last could be present only in the upper part of the mantle. Most authorities in the field favor dunite for the lower part of the mantle. The composition of the core is also limited by density considerations.

The density of the earth as a whole is 5.5 and that of the surface rocks is 2.7. The inner core must have a density of 11 or 12 or possibly even more to give an average density of 5.5. By analogy with meteorites the core is assumed to be made up largely of iron with a few per cent nickel. It is reasonable to assume that the core is made of a material abundant in the crust. Whether it is or not, the existence of a liquid core having a density several times that of silicate rocks is now accepted. The situation is very similar to that of a blast furnace. In its solidification from a wholly liquid earth, the iron sank to the center, with a "slag" of heavy iron and iron-magnesium silicates forming around the free iron phase (which is immiscible with the iron silicate phase) and a "slag" of lighter silicates forming the outer part.

One cannot be too dogmatic about the constitution of the interior of the earth, nor too free with one's imagination concerning it. Solution of the problem calls for expert knowledge; the speculations of the ignorant or of those with a little knowledge are useless.

We can now turn our attention to the three fundamental processes that are operating to alter the face of the earth, vulcanism, diastrophism, and gradation. The first two involve energy from a source within the earth; the third involves energy from a source outside the earth, that is, energy from the sun.

Exercises

1. Suppose that someone postulates that the core of the earth is made of an element that has not yet been discovered here on earth. Considering all that you have so far learned about the periodic chart and the structure of atoms, what are the probabilities that the postulate is correct?

2. Is the concentric zonal structure of the earth consistent with the concept of its having once passed through a molten stage? Explain.

3. What is the evidence that the earth's crust has a natural lower boundary?

4. Differentiate between primary and secondary waves.

5. What two factors govern the speed of primary and secondary waves?

6. In what part of the earth do the waves travel fastest? Why?

7. (a) What happens to the transverse wave when it strikes the core? How do we know?
   (b) What happens to the longitudinal waves?

8. Why are the paths of P and S earthquake waves curved?

9. What is the average density of (a) the earth as a whole, (b) the crustal rocks, (c) the core?

10. What is the volume of the core with respect to the total volume of the earth?

11. List the evidence for the composition of the core.

12. What method of investigation developed since World War II has greatly improved our knowledge of the crust of the earth?

13. What is the Mid-Atlantic Ridge? What are some of its characteristics?

14. What sort of lava, if any, is erupted in these ridge and rift areas? Describe this lava by mentioning color, relative density, grain size, and essential mineral content (see Chapter 30).

Energy Within the Earth: Volcanism and Diastrophism

Chapter

32

The external phenomena of volcanism, displayed either by spectacular eruptions of volcanoes or the quiet bubbling of lavas in their craters, and the tremendous damage done to the works of man by some earthquakes attest to the fact that the earth has enormous energy stored within it. The source of this energy and the manner in which it is enabled to manifest itself are not entirely clear. We will defer discussion of these aspects until some of the observations of volcanism and diastrophism have been presented; it will be more meaningful then.

Volcanism: Extrusive Activity

The external phenomena of volcanism may be viewed in many parts of the earth today. Spectacular as the extrusive activities of some volcanoes may be, they are only superficial manifestations of the geologically far more important deep-seated processes responsible for the formation and intrusion of enormous

555

bodies of molten material into younger rocks. The composition of this molten material, called magma when deep in the crust and lava when it is extruded, has been discussed in Chapter 30. The difference between magma and lava is in their gaseous content. The gases—chiefly water vapor, but also carbon dioxide, carbon monoxide, hydrogen, sulfur vapor, and many others—are kept dissolved in the magma at depths where the pressure is high but escape when the pressure is released as the magma comes to the surface. Lava is, therefore, magma that has lost most of its gaseous content (Fig. 32-1).

The gases are important for several reasons. One is that they are the cause of the violence of many eruptions. If magmas contained no gases, extrusive volcanic activity would be limited to the quiet extrusion of lava. Volcanic explosions are due to the extremely rapid expansion of large volumes of gases under high pressure (as are explosions of any sort). The gases may be so abundant that there is an explosive foaming like that in a warm bottle of soda pop that is violently shaken and then opened. This foam freezes on exposure to the atmosphere. This frozen foam we call *pumice*.

Volcanoes are vents (craters) in the earth's crust from which gases, liquid lava, or solid materials are ejected; the latter two form a conical hill or mountain about the crater. The cones may vary from a few tens of feet in height to more than 5 mi. They are cone-shaped simply because more of the ejected material falls (if solid) or solidifies (if lava) close to the crater. The solid ejecta is commonly a great cloud of volcanic "ash" chiefly the result of instantaneous freezing of a fine liquid lava spray thrown into the air, sometimes to a height of many miles. It falls as "dust" or "ash." Larger particles fall as "cinders" or lapilli. Sometimes the lava thrown out

Fig. 32-1. Frozen Lava at Kilauea, Hawaii. The lava is a type that forms relatively smooth rounded, twisted, or pleated surfaces. It solidified as it poured over a low cliff. (U.S. Geological Survey photo by H. T. Stearns.)

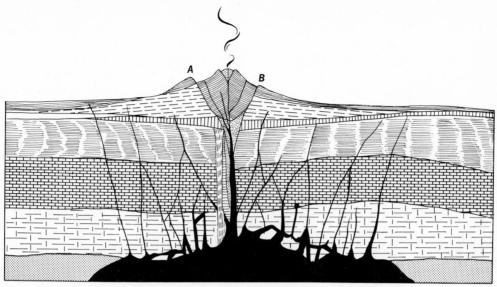

Fig. 32-2. Inferred Conditions Below Vesuvius. The magmatic reservoir and the dikes extending from it are shown in black. Vesuvius had been built up inside the explosion pit (caldera) of an older volcano, Monte Somma, which "blew its top" in A.D. 79, burying Herculaneum and Pompeii in volcanic ash and cinders. Parts of the rim of Monte Somma are shown at *A* and *B*. A volcano is an unusual kind of mountain, formed by accumulation of debris ejected from within the earth, rather than by diastrophic processes. (After Rittman.)

is in the form of large clots that solidify while spinning through the air; they fall as volcanic "bombs." Sometimes masses of lava previously solidified in the throat of the volcano are thrown out as solid blocks weighing a ton or more, and for a distance of as much as a half mile.

Monte Somma literally blew its top in A.D. 79, burying Herculaneum and Pompeii and much of their populations under a thick layer of ash. A new volcano was then built up on the inside of the remnants of Monte Somma; its name is Vesuvius (Fig. 32-2). Scores of similar explosions have occurred elsewhere in the world since (Fig. 32-3). Krakatoa, in the East Indies, blew up in 1883. Over a cubic mile of rock was thrown into the air, some of it to a distance of 17 mi. The "dust" circled the earth and took three years to settle. The noise of the explosion was heard 2500 mi away.

Hundreds of volcanoes are quietly active today. Our fiftieth state, Hawaii, is composed *completely* of volcanoes. The island of Hawaii is a composite of five of them, the highest of which stands nearly 14,000 ft above sea level. Their bases rise from the floor of the Pacific more than 14,000 ft *below* sea level. Thus, these volcanoes range up to 28,000 ft above their bases; they are the greatest volcanoes on the face of the earth. Two of the five, Mauna Loa and Kilauea, are still active. The other three are dormant or extinct. All the other Hawaiian Islands are also volcanoes. The lava erupted from all of them was low silica magma, and so was very fluid. The result is that the cones that have been built from them slope so gently that it is hard to believe that all of the people in the state of Hawaii live on the slopes of volcanoes.

The best known infant among volcanoes is

Fig. 32-3. Crater Lake, Crater Lake National Park, Oregon. A volcano much higher than the present remnants "blew its top" some 5000 years ago. Before its activity ceased, a small new volcano (Wizard Island) was built up inside the crater (caldera) of the old. It rises 2500 ft above the floor of the crater. The lake is surrounded by cliffs nearly half a mile high and is 5 to 6 mi across. The water in the lake is meteorological in origin. (Oregon State Highway Department photo.)

Paricutín,[1] 200 mi west of Mexico City. It began its life in 1943 and became inactive nine years later. Meanwhile, it had built a cone nearly half a mile high and devastated the countryside for miles around with deposits of volcanic ash and lava flows. It is the only volcano in history that has been intensely studied by geologists from the day of its birth. Will it become active again? Only time will tell. Some volcanoes erupt once and then become extinct. Others may lie dormant for hundreds of years, as, for example, Monte Somma before A.D. 79. Mount Lassen, in northern California, last erupted in 1915. It is

the only active volcano in continental United States except for Alaska—which has several.

In addition to the extrusive activity of volcanoes there are the fissure eruptions of plateau basalts. They build no well-defined volcanoes. Instead the lava, which is always of the very fluid basaltic type and so flows readily, spreads out in great horizontal sheets (Fig. 32-4). One such fissure eruption took place in Iceland in 1783. The lava welled up out of a crack in the earth's crust and spread out in a sheet 12 to 15 mi wide and 100 ft deep.

There have been great fissure eruptions in past geologic times. The lavas from one of them today form the great Columbian Plateau in the northwestern United States. Some tens of thousands of cubic miles of lava were poured

---

[1] A still younger volcano came into existence in 1965 off Iceland.

Fig. 32-4. Lava Tubes, Craters of the Moon National Monument, Idaho. Here the lava surfaces froze, but the lava continued to flow underneath, eventually draining away and leaving hollow tubes. A pencil (left of center) gives the scale. (Photo by John Shimer, Brooklyn College.)

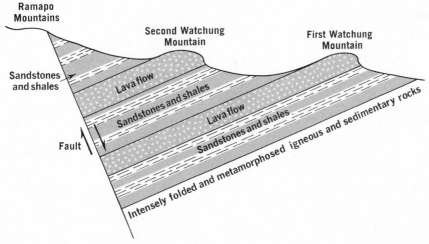

Fig. 32-5. Ancient Buried Lava Flows Exposed by Erosion, First and Second Watchung Mountains, New Jersey. The surface was approximately level when these flows were extruded. The first flow was buried by hundreds of feet of sandstone and shale before the second flow was extruded. It, in turn, was buried by similar sediments. Later much of the eastern United States was tilted westerly, then deeply eroded, exposing tilted edges of the flows.

out, filling the valleys and burying the hills. In northeastern New Jersey there are the remnants of two major and several minor outpourings of basaltic lava some 200 million years ago. The eroded edges of the two major flows form First and Second Watchung Mountains in New Jersey (Fig. 32-5).

All the fissure eruptions, as well as all the lavas poured out from volcanoes rising from the floors of the true ocean basins, consist of the low silica rock known as basalt.

Volcanism: Intrusive Activity

We cannot, of course, directly observe intrusive activity. Moreover, we would not know anything about it if deep erosion had not taken place. Magma, once formed at depth, is under terrific pressure. Since it is a mobile liquid, it will escape to regions of lower pressure if any route is available. This region of lower pressure is always upward. Sometimes the magma reaches the surface, giving us the volcanic phenomena we have described. But it may work its way up toward the surface until its energy is spent without any great quantity of it reaching the surface. It may then solidify in place, forming a huge body of rock that we call a *batholith* (Figs. 31-3 and 32-6). It will have cooled and crystallized extremely slowly to give a coarse-grained rock called granite. These granitic batholiths may be as much as several hundreds of miles long, several tens of miles wide, and several miles deep. How deep we do not know, for erosion has nowhere cut deep enough to expose the rocks below a batholith. The home of the batholith is in the cores of the great mountain ranges of the earth.

At one time or another during the past three billion years, batholiths have intruded into every portion of the continental areas of the earth. The vast majority of them are composed of granite. From these batholiths tongues of

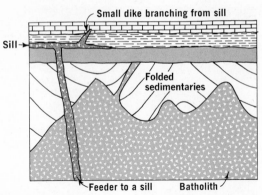

Fig. 32-6. Vertical Cross Section of a Batholith Intruded into Folded Sedimentary Rocks. The sill cuts across the batholith and so is younger. The small dike branching from the sill proves that this igneous body is an *intrusive,* not a buried *extrusive* as in the case of the Watchung lavas (Fig. 32-5). Which is older, the batholith or the folded sedimentary rocks? How can you tell?

magma have been forcibly injected into fractures in the rocks above, the enormous pressures widening the fractures. If these tongues are tabular in shape and cut across the structures of the rock they intrude, they are called *dikes* (Figs. 32-6 and 32-7). The presence of great numbers of dikes intruded into the overlying rocks (as in the rocks of northern New York City) is evidence that a great batholith lies below.

If the magma more readily spreads between the layers of sedimentary rock, lifting them up if they are horizontal or nearly so, and so solidifies in *the form of a sheet,* we call the intrusion a *sill* (Fig. 32-6). A sill does not cut across the layers (except locally) as does a dike. Vertical sills are possible, and so are horizontal dikes. The best known sill in North America, perhaps in the world, is the one whose eroded edge now forms the Palisades of the lower Hudson River (Fig. 32-8). This great sill is some 40 mi long, extending from Staten Island on the south to Haverstraw, New York, to the north. It is well over a thousand feet thick in its thickest part and ends both in the north

Fig. 32-7. Basalt Dike Cutting Granite, Cohasset, Massachusetts. The granite was intruded into still older rocks (not shown) in a different period of igneous activity. The dike extends as a great tabular sheet downward, connecting somewhere at depth with a larger body of similar rock. But the granite and the dike are exposed only because of deep erosion. (Photo by John Shimer, Brooklyn College.)

and south by thinning out. How great its third (east–west) dimension originally was is unknown, but it must have extended east of the Hudson for many miles.[2] To the west it disappears beneath the intruded sandstones and shales of the Newark Series, where it either extends to the eastern base of the Ramapo mountains where it ends against a fault, or it thins gradually to zero before reaching the fault (Fig. 32-5).

Both the sill and the intruded rocks dip 10° to 15° in a westerly direction; thus, the sill lies deeper and deeper in that direction. When this sill was intruded the Hudson River had not yet been formed, and there were at least 2 to 3 mi of sandstones and shales above it. Only because of deep erosion has it become exposed. The rock composing it is a basaltic type called *diabase*. At both the base and the top

[2] In the part of the Connecticut River Valley south of the Massachusetts border there is a similar sill, comparable in thickness and with all of the associated features of the Palisades Sill except that the rocks dip easterly. Were they once connected with the Palisades rocks, forming a great arch whose center has been removed? The concept is tempting but need not have been that way—and probably was not.

of the sill, where it cooled fastest and so is fine-grained, it is indistinguishable from basalt. It contains the minerals dark-colored feldspar (labradorite) and pyroxene, with lesser amounts of amphibole, biotite, and olivine.

When this great sheet of magma crystallized and cooled, it contracted. So huge a sheet could not contract as a unit; for one thing, it was welded to the rocks above and below. The stresses set up by contraction were too great for it to withstand, so a great series of fractures (called *joints*) developed. The major fractures formed perpendicular to the cooling surfaces, or to the top and the bottom of the great sheet, and in a more or less hexagonal pattern (Fig. 32-9). Weathering has widened the joints on the exposed surfaces so that when the Palisades cliff is viewed from in front, it appears

as a series of gigantic columns (or stakes) driven into the ground like a palisade, hence the name.

The abundance of extrusive activity today implies that intrusive activity is still going on. Beneath all active volcanoes there must be reservoirs of magma, some of which are probably large enough to be called batholiths, that are still in the process of cooling. Such features as the geysers of Yellowstone National Park, Iceland, and New Zealand indicate that there are bodies of igneous rock at shallow depths (even less than 100 ft) so hot that water soaking down to them is heated to the boiling point and above. The evidence seems to indicate that there never has been a time in the history of the earth when some volcanic activity, intrusive or extrusive, was not taking place. Before

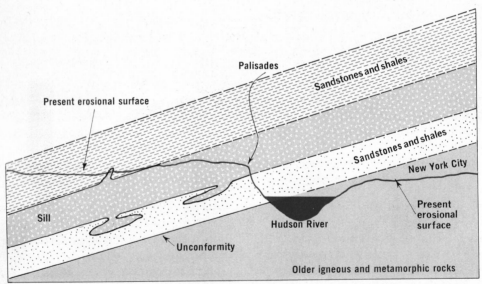

Fig. 32-8. The Palisades Sill. A sill in sedimentary rocks is intruded between the layers (strata) instead of cutting across the layers in the manner of dikes. Note carefully the position of the present erosional surface. Originally the sill extended far to the east over where New York City is now. Erosion of a minimum thickness of 3 mi of rock was necessary to produce the present topography. The Hudson River originated too late to play much part in the removal of this rock. Note the small protrusions from the sill into the sedimentary rocks in the left half; the upward one is proof of intrusion, rather than extrusion followed by burial under later sediments.

Fig. 32-9. Devil's Tower, Wyoming. This mass of igneous rock towers 865 ft above the surrounding countryside. Note the fluted columnar structure, called jointing, due to contraction on cooling of the original magma. The tower may have been formed by solidification of magma in the throat of a volcano, or it may have been a "finger" of magma pushed up into overlying sediments. In any case, it now stands higher than the surroundings because it is composed of rock more resistant to weathering and erosion than the rock which once enclosed it. (U.S. Department of the Interior National Park Service photo by Jack E. Boucher.)

we investigate the sources of the energy, we will briefly consider diastrophism, and then discuss causes, the problems of origin, and so forth, together.

Diastrophism

By the time students are of college age they have read accounts of more than one disastrous earthquake somewhere on earth. Earthquakes are much more common than that, for the seismologists tell us that the earth is trembling all of the time. Almost all of these tremors are minor, do no damage to the works of man, and so do not get in the newspapers. Over one seven-year period, California averaged 75 earthquakes per month; Japan has about 4 per day. The average for the whole earth is an earthquake about every two minutes. The great majority are the merest of shivers, not vigorous enough for people to feel or hear them. About 1000 per year cause some damage, most of it comparatively trivial. About one per year borders on the catastrophic, and one or two per century may represent the greatest of cataclysms ever to be inflicted on man by nature. The worst on record occurred in Shensi Province, China, in 1556 in which the death toll was estimated to be 830,000. Other disastrous earthquakes include the following: Calcutta, India, in 1737 with a toll of 300,000, Kansu Province, China, in 1920 with a toll of 180,000, Japan in 1923 with a toll of 143,000, Sicily in 1908 with a toll of 82,000, and Peru in 1970 with a toll of 70,000.

Actually, however, few people are killed, or even injured, directly by the quake. Most are killed by the toppling of buildings, particularly those of stone without a steel framework, or when ruptured dams, avalanches, and vast rivers of mud bury whole villages in a matter of minutes. Elsewhere the chief damage was done by fires started by overturned oil lamps, broken gas mains, and broken power lines, fires that could not be put out because of broken water mains. The answer in part is to build structures in earthquake-prone areas that can withstand the shocks. Steel frames are best for tall buildings and wooden frames for dwellings. Moreover, they should be placed on solid bedrock, not on loose soil or on filled land no matter how well packed. Neither gas mains nor water mains should cross earthquake fractures unless other sources of supply are impossible.

Scientific research on the behavior of earthquake waves has been going on for a century or more, but only in the last ten years have they seriously began the research that could lead to the exact prediction when and where an earthquake would take place. This research is centered at the United States Geological

Survey's new earthquake laboratory in Menlo Park, California, the National Center for Earthquake Research. Dr. John H. Healy, a member of the staff, says, "I feel that it is unlikely that the crust ruptures with a bang, without any warning. Most likely the warning is to be found in the pattern of very small earthquakes we are now detecting, or in some change in the earth's shape, or in some change in the properties of rocks under stress." Guided by such reasoning, instruments have been developed to sense and record the different phenomena associated with earthquake zones. A breakthrough is expected by 1975 or shortly thereafter.

Earthquakes represent an unusual kind of diastrophic activity in that the movements involved are sudden; they take place in a matter of seconds. These movements occur along fractures in the earth's crust, fractures that may be some miles, tens of miles, or even hundreds of miles long and that extend downward into the earth's crust for some few miles. The frac-

ture, together with the resulting horizontal and/or vertical displacement of the rocks on one side with respect to those on the other, is known as a *fault*. The magnitude of a single displacement may be a few inches, a few feet, or even a few tens of feet; the largest in historic times has been about 45 ft.

Repeated displacements along the same fault over millions of years have resulted in total displacements of several miles. Great fault block mountain ranges like the Sierra Nevada (Fig. 32-10) and countless smaller ranges in the Basin and Range Province of Utah, Nevada, southern California, and parts of Arizona and New Mexico have been formed by repeated displacements. The continuity of many rock formations is broken and displaced (offset) by faults. Thus, rock strata, dikes, sills, coal seams, and veins of gold and other valuable minerals may end against a fault. Where they are continued on the other side may be obvious to anyone, or it may be a problem that baffles even the most astute of geologists.

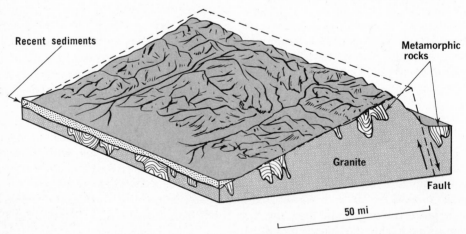

Fig. 32-10. The Sierra Nevada Fault Block. The Sierra Nevada Mountains are formed from a single great fault block 400 mi long and 80 to 100 mi wide. During a long period of faulting the western side of the block was tilted some 20,000 to 25,000 ft higher than the eastern (see arrows at right). Erosion during the very long period of faulting and since has greatly reduced its height. Mt. Whitney, California, the highest mountain in the continental United States (excluding Alaska), is in the Sierra Nevadas. The rock is largely granite, formed from a great batholith intruded into older rocks.

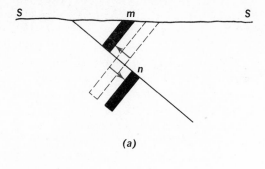

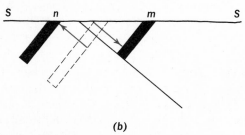

Fig. 32-11. Veins of Ore Displaced by Faults. Relative movements along the faults are shown by the arrows. The present deeply eroded surface of the earth is indicated by *SS*. Mines at *m* run out of ore against the faults. (*a*) Search for the displaced vein must be made at a lower level because the left side has moved *down* relative to the right. (*b*) Here the continuation of the vein is at *n* because the left side has moved *up* relative to the right. Somebody else is probably mining it.

Many a mining venture has failed because the ore-bearing vein was lost by faulting (Fig. 32-11).

Faulting, with the resulting earthquakes, represent only one type of diastrophic activity. *Diastrophism includes all of those normally large-scale movements of the earth's crust that result from forces acting from within the earth.* In addition to faulting there are the warping movements and those due to the folding of rock strata. Warping consists of large-scale vertical uplifts or subsidences. They are called warps because the movements commonly in-

volve large parts of continents, with the result that some parts are uplifted more than others. The Colorado Plateau includes an area of over 200,000 mi² (four times the size of New York State); it has been uplifted considerably more

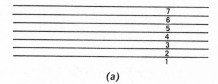

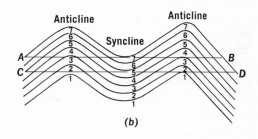

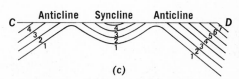

Fig. 32-12. Simple Folding of Sedimentary Rocks. (*a*) A series of sedimentary rocks have been deposited in horizontal layers in a shallow seaway. (*b*) Compressive forces have folded them into anticlines (upfolds) and synclines (downfolds). Future erosion surfaces are indicated by *AB* and *CD*. (*c*) Erosion to the level of *CD* has taken place. Note that the anticlines and the syncline still exist even though the surface is level; folds are structural features of the rocks, not topographic features. If a geologist were to walk across the surface shown in either (*a*) or (*b*), he would see the top formation only, whereas in (*c*) he would see the upturned edges of the whole sequence of formations shown in (*a*) and (*b*). Thus folding, followed by deep erosion, causes formations to be exposed at the surface that otherwise would be deeply buried.

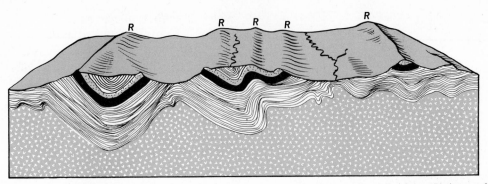

Fig. 32-13. Eroded Simple Folds in the Appalachians. Note that the position of ridges (*R*) is not determined by the positions of the anticlines and synclines but by the outcrop of the colored layer. This layer is more resistant than the others. On the right it forms a ridge even though it is in the center of a syncline. (After Arthur Keith, U.S. Geological Survey.)

than a mile above sea level in the last 60 million years. Most plains and plateaus owe their present elevations to warping. The geologic history of every continent is involved with upwarpings and downwarpings, with the emphasis on the former to offset the lowering by erosion. In general, the downwarpings have been far more local than the upwarpings.

The most conspicuous consequences of diastrophism are the great folded mountain ranges of the earth (Figs. 32-12 and 32-13). These include the Appalachians, the Rockies, the Andes, the Alps, the Himalayas, the Carpathians, the Pyrenees, and a vast number of others. The most common types of rock found in them are either sedimentary rocks or meta-

Fig. 32-14. Complex Folding of Sedimentary Strata. This is the kind of folding one sees in the Alps. The colored lines represent the former extension of the limestone (marble) layer. The folding has been intense enough to metamorphose the rocks.

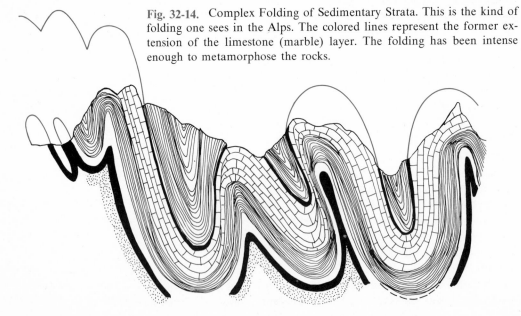

Fig. 32-15. Eroded Anticline, Hancock, Maryland. Only small anticlines can be shown in photographs. (U.S. Geological Survey photo by C. D. Walcott.)

morphosed sedimentary rocks (Fig. 32-14). The more complex the folding, the more the rocks have been metamorphosed. In some, as in the high peaks of the Front Range of the Rockies (Pikes Peak, for instance), coarse-grained igneous rocks are exposed in the core because of removal of other rocks by erosion. The sedimentary rocks often contain fossils of marine animals; in fact fossils of the various kinds of marine life are found in the rocks composing one or another of the great mountain ranges of the earth.

Although upwarpings have contributed to the dizzy heights of mountains, a theory that the mountains are caused by these uplifts is not consistent with the mountain structures and mountain patterns. For example, if the Appalachian folds were "unfolded," that is, if the strata were stretched back into their original horizontal positions (Fig. 32-12), the mountain belt would be more than 50 mi wider than it is at present. All folded mountains (and most of the great mountain ranges are folded mountains, simple or complex) tell much the same story. All are essentially composed of sedimentary rocks, for they are the layered rocks, and only layered rocks can be truly folded (Figs. 32-15, 32-16, and 35-5). Lateral squeezing has been the cause of the buckling into anticlines and synclines, and commonly

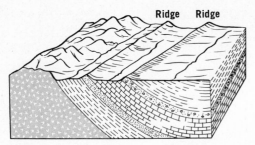

Fig. 32-16. Ridge and Valley Structure Characteristic of Fold Mountains. Only one half of the fold and part of an igneous core are shown. The ridges and the rocks of the core stand higher than the valleys because of the greater resistance of the rocks to weathering and erosion. The ridges are of sandstone and conglomerate, the valleys are carved in limestone and shale. Note that the whole top of the fold has been removed by the processes of weathering and erosion, exposing the granite in the core.

has been the cause of thrust faulting; the uplift has been, at least in part, a result of the squeezing.

The Origin of Mountains

The layman applies the term mountain to any land area that stands conspicuously above its surroundings if it has a narrow summit level. Many such areas, for example, the Catskill Mountains of New York State and the Allegheny Mountains of Pennsylvania (not to be confused with the Appalachians), are remnants of the long-continued erosion of highland areas; we may call them residual mountains. Volcanic mountains are mountains of accumulation; they are simply great piles of volcanic ejecta resting on other rocks of the earth's crust or on the sea floor. We are not concerned here about any problem involved in the origin of either residual or volcanic mountains.

The geologist applies the term *orogeny*

(mountain-making) to the formation of a complex system of long ranges or ridges of highland areas by the folding and faulting of great thicknesses of layered rocks, chiefly of sedimentary origin, that compose them. The various units of the system have similar characteristics of form, structure, composition, and alignment, and a similar origin and subsequent geologic history. These are the great fold mountain systems of the world, many of them made complex by intense folding accompanied by thrust faulting (chiefly) and igneous intrusion on a gigantic scale. Examples of such systems are the Appalachians, the Rockies, the Andes, the Himalayas, the Alps, the Carpathians, the Pyrenees, the Hindu Kush, and scores of others.

All fold mountains, simple or complex, have had their beginnings in broad down-warped areas some few scores or hundreds of kilometers wide and some thousands of kilometers long, which were filled with sediments washed down from adjacent highland areas, and whose bottoms sank as they were filled. Such great troughs are called geosynclines. The slow down-warping was intermittent rather than steady. The sides of the great trough were gently sloping with angles not more than a few degrees from the horizontal. The term *geosyncline* refers not only to the trough itself but also to the sediments deposited in it (Fig. 35-3). In time the sediments were converted to solid rock by a variety of processes. The types of sediment originally deposited (chiefly pebbles, sand, silt, clay, and lime), the fossils of marine life found in them, and structures such as ripple marks and mud cracks, all indicate shallow water deposition, in water usually less than 600 ft deep. Nevertheless, because sinking more or less kept pace with filling, or vice versa, as much as 40,000 ft of sediments were deposited in some ancient geosynclines.

Consider the Appalachian Geosyncline, which stretched southwestward from Newfoundland to Alabama. The source of the coarser sediments (and much of the finer) lay to the east. The source was a highland area, probably an island arc, that was eroded to a lowland area and then re-elevated several times throughout its 300 million yr history. The gradation of the sediments, coarsest to the east, finest to the west, attest to the position of the source, and the enormous volume of them attest to its size and repeated elevation.

This brings us back to the repeated advances and retreats of the sea over the continents. We may view the advances as the result of ocean basins that were somewhat overfull becoming shallower, spilling the sea over the lowlands of every continent at the same time. The retreats could result from the deepening of the ocean basins, which would draw the water off the lowlands into the ocean basins proper, leaving the continents with no submerged continental shelves.

While this explains why the advances and retreats took place, it still leaves us with the problem of the cause of the alternate shallowing and deepening of the basins. As might be expected, the deepening can be correlated, in part at least, with the times of most rapid mountain-building. The problem is complicated by the fact that mountain-building has not been so exclusively confined to certain epochs as was once believed. It seems to have been going on in one place or another in every epoch, although there is little doubt that it has been more widespread and more intense in some epochs than in others.

Neither geologists nor physicists are yet in full agreement on any theory than can explain the forces involved. Tremendous amounts of energy are required to fold and elevate huge rock masses into high mountain ranges, amounts that the mind cannot conceive. What is the origin of the energy? How is it applied to accomplish the compression needed to fold, fault, or elevate rock masses? What accounts for the intrusion of the great batholiths into the cores of the mountain ranges at one stage or another of the orogenic (mountain-building) cycle? All geologists agree that mountain-building of the fold type is essentially the product of horizontal compression, which reduces the diameter and the circumference of the earth, but they have not yet agreed on the cause. As associated question is this: Why should a lowland area like the Appalachian Geosyncline whose elevation alternated between a few hundred feet below sea level and a few hundred, perhaps a thousand, feet above sea level a score or more times during a period of 300 million yr, eventually become a persistent highland area several thousands of feet above sea level—one that was re-elevated after erosion lowered it at least three times in the 200 million yr following the demise of the geosyncline? Answers to this question may be more difficult to find than those to the original question of mountain building.

The Thermal Contraction Theory of Mountain Building

The thermal contraction theory is much the oldest theory of mountain building. It assumes that the earth was once completely molten and that it has been cooling and contracting ever since. In time the outer few miles (the so-called crust) solidified and became cold; it could not shrink anymore. Meanwhile, the inner part continued to cool and shrink as its heat was very slowly conducted through the solid crust. The crust eventually got too big for the shrinking inner part; gravity (which never rests) pulled the crust centerward until it collapsed to fit the inner part. These collapses gave rise to compressive and wedging effects that produced folds, faults, and upwarps.

The theory is an old one and has had many adherents, for it is an extremely reasonable one. There are a number of objections, however, one of which is that it fails to provide for enough shrinking of the crust to account for all of the foreshortening that has taken place. The study of the behavior of earthquake waves led to another objection. The theory assumed a relatively thin crust of about 50 to 100 mi; all below it was molten. This gave a very handy explanation for the origin of magmas and lavas. The discovery that the transverse waves of earthquakes, which cannot be transmitted through liquids, are freely transmitted to a depth of about 1800 mi shook the confidence of the adherents to the theory. Another objection is that there is considerable doubt that the earth is cooling off. The evidence from radioactivity (Chapter 36) suggests that the earth is heating up. All rocks contain minute amounts (at least) of radioactive elements that spontaneously disintegrate into other atoms, giving off energy that is converted to heat energy. If the amount of this heat has been significant throughout geologic time, that fact would be fatal to the thermal contraction theory, for this theory demands a cooling earth, not one that is getting hotter. The theory also fails to account for fault block mountains like the Sierra Nevada and scores of other ranges throughout Utah, Nevada, New Mexico, Arizona, and Mexico. These are mountains whose origin involved tensional forces rather than compressional forces. The thermal contraction theory is on the decline at present, chiefly because of the rise of one or more conflicting theories.

The Theory of Convection Currents

The concept of convection currents in the mantle of the earth has been used not only to explain the formation of geosynclines and the complex mountain ranges that are formed from them but also to provide a physically acceptable basis for the theory of continental drift (p. 579). This mantle is intensely hot, hot enough to be molten if it were not for the extremely high pressures that are estimated to be more than 25 million $lb/in.^2$. Although solid, the mantle material must possess a limited plasticity that would allow it to move upwards in places at a very slow rate, possibly only a few centimeters per year. Because the crust of the earth is much too rigid to allow convection currents to develop in it, an upward-moving current would be deflected horizontally, part of it in one direction and part in another. Convection currents commonly occur in pairs; each pair is called a convection cell.

Thus heat is transferred upward by the mantle material toward the base of the crust; this material moves horizontally beneath the base of the crust until it reaches a region where it turns downward. The process operates like the water in a deep pan on the stove; the bottom water heats first, expands, and moves upward as the cooler water at the top decends. It is postulated that the descent of the mantle material drags the crust downward very slowly, initiating a geosyncline whose bottom slowly continues to sink as it is being filled with sediments eroded from not too distant highland areas. As the geosyncline sinks, the bottom sediments in it are moving into a hotter zone. This heating would probably cause expansion, which in turn would cause crumpling (folding) of the strata above the zone of melting, and uplift to produce mountains. These strata would be hot enough to yield plastically, and so the observation of thick, seemingly rigid yet closely folded layers of rock in mountain regions is explained satisfactorily. The molten material near the base of the crumpled zone could then intrude the overlying strata, and this would explain the observation that the "home" of the great intrusives, chiefly granite, is in the cores of the great mountain ranges of the earth.

The mantle convection cell theory does not

require that any one cell should have a thickness equal to the entire depth of the mantle, about 1800 miles. It is quite widely accepted among geologists that the mantle has several layers, or seismically discontinuous zones, which may differ from each other in physical or chemical characteristics or both. Thus there are probably several layers of convection cells. They would not be stacked vertically one above another but, rather, offset from each other to some extent. Such a mechanism would transfer heat energy from the deep interior to the geologically active region near or at the earth's surface. Evidence from the study of earthquake waves seems to validate this theory. Current estimates of the thickness of the uppermost convection cells, just below the crust, range from about 10 miles to several hundred miles.

The Theory of Continental Drift

Late in the 19th century Antonio Snider attempted to explain the apparent matching of the shoreline of western Africa with that of eastern South America (Fig. 32-17) by proposing a theory of continental drift. Nothing came of it. Alfred Wegener, a German meteorologist, revived the theory in 1912. The theory assumes that all of the lands of the earth were once joined to form a single continent, which Wegener called Pangaea (Fig. 32-18). This continent split into northern and southern parts called Laurasia and Gondwanaland (Fig. 32-19). These landmasses later split into smaller fragments, which drifted apart (Figs. 32-20 and 32-21), and these fragments form our present continents (Fig. 32-22).

How Pangaea was formed in the first place is outside the scope of the theory. The theory postulates its presence deep in the southern hemisphere during late Paleozoic time (see the geologic time scale, Fig. 35-1). Wegener could

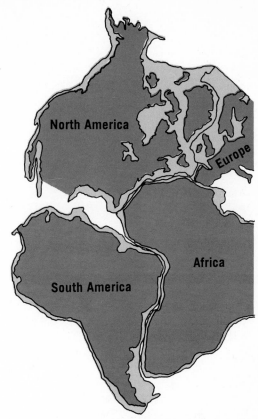

Fig. 32-17. The Fit of the Modern Continents on the East and West Sides of the Atlantic Ocean. The approximate fitting of the east coast of North America into the west coast of Europe and the east coast of South America into the west coast of Africa can be seen on any map. The fit becomes still better when the continental shelves and slopes are taken into account. Land masses are indicated by darker color, continental shelves and slopes by lighter color; nonfitting regions are white. (From a map by Tom Cardamone for *Fortune*. Fit of continents based on the map by Sir Edward Bullard, J. E. Everett, and A. G. Smith of Cambridge University.)

then explain the evidence for extensive glaciation in parts of southern Africa that are now much too close to the equator for it to have occurred if Africa had been in its present loca-

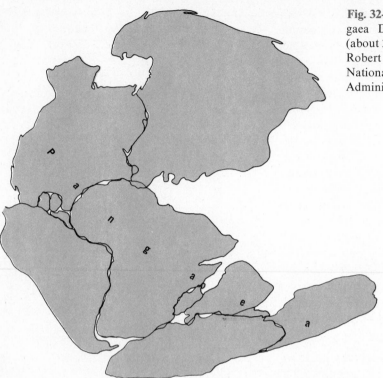

Fig. 32-18. Possible Outline of Pangaea During the Permian Period (about 225 million years ago). (From Robert S. Dietz and John C. Holden, National Oceanic and Atmospheric Administration.)

tion at that time. No one has suggested where Pangaea might have been during the more than 3 billion yr preceding the Permian glaciation. The theory assumes that Pangaea began to break apart in the Triassic period, as much as 200 million yr ago. About the same time Pangaea may have started moving northward, thus moving southern Africa out of the south temperate zone, where glaciation could have occurred, into the tropical zone. Why the dispersal began when it did after the existence of a single landmass for so long is an unanswered question.

To validate the theory of continental drift—note that we do not say prove—we need a sufficient number of observations that can be explained by the theory in a more reasonable manner than by any other theory. A mechanism within the realm of possibility by which the drift could take place is not an

absolute necessity but it is of great help in the validation of the theory, especially if the observational evidence is weak.

We have mentioned the original observation that started Wegener thinking about continental drift—the close fit of the eastern bulge of South America into the Gulf of Guinea on the western coast of Africa. If this matching is done at a level of 2000 meters below present sea level, the fit is much more impressive (Fig. 32-17). The fit of Europe and North America is not nearly as close, but it is well within the realm of possibility.

The Climatic Evidence

We have mentioned briefly the Permian continental glaciation in South Africa. (The distinction between mountain glaciation and continental glaciation is made in the next chapter.) The evidence for continental glaciation consists of widespread deposits of boulders, pebbles, sand, and clay with no evidence of sorting or layering. These deposits may be found on hill and valley alike, show no relationship in kind to the underlying rocks, and may lie on bedrock that has been prominently striated by boulders embedded in the undersurface of the glacier. No competent geologist ever questions the origin of such deposits. Deposits like these are found in South Africa and in South America in areas that are now less than 20° from the equator. The continental drift theory assumes that they were made when Pangaea lay far to the south of Africa's present position.

Another line of climatic evidence comes from the distribution of fossil coral reefs. Today coral reefs are restricted to warm, clear, marine waters not more than 30° from the equator. Fossil coral reefs are found in areas as far north as Alaska. The supposition is that these reefs were formed when the continents were far to the south of their present locations. Extensive coal deposits in the far north are also easily explained by the same supposition.

Other Fossil Evidence

The fossil evidence shows that following the period of glaciation mentioned above, there

Fig. 32-19. Probable Appearance of Laurasia and Gondwanaland During the Triassic Period (about 200 million years ago). The Laurasian landmass comprised what is now North America, Europe, and part of Asia; Gondwanaland included present South America, Africa, India, Antarctica, and Australia. (From Robert S. Dietz and John C. Holden, National Oceanic and Atmospheric Administration.)

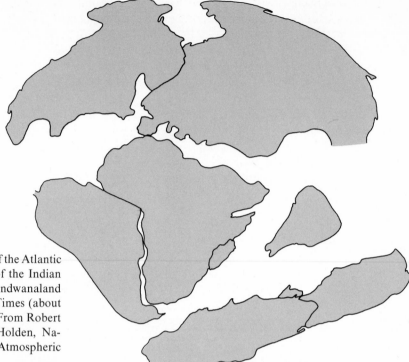

Fig. 32-20. Formation of the Atlantic Ocean and Separation of the Indian Subcontinent from Gondwanaland Began During Jurassic Times (about 135 million years ago). (From Robert S. Dietz and John C. Holden, National Oceanic and Atmospheric Administration.)

developed a flora of primitive land plants that became widespread. Fossils of this flora have been found in South America, Africa, Australia, Antarctica, and even in India. This flora is very uniform in composition, and differs considerably from the flora that developed in the northern hemisphere at the same time. The distribution of these plants is easily explained by assuming the existence of Laurasia and Gondwanaland during this time. There is also some similar evidence from fossil reptiles and amphibians, which we will not elaborate here. If these two landmasses did not exist, then there must have been some sort of land bridge that connected these areas across which the single uniform flora could have migrated.

Evidence from "Broken" Mountain Ranges

Some ancient mountain ranges stop abruptly at continental borders. The Cape Mountains of South Africa end on the west coast of Africa, and the Sierra de la Ventana Mountains of Argentina end abruptly on its eastern coast. The two ranges are composed of rocks of about the same age and composition, and having the same structure. Likewise our own Appalachians end abruptly on the coast of Newfoundland. Mountains of the same age and structure occur in northwestern Europe; these could have been continuous with the Appalachians before Laurasia split apart.

The Demise and Revival of the Theory of Continental Drift

Wegener regarded the continents as relatively light granitic plates "floating" in a denser basaltic substratum. Put in other words the continents are low density crustal "icebergs" suspended in the denser mantle. The mantle was thought to be plastic enough to

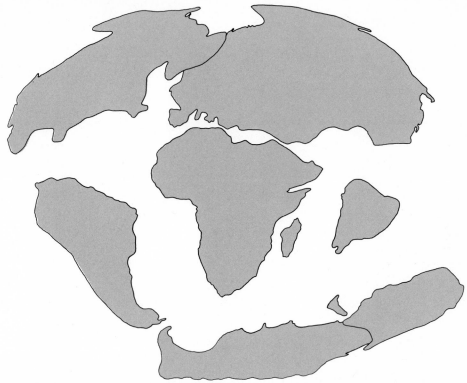

Fig. 32-21. The Continents During Early Cretaceous Times (about 65 million years ago). The South Atlantic has become recognizable, and India is drifting toward the southern edge of Asia. (From Robert S. Dietz and John C. Holden, National Oceanic and Atmospheric Administration.)

yield to small but persistent forces, and so allow the continental plates to slide over it. However, try as he might, he could not propose any force or set of forces that would start the continents moving. Moreover, there were alternative explanations for most of the fossil evidence, and the supposed fit of the continents could be assigned to chance. Also, the thought of huge continents moving such great distances staggered the imaginations of most.

As a result, interest in his theory petered out about 1930, although some South African and South American geologists continued to consider the theory more or less seriously. However, interest in the theory was revived in the late 1950's and early 1960's until by the early 1970's it was regarded as phenomenally great.

For one thing the concept of convection currents in the mantle became scientifically acceptable. Of greater importance were the many facts that came from research in the fields of submarine geology, paleomagnetism, and heat flow, research that began in the early 1950's and is continuing at a great rate today.

Submarine Geology

Submarine geology has been discussed in the previous chapter in the section on Structure of Ocean Basins. We can add little here that is descriptive, but we can do a bit of theorizing about the midocean ridges and rifts. The most important is the mid-Atlantic ridge and rift. Other rifts extend into the continents,

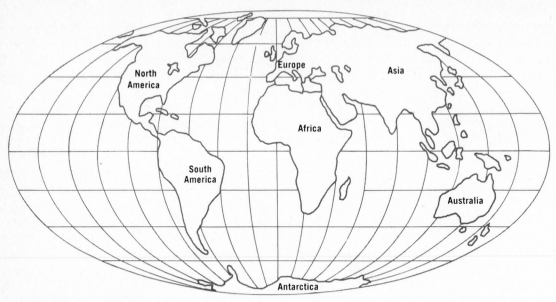

Fig. 32-22. The Continents and Oceans Today (Cenozoic era). Early in the Cenozoic, India "collided" with Asia and Antarctica separated from Australia.

for example, the Red Sea and East African rift valleys and the Gulf of California. These rifts are in regions where the crust seems to have been pulled apart. If this supposition is correct, then they could have a convection current origin (see Fig. 32-23); that is, when the pair of upwelling currents reached the bottom of the crust, they would separate, pulling the crust apart to create a central rift valley such as that shown in the figure. One important point about these ridges is that whereas mountain ranges on the continents are apparently produced by compressional forces, these submarine ridges are apparently produced by tensional forces. If these convection currents are capable of producing rifts in the earth's crust, then the currents could be considered as the mechanism causing continental drift. There are a number of geophysical data that support this concept. One is the abnormally high heat flow along the trend of the rifts.

Geological evidence indicates that Lower (Baja) California once formed a part of the mainland that has since rifted away. Both the Gulf of California and the Red Sea have crustal structures that are essentially oceanic in character, and so the bottoms of these two narrow belts of water represent true parts of the ocean basins in the process of formation; they are not considered to be parts of continents that have been submerged. Is the Atlantic Ocean itself such a rift?

Following this idea further we can picture the convection currents, having reached the base of the crust, traveling horizontally in opposite directions and carrying the split-apart continents with them. For example, an eastward-flowing current would carry Africa in that direction and westward-flowing current would carry South America in the opposite direction. As the rift between the two continents widened, hot plastic mantle material would rise to partly fill the void. This mantle material would thus escape the high pressure prevailing deeper in the mantle; hence its melting point would be reduced enough to allow the upper part to melt and form basaltic lava. When cooled sufficiently, the upper part would solidify to form a new submarine crust through which molten lava could break in places to form volcanoes. Both this newly formed crust and the volcanoes built upon it would be carried away east and west by the oppositely traveling convection currents.

In the interest of clarity in the presentation of these ideas and the extension of them, let us indulge our imaginations to a high degree by going backward in time to the original undispersed Pangaea. We need to remember that (1) the average thickness of the crust is about 35 km, (2) the upper part of the crust is composed of sial (Chapter 31), which is about 10% less dense than the sima that forms the lower part, and (3) the crust is, in general, too rigid to allow plastic flow like that in convection currents. We will ignore the ocean waters for the time being.

We will assume, then, that one or more rising convection currents came up against the bottom of the crust of the primeval landmass of Pangaea. There each rising current split into two currents, which were deflected horizontally in opposite directions. In time such oppositely directed currents could cause the crust of Pangaea itself to split and the parts thus formed could be carried away from each other. The first split appears to have occurred during the Permian period and produced a northern section, Laurasia, and a southern section, Gondwanaland.

Now we will assume that another, later, upwelling current (or pair of rising currents) caused splitting along what we now call the Mid-Atlantic Ridge. The Americas would be pulled westward, Africa and Europe eastward, forming a gap between them. This gap would be about as deep as the crust of the earth is thick. The top of the mantle would be exposed on the floor of the gap. This intensely hot plastic mantle material, relieved of the enormous pressure that had been exerted on it by the crustal rocks, would quickly rise in the gap until isostasy was reached. Note that the sea

would now have a new floor within the gap, and that as the continents drifted farther and farther apart, the new floor would spread to keep pace with the drift. Note also that this floor is younger than any of the rocks forming the continents. The processes of weathering and erosion (Chapter 34) would be operating on the continents, and some of the resulting sediments would be deposited on the new sea floor. The life cycle of these sediments began with their deposition; they must be younger than the split-up of Laurasia and Gondwanaland. If this split-up started in late Jurassic time (Fig. 32-20), and if the Atlantic Ocean basin has indeed been formed by continental drifting, then there can be no sediments older than late Jurassic on the Atlantic floor.[3] Extensive drilling from ships in the Atlantic floor has been going on for years, and depths of more than 3300 ft have been reached without encountering any sediments older than Jurassic. Thus, this split is presumed to have started in the Jurassic period and to have continued through the Cretaceous period; it may still be in operation to this day. Both Laurasia and Gondwanaland split, though not necessarily simultaneously or at the same rate.

Let us now return to reality. In our imagination we compressed millions of years into a few days. Doing this made little difference in the sequence of events as we related them. The gap developed centimeter by centimeter, and the hot plastic mantle material rose to keep pace with it. The sediments deposited were not all derived from the drifting continents; much of it was formed from the shells of microscopic marine organisms and of dust blown into the sea. If the Atlantic Ocean and the continents have always been as they are today, the blanket of sediment on the sea floor should be several miles thick. Drilling shows very little sediment in the central areas and

---

[3] How sediments are dated is discussed in Chapter 35.

only a half-mile veneer of it near the ocean borders.

The Evidence from Heat Flow

If the earth has a molten iron core, there must be heat flowing from this core outward to the surface. The earth should be cooling unless there is an additional source. We have already mentioned the heat generated by radioactivity. (For further information, see Chapter 36.) We may classify continental rocks as essentially granitic in composition, and oceanic rocks as essentially basaltic. Granitic rocks contain a much higher percentage of radioactive minerals than do basaltic rocks. The effects of radioactive heating should be more apparent in continental rocks than in oceanic rocks. It follows that the *average* rate of heat flow should be greater from the continents than it is from the ocean basins. Actually the average rate is about the same, but that from those parts of the basins that are far from oceanic ridges, like the mid-Atlantic, is only a fifth of the overall average. Therefore additional heat must come from the ridges. Measurements show that in the vicinity of the ridges the heat flow is 5 to 10 times the overall average. Thus the data from heat flow support the ideas expressed elsewhere about ridges and rifts.

The Evidence from Paleomagnetism

It has long been known that some rocks have weak magnetic fields whose orientation can be determined by sensitive instruments. For example, ordinary basalt contains many small grains of the mineral magnetite, each of which is a natural magnet.[4] In a single piece of basalt the magnetic poles are all aligned in the same directions. If such a piece is heated to about 500°C (called the Curie point), its magnetism

is destroyed. If it is then cooled in a sufficiently strong magnetic field, the grains become magnets again with their poles aligned parallel to the field.

In nature basalt results from the crystallization of a low-silica lava at a temperature of about 1000°C. At this temperature the magnetic grains have no polarity, but as the rock cools and solidifies, each magnetite grain acquires the polarity of the earth's magnetic field when the temperature drops below 500°C. The direction of this polarity is maintained indefinitely as long as the rock is not moved[5] nor again heated to the Curie point. This magnetic property of the rock is called *remanent ferromagnetism*. Hematite, another oxide of iron, has a much weaker ferromagnetism than magnetite. Rocks other than basalt may contain grains of magnetite and/or hematite and so show remanent ferromagnetism.

Rocks with remanent ferromagnetism are widely distributed over all continents. If the remanent ferromagnetism of rocks of the same age in a specific continent are studied and mapped, one can plot where the magnetic poles were with respect to that continent at the time those rocks were formed. If rocks in the same continent but of a different age are studied in the same manner, one can plot the position of the earth's magnetic poles during that age. If the positions do not coincide, then one is faced with the conclusion that the magnetic poles have not remained fixed with respect to that continent during the time interval between those two ages. In Great Britain such plots show a "wandering" of the magnetic poles from a point in the mid-Pacific in the Paleozoic Era through eastern Asia and into the Arctic Ocean where it is now. Plots based on the rocks of North America of the same ages also show a wandering but along a different path.

---

[4] Some bodies of rock contain enough magnetic minerals that an ordinary compass cannot be used in their vicinity.

[5] It may be moved by forces involved in faulting or folding. Loose pieces that may be moved by man must be ignored.

Why should these paths be different? There are two possibilities: (1) the magnetic poles have shifted their positions during that interval, or (2) the continents have shifted their positions with respect to the poles. If North America is shifted about 30° to the east, the two paths do approximately coincide. The so-called polar wandering is usually interpreted in reverse; it is the continents that have wandered while the magnetic poles remained fixed. Studies of remanent ferromagnetism made in other parts of the world, however, reveal paths that do not jibe, so the study still goes on.

Another facet of these studies shows alternate reversals of the north and south magnetic poles at intervals of somewhat less than a million years. We need here to recall how the sea floor spread as the continents drifted, and that this floor consisted of basalt, a rock that shows remanent ferromagnetism. The magnetic pole reversals of more or less regular intervals of time should show up in a series of alternate striped patterns on the spreading sea floor, one stripe with the north magnetic pole oriented in one direction, then another stripe with the pole oriented in the opposite direction. The width of a stripe should be proportional to the length of time between reversals. Such stripes should appear on both sides of the Mid-Atlantic Ridge. Investigations show that they do. Thus we have another fact to support the theory of continental drift, even though there is at present no explanation of the above reversals.

Mountain Building and Continental Drift

We have mentioned that the original chief objection to the drift hypothesis was that it was physically impossible for a continent to "sail like a ship" through the material forming the top part of the mantle. Sea floor spreading as we have described it eliminates this difficulty; continents never move through the top of the mantle—they either move along with it as they "ride" a horizontally moving convection current or they stand still at the place where the convection current ceases to move horizontally but instead turns downward toward the bottom of the mantle. This convection current turns downward because it has met another such current moving in the opposite direction (Fig. 32-23). (If there is an upward-moving

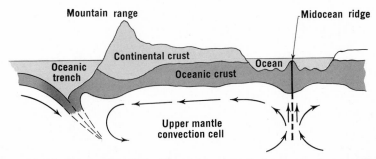

Fig. 32-23. Upper Mantle Convection Cells. The rising currents in a pair of convection cells split near the base of the oceanic crust, pulling the crust apart and forming a rift. Basaltic magma rising through this rift piles up as it hardens to form the midocean ridge. In places volcanoes may form. The horizontal current on the upper side of the cell carries a continental plate (of lighter material) "drifting" along with it. Where this current meets the oppositely directed horizontal current of an adjacent cell, both currents turn down, pulling some of the heavier material of the lower crust along with them and forming an oceanic trench. However, the lighter material of the upper crust piles up to form simple or complexly folded mountain ranges.

convection current in one place, there must be a downward-moving one somewhere else.) The drifting continent has a great deal of momentum; the light crustal rocks pile up at the front margin to form mountains, while the ocean floor is pulled downward by the descending currents to form a trench (p. 549). The Andes Mountains are considered to have been formed in this manner. Perhaps there is another continent "riding" on the oppositely moving current. The great Himalaya Mountains are believed to have been folded and uplifted by a collision between Asia and India, which at the time was a separate continent by itself.

The Theory of Plate Tectonics

The modern theory explains most of the facts we have just related by combining the main ideas about convection currents with the main ideas of continental drift. It is called the theory of plate tectonics. A summary of the theory is all that is necessary here; we have already discussed some aspects of it. Rising convection currents divide into two oppositely directed horizontally moving currents when they reach the bottom of the crust. In doing so they exert tensional stresses on the crust that are great enough to tear it apart; a ridge-rift valley system eventually forms. As the continents are pulled apart, the upwelling mantle creates new ocean floor. The opposing currents with continents "riding" on or in them can be visualized as plates. These plates originate at the ridges (or rises). When two oppositely moving plates meet head on, one slides over the other. The upper one remains horizontal or is tipped upward slightly while young fold mountains may be formed along the front margin. The lower one is bent downward and largely destroyed by "melting" as it encounters

more and more of the hot plastic mantle. A deep sea trench may be formed by the descending convection current. The whole earth is assumed to be divided into a number of separate plates; new ones are being formed and old ones are being destroyed. Two plates may slide past each other. We have mentioned the Gulf of California with its new sea floor forming as the peninsula of Baja California drifted away from Mexico. The great San Andreas fault, which can be traced more than 600 mi, is aligned with the western side of the Gulf of California. The fault is a side-slip movement with the western side moving northwestward. Perhaps Baja California and a sliver of southern California lie on a separate plate that will eventually be pulled loose from the mainland. Perhaps a great many of the California earthquakes are caused by this tearing away. Perhaps the westward-moving south American plate is encountering an eastward-drifting oceanic plate that it is overriding. (Plates do not have to have continents riding on them.) Such an encounter could explain the origin of the Andes Mountains and the many disastrous earthquakes that occur in western South America. In these encounters there is a great deal of friction; the heat generated may be great enough to cause melting of the rocks at depth without recourse to the heat brought up by convection currents. The many volcanoes along the west coast of South America could be explained in this way.

There is a vast amount of evidence in favor of the theory of plate tectonics that we are unable to present. Part of it is much too complex for us. Part of it is too fragmental to mention; intensive research going on now will eventually piece it out. Many of the researchers believe that the evidence so far uncovered is sufficient to validate not only the theory of continental drift but also the continental plate theory of mountain building.

Exercises

1. What is the direct cause of any volcanic explosion?
2. What is a fissure eruption?
3. In many active volcanos the molten material in the crater may be observed to be "boiling."
   (a) Considering what you have learned about boiling, would you expect this to be true boiling?
   (b) If not, what is it? Explain.
4. Volcanic ash is the abrasive used in the common kitchen scouring powders. Precisely why should it make such a good abrasive?
5. For geysers to erupt water and steam high in the air, part of the water must be heated *above* the normal boiling point. What conditions must exist below the surface for this to be possible?
6. Criticize the following statement, giving your reasons: The eruption of a geyser may be considered to be a volcanic eruption in which the molten material is water instead of magma or lava.
7. Differentiate between a dike and a sill.
8. Both sills and lava flows may be horizontal or tilted sheets of igneous rock lying between beds of sedimentary rock. How is it possible to distinguish one from the other?
9. In what sorts of regions are batholiths most likely to be exposed? Give two very different reasons.
10. What kind of rock forms (a) most batholiths, (b) most of the great lava flows?
11. How can you distinguish batholiths and lava flows from each other?
12. Differentiate between an intrusive rock and an extrusive rock.
13. (a) What is a batholith?
    (b) Of what rock are most batholiths composed?
14. Where is the "home" of the batholith?
15. (a) What is a fault?
    (b) How are faults related to earthquakes?
16. (a) What other types of diastrophic activity are there besides faulting?
    (b) One series of horizontally deposited sedimentary rocks has been elevated by being upwarped. Another similar series has been elevated by folding. In what fundamental way would these two regions differ geologically?
17. (a) Define diastrophism.
    (b) Name three types of diastrophic activity.
18. Name two prominent folded mountain ranges in North America, and one great fault block mountain range.
19. Suppose that you lived in a low-lying sea coast. If you awoke one morning to find the waters of the sea lapping at your doorstep, you would have to assume either that the land had sunk or that the sea level had actually risen. How could you find out which?
20. If you concluded (in exercise 19) that the sea had actually risen, how could you explain it, considering the fact that the total volume of water on the earth is constant?
21. Changes of sea level have taken place without any diastrophic activity whatever. For example, during the last ice age, the sea level dropped as much as 200 ft. Explain.
22. May rock at depth be at the same temperature but solid in one case and molten in the other? Explain.
23. The melting of rock at depth causes an increase in volume. The magma must therefore have a lesser density. Would this have any effect on its tendency to move upward? Explain.

24. If a new volcano were to form in the United States, in what state do you think it would be? Justify your answer.

25. What is the chief assumption of the thermal contraction theory of mountain-building? What are two chief objections to this theory?

26. (a) What is an upper mantle convection cell?

    (b) What two types of such cells are possible?

27. How is it possible for convection currents to form in the mantle but not in the crust?

28. (a) What effect do upwelling convection currents seem to have on the earth's crust; for example, at the Mid-Atlantic Ridge?

    (b) How is this ridge related to the rift area of the same name?

29. Large land areas have shifted considerable distances in the recent past as well as in the ancient past. Cite one such instance.

30. What is the relationship of the theory of convection currents to the theory of continental drift?

31. Where do ranges of mountains form with respect to the drifting continents?

32. (a) What type of energy is necessary for convection cells to operate and for continents to drift?

    (b) What is the probable source of this energy?

33. How do the facts of paleomagnetism support the concept of continental drift?

34. The expression "migration of the poles" has been used in discussions of continental drift. Has this migration been apparent or real? Explain. (*Hint:* First define a pole.)

35. Considering the immense inertia of the earth, we can see that it would take a very considerable force to change the axis of the earth's rotation. So far as we can see, is any such force available?

36. State three lines of evidence that led Wegener to postulate continental drift.

    (a) What lack caused it to founder in the 1920's?

    (b) Why was the theory rejuvenated in the late 1950's and early 1960's?

    (c) What is its present-day status?

Natural Large-Scale Energy Transformations: Weather and Climate

33

Energy: Source and Distribution

The source of all the energy that makes life possible on earth is the sun. Without enough of its energy and an adequate atmosphere and immense oceans (of water) to absorb it, this would be a cold dead planet just as Jupiter, Saturn, Uranus, Neptune, and Pluto are. Solar energy evaporates enormous quantities of water from the oceans, much of which, carried by winds over the lands, is ultimately condensed to rain and snow. This solar energy plus atmospheric moisture makes possible chemical weathering, which in turn provides the earth with its soil. The sun's radiant energy, via photosynthesis, makes plant life possible on earth, and plants in their turn supply animals with their energy.

The distance of the earth from the sun is more than 10,000 times the earth's diameter. The sun's rays, therefore, are very nearly parallel when they reach us (Fig. 2-21). If the earth were perfectly flat with its surface at right

583

angles to these rays, the noonday sun would appear directly overhead everywhere; every square mile of the earth would receive the same amount of solar energy each day. That the noonday sun is not at the same elevation above the horizon everywhere at the same time is proof that the earth's surface is curved. This curvature is a chief factor in causing the great inequality in the amount of solar energy received in various parts of the earth. From this inequality temperature differences arise, causing differences in air pressure, which in turn cause winds.

Winds transport the water vapor evaporated from the oceans over the lands, where it may be condensed to fall as rain or snow. Winds also transport heat from warmer to cooler regions, and return the cold air to the warmer regions to be heated again. Winds also cause ocean waves and long-shore currents that erode the shore lines. Winds start the great oceanic drifts of sea water, for example, the Gulf Stream, and together with the configuration of continents and the rotation of the earth determine their courses, courses that change the habitability or inhabitability of continents. Winds themselves are a minor agent of erosion; their climatic functions greatly overshadow their direct geologic functions.

Weather vs. Climate

Weather refers to the atmospheric conditions of the moment or, at best, over a short period of time. The weather of any place is the sum of such atmospheric conditions as temperature, air pressure, winds, atmospheric moisture, and precipitation over a short period. *Climate* is sometimes said to be average weather over a longer period of time. This is not strictly true, for it fails to give proper consideration to the extremes. It is conceivable that the factors that govern weather of two regions could average out the same from year to year and those

regions yet have very different climates. For example, consider the temperature factor alone. The average for New York City is 52°F and that for Seattle is 51.4°F. Yet you would have far more need of an overcoat in winter and an air-conditioning system in summer in New York than you ever would in Seattle.

Effects of Motions and Orientation of the Earth

The effects of motions and orientation of the earth have already been dealt with in Chapter 2. The student is strongly advised to read this chapter again, especially pp. 29–36.[1] The two motions are, of course, rotation and revolution. The orientation is that of the earth on its axis with respect to the plane of the ecliptic and the constancy of this relationship during a complete revolution.

Troposphere, Stratosphere, and Ionosphere

The earth's atmosphere has a layered structure. Three major layers are recognized, the troposphere, the stratosphere, and the ionosphere (Fig. 33-1). In the middle latitudes the troposphere extends upward from the surface of the earth to an altitude of 6 or 7 mi. In it we find most of our atmosphere, atmospheric moisture, dust, wind, clouds, fog, haze, storms, and precipitation. In it there is also a strong vertical mixing of the atmosphere. A study of weather and climate is very largely a study of this zone. Hence practically all that follows in this chapter has to do with this zone.

Above the troposphere and extending upward above it for some 30 to 35 mi is the stratosphere, a region with a cold, clear, rarefied atmosphere, almost without water vapor or dust. Its chief point of interest is the pres-

---

[1] Some of the questions at the end of this chapter are based on the assumption that you have read these pages.

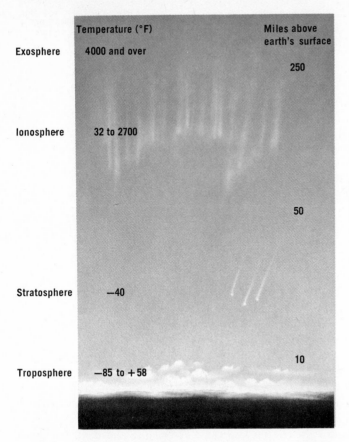

Exosphere   Temperature (°F)

4000 and over

Ionosphere   32 to 2700

Stratosphere   —40

Troposphere   —85 to + 58

Miles above
earth's surface

250

50

10

Fig. 33-1. Atmospheric Zones and Beyond. The top of the troposphere ranges from a height of 10 or 12 mi at the equator to 5 or 6 mi at the poles. In it the temperature generally decreases with altitude.

ence of a layer of ozone whose maximum density is at about 15 mi. Ozone is a form of oxygen whose molecules are O_3, an entirely different substance from O_2. Ozone is formed by the action of ultraviolet light on O_2. It is such an excellent absorber of the photons of ultraviolet radiation that relatively few of them reach the earth. Too much of this shortwave radiation from the sun would be fatal to man. The temperature of the upper part of the stratosphere is higher than that on earth.

The ionosphere is chiefly a region of charged particles, ions, and electrons, created chiefly by the interaction between the air molecules and the ultraviolet radiation from the sun. The density of the ionized particles is less than $1/1000$ that of the earth's atmosphere at sea level. It grades imperceptibly upward into interplanetary space as the density of the atmosphere becomes immeasurably thin. Its temperature is high, high enough to cause astronauts and artificial satellites trouble were it not for its extremely low density.

The ionosphere was not known before Marconi's invention of radio communication—about 1902. Meteorologists of the time predicted failure for Marconi's attempt to send a message via the atmosphere to the United States from Europe. Electromagnetic waves travel in straight lines, and so could not follow the curvature of the earth. They would pass high in the air above any receiving apparatus in the United States. Nevertheless the waves did reach the receiving apparatus. To do this, the astonished meteorologists reasoned, the waves had to be reflected back to earth by

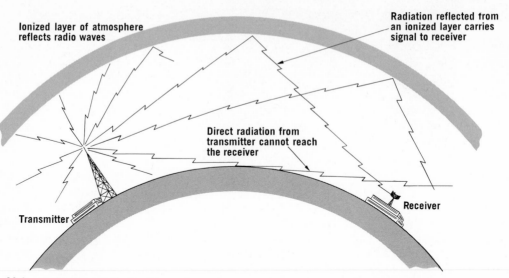

Fig. 33-2. Reflection of Radio Waves from the Ionosphere. This reflection makes long distance radio transmission and reception possible. The existence of such an ionized layer was deduced from the fact that Marconi succeeded in sending messages across the Atlantic Ocean. TV waves are not reflected because they have unsuitable wavelengths.

some reflecting layer of the high atmosphere (Fig. 33-2). Proof that such a layer (or layers) existed did not come before 1924. There are actually four such layers but we need not concern ourselves with them here. Because the ionosphere has these reflecting properties, radio communication around the world is possible. The shorter TV waves are not reflected by the ionosphere; TV waves therefore have a relatively short range; they are limited by the horizon.

Elements of Weather and Climate

Air Temperature

Two factors govern the amount of solar energy received at any one place at any one time. They are (1) the angle at which the sun's rays strike the earth (see Fig. 2-21) and (2) the relative lengths of day and night. Both are functions of the latitude of the place in question. Our summers are warmer than our winters, not only because the sun's rays are nearer the vertical, but because the days are much longer in the higher latitudes. The earth has more time to heat up during the hours the sun is above the horizon and less time to cool off at night when it is below the horizon. Conversely, winters are colder not only because the sun's rays are more slanting, but because there are fewer hours of sunlight and more hours of darkness. At 40°N latitude there are about 15 hr of sunlight and 9 hr of darkness on June 21, 9 hr of sunlight and 15 hr of darkness on December 22. With the dates reversed, the same is true at 40°S latitude.

Much of the sun's radiant energy is reflected back into outer space by clouds and by dust particles before it reaches the earth. The sun's energy that reaches the earth consists of electromagnetic radiation (photons); most of them have wavelengths in the visible and infrared part of the spectrum. Only the longer of these wavelengths are capable of heating the atmosphere directly. However, the earth absorbs the shorter wavelengths, is warmed by them, and reradiates part of this heat back into the atmosphere.

Since the reradiated wavelengths are longer[2] than those absorbed, they are much more effective in heating the atmosphere. They can be absorbed by the molecules that make up the atmosphere, more so by the molecules of water vapor and carbon dioxide than by those of oxygen and nitrogen. Absorption of the infrared rays makes the molecules move faster, and collisions of these faster moving molecules make other molecules move faster, and so the temperature rises. Remember that heat is molecular motion (Chapter 13). The so-called "greenhouse" effect is due to the fact that glass admits the shorter wavelengths that are absorbed by materials inside the glass enclosure. These materials reradiate the absorbed energy as longer infrared rays, which do not readily pass out through the glass. This explains why the inside of cars parked in the sun even on a cold winter day are warmer than the outside.

Water surfaces differ from land surfaces in their properties of absorption and reradiation of heat, even when they lie side by side. Each receives the same amount of insolation (solar energy), has the same thickness of air above it, and is affected by the same major wind system. Yet summer is hotter and winter colder on the land than on the water. There are several reasons. Water reflects more of the sun's rays than the soil and rocks, and so absorbs less. Water has a specific heat (Chapter 11) four times that of soil and rocks, so its temper-

ature is not raised so rapidly nor so much. Water circulates, whereas the soil and rocks do not. Thus, there is a much greater thickness (depth) of water to be heated. Moreover, water constantly evaporates. Because evaporation is a cooling process, it helps to keep the water cooler than the land. But when night or winter comes, the land cools more rapidly than the water, and so the air over the land is cooler than the air over the water.

Within the troposphere temperatures are lower at high altitudes than they are at lower altitudes, other things being equal. This is in part owing to greater distance from the radiating earth, and in part to the lesser density of the atmosphere. There are fewer molecules at higher altitudes to absorb the heat. The average decrease is about 3.3°F per 1000 ft in the troposphere. In hot deserts the air cools quickly after sundown because there are relatively few molecules of water vapor in it to condense and release heat as they do so. In humid climates where clouds are more prevalent at night, they act as blankets to prevent heat from escaping.

Air Pressure

Pressure differences are far more significant in relation to weather and climate than are the absolute pressures. There is a continuous variability of pressure at the same place from hour to hour as the temperatures rise from those of early morning to a high and then decrease with the coming of night. Pressures also change locally with the seasons. Moreover, average pressures differ in different parts of the earth; for example, they are lower at the equator than elsewhere. All these pressure differences arise from the fact that the earth's surface is unequally heated by the sun. Aside from the inequalities due to the earth's curvature and to the land and water differences in absorption and reradiation of heat, there are the more

---

[2] On p. 351, we saw that the hotter the radiating body the shorter the dominant wavelengths emitted. Thus, the earth, being cooler than the sun, radiates only the longer wavelengths. Reradiation must not be confused with reflection. The latter involves no absorption.

local causes due to differences in the absorbing and reflecting abilities of different types of land surfaces. Plowed fields or stretches of barren sand, for example, absorb more heat than do forested or grass-covered areas. As it is the reradiated rays that warm the atmosphere, the more heat that is absorbed by the earth, the faster the air above it is warmed. Warm air tends to produce low pressure in an open system where it is free to expand, and cold air tends to produce high pressure in the same system where it is free to contract. Thus, air pressures are relatively high over the oceans in summer as compared to those over the continents, because land areas heat up faster than water areas. In winter the reverse is true.

One result of this tendency for warm air to create low pressure is that the region about the equator forms a belt of low pressure, called the equatorial low, or, less formally, the doldrums. Here the warm air rises, expanding as it does so; the chief air movement is upward. It is a region (except at high elevations) of much calm; whatever winds there are, are light and variable in direction.

As might be expected, the cold polar regions are regions of high pressure. In such regions the chief movement of air is downward and outward. In between the poles and the equator there are other pressure belts, the most important of which are centered between the 25° and 30° parallels on either side of the equator. These are the subtropical high-pressure belts. These belts are not continuous but are broken into a series of high-pressure cells (Fig. 33-3). As in all high-pressure areas the movement of air is downward and outward. Like the equatorial low, they are regions of much calm, and

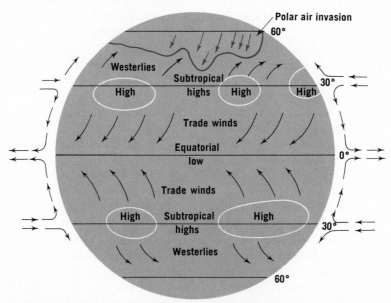

Fig. 33-3.   Wind and Pressure Belts. The boundaries between them cannot be shown, even approximately, partly because of their migration with the sun and partly because of the irregular distribution of land and sea. The equatorial low pressure belt is well developed everywhere, the trade winds are well developed except in the Indian Ocean, the subtropical high pressure belt is broken up into a series of high pressure cells, and the westerlies are highly variable from any viewpoint. Nevertheless, the student should memorize the broad features of the diagram if he wishes to have even a superficial understanding of world climates.

whatever winds there are, are usually light and variable. The reason for the high-pressure belt at these latitudes (often called the horse latitudes) is at present an inadequately explained effect of the earth's rotation.

Movements of the Air: Winds and Currents

The immediate results of pressure differences are winds and air currents. The term *wind* refers to horizontal movements of the air, whereas the term *air currents* refers to vertical movements. These air currents are called convectional currents. The winds always blow from regions of higher towards regions of lower pressure, tending to equalize the pressure. The greater the pressure difference, the stronger the wind. A difference equivalent to 2 in. of mercury is sufficient to cause the violent winds of a hurricane.

Although the differences in pressure govern the general direction of the movement of air masses, the rotation of the earth exerts a strong influence also. The fundamental reasons for this deflection are discussed in connection with the Foucault pendulum experiment in Chapter 2. The result is that the winds are deflected to the right[3] in the northern hemisphere, to the left in the southern; the trade winds that would normally blow towards the equator from both the north and the south are deflected so that they become the northeast trades in the northern hemisphere and the southeast trades in the southern (Fig. 33-3).

The trade winds are the most constant winds on earth in both velocity and persistence. This belt provided a splendid route for westward travel in the days of sailing ships. The wind velocity rarely rises above 15 mi/hr. At times hurricanes (in the western Atlantic) or typhoons (in the western Pacific) move across

them. The trades arise in the subtropical highs; the air to nourish them comes from the descending currents in the high-pressure cells in the horse latitudes.

A part of these descending currents of air in the subtropical high-pressure cells moves northward (northern hemisphere) and is quickly deflected to the right (east) because of the earth's rotation. *These winds are the westerlies.* Locally the winds in the belt of the westerlies may be from any point of the compass. Nevertheless, the prevailing direction is always from the west, southwest, or northwest, and so they are sometimes referred to as the prevailing westerlies. The result is that in this belt the movement of weather is from west to east. Therefore, west coast climates in the belt of the westerlies are controlled by oceanic conditions to the west of them, whereas east coast climates are controlled by the continental conditions to the west of them.

In winter the southern edge of the belt of the westerlies shifts southward over northern Florida so that great tongues of cold air moving southeastward from northwest Canada frequently penetrate even into southern Florida before they warm to the normal temperatures of that region. In the west the southern shift of the westerlies brings southern California into a zone of more rain so that most of the comparatively little rain that the area gets falls in winter. The northward shift in summer brings the area into a dry subtropical zone. In southeastern United States the northward shift of the westerlies leaves the area in a zone of copious rainfall and warm to hot temperatures.

Air Masses and Fronts

A large body of air that has acquired definite characteristics from lying over a large uniform surface of the earth until it is in equilibrium with the surface with respect to temperature and moisture content, is called an *air mass*.

---

[3] The direction of a wind is, of course, that from which the wind is coming. Thus, to apply this rule (known as Ferrel's law) one should imagine oneself to be standing with one's back to the wind.

One with a source over northwestern Canada will be cold and dry, one with a source region over the North Pacific will be cold and humid, whereas one whose source is over the southwestern United States will be warm and dry, and one whose source is over the Gulf of Mexico will be warm and humid. Occasionally one whose source is over the northwestern Atlantic will edge westward far enough to affect New England and the other North Atlantic states. Such air masses retain these characteristics to a large degree even after they move away from their source regions. Lower pressures in surrounding regions start them moving.

An air mass moving down from the north or northwest commonly comes in contact with an air mass moving up from the south or southwest. There is little mixing of the air between the two masses. They may move in part side by side but in different directions, or they may meet at some angle. The warmer air rises above the colder denser air. There is, therefore, a boundary surface between the air masses that always slopes upward from low pressure centers. The line formed by the inter-

section of this surface with the ground is called a *front* (Fig. 33-4). The boundary or contact zone between two air masses of unlike characteristics is always one of disturbance. The boundary surface is a gently sloping one, more gentle along a warm front[4] than a cold one. If the warmer air mass is actively pushing ahead, displacing the colder air and pushing it forward as it rises above it, the front is a warm one. The warm air, sliding up a gentle slope, cools slowly, causing precipitation to occur as a slow steady drizzle. The temperature of the air ahead of it either remains constant or it rises. If it is the colder air mass that is actively pushing ahead, wedging itself beneath the warmer air as it displaces it by forcing it upward, the front is a cold one. The more rapid and irregular ascent of the warm air up a steeper slope cools the air quickly, causing considerable turbulence and more concentrated precipitation. In any case, it is the air mass that is the "aggressor" that is the chief determiner of the character of the front. As

[4]The slope of the boundary surface may vary from 1:100 to 1:200; that is, its rise may be 1 ft or less per 100 ft.

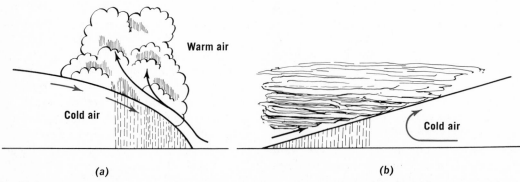

(a)   (b)

Fig. 33-4. Fronts. (*a*) A cold front. A mass of cold air is aggressively pushing in under a mass of warm air. The rising moisture-laden mass of warm air is pushed upward and cooled; part of its water vapor is condensed and falls as rain or snow. (*b*) A warm front. The warm air is aggressively moving toward a mass of cold air. Since it is less dense, it rises up over the cold air along a gently sloping front. As it does so, it is cooled; part of its water vapor is condensed and falls as rain or snow.

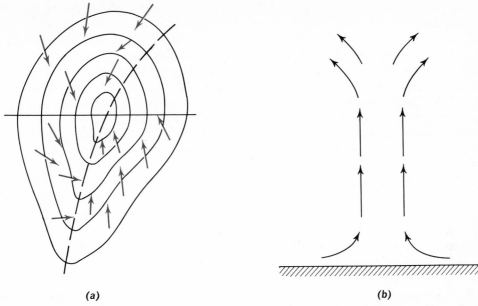

(a) *(b)*

Fig. 33-5. A Cyclone. (*a*) The closed black lines are isobars, lines of equal pressure. Since the lowest pressure is at the center, the air moves inward from all direction toward the center, spiraling as it does so in accordance with Ferrel's law. The broken line indicates the northerly path along which the cyclone is traveling. (*b*) At the center the air rises and is cooled, commonly below the dew point.

weather travels from west to east in the United States, a front with the cold mass to the west and a warm mass to the east is a cold front, and one with the cold mass to the east and a warm mass to the west is a warm front. If one front overtakes another, bringing three air masses close together, an occluded front results. The middle air mass is warmer than the other two, and so is lifted above the cooler masses.

Cyclones and Anticyclones

Within the belt of the westerlies large pressure systems are constantly developing as a result of the meeting of air masses having widely different characteristics of temperature, density, and moisture content. These systems vary from nearly circular to elliptical in shape, and are several hundred to a thousand or more

miles long. They are the cyclones (lows) and anticyclones (highs) that are seen on every weather map of the United States. The lows are great low-pressure centers into which the air from surrounding regions of higher pressure spirals and moves upward. The spiraling is to the right in accordance with Ferrel's law (Fig. 33-5a). The essential condition for such a low seems to be the presence of two air masses adjacent to each other, with markedly different temperatures and humidities, and moving in different directions. A "kink" in the front may be caused by a number of things, for example, the topography. Once started, it may develop into a cyclone.

Anticyclones also start as "kinks" in fronts. They are huge centers of high pressure in which cooler descending air spreads out near the surface of the earth in all directions. In the United States and Canada they have their beginnings in surges or wedges of cold air moving southward from polar regions. They commonly develop along with the lows when these wedges encounter a warmer air mass.

Cyclones and anticyclones travel a generally easterly course across the United States, often following one after the other, especially in winter. So numerous are they that they form the main flow of the westerlies across the United States. They are like the eddies in a turbulent stream. The speed with which they move is highly variable but 600 mi a day is a fair average.

Modern Views on the Planetary Circulation of the Atmosphere. If the earth were all water or all land of uniform topography and not rotating, the circulation of the atmosphere would be simple. Warm air rising at the equator would drift poleward at high altitudes, descend in the polar regions and move along the surface towards the equator. This would be a simple one-cell system. The rotation of the earth, combined with the distribution of land and sea, with most of the land in the northern hemisphere, breaks this idealized system up into a system so complicated that it is not yet completely understood.

Until World War II it was believed that the circulation consisted of a three-cell system in each hemisphere. The equatorial low, northeast trades, subtropical high, belt of the westerlies, polar easterlies, and polar high formed the primary wind system in the northern hemisphere. The cyclonic and anticyclonic circulation was designated a secondary system superimposed upon the primary system, and almost entirely confined to the belt of the westerlies.

Research during and since World War II has destroyed this reasonably simple model, chiefly by giving us more information about air movements at high elevations. The winds at high altitudes that were thought to blow in directions opposite to those on the surface in

order to complete the circulation were found to be weak or absent. The cyclonic and anticyclonic circulation is now assigned a major role in the belt of the westerlies. The jet stream at high elevations in this belt flows at high speeds (up to 300 mi/hr) in the same easterly direction as do the westerlies. Much research needs to be done, and more data need to be accumulated, before present ideas are sorted out, evaluated, and classified.

Precipitation and Humidity

Included under precipitation are rain, snow, hail, and sleet; included under humidity are atmospheric moisture, clouds, fog, and dew. The amount of rainfall per year varies from 450 in. or more in Assam province, India, to less than $\frac{1}{2}$ in. in the Atacama Desert of northern Chile. The amount of moisture that air can contain in the form of water vapor is dependent on the temperature; warm air can hold far more than cold. The ratio between the actual amount of moisture in the air and the amount that it can hold at a given temperature is called relative humidity. Thus, the relative humidity is said to be 50% if the air contains just half the moisture that it is capable of holding at that temperature. If the temperature drops and the total amount of moisture in the atmosphere remains the same, the relative humidity increases. The temperature at which the relative humidity reaches 100% is called the *dew point*. Further cooling results in precipitation. Since grass, leaves, and so forth cool off at night more rapidly than the atmosphere, the air in contact with them may be at the dew point while the air elsewhere is well above it. Dew therefore is precipitated on them.

It follows that in order to produce significant precipitation of any kind, a large air mass must be cooled below the dew point. There is only one way a large air mass can be sufficiently cooled and that is to cause it to rise to a higher altitude. There are three ways by which air masses can be forced to rise to higher altitudes; each gives rise to a particular type of precipitation, as follows:

Convectional Precipitation. Air warmed to a higher temperature than the surrounding air rises more or less vertically. As it rises, it expands and is cooled. How much cooling must take place depends upon the amount of moisture in the air and its original temperature. Large patches of plowed land or other bare ground or great stretches of concrete, brick, and stone heat up faster than green fields and woodlands. The air above them is warmed more than the air above adjacent areas. It is, therefore, less dense and so rises; cooler air from the adjacent regions moves in, is in turn warmed, and so rises. A vertical current of air is thus set up. If the rising air is cooled below the dew point, precipitation occurs. This type of precipitation is at a maximum in the equatorial low (doldrums). It is also the type that gives us our summer thunderstorms.

Orographic Precipitation. A moving air mass will be forced to rise if it encounters a mountain range or other high area in its path. As it rises, it expands and is cooled, possibly below the dew point. If so, the resulting precipitation is termed *orographic,* which means "related to mountains."

After crossing the mountains the winds descend and are warmed. This increases the capacity of the air to hold moisture. Thus, the areas on the leeward sides of mountain ranges are commonly desert areas if the mountains are high enough. A fine example is that furnished by winds from the Pacific crossing the Sierra Nevada range along the California-Nevada boundary. In the central and northern parts of California, heavy rainfall is experienced on the western slopes of the mountains, whereas the Nevada side of the range is dry.

In its general character much orographic rainfall is like that of the convectional type. The moisture-carrying trade winds do not bring rain unless mountain ranges lie across their paths, because they are blowing from cooler regions to warmer regions; that is, they are blowing toward the equator. The same is true of the summer monsoons in southern and southeast Asia. They blow from the cooler ocean toward the warmer land, yet the heaviest rainfall anywhere in the world results when the monsoons rise to cross the towering Himalaya Range.

Cyclonic and Frontal Rain. We have already discussed cyclones and fronts. In a warm front the advancing warm air rises along a gently inclined slope of a wedge of cold air. Cooling by expansion takes place slowly. If the warm air is dry, little or no precipitation may result. Most generally the warm air is moist so there is rain ahead of the advancing front. When the front passes, the weather generally clears, partly at least, and commonly there is a rise in temperature.

In a cold front warm air is being replaced by an advancing wedge of cold air, which pushes in beneath the warm air. Thus, the slope of the boundary surface between the two air masses is backward instead of forward as in a warm front; it is also steeper. Most of the rain falls along the front or close to it in a zone that is much narrower than that in a warm front. After the front has passed, the weather clears, and there is usually a sharp drop in the temperature. The winds commonly change from southwesterly to northwesterly.

As we have already learned, cyclones develop along fronts. In them the air at the center is rising, expanding, and being cooled. If cooled below the dew point, cyclonic rain falls. Since fronts and cyclones are so intimately related, it is difficult for us to make any distinction between cyclonic and frontal rainfall.

Most of the rainfall in the United States, except that in the summer months, is cyclonic or frontal.

Hurricanes and typhoons are violent tropical cyclones of comparatively small area. They originate over the oceans along the boundaries between the equatorial low and the trade winds. Tornadoes are the most violent of all storms; winds within the funnel cloud may reach 500 mi/hr, whereas the tornado as a whole may travel less than 40 mi/hr. Inside the funnel the air pressure is so low that houses in the tornado's path explode from the pressure of expanding air within them. Tornadoes are miniature storms, rarely much more than one quarter of a mile wide, and never lasting more than an hour; most last only a few minutes.

They commonly occur along cold fronts. They are also confined very largely to the United States, almost all of them forming east of the Rockies.

In all violent storms a great deal of energy is expended. What is the source of this energy? If we remember that about 540 cal of heat are absorbed in evaporating 1 g of water, and that this energy is released when condensation takes place, it is easy to account for the enormous amounts of energy expended during a violent storm.

"Migration" of the Sun

One of the *apparent* motions of the sun is a northward advance from December 22 to June 21 and a southward advance from June 21 to December 22. Since solar energy is responsible for varying weather and climate, and the distribution of this energy is profoundly affected by the apparent migration of the sun, the temperature, pressure, wind, and rainfall belts migrate with the sun. The boundaries between these belts shift northward in the northern summer and southward in the north-

ern winter. Regions that have alternating wet and dry seasons are located such that these shifting boundary lines cross them. Thus, southern California and the Middle East lie in the dry subtropical belt during the summer and in the more humid belt of the westerlies during a part of the winter.

Ocean Currents

A great ocean current like the North Atlantic Drift (Gulf Stream) is set in motion by winds blowing in a constant direction. Once well developed it has an enormous momentum that may carry it across wind belts where the winds are not favorable. The courses of ocean currents are affected by the configurations of continents. The currents are great distributors of heat, some carrying warm waters far to the north, some bringing cold waters down from the north. Europe, for example, is largely farther north than the United States, but much of it has average temperatures far above those of the corresponding latitudes in the United States because of the Gulf Stream.

Exercises

1. Why should the amount of solar radiation (insolation) received per unit area per unit time be so much greater at your latitude than it is at the North Pole on June 21?
2. What are the two great climatic functions of the winds?
3. Suppose the earth rotated once on its axis in one of our months.
   (a) What do you think the climate would be like in your area?
   (b) What effect would this have on life?
4. (a) Distinguish between stratosphere, troposphere, and ionosphere.
   (b) What is the importance of the ionosphere?

5. List the elements of weather and climate.
6. What two factors govern the amount of solar energy received at any one place at any one time?
7. (a) What two constituents of the atmosphere are the best absorbers of heat?
   (b) Relate this fact to the rapid cooling of desert areas after sundown.
8. Is the atmosphere heated directly by the sun? Explain.
9. Water surfaces heat up more slowly and cool off more slowly than land surfaces. Why?
10. What is the fundamental cause of differences in air pressure in different areas?
11. Warm air tends to produce low pressure and cold air to produce high pressure. Explain.
12. What is the chief movement of air (a) in the doldrums, (b) the more remote cause?
13. What is (a) the immediate cause of winds and, (b) the more remote cause?
14. (a) Describe the trade winds.
    (b) Where do they have their origin?
    (c) What happens to the air that forms them?
15. What is Ferrel's law as applied to winds?
16. What is the origin of the westerlies? Compare them with the trade winds.
17. What is (a) an air mass, (b) a front?
18. Distinguish between a warm front and a cold front.
19. Compare cyclones and anticyclones with respect to air pressure, directions of air movement, temperature, and likelihood of bringing rain.

20. It is commonly said that an easterly (northeast, east, southeast) wind brings rain in eastern and northeastern United States. Where is the storm center with respect to an area where such rain is falling, and in what general direction is it traveling?
21. In the Northeastern quarter of the United States the center of a cyclonic low passes to the south of you. If it is winter, you will probably receive snow, whereas if the center passed to the north of you, you would probably receive rain. Explain.
22. (a) What is relative humidity?
    (b) Is it directly or inversely proportional to the temperature?
    (c) What is the dew point?
23. Explain the three types of rainfall. What areas in the United States experience each?
24. The great deserts of the world lie in the horse latitudes and the northern part of the trade wind belts that lie just to the south of them. Explain.
25. Many believe that if the Gulf Stream shifted its course somewhat farther north in the western Atlantic the coastal climate of northeastern United States would be warmer. It is doubtful that there would be much temperature difference, but it is reasonably certain that the east coast would experience stormier weather and more snow in the winter. Explain. (Hint: The northeastern part of the United States lies in the belt of the westerlies.)

Natural Large-Scale Energy Transformations: Weathering and Erosion

34

Nothing is constant but change.
ANON

The processes of gradation are generally opposed to the processes of volcanism and diastrophism. For purposes of convenience we may call the latter two constructional processes. Their net effect is to change the elevation of the lands with respect to the seas, to fold the enormous thicknesses of sedimentary rock strata that have been deposited in shallow troughs (Fig. 32-14) into great mountain ranges, and to elevate other areas by vertical uplift or by block faulting into plains and plateaus and fault block mountains, some of which are at present a mile or two or even more above sea level. Other areas have been downwarped or down faulted below sea level but at present the effects of elevation are far more extensive and impressive than those of subsidence.

The net effects of gradation are ultimately to reduce these elevated land areas to surfaces of low relief. The gradational processes, which for convenience we may call destructional forces, begin long before the constructional forces have come to a halt; in fact, they begin as soon as an area is uplifted an appreciable

596

distance above sea level, and they never cease until the area is reduced to near sea level again. Mountains therefore never reach their greatest potential height, for much erosion has taken place to reduce them before the mountain-building forces have completed their work.

The whole of geologic time has been a constant "struggle" between the constructional and the destructional forces. For long periods of geologic time the constructional processes have been dominant so that mountains were formed and the continents elevated, giving the lands a considerable relief. For other long periods of time the destructional processes have been dominant, with the result that the highlands have been brought low. Intermittent briefer periods of uplift may have delayed the processes of degradation, but there have been times when whole continents were reduced to near base level (defined as the lowest level to which a stream can erode its channel). The earth has just passed through a great period of mountain-building, a period that is not yet ended. The result is that the earth is now in an exceptional stage of its history; the continents are abnormally large and at a higher average elevation than usual; the highland areas are larger and the mountains more lofty and rugged; the climate is more varied. The landscape is therefore more variegated and the scenery grander than for the average of geologic time.

All in all we are living in an unusually interesting period of the earth's long history. The conclusion that the constructive processes have not yet died down is warranted by the great number of volcanoes that are still active, by the enormous number of earthquakes each year, and by the number of areas where elevation or subsidence are still taking place.

The agents of gradation may be divided into two groups according to whether the role they play is an active or a passive one. The passive (or static) agents are the atmosphere—oxygen, carbon dioxide, and water vapor—freezing waters, roots of trees, organic acids, and gravity. We might also add to this list that part of the rain or snow which acts as a wetting agent, keeping the soil and rocks moist to greatly varying distances below the surface and hence more susceptible to chemical change. The active (or dynamic) agents are groundwater, streams, glaciers, ocean waves, and longshore currents and the wind.

Energy Sources and Transformations

Solar radiation creates all these agents except gravity, either directly or indirectly. The action of the atmospheric agents, oxygen, carbon dioxide, and water vapor, and the action of the organic acids formed by decay of once-living organisms, are chemical in nature. Heat speeds them up; on a sunless earth chemical activity would be at a standstill. There would be ice but no freezing of water, and there would be no roots of trees.

All the active agents are dependent on wind; none could exist in a windless world. Streams, glaciers, and groundwater obtain the water or snow that forms them from water evaporated from the oceans by solar energy. Winds and air currents are needed to carry this water vapor to high altitudes and over the lands, where it may fall as rain or snow. Most water that falls as snow is melted by solar energy; that which is not becomes glaciers, which move to lower altitudes or latitudes where they are eventually melted by solar energy.

Once the rain falls on the earth its further movement is governed by a number of factors. Some is evaporated and returned to the atmosphere, the percentage depending on the temperature and humidity. Some soaks into the soil and is absorbed by the roots of plants, which either use it in photosynthesis or transpire it back into the atmosphere. Some is carried on down to a zone where the rocks and soil are saturated, to become a part of the groundwater. The percentage that becomes groundwater is controlled by the slope of the land, the amount and kind of vegetation (which acts as a sponge to soak up water), and by the porosity and permeability of the soil and rocks. In a flat country all of the water is disposed of in one or the other of the last two ways.

Where there are slopes there is some run-off into the lower places to form streams. The steeper the slopes, the greater the percentage of run-off. The energy of streams is both kinetic and potential; the higher above sea level, the greater the potential energy, and the steeper the slopes the greater the kinetic energy at any one point. The kinetic energy reaches a maximum in waterfalls. It is the kinetic energy of winds and air currents, derived from solar energy, that carries the water vapor to high elevations, thus giving it potential energy. Once the vapor condenses, the force of gravity takes over, and under this influence much of the water finds its way back to the sea whence it came.

Ocean waves and longshore currents are both caused by winds. Winds do some gradational work of their own directly, but their indirect effects are vastly more important. It is apparent that almost all the energy of the gradational agents can be traced back through a series of transformations to solar energy. In this respect the gradational agents present a contrast to volcanism and diastrophism, both of which have their sources of energy within the earth.

Processes of Gradation

Gradation is essentially a leveling process. The leveling can be accomplished in two ways,

by removing material from the high places and by using it to fill in the low places. Removal from high places is called *degradation;* filling the low places is called *aggradation*. The gradational processes consist of weathering, masswasting, and erosion; the aggradational processes consist of deposition, sometimes, as we have seen, called sedimentation.

Weathering

Weathering consists of a complex set of passive processes by which rocks are disintegrated and decomposed. Weathering goes on all about us, affecting not only the works of nature but the works of man. The crumbling of buildings and their foundations, the rusting of bridges and all things made of iron or steel, the blurring of inscriptions on gravestones and monuments, and the heaps of boulders at the bases of cliffs, all attest to the slow but inexorable processes of disintegration and decomposition. The agents of weathering cannot be neatly and precisely enumerated. They have been listed in a preceding paragraph. The processes of weathering may be divided into two groups, disintegration by mechanical or physical means and decomposition by chemical means.

Chemical weathering is brought about by the processes of hydration, carbonation, and oxidation. Hydration, the union of water with other elements in the mineral, is most important, for neither oxidation nor carbonation can be effective without it. Through these processes new minerals are formed from the old; the new minerals are more stable than the old under the conditions that exist at the surface of the earth. Minerals that are already stable do not weather chemically. The chemical weathering of the feldspars has been discussed in Chapter 30. Chemical weathering is necessary for the production of soil (Fig. 34-1). Ground up unweathered igneous rock is not true soil.

Mechanical weathering consists of those processes that break up rock into smaller pieces without changing the composition. In temperate latitudes or at high elevations where there is considerable alternate freezing and thawing during the late fall, winter, and early spring this is best done by frost wedging. Rain water or water from melting snows fills the pores and crevices of rocks. When it freezes, it expands, exerting a wedging effect, which, on steep slopes or cliff faces, may cause blocks of rock of all sizes to loosen and roll down the slopes to form talus slopes (Figs. 34-2 and 34-3). Roots of trees, growing on such slopes, grow down into cracks and their roots help the wedging process along during the nonfreezing months.

The volume changes brought about by the chemical weathering of minerals also cause a

Fig. 34-2. Mechanical Weathering of Columnar Basalt, Devil's Post Pile, Sierra National Forest, California. The columnar structure results from jointing during contraction on cooling of a nearly horizontal igneous body. The mechanical weathering process is that of frost wedging. The pile of debris is called a talus. (U.S. Forest Service photo.)

wedging effect that pries mineral fragments loose. The volume changes are brought about by union of the minerals being weathered with atmospheric moisture, carbon dioxide, and oxygen. Since rock broken into smaller fragments exposes a larger surface area to the action of the atmosphere than do the larger fragments, mechanical weathering enables chemical weathering to proceed at a faster pace.

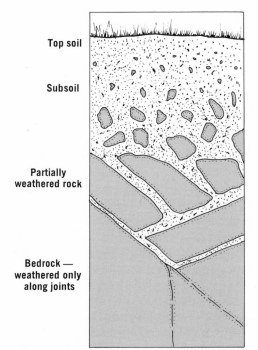

Top soil

Subsoil

Partially
weathered rock

Bedrock —
weathered only
along joints

Fig. 34-1. Residual Soil Profile. Residual soil is soil formed in place. The top soil consists of well-weathered rock, humus (partially decayed vegetable matter), and bacteria of many kinds. Soils in humid regions are normally thicker than in arid regions.

Masswasting

The term *masswasting* refers to the downslope movements of weathered rock debris under the influence of gravity alone. The en-

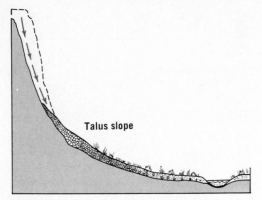

Fig. 34-3. Masswasting, the Downslope Movement of Weathered Material. Jointed blocks of rock, loosened by frost wedging and root wedging of trees, fall and accumulate in heaps near the bottom of the cliff, forming a talus composed of sliderock. From then on, chemical weathering and the slow downward creep of the weathered material, which is gradually becoming soil, dominate. Rainwash plays an important role in transporting the soil into the stream, which may carry it to the sea.

ergy transformations are from potential to kinetic to heat. The effects of masswasting are especially noticeable at the foot of cliffs or steep slopes where heaps of angular boulders of "sliderock" loosened from the cliff by frost or root wedging accumulate. This sliderock forms a talus slope. More important but far less obvious is the slow movement (*creep*) of soil formed by chemical weathering down slopes (Fig. 34-4), especially where the debris is subject to soaking rains followed by alternate freezing and thawing. The net effect of creep is to make the soil cover thinner on and near the tops of hills than it is farther downslope.

More spectacular but far less important are the landslides, in some of which millions of tons of rock and rock debris may move distances of a mile or more in a matter of seconds. They are largely confined to steep mountain regions. Masswasting of any type is obviously lacking in a level region. The net effect of masswasting is to reduce the land areas to

gentler slopes that are not strikingly higher than the level of the floor of the valley that lies at the foot of the slopes (Fig. 34-3). Much of the load of rock debris carried by streams is furnished by masswasting.

Groundwater

The only important source of groundwater is the rainwater or meltwater of snows that sink into the ground to fill the crevices and pore spaces in soil and rocks. The amount depends on a number of factors, such as the slope of the land, the amount and kind of vegetation the porosity and permeability of the soil and rocks, and how rapidly the rain falls. If there is sufficient rainfall, the water that soaks down through the soil and rocks reaches the water table (Fig. 34-5), which is the surface below which the soil and rocks are saturated. The depth to the water table increases or decreases with the amount of rainfall. If the water table is at the surface, a swamp develops.

The geologic work of groundwater is largely

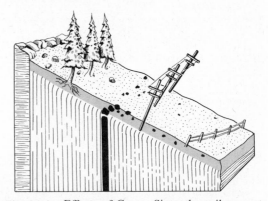

Fig. 34-4. Effects of Creep. Since the soil nearest the surface creeps faster than that at depth, trees, poles, and fence posts anchored in it are tilted downward. When the soil on such a surface is water-soaked and freezes at night, expansion takes place at right angles to the surface, not vertically upward. When melting takes place, the contraction is vertically downward. The result is that each particle moves a tiny bit farther downslope after each melting.

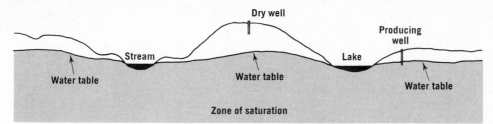

Fig. 34-5. The Water Table. The water table is the upper surface of the zone of saturation. This surface, misnamed a table, is a subdued replica of the land surface; that is, it rises and falls with the topography but not so greatly. To obtain water a well must be sunk below the water table in rock or sediments that are permeable to water. Note that the water table intersects the surface of all permanent streams and lakes. Therefore it is the source of most of their water.

Fig. 34-6. Sinkhole in Limestone. Groundwater, seeping along joints in the rock, slowly dissolved the calcium carbonate of which limestone is composed. Of the common rocks only limestone and marble are soluble enough for sinkholes to develop in them. (U.S. Geological Survey photo.)

confined (1) to carbonate rocks such as limestone and marble, and (2) to the solution of the soluble salts formed during the process of chemical weathering. Pure water is ineffective in dissolving the (calcium) carbonate rocks, but rain falling through the atmosphere dissolves some CO_2, forming a weak solution of H_2CO_3 (carbonic acid), which is effective. Almost all caverns and caves are formed by solution in limestones and marbles.

Sinkholes (Fig. 34-6) are extremely abundant in some limestone regions. Limestones and marbles were originally formed by precipitation from solution of the soluble products of weathering. The products, largely salts of various kinds, are carried by groundwater into streams; the streams carry them to the sea. This is the reason that the seas are salty. The Mississippi River alone carries nearly a quarter of a million tons of dissolved material down to the sea each year. Thus, the seas get a bit saltier each year.

Groundwater is of extreme importance to man, for without it few areas of the earth would be inhabitable. In large areas of the earth man is completely dependent on well water for his existence. In other areas he is dependent on streams and lakes for his fresh water, which, in their turn, are largely dependent on groundwater for their supply. The availability of fresh water for human and animal consumption has long been a limiting factor in population growth in many areas, and as the population increases, it is becoming an important factor almost everywhere. The possibility of ever desalting ocean waters at a cost that makes their use for purposes *other* than personal human consumption or in industry practicable is largely wishful thinking. The amount of water needed per acre for agricultural purposes even under highly controlled conditions is enormous. At $1.00 per 1000 gal at the plant, the cost per acre would range up to $100 or more. To the cost of desalting there

would have to be added the cost of distribution, which is always uphill from sea level. Moreover, the areas that need water for agricultural purposes are arid to semiarid and their water loss by evaporation is exceptionally high.

Stream Erosion

Streams are the chief means of returning the water evaporated from the ocean, which falls on the land, back to the ocean again. The energy of a stream is both potential and kinetic. As it flows, potential energy is converted into kinetic, and kinetic energy is converted partly into work as rock debris is transported

Fig. 34-7. Gully Development on Grassy Slope in California. This tributary to some larger stream is slowly extending itself up the slope. It is also being widened and deepened. There is water in its channel only during, and a short time after, a rain. When the channel has been cut below the water table, it will be a permanent stream. (U.S. Geological Survey photo.)

downstream, and partly into heat. Man uses the energy of running water for transportation and for generating hydroelectric power.

The erosional work of a stream consists of the removal of rock debris, the transportation of this load downstream, and its ultimate deposition, usually in deltas or on the continental shelf. The removal is accomplished in several ways, (1) by washing loose material away just as water from a hose can be used to remove a pile of sand from a sidewalk, (2) by abrasion, and (3) by solution. Most important in the early stages of a stream is abrasion. This is accomplished by the sand or pebbles striking against the bottom or sides of the channel. By such abrasive action the stream acts like a saw as it cuts its valley deeper and deeper (Figs. 34-7 and 34-8). The rapidity of the cutting depends on the volume of water, its velocity, the hardness of the rocks in which the valley is being cut, and the quantity and kind of sand by which the cutting is done. The sand acts

as a necessary tool, for water by itself can do no cutting. The faster the flow, the more rapid the cutting. Doubling the velocity not only doubles the number of particles of sand striking bedrock per unit of time, but causes them to strike twice as hard. Moreover, the water can carry not only more particles per unit volume, but larger particles as well. Since the velocity of a stream increases greatly with an increase in volume (due to heavy rains), it is no wonder that streams do most of their work during high-water stages.

As the stream cuts its valley deeper, it reduces its average gradient (slope measured in feet per mile), for streams in most regions cannot cut below sea level. In reality, they can reduce their channels to sea level only in their lower parts, for a stream must have a gradient, however gentle, down which to flow. The level below which a stream cannot cut is called base level. As a stream nears base level in its downcutting, it begins to swing more and more from

Fig. 34-8.   Gullying at Ducktown, Tennessee. The forest and vegetation cover has been destroyed by the sulfurous fumes of a nearby copper smelter. With nothing to anchor the soil in place, erosion has been rapid. Note the intricate system of branching gullies. (U.S. Geological Survey photo.)

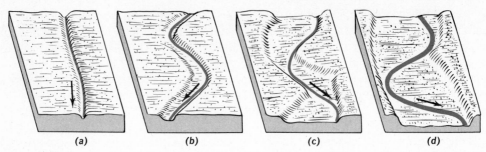

Fig. 34-9. Valley Development. The stages shown are (a) early youth, (b) late youth, (c) early maturity, and (d) full maturity. In early youth the stream valley is V-shaped, either straight or with irregular curves. Note that in (b), (c), and (d) the stream is eroding the valley walls on the outsides of the curves, which are slowly being transformed into sweeping meanders. By maturity the original narrow V-shaped valley has been altered to a wide flat-floored valley. (Modified from Longwell, Knopf, and Flint, *Physical Geology,* John Wiley and Sons, New York, 1939.)

side to side, thus widening its valley (Fig. 34-9), changing it from a V-shaped to a flat-floored valley that slowly gets wider and wider. In the process the stream itself accentuates any original irregular curves into smooth-swinging curves called meanders, thus increasing its own length (Fig. 34-10).

Meanwhile, the many tributaries and their subtributaries have been developing into a full-fledged drainage system. Weathering, mechanical and chemical, has been slowly going on in all of the interstream areas, and mass-wasting has been slowly moving the weathered debris down the slopes into countless rills and brooks and creeks, which carry it via the large tributaries into the master stream. The master

Fig. 34-10. Meanders in Trout Creek, Yellowstone National Park. One or the other of two cutoffs is imminent. (U.S. Geological Survey photo.)

Fig. 34-11. Uplifted Peneplain. Canyon de Chelly, New Mexico. The upper surface is the peneplain. Note the strata are inclined (dipping) to the right, and that the peneplain truncates their upturned edges. After peneplanation the area was uplifted, and a new cycle of erosion initiated. If the uplift had not occurred, the erosional effects seen in the foreground could not have occurred.

stream carries the load, most of it in suspension, down to its mouth and usually into the sea where it is deposited to form a delta, which is built out across the continental shelf. Ocean waves and currents may drift part of the mud and sand for many tens (and even hundreds) of miles, spreading them far and wide across the continental shelf. Thus, the continental shelves become the great repositories of the sediments eroded from the lands. The lands themselves become lowered, reduced eventually to a gently undulating surface called a peneplain (almost a plain). Here and there erosional remnants called monadnocks[1] may be left standing well above the surrounding region, either because they are of harder rock, or because there always has to be some last part to be removed.

[1] In dry regions where the rock layers are essentially horizontal, they are called mesas if flat-topped, or buttes if they are otherwise.

The time necessary to peneplain an area is highly variable, but it is always measured in millions, more commonly tens of millions, of years. Vulcanism and diastrophism may interrupt the process before it is complete, thus initiating a new cycle of erosion. Even if peneplaination is accomplished, diastrophism, possibly accompanied by vulcanism, eventually gets the upper hand and rejuvenates the streams by elevating and tilting the area. This has been done fairly recently, geologically speaking, and so there are no true peneplains anywhere at present (Fig. 34-11).

The rock debris that forms the load for streams is not transported downstream in one fell swoop, but is picked up and deposited, picked up again, and so on because the flow of the stream is turbulent. For a given velocity a stream can carry only so much of a load; any decrease in velocity will cause it to drop part of the load. The amount carried by large streams in time of high water is enormously greater than at low water. Fast-flowing streams may carry boulders a foot or more in diameter, and they may roll boulders several feet in diameter along their bottoms. Blocks of concrete from broken dams, weighing thousands of tons, have been carried a mile or two downstream.

Any decrease in velocity causes a fully loaded stream to deposit. A heavily loaded stream coming down out of mountains where the gradient is steep onto a more level area at the foot of the mountain will have its velocity suddenly checked by the abrupt change in gradient causing the stream to dump most of its load, filling up the channel. It then spills over, forms a new channel, fills it up, and repeats the process over and over again. Thus a fan-shaped deposit is built up, called an alluvial[2] fan (Fig. 34-12), which is sometimes likened to a delta built on land. As the mountains will in time be lowered by the processes of gradation, fan-building will also cease. Eventually the fan will itself be removed, as all of the rock and rock debris that lie above base level are removed to a more or less final resting place in the delta at the mouth of the stream or elsewhere on the continental shelf.

Glaciers

For a glacier to form, all that is needed is to have more snow fall in winter than can possibly melt in summer over a long enough period of time. Glaciers can even exist in equatorial regions if the mountains are high enough. The residue accumulated over the years becomes packed and otherwise transformed into ice. When the accumulation is big enough it will start to move under its own weight. If the region of accumulation is at the

---

[2]Alluvium is a general name for stream deposits of any kind.

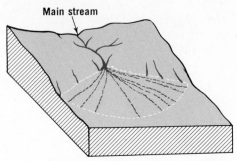

Main stream

Fig. 34-12.   Alluvial Fan. The steep gradient of a mountain stream is abruptly reduced as it leaves the mountain. As a result its velocity, and hence its transporting ability, is greatly diminished. It cannot carry all of its load; it drops some, filling up its channel, and swings over into a new one. Swinging back and forth from one mountain wall to the other builds up the deposit in the shape of a fan. The fan consists of gravel (closer to the mountains), sand, and clay (farther out).

heads of mountain valleys (Fig. 34-13), glaciers of the alpine type (also called mountain glaciers or valley glaciers) will move down the valley until the rate of melting of the ice front equals the rate of advance. Such valleys were originally made by streams while the mountains are being uplifted. The glacier transforms them from V-shaped to U-shaped valleys (Fig. 34-14), straightens them out, and otherwise alters them in a characteristic manner, so much so that after the glaciers have disappeared the region bears the unmistakable marks of glaciation for tens of thousands of years.

If the region of accumulation is not in the mountains but, say, in a relatively level area of some tens of thousands of square miles in extent, the ice will eventually spread out in all directions under its own weight. The great ice sheets of the Pleistocene epoch, the last of which disappeared from the United States less than 12,000 years ago, did just this. Accumulating in the area a bit south of the Arctic Circle, these great sheets, a mile or two thick, moved north, south, east, and west. The

Fig. 34-13. Birthplace of Alpine Glaciers. The snow accumulates high up in the mountains, avalanching from the higher slopes down into the heads of the valleys. Much of it is transformed into ice. If more snow falls every winter than can melt in the summer, it accumulates until the whole mass begins to move under its own weight. Note the rock debris formed by frost wedging. (U.S. Geological Survey photo.)

Fig. 34-14. U-Shaped Valley, Wasatch National Forest, Utah. Valleys of this shape are never formed by streams. This was once a V-shaped stream valley that was remodeled into a U shape during the last ice age. Glaciers do not originate their own valleys. (U.S. Forest Service photo.)

scratches (glacial striae) left on the bedrock they passed over attest to these directions of movement. They moved down into northern United States, reaching New York City in the East, and the Ohio and Missouri rivers to the Midwest. The mountain glaciers of Glacier National Park (Montana), of Mt. Rainier, Mt. Baker, Mt. Shasta, and others are shrinking remnants of this last ice age.

Glacial erosion is accomplished chiefly by the great weight of the ice pressing down on the boulders and pebbles that it is dragging

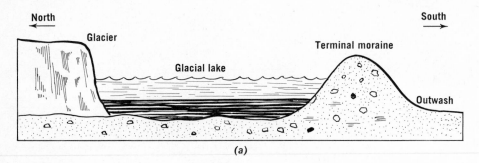

(a)

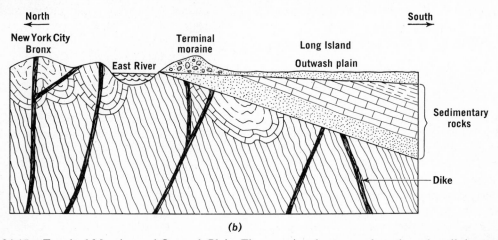

(b)

Fig. 34-15. Terminal Moraine and Outwash Plain. The great ice sheet moved southward until the rate of melting of the ice front equaled the rate of advance. The glacier was then *apparently* motionless but its movement dragged debris along the bottom, piling it up in the form of a ridge (terminal moraine) paralleling the ice front. The moraine is composed of glacial till. It consists of boulders, gravel, sand, and clay, unsorted and unstratified. (*a*) Eventually the rate of melting exceeded the rate of advance and the glacier began an apparent retreat. A glacial lake developed between the ice front and the terminal moraine. When melting was rapid, the lake overflowed in countless places, washing the finer debris (mostly sand and clay) out, depositing it far and wide beyond the moraine. Thus an outwash plain is built. (*b*) The terminal moraine (in New York City and vicinity) accounts for the hilly character of northern Long Island, and the outwash plain for the flat terrain of southern Long Island. Beneath these glacial deposits lie sedimentary rocks that are missing in Manhattan and the Bronx. Beneath the sedimentary rocks, however, are the same metamorphic rocks (gneiss, marble, schist) that form the foundation rocks of Manhattan and the Bronx. Countless coarse-grained granite dikes (pegmatite dikes) intrude them.

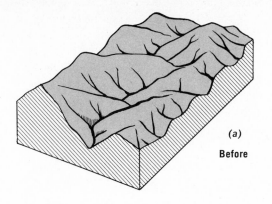

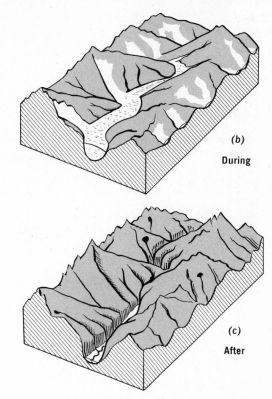

Fig. 34-16. Before, During, and After Alpine Glaciation. Compare the more rounded topography resulting from stream erosion in (*a*) with the highly angular topography resulting from glacial erosion in (*c*). Note also the change in the main valley from V-shaped to U-shaped.

along beneath it as it very slowly advances. These boulders and pebbles are ground to pieces, to fine rock flour as in a great grinding mill; new ones are being constantly picked up as the glacier moves forward like a giant bulldozer. We have said that a glacier's farthest line of advance will be located where the rate of the melting back of the ice front equals the rate of advance. It is here that the terminal moraine is formed (Fig. 34-15), a great deposit of unsorted and unstratified boulders, pebbles, sand, and clay (called glacial till). The form is highly irregular but is generally ridgelike.

The terminal moraine of the last ice sheet can be traced from the eastern end of Long Island to the Rocky Mountains; stretches of it have been removed in places. The area to the north bears abundant evidences of glaciation, that to the south, none. Glaciers of the

ice sheet type smooth out the topography by removing loosened material from the high places and depositing it in the low places. In doing so they form innumerable lake basins by irregular gouging and deposition. The vast majority of the lake basins of the world are glacial in origin. Alpine glaciers, on the other hand, make the topography more angular (Fig. 34-16); the result is some of the most spectacular scenery on earth.

Wind

As we have already stated, the climatic and indirect effects of the wind greatly exceed their direct geologic effects. There are few places in the world where wind erosion is more important than stream erosion. Essential conditions are a truly arid climate, strong winds, and a

Fig. 34-17. Crescent-Shaped Sand Dunes, Biggs, Oregon. Such dunes, called barchans, are formed in regions where the supply of sand is not too great and the wind is constant in direction. Here the wind was blowing from left to right. (U.S. Geological Survey photo.)

Fig. 34-18. Ancient Sand Dune Deposit, Utah. The sandstones that form the towering cliffs in Zion National Park were deposited as dunes by the wind 125 million years ago. Note the irregularity of the beds (cross-bedding), a characteristic of dune deposits. (U.S. Geological Survey photo.)

supply of hard sand grains, for example, quartz, to do the abrasive work. Because winds blow more sand along the ground than higher up, projecting pieces of rock get cut away at the bottom faster than higher up, producing erosional features that are called pedestal rocks.

In dry areas where the vegetation cover has been removed, the soil may be picked up and carried away, causing dust storms. This process is called deflation. The wind-blown hollows formed by it are called blowouts. Sand deposits made by the wind are called dunes. They may be crescent-shaped or irregular in form (Figs. 34-17 and 34-18). Dunes may be formed at times in humid climates if there is an abun-

dance of sand not anchored down by vegetation, as along some beaches.

Ocean Waves and Currents

Both ocean waves and currents are erosional agents caused by the wind. They are effective only along the edges of the lands, continents, or islands, or along the shores of very large lakes. Most of the erosional work of waves is accomplished during heavy storms (Fig. 34-19). Strong waves can pick up pebbles and boulders and throw them at cliffs. Gradually the cliffs are eroded back, the broken debris being broken further and ground finer until

Fig. 34-19. A Wave-Cut Cliff and Sea Arch Carved in Sandstone Along the Oregon Coast. (Oregon State Highway Department photo.)

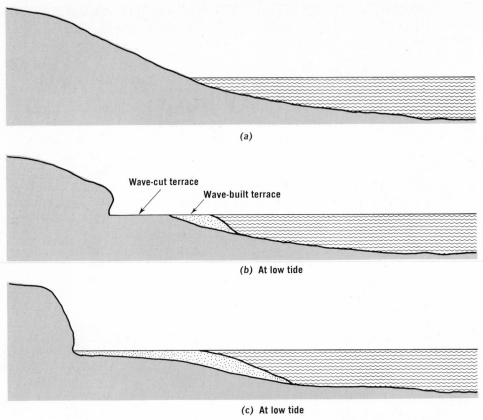

(a)

(b) At low tide

(c) At low tide

Fig. 34-20. Wave Erosion. (*a*) Hypothetical newly submerged area in which no wave erosion has yet taken place. (*b*) The waves have cut the land back, forming a wave-cut cliff and a wave-cut terrace. The wave-built terrace consists of the debris removed to form the cliff and the wave-cut terrace. (*c*) A later stage. As the cliff is cut back farther and farther, the waves lose more and more energy as they drag over the long terrace, thus reducing the rate of cutting.

the outgoing undertow (return current) can carry it farther out to sea, where it is eventually dropped into water too deep for waves to disturb it (Fig. 34-20). The chalk cliffs of Dover have been eroded back more than two miles since the time of the Norman conquest in 1066.

Winds blowing at an angle to the shore set up currents that run parallel to the shore but some little distance from it. These are the longshore currents. They drift sand along the bottom, often piling it up in submarine bars across the mouths of bays. In time of storm the submarine bar may be built up above normal sea level. It is then called a spit. Some well-known spits along the Atlantic Coast are Sandy Hook (across the mouth of New York Bay), Rockaway spit (across Jamaica Bay, Fig. 34-21), and Cape Cod. To protect these spits from destruction by the agent that built them, man builds jetties at right angles to the shore. They keep the longshore currents away from the shore.

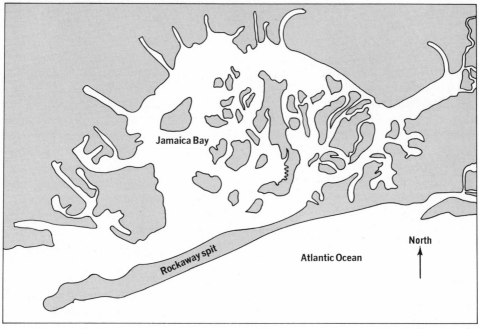

Fig. 34-21. Spit Formation. Longshore currents from the right drifted sand across the mouth of the bay building at first a submarine bar, which later, in time of storm, was built up above sea level. This particular spit is the Rockaway spit in south Brooklyn and Queens, New York City. The bay is Jamaica Bay. Man-made features have been largely eliminated.

Exercises

1. Mountain ranges never reach their greatest potential height. Why?
2. Distinguish (a) between an agent and a process of gradation, (b) between a depositional feature and an erosional feature.
3. Classify each of the following as agent, process, erosional feature, or depositional feature. For each state the particular agent and the particular process.

atmospheric moisture	valley
hydration	creep
masswasting	frost wedging
talus	fan
delta	peneplain
canyon	monadnock
sinkhole	striae

dune	abrasion
longshore current	deflation
moraine	spit
decomposition	disintegration

4. If the agents of gradation are effective in reducing the lands, and the earth is so old, why is the whole earth not a peneplain?
5. Trace *all* of the energy transformations that result in a delta being formed by a stream.
6. A dark-colored feldspar in an igneous rock contains some calcium and oxygen, among other things. Eventually some of these two elements end up as $CaCO_3$ (calcium carbonate) in the ocean waters. List the intervening events.
7. Distinguish carefully between mechanical and chemical weathering.

8. Quartz does not weather chemically. Neither does the mineral calcite. Why?

9. (a) What is a talus?
   (b) How is it produced?

10. In humid climates the slopes of hills are more rounded (less angular) than they are in dry climates. Moreover, bedrock is less likely to be exposed in the lower half of the hills. Explain.

11. How deep (not in feet) must a well be to furnish a steady supply of water?

12. The greatest of all water reservoirs on the lands is the soil and rocks of the earth's outer crust. Explain.

13. In a region where there is plenty of rainfall what would determine the lower limit of the water table?

14. (a) Mammoth Cave in Kentucky was carved by what agent?
    (b) In what kind of rock? Why not some other kind?

15. List three ways by which a stream erodes. Which is most important where the channel is cut in bedrock?

16. Through one 5-mi section of the Grand Canyon the Colorado River drops about 62.5 ft. What is its average gradient?

17. How are stream valleys widened (a) at the bottom, (b) at the top?

18. Most streams in humid climates keep flowing steadily even though it may not have rained for a month or two. Where do they get their supply of water?

19. (a) How does a stream carry most of its load?
    (b) What causes a stream to deposit?

20. (a) How and where is an alluvial fan built?
    (b) A delta?

21. Ice is a soft mineral, softer than most rock minerals, yet a glacier erodes the bedrock beneath it. How?

22. Alpine glaciers never originate new valleys; they only remodel pre-existing valleys. Explain.

23. When a geologist sees a deposit made directly by a glacier, he need rarely ask, "Could some other agent have made it?" Why is this so?

24. Of what sorts of materials are terminal moraines made?

25. How do glaciers form lake basins?

26. Northern New Jersey was glaciated by a great ice sheet but southern New Jersey was not. List as many pieces of evidence as you can that would tend to prove this statement.

27. The indirect erosional effects of the winds are vastly more important than their direct erosional effects. Explain.

28. (a) By what two methods do winds erode?
    (b) Name one erosional feature produced by each method.

29. Explain how a spit is formed.

30. The earth is more than 3 billion years old, yet it is highly unlikely that any river flowing today is much more than 60 to 70 million years old, and most are much less than that. Explain.

31. (a) How are ocean waves formed?
    (b) Longshore currents?

32. The presence of true soils on the moon would imply what?

The Search for the Past

It is easy to see that the science of geology as we have dealt with it so far, is to a large degree the application of the principles of physics and chemistry. The study of rocks and minerals is almost exclusively a study of the principles of chemistry. The study of the interior of the earth and the three fundamental processes acting to alter the face of the earth involves many of the principles of physics. It is only the application that is different.

That part of historical geology that deals with paleontology, the science of ancient life, depends in large part upon the science of biology, for anyone who wishes to make a detailed study of the life of the past must first study the life of the present. Geology, however, is not entirely the application of the principles of other sciences, for none of them attempts to decipher past events. The geologist is concerned with questions that the physicist, the chemist, and the biologist would not think of asking unless he was consciously trying to be a geologist also.

Consider a mountain range. The chemist would be concerned with the composition of

False facts are highly injurious to the progress of science, for they often endure long; but false views, if supported by some evidence, do little harm, for everyone takes a salutary pleasure in proving their falseness; and when this is done, one path toward error is closed and the road to truth is often at the same time opened.
CHARLES DARWIN

the minerals that form the rocks, their origin, and so on. The physicist would be concerned with the forces that caused the mountain range to be formed, the conditions at depth that would allow such a range to stand so high above the surrounding region, and similar problems. The biologist and/or the paleontologist would be concerned chiefly about the fossils the strata contained. The geologist, however, would be concerned not only with all of these problems, but with many others such as these: Why are many mountain ranges composed of sedimentary rocks on their flanks with igneous rocks in their cores? What sequence of events preceding the making of the mountain range allowed the enormous thicknesses of both continental and marine sediments that form the mountains to be deposited? What sequence of events followed the making of the mountains that allowed the individual ridges always to be composed of resistant rock and the intervening valleys of weaker rock? And many more.

These questions involve the methods and principles of the search for the past, a search that we more formally call historical geology. Because the pages that we can devote to it are few, we will confine our discussion to some of these methods and principles rather than to the facts of historical geology. The problem of accumulating the facts and arranging them in a proper time sequence are many and complex.

The Age of the Earth

The earth is unimaginably old, more than four billion years. The method of dating it is such that the best geologists can do is to determine the minimum age, not the maximum age. To understand the method one needs to know something about radioactivity. Since this subject is discussed at some length

in Chapter 36, the discussion of the method will be postponed until then.

Fossils tell us nothing about the absolute ages of rock formations except that the earth is a great deal older than we once thought it was. Fossils do tell us, however, a great deal about the relative ages of rock formations; they can tell us that one formation is older or younger than another. The problem will be understood better after the law of organic correlation has been studied. The history of man, civilized and uncivilized, becomes more fragmentary and dimmer and dimmer the farther back we go in time, until we lose all trace of him except for the fossils of his distant ancestors. In the same manner, the history of the earth becomes dimmer and more fragmentary until we have little or no record of its first billion years.

Think of a book originally having at least 4000 pages, with a million years of earth history recorded on each page. For the first 2000 pages there is not a single complete page. Moreover, all of the earlier chapters have been forever destroyed. It is not until we reach the last eighth of the book that we begin to have complete chapters, but even there many of the pages are fragmentary and some are missing. We might more properly say that all the pages are fragmentary, but that their fragments have been scattered over the earth, some forever destroyed, some still in existence although still undiscovered. The great majority of these later pages have been discovered and pieced together to give us a reasonably coherent history of the last one sixth of geologic time.

It is the problem of the trained geologist to collect the missing fragments for each region if they are still in existence and, if not, to try to reconstruct as best he can the record of the missing parts from the evidence he has and from that of neighboring regions. Considerable amounts of the missing records now lie buried beneath younger sediments, either in our plains and plateaus where the strata are horizontal, or beneath younger strata on the continental shelves.

Orderly Sequence of Deposition

We might very well ask how so much of the record came to be destroyed. Before answering, we might better ask what the record consists of. Suppose that two billion years ago the area now occupied by North America consisted of two great highland areas, one in the east and one in the west with a great lowland area in between. Suppose also that this lowland area consisted of a great central shallow seaway with a broad comparatively lowland area on each side between it and the highland areas. Streams flowed down from the highlands and into the sea, carrying with them the products of weathering and erosion and depositing them. To keep pace with the filling, let the floor of the seaway slowly sink, not so much because of the weight of the sediments but because of the action of the forces that caused the basin in the first place. Let uplift of the highland area keep pace with erosion, and let us assume that once sediments were deposited they remained uneroded to the present day.

Assume that life evolved in the sea, first plants, then simple marine invertebrates, then more complex invertebrates, and finally finned vertebrates. Let these be followed by plant life on the land and land-dwelling invertebrates. Eventually come the land-dwelling vertebrates, first the amphibians, then the reptiles, and then the birds and the mammals almost together (see Fig. 35-1). In all cases the remains of the hard parts of many of these plants and animals would be preserved in the sediments. Quick burial by fine-grained sediments after death would preserve some of each group. If this situation existed, the sediments would contain a reasonably complete record not only of their own history but much of that of the highland areas that supplied the sediment. Entombed in the sediments would be a complete record of the evolution of life. Since sedimentation was continuous, with no erosion of the sediments, there would be no gaps in the record. Our only problem would be to get at the record, for there would be many tens of thousands of feet of sediments, all more or less in horizontal layers.

If this seaway prevailed today and we were here to contemplate it, we would actually know less than we do about the history of the earth, for most of it would be unavailable. But the record would still be there, fully preserved instead of fragmentary; there would be no gaps in the orderly sequence of deposition.

From this hypothetical situation we should gain some understanding of what the record of earth history consists of and how it is preserved. Such a record would be complete as far as life is concerned, but the igneous and metamorphic history would be incomplete. There is no hypothetical picture that we can think of that would allow all phases of earth history to be preserved, because you cannot have sediments deposited without erosion, and you cannot have erosion without some destruction of the record.

Availability of the Geologic Record

In fact, diastrophism followed by erosion is responsible for the availability of much of the geologic record. Consider the Grand Canyon area (Fig. 35-2). The rocks exposed at the surface on the north side of the canyons are limestones containing fossils of marine animals. They are now a mile and a half above sea level. Other rock formations once above them have been removed by erosion. The

Era	Period	Type of life	Approximate length of each interval (millions of years)
Cenozoic	Quaternary* Recent Pleistocene	Invertebrates, fishes, amphibians, reptiles, birds, mammals (including man)	2.5+
	Tertiary* Pliocene Miocene Oligocene Eocene Paleocene	Invertebrates, fishes, amphibians, reptiles, birds, modernized mammals (except man)	63
Mesozoic	Cretaceous	Invertebrates, fishes, amphibians, reptiles, birds, "archaic" mammals	71
	Jurassic	Invertebrates, fishes, amphibians, reptiles, primitive mammals	54
	Triassic	Invertebrates, fishes, amphibians, primitive reptiles	35
Paleozoic	Permian		55
	Pennsylvanian		45
	Mississippian	Invertebrates, fishes, primitive land-dwelling vertebrates (the amphibians)	20
	Devonian		50
	Silurian	Invertebrates, primitive vertebrates (the fishes)	35
	Ordovician		70
	Cambrian	Marine invertebrates	70
Precambrian eras		No certain fossil record of animal life	4030

*The Quaternary and Tertiary periods are further divided into epochs.

Fig. 35-1. The Geologic Time Scale. The order of succession of animal life is based on fossil evidence. Note that the total time shown in more than 4 billion years.

forces of diastrophism elevated these limestones (and all the associated rocks) at least a mile and a half. Yet these limestones would not now be exposed to man's observations if erosion had not removed the overlying rocks, and the rocks below the limestones would be hidden if the Colorado River had not cut a deep canyon into them.

Thus, streams cutting their valleys into rocks expose them to our view. Still, deep valleys like the Grand Canyon are few, and even the deepest are cut little more than a mile into the earth. If horizontally deposited sediments[1] are folded and then eroded (Fig. 32-12), then

[1] Most sediments are deposited in nearly horizontal layers.

the older layers may be exposed at the surface even though the surface is level. Note in the figure that if erosion had cut only to the line *AB*, no formations below 3 would be exposed. Erosion to *CD* exposes them all. The result is that one can walk across the surface from *C* to *D* and see formations exposed right at the surface that may once have been as much as 3 miles below the surface (Fig. 32-12*a*).

In New York City the schists and gneisses that represent the roots of an ancient mountain range are exposed in the parks of Manhattan and the Bronx, whereas across the East River on Long Island these rocks are buried by younger sediments of varying thicknesses (Fig. 34-15*b*). The schists and gneisses are intruded by countless pegmatite dikes but none of them penetrates the younger sediments. Thus, the older rocks reveal something of the igneous and metamorphic history of a region that was once a highland area but on Long Island where the younger rocks have not yet been eroded away, the story the older rocks have to tell is hidden from us. Erosion, therefore, is both detrimental and useful to man's search for the past.

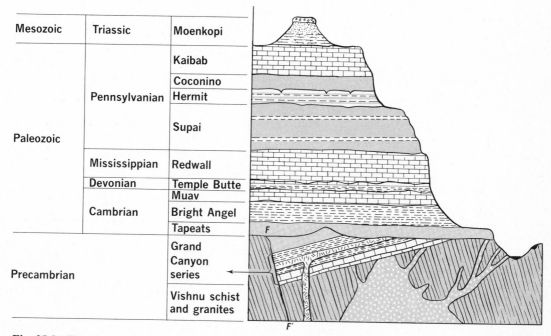

Mesozoic	Triassic	Moenkopi
Paleozoic	Pennsylvanian	Kaibab
		Coconino
		Hermit
		Supai
	Mississippian	Redwall
	Devonian	Temple Butte
	Cambrian	Muav
		Bright Angel
		Tapeats
Precambrian		Grand Canyon series
		Vishnu schist and granites

Fig. 35-2. The Grand Canyon. Much of the geologic history of the Grand Canyon area is decipherable from the rocks exposed on the south wall. We cannot possibly present it all here. None of the last 100 million years and more is portrayed, and there are great gaps in the record, represented by unconformities. The greatest is that between the Cambrian and the Precambrian. Another exists within the Precambrian itself. You can locate others if you know the geologic time scale (Fig. 35-1). Much about the conditions of deposition can be inferred from the fossils. All formations contain a few at least except the Precambrian. The formations below the Supai contain marine fossils, indicating the presence of the sea in the area. The Supai and Hermit show evidences of stream deposition, not only by fossils, but also by other characteristics; the Coconino is obviously a dune deposit of sand made by the wind. The Kaibab indicates the return of the sea, and the Moenkopi a retreat of the sea again. Later chapters of the history of the region are contained in rocks to the north. The cutting of the canyon itself was started about 1 to 2 million years ago.

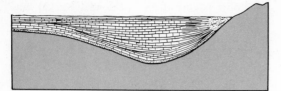

Fig. 35-3. The Geosynclinal Concept. To the right (east or southeast in the case of the Appalachian geosyncline) was the borderland area, the source of the sediments that were produced as the result of weathering, masswasting, and stream erosion. Streams carried the sediments down into the periodically subsiding basins, building great deltas out into them. When filling got ahead of sinking, the sea was driven out; when sinking got ahead of filling, the sea returned. Note that the coarser sediments are nearest the source.

Geosynclinal Concept

We used a hypothetical North America to demonstrate some of the problems that man has in gaining access to the geologic record. There were elements of truth in the situation presented. Beginning some 500 million years ago there was a highland area in eastern North America broken up into a chain of volcanic islands, and to the west of them there was a shallow trough, in which sediments eroded from the islands accumulated in great thicknesses. Such a trough is called a geosyncline. Its bottom sank from time to time to keep pace more or less with filling (Fig. 35-3).

At times sinking got ahead of filling and a shallow sea covered the floor of the geosyncline in whole or in part. At other times filling got ahead of sinking and so the sea was driven out for some millions of years. Coupled with such advances and retreats of the sea were other advances and retreats caused by diastrophism as the highland areas were uplifted from time to time after being eroded down almost to the peneplain stage. While the sea was absent the previously deposited sediments were subject to erosion, so that there are now gaps in the geologic record.

This series of events was spread over some 300 million years, during which time the total thickness of sediments deposited in some parts of the geosyncline reached 40,000 ft. In the end these sediments were folded (Fig. 35-4) into a great mountain range, the remnants of which we today call the Appalachian Mountains.

The folding was completed about 225 million years ago. Curiously enough, the mountains were highest in those areas where the sediments accumulated in greatest thicknesses. Careful study reveals that most of the other great mountain ranges of the earth were formed from great thicknesses of sediments accumulated in other geosynclines. Therefore if we understand the history of one of these ranges, we understand, in general, the history of them all. It is chiefly the details that are different. The original Appalachians have since been peneplaned, uplifted, peneplaned again, uplifted, and peneplaned a third time. Once again uplift came, and they are at present undergoing a fourth peneplanation. Since the last uplift erosion has cut deeply into the belts of weaker rocks, leaving the more resistant ones to stand up as ridges (Fig. 32-13).

Fig. 35-4. Generalized Abbreviated History of the Appalachian Mountains. (*a*) Streams from highland areas (Appalachian) transported sediments to the Appalachian geosyncline where they accumulated in thicknesses up to 40,000 ft over a period of some 300 million years. (*b*) Lateral compression from the southeast caused the weakest rocks (the sediments) to crumple into anticlines and synclines, and to fault, forming the original Appalachians. (*c*) Peneplanation of the area. (*d*) Uplift of eastern North America initiated a new cycle of erosion. The weaker rocks were eroded out faster than the more resistant (see Fig. 32-16), leaving the latter standing up as ridges. (Actually there have been at least three peneplanations with an uplift following each.)

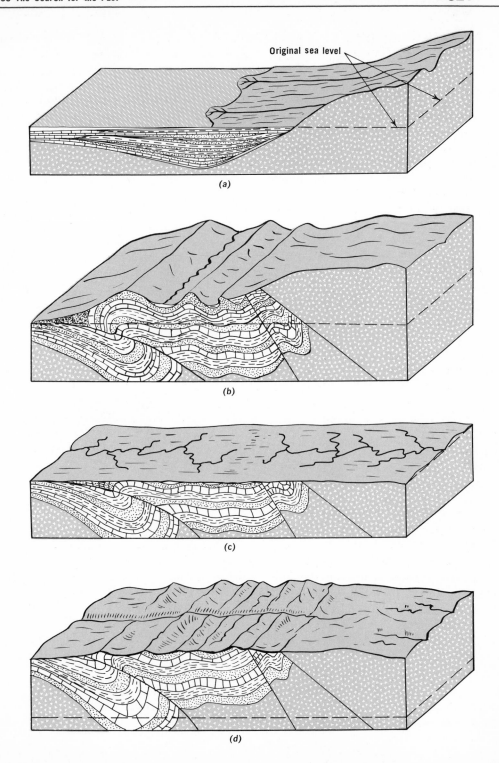

Original sea level

(a)

(b)

(c)

(d)

Some Principles of Historical Geology

Law of Superposition

We have already noted that sedimentary rocks are deposited in successive layers that are usually not far from the horizontal. It follows that in any sequence of sedimentary rock formations not disturbed by diastrophic forces other than uplift, the oldest strata will be at the bottom, the youngest at the top. This is sometimes referred to as the law of super-position. In cases where the strata have been deformed by folding or faulting, the law still holds. In some cases the strata have been so complexly folded that the folds have been overturned; older strata have come to lie on younger strata, or they may simply stand vertically. One type of fault can also produce the same result. In such cases the law does not hold. Usually the geologist can apply some method or principle to give him the relative ages.

Law of Igneous Intrusion

We have noted that the rocks of New York City are intruded by countless dikes but that on Long Island there are younger strata with no evidence of such intrusions (Fig. 34-15b). It follows that the dikes were intruded before the younger strata were deposited. It also is self-evident that the dikes are younger than the schists and gneisses. This is an example of the law of igneous intrusion, which simply states that the intrusive rock is always younger than the intruded rock. In Fig. 32-8 an igneous body lies between layers of sedimentary rock. If it is intrusive, then it is not only younger than the rocks below it but also younger than the rocks above. The problem is to prove that it is intrusive, for there is a possibility that it could have been poured out on the surface as

a lava flow, or series of lava flows, and then buried by later sediments.

If we note the projections extending from the sill into the rocks both above and below, we see that it must be intrusive. Moreover, the sediments in contact with the sill at its top show the effects of the heat of the igneous body. They must therefore have been present earlier.

Principle of Unconformity

We have already spoken about the gaps in the record that have been caused by erosion. If the eroded strata have been covered by younger strata, the surface between the two series of strata is called an unconformity. Formally defined, an *unconformity* is a surface of erosion or nondeposition that separates younger from older beds. Consider Fig. 34-15b. It is obvious that there is a great gap in the geologic record between the time of the for-

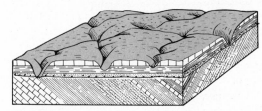

Fig. 35-5. A block diagram showing an unconformity. It is clear that the horizontal strata could not have been present when the inclined layers were folded. After folding the area was peneplaned. This erosion surface is indicated by the colored line. Later the horizontal sediments were deposited on the erosion surface. Thus, this surface is a *surface of erosion* that separates younger from older beds. Such surfaces are unconformities. An unconformity indicates a time gap in the orderly sequence of deposition. This gap may be millions, tens of millions, or even hundreds of millions of years long. The fossils in the horizontal layers (if any) will be different from those in the folded layers because plants and animals are continually evolving.

mation of the original rocks from which the schist and gneiss were derived and the time of deposition of the strata in contact with them on Long Island. During that time the original rocks must have been folded, metamorphosed to schist and gneiss, and peneplaned. (Actually far more has happened than that, but a study of these rocks alone will not reveal it.) Other unconformities are shown in Figs. 32-6, 32-8, and 35-5. Several unconformities are shown in Fig. 35-2. The gap in the record indicated by the unconformity may vary from hundreds of thousands of years to a billion or even more.

Law of Organic Correlation

Assemblages of fossils and, sometimes, single fossils may be used to determine the relative ages of formations in one area with respect to those in other areas. The principle assumes[2] that evolution has taken place, so that the differences in the fossils in marine strata at the bottom of a high cliff and those in marine strata at the top of the cliff are explainable by the changes that evolution had wrought during the time the whole sequence was being deposited.

Consider the geosyncline described earlier in this chapter. Suppose the sea has been present for a long time. Marine animals have lived and died, and the remains of many have become entombed in the sediments. Now let the sea retreat for some millions of years. Evolution goes steadily on during these millions of years, and when the sea returns, it brings with it all the new forms of marine life that have evolved. Some of them will be preserved as fossils in the new sediments, fossils that will

[2] Whether evolution has or has not taken place is no longer subject to question among scientists. It is an accepted fact because of the overwhelming amount of evidence that has been accumulated. Scientists may argue about how evolution has taken place but never whether it has taken place or not.

be different from those in the beds below them.

Millions of years later, perhaps hundreds of millions of years later, suppose that two groups of strata are exposed to investigation by geologists. A geologist in Georgia collects fossils from the two series of strata, carefully listing and describing them and the formations in which they are found; he eventually publishes his findings. Another geologist in Pennsylvania reads the article and finds the fossils described are identical for the most part with some he has collected from two series of strata in his state. He assumes that his strata are the same age as those in Georgia. He is simply using the law of organic correlation, which states that *if two sedimentary formations have the same assemblages of fossils, they are the same age.* Paleontologists may designate two formations as being the same age even though they differ in age by as much as a million years.

This law of organic correlation has been established and verified by thousands of geologists working in all parts of the earth during the last 150 years. By use of the law the geologist can determine the distribution of land and sea at various times during the past. In other words, he can construct paleogeographic maps. Unfortunately not all sedimentary rocks contain fossils, so that correlations with other formations are not always possible. Moreover, strata containing fossils of land dwellers cannot ordinarily be correlated with strata containing fossils of marine dwellers. However, indirect correlations can be made in some cases.

Uniformitarianism vs. Catastrophism

All the early peoples of the earth believed in some form of special creation for both the earth and themselves. In Western Europe the belief that the earth was created essentially as is prevailed even among most men of science until near the beginning of the 19th century. It was heresy for Christians to believe that the earth was more than 6000 years old. Mountains were believed to have originated within a short span of time, a few weeks at most, with catastrophic results in the surrounding regions. Great cataclysms split the earth wide open in places forming the great canyons that some rivers flowed in. Great floods were called on to explain the location of strata containing marine fossils on the tops of mountains, the distribution of boulders that we now know to have been left by one of the great ice sheets, and many other geologic phenomena.

The fact that fossils in some strata were entirely different from those in strata directly above created a problem that was "solved" by assuming a catastrophe that wiped out the earlier forms, necessitating another creation. As more knowledge was gained, more and more catastrophes were called for, until the number reached 27. Long before, however, almost all geologists and biologists had forsaken the catastrophism concept, for even the most casual dabbling in geology had revealed indisputable evidence that the earth was more than 6000 years old.

The first important dissenter from the catastrophism concept was the Scotsman James Hutton, the founder of modern geology. Hutton obtained his facts first and drew his conclusions afterward, as do all true scientists. He could find no evidence of any process that took place in the past that was not going on at present. He could find "no vestige of a beginning, no prospect of an end." He came to the conclusion that the present is the key to the past. No great floods, no great cataclysms were needed, but only the processes that are operating today. This is the essence of the concept of uniformitarianism. Hutton's work was carried on by Sir Charles Lyell, who championed Hutton's ideas and added much evidence of his own. Shortly after Darwin had advanced his theory of evolution in 1859 (a theory that introduced into the field of biology the same general concept of uniform change), the law of uniform change (uniformitarianism) was widely accepted. It involves the fewest awkward assumptions and gives the simplest explanation of all the available facts.

Exercises

1. What is meant by the geologic record?
2. Explain how erosion and diastrophism have together made more of the record available, while they at the same time have destroyed much of it.
3. (a) List the order in which the various types of life, plant and animal, invertebrate and vertebrate, appear in the fossil record.
   (b) Does this succession support the concept of evolution? Explain.
4. (a) What is meant by a gap in the orderly sequence of deposition?
   (b) What causes the gaps?
5. Much of the geologic record that has been preserved is unavailable to man, and always will be as far as modern man is concerned. Explain by stating where these records may be and why they are unavailable.
6. Where would you expect to find the best record of geologic events during a 500 million year interval preserved and available to man, in a level plain or plateau, or in a rugged mountain region? Explain.
7. (a) In Fig. 34-15b, why are the upper rocks on Long Island not folded as are the lower ones?
   (b) What do you call the surface separating the folded rocks from those above them?

8. What is a geosyncline? How can such a shallow trough accumulate so great a thickness of sediments?

9. (a) List the general sequence of events from the time of formation of a geosyncline until its final destruction.
   (b) In what way was it destroyed? (Note that what had so long been an area of deposition finally became an area of erosion.)

10. Study Fig. 35-4 carefully, noting that the ridges in (b) (what is a ridge?) are the upfolds, whereas in (d) they are composed of the resistant sandstones and conglomerates; the valleys in (b) are the downfolds, whereas in (d) they are composed of the weaker shales and limestones.

11. (a) Can one apply the law of superposition to vertical strata? Why or why not?

12. The question as to whether a dike is intrusive or not never arises, but every sill has to be carefully checked. Explain.

13. (a) What is an unconformity?
    (b) What is its significance as far as the geologic record is concerned?

14. Locate an unconformity in Fig. 35-2.

15. An area is vertically uplifted a few tens of feet above sea level. The uplifted sediments contain fossils. It remains that for some millions of years. Would it be an area of erosion or an area of deposition, or neither?

16. Finally this same area sinks beneath the sea again for a long period of time, and is then again uplifted. A geologist examines the rocks thousands of years later.
    (a) Could he find a record of the first uplift?
    (b) If so, what would it be?
    (c) Could he estimate the length of time of the first emergence? How?

17. Do fossils give us the absolute age of rocks? Explain.

18. Would you expect to find fossils of dinosaurs and horses in the same formation? Why or why not?

19. A newspaper carried an account of fossil bones being found in a nearby area. They were reported to be dinosaur bones. A local geologist, who had not read the account, was asked about it. His first question was the whereabouts of the locality of the find. On being told, he said, "They can't possibly be dinosaur bones; they are probably mastodon bones." His listeners, all nongeologists, protested that he was much too dogmatic in his answer. Yet he turned out to be right. Any geologist familiar with the local geology would have given the same answer, and just as quickly. Can you think of a reason why?

20. Why was the concept of catastrophism necessary to those who believed the earth to be only 6000 years old?

21. State the law of uniformitarianism (law of uniform change).

PART VIII

Starlight and Nuclear Energy

Natural Radioactivity and Modern Alchemy

We now return to the structure of atoms. Our previous concern with atomic structure was almost exclusively with the arrangement of the electrons, particularly with the arrangement of the outer electrons and the consequences thereof. It seemed better to go directly from the study of these arrangements of electrons to their role in chemical reactions rather than to the study of the atomic nuclei. During chemical reactions the role of the nucleus is a passive one (except in the case of the hydrogen atom, to which we will turn our attention shortly). Moreover, consideration of the energy within nuclei at this point can lead us directly into the energy within stars, our closing topic.

That there was considerable energy within the nucleus was made evident by the phenomena of radioactivity. The ejection of both alpha particles and beta rays at high speeds and the emission of high-energy gamma rays, the most penetrating of all electromagnetic radiation, could mean only that considerable energy resided in the nucleus. The fact that large

> A hypothesis or theory is clear, decisive, and positive, but is believed by no one but the man who created it. Experimental findings, on the other hand, are messy inexact things which are believed by everyone except the man who did that work.
> **HARLOW SHAPLEY (1935)**

629

numbers of positive charges were packed tightly in nuclei suggested that large amounts of energy were needed to hold them together. Einstein, in his discussion of relativity in 1905, had stated the equivalence of mass and energy in his now famous equation

$$E = mc^2$$

where m is mass and c is the velocity of light (3×10^{10} cm/sec). If they are equivalent, then under certain circumstances they should be interconvertible. Our problem is to see what those circumstances are.

The hydrogen atom is the only reactive atom with just one shell (a K shell) and with only one electron in that shell. Loss of that electron leaves a bare nucleus consisting of one lone particle, a positive hydrogen ion that Rutherford named a proton five years before it was discovered in 1919. Moseley had discovered (p. 416) that the number of positive charges on the nucleus was equal to the atomic number. This made it possible to define *an element as a substance whose atoms all had the same number of unit positive charges on the nucleus.* Since charges do not exist apart from matter, some particle (or particles) had to be associated with the charge (or charges). Some particle had to carry only one unit charge; it was this particle to which Rutherford gave the name *proton.* Its existence in 1914 was based on pure reasoning. Eventually the word *proton* was substituted for the word *charges* in the definition of an element.

Discovery of the Proton

Part of what is said here is a repetition of the same topic in Chapter 19. There we merely needed to know what protons and neutrons are, whereas here they form the essential theme of the chapter. We offer no apologies for the repetition since it serves the interest of clarity.

Research on the structure of the nucleus was performed by Rutherford and others, chiefly by bombarding various kinds of atoms with alpha particles (doubly charged helium ions) from a radioactive source. Rutherford used such ions to bombard nitrogen atoms in a closed tube. He used pure nitrogen in the tube. His source of alpha particles was a small piece of a radioactive compound of radium, which may be likened to a minute battery of guns. This "battery" was mounted in one end of a closed tube so that the alpha particles that it spontaneously emitted could be "fired" toward a movable fluorescent screen mounted in the other end of the tube. Rutherford used a microscope focused on the screen to watch for flashes of light (scintillations) caused by high speed particles (about 10,000 mi/sec), alpha particles and others that might be created by the bombardment. (The nitrogen molecules had only their normal thermal energies.)

The atomic weights of helium and nitrogen are 4 and 14, respectively. The ratio of their nuclear masses is therefore 4:14. Rutherford expected that the alpha particles would be stopped, or greatly slowed down, when they struck the much more massive nitrogen particles. When the screen was not more than 7 cm from the "battery," many of the alpha particles hit the screen, causing the expected scintillations. Only a few were observed at greater distances, and these only when the screen was moved to a distance of 30 cm or more. These could be neither alpha particles nor nitrogen atoms that had been struck and given higher speeds by collisions with alpha particles, for the latter were not nearly massive enough to do that. Rutherford substituted other gases for the nitrogen, but no long-range particles were

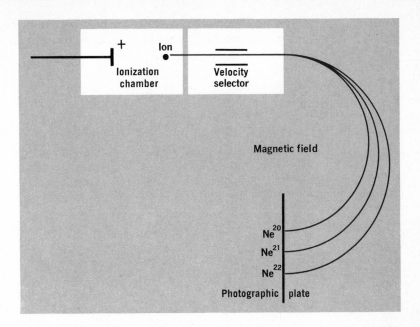

Fig. 36-1. Principle of the Mass Spectrograph. Ions are produced from neutral atoms in the ionization chamber. The velocity selector is basically an electric field. The curving paths are produced by a continuous deflection in a magnetic field (perpendicular to the plane of the paper). The lighter atoms are deflected more than the heavier ones.

detected.[1] Clearly, then, the scintillation effects were related to one particular gas, nitrogen, and the particles causing it had to be less massive than alpha particles. The only particles known to be less massive are hydrogen nuclei, which have masses about one fourth those of alpha particles. All Rutherford had to do now was to prove that he had hydrogen nuclei in the tube.

The year was 1919,[2] and it was that year that Francis Aston invented an instrument

called the *mass spectrograph*. It recorded the masses of atoms directly on a photographic plate. It was designed to do the kind of a job that lay before Rutherford—to separate atomic particles of different masses, charges, and velocities from one another, and determine their q/m. This is done by passing the particles through electric and magnetic fields (Fig. 36-1). Neutral particles, like those of nitrogen, pass through unaffected. The principle is the same as that J. J. Thomson used in his discovery of the electron (p. 306). Thus Rutherford was able to isolate and measure the q/m of the nuclei of his unknown particles (the ones causing the scintillations). It was the same as for hydrogen nuclei, and therefore the particles must be hydrogen nuclei. An instrument called a cloud chamber, invented about 1912 by C. T. R. Wilson, one of Rutherford's assistants, was used to verify Rutherford's conclusion that alpha particles actually did strike nitrogen atoms and knock hydrogen nuclei out of them.

The final conclusion was that in some way the helium nuclei (alpha particles) were ab-

[1] One might very well ask, "Why?" Nitrogen has only seven protons in its nucleus. All other gases except helium (whose ions he was using as "bullets") and hydrogen have more. Helium ions (alpha particles) have two positive charges on their nuclei, nitrogen has seven. At close range these particles tend to repel one another. This repulsive force is not great enough to prevent high-speed alpha particles from entering the nitrogen nucleus. Other gaseous elements with more charges on their nuclei could prevent such entry.

[2] Moseley's discovery was made in 1913, and Rutherford's discovery of the proton in 1919. The gap in time is explained by the intervention of World War I, 1914–1918. Both men were engaged in work connected with the war. Moseley was killed in World War I.

sorbed by nitrogen nuclei and the product transformed into something else, as shown by the following nuclear reaction:

$$_7N^{14} + {}_2He^4 \rightarrow {}_9F^{18} \rightarrow {}_1H^1 + {}_8O^{17} \quad [36\text{-}1]$$

In nuclear equations the subscripts refer to atomic numbers and the superscripts to mass numbers. The mass number of an atom is the whole number nearest the atomic weight. It should be carefully distinguished from an atomic mass unit (amu). If 6.02×10^{23} atoms of C^{12} weigh 12 g, then one atom of C^{12} weighs $12/(6.02 \times 10^{23})$ g. A new unit equal to $\frac{1}{12}$ of this weight is called an atomic mass unit:

$$\frac{1}{12} \times \frac{12}{6.02 \times 10^{23}} = 1.66 \times 10^{-24} \text{ g}$$
$$= 1 \text{ amu}$$

The mass number of ordinary hydrogen is 1 and its atomic weight is 1.008. The actual mass of the hydrogen atom is, therefore, $1.008 \times (1.66 \times 10^{-24})$ g. Hydrogen has a mass number of 1 and has a mass of 1.008 amu; carbon-12 has a mass number of 12 and a mass of 12 amu. Like chemical equations, nuclear equations must be balanced; both the sum of the subscripts and the sum of the superscripts on the two sides must be equal.

Note that in Eq. 36-1 the nitrogen nucleus momentarily absorbed the helium nucleus, making the charge on the new nucleus 9 (which by definition must be that of fluorine), and giving it a mass number of 18. This is not regular fluorine—that has a mass number of 19—but an isotope, which is unstable. The assumption that a nitrogen nucleus can absorb an alpha particle is bolstered by the fact that radioactive atoms eject alpha particles. F^{18} at once splits into two unequal parts, one a hydrogen nucleus (to which Rutherford applied the term proton) and the other an isotope of oxygen. This is the old dream of the al-

chemist—a transformation of one element into another—although it was not that of a baser element into gold.

The Wilson Cloud Chamber

As we have said, the Wilson cloud chamber enabled Rutherford to demonstrate the presence of hydrogen nuclei. It has been, and still is, an extremely important instrument in atomic research. The marvelous thing about it is that it allows a nuclear event to be observed with the naked eye, and photographed.

The working principle of the cloud chamber is easy to understand for anyone who has seen the exhaust gases of a high-flying airplane leave a vapor trail across the sky, a trail that slowly expands and then is dissipated. Tiny particles in the exhaust gases act as centers of condensation on which invisible water vapor precipitates to form tiny water droplets. Natural clouds are formed the same way. In dust-free air, clouds cannot form. As early as 1897 Charles Wilson showed that electrically charged particles, for example, ions, can act as dust particles on which the condensation of minute water droplets can take place in air that is saturated. We learned that the expansion of a gas is a cooling process (p. 212). A sudden expansion and cooling of a fixed volume of *filtered* air inside the chamber is achieved in the apparatus shown in Fig. 36-2a by simply lowering the piston (on which a few drops of water have been sprinkled to insure saturation of the air). With the cooling, the already saturated air becomes supersaturated with water vapor, and so will condense upon any particles available. An alpha particle, or any other particle energetic enough to create ions, that passes through the chamber will leave a vapor trail marking the path that it took (Fig. 36-2b). The Wilson cloud chamber was a fabulous invention for the experimental atomic physicist. Rutherford thought of it as "the most

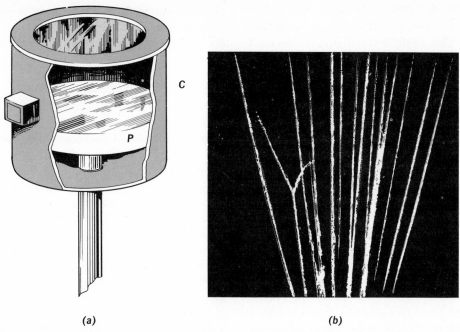

(a)   (b)

Fig. 36-2. The Wilson Cloud Chamber. (*a*) *P* is a movable piston inside a small cylinder, *C* (the chamber). *C* is filled with a gas saturated with water vapor. When the piston is quickly lowered, the gas expands, cooling the vapor (see p. 212) and the gas, producing a supersaturated condition. The excess vapor will condense onto any tiny foreign particles in the gas. Charged particles are constantly emanating from the radioactive mineral that has been placed in the small box attached to the cylinder; the vapor condenses on them, forming a fog. Since the particles are shot out of the mineral at very high speeds, they leave fog tracks (or trails) that are visible through the glass window. (*b*) Fog trails of charged particles (chiefly alpha particles) passing through a cloud chamber. (Drawn from a photograph by P. M. S. Blackett of the Cavendish Laboratory.)

original and magnificent instrument in the history of research." The original model had one fault: After every expansion of the air in it, the equipment had to be returned to its starting point before it could be used again. Hence continuous observations could not be made. In time it was replaced by the diffusion cloud chamber, an instrument that allows continuous observation and photographs to be made of the nuclear events whenever they occur. In 1952 Donald A. Glaser, an American physicist, invented the bubble chamber, which also allows one to observe and photograph a nuclear event. Very clear pictures can be ob-

tained with it. He got his inspiration after he had stared long and hard into a glass of beer, watching the bubbles form. It won him a Nobel prize in 1960.

Discovery of the Neutron

The mass number of the hydrogen nucleus (a proton) is 1, whereas that of helium is 4. If it is the proton that carries the positive charge, then helium's two protons account for only half of its mass. What constitutes the other half? Two possibilities exist. It can consist of one particle with a mass equal to 2 amu or of two particles each with a mass equal to 1 amu. That there were two particles each approximately equal to 1 amu instead of one particle of 2 amu could be inferred from the fact that beryllium has a mass of 9 amu, 4 of which can be accounted for by its 4 protons, the other 5 either by 1 particle of 5 amu (which can easily be disproved) or by 5 particles of 1 amu each.

The unknown particle was first inferred to be some sort of a proton-electron combination. Such a particle would be about the right size, it would be electrically neutral, and it would account for the source of the beta particles (electrons) emitted during natural radioactivity. It would also explain why the ejection of a beta particle would increase the atomic number of the atom by one, for the proton left behind with no electron to neutralize it would add an extra charge to the nucleus. This hypothetical proton-electron combination was named the neutron even before it was discovered. The search for it continued for years. In 1930 the daughter of Marie Curie and her husband (F. Joliot) were bombarding the metal beryllium with alpha particles. No protons were ejected, but a new type of radiation of greater energy than any yet known was detected. If a plate of paraffin (a hydrocarbon) was placed in its path, the new radiation ejected protons from it. This new radiation did not leave tracks in a cloud chamber and it was wholly unaffected by electric and magnetic fields. The discoverers came to the conclusion that this radiation was electromagnetic in character.

In 1932 Chadwick, a former assistant of Rutherford's, proved that the high energy of this radiation could not be accounted for by assuming that it was electromagnetic in character, but that the energy could be explained by assuming that the radiation was composed of particles with masses slightly greater than that of protons, but with no charge. Further research convinced the investigators that it was the long sought for neutron. The reaction can be written as follows:

$$_4Be^9 \; + \; _2He^4 \; \rightarrow \; _6C^{12} \; + \; _0n^1$$

where $_0n^1$ is the neutron.

The difficulty of its detection lies in its tiny size and in its electrical neutrality. Because of these properties it has great penetrating ability; neutrons cannot be contained in any container. Having no charge, a neutron does not ionize a gas except by a direct hit and so does not readily lose its energy. In a head-on collision with a proton, all or nearly all of its energy is transmitted to the proton. The neutron has a mass number of 1 and zero charge; it is therefore represented by $_0n^1$.

We can now redefine atomic mass number as the sum of the numbers of the protons and of the neutrons in a nucleus. If we use the term *nucleon* to refer to either a proton or a neutron, we can say that the mass number is the number of nucleons in the nucleus. As the atomic number, given by the subscripts in nuclear formulas, is the number of protons in the nucleus, the difference between the atomic and the mass numbers represents the number of neutrons.

Discovery of the Positron

After the discovery of the neutron it was believed that the fundamental particles were all known. Since that time (1932) a host of other particles and antiparticles have been discovered and called fundamental even though we may think that elementary is the better term for them. Most are strange particles that have no place in the scheme of the atom as presented here. The situation is rather chaotic at present. Research still goes on in the hope that order will eventually replace the present confusion. We will content ourselves here with a brief discussion of three of the most stable of these particles, the positron, the antiproton, and the neutrino.

Positive electrons, now called positrons, are just like ordinary negative electrons except that they carry a positive charge. They were predicted by P. A. M. Dirac of England when he advanced a highly speculative theory in which he was trying to extend the wave mechanical theory of atoms to include relativity considerations. His theory gave a very satisfactory description of the electron's properties but it required the existence of an "antielectron," a positively charged electron. Search for the particle was successful in 1932, when C. D. Anderson discovered it while he was observing cloud chamber photographs in his cosmic ray[3] research. The photograph, accepted as unequivocal proof for the existence of positrons, shows the typical ionization track of an electron, but its magnetic deflection is precisely opposite to that for an electron.

In a complete vacuum a positron would exist forever, but here on earth it quickly meets an ordinary electron, to which it is attracted because of its opposite sign, and is annihilated. This does not mean that the two particles are neutralized; they disappear completely but not into "nothingness," for two gamma-ray quanta appear in their place. Thus matter was converted into radiant energy. The appearance of a real positron apparently disappearing into "nothingness" caused investigators to look for the opposite event, the creation of e^- and e^+ from gamma ray quanta. They found it—a high-energy gamma ray hit a massive atom of lead, passed close to the intense electric field

[3] Cosmic rays are a very penetrating radiation coming from outer space. That they were extremely penetrating means they have very high energies. Not all cosmic rays are alike. Most are probably atomic nuclei. The problem of cosmic rays is much too complex to be presented here.

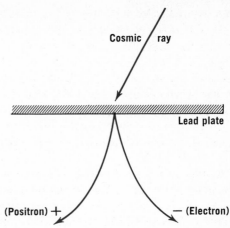

Fig. 36-3. Discovery of the Positron. A cosmic ray from outer space entered the lead plate and passed close to the nucleus of a lead atom. The intense electric field of this nucleus caused the ray (probably a gamma ray photon in this case) to disintegrate into an electron and a positron. A magnetic field below the plate caused these oppositely charged particles to diverge.

of a lead atom (with its 82 protons), and was transformed into the two electrons, e^- and e^+ (Fig. 36-3). The process is called pair production, or pair creation. This is a conversion of energy into matter in accordance with Einstein's equation, $E = mc^2$. It has since been found possible to "create" electron-positron pairs out of radiant energy when photons are subjected to extremely powerful electromagnetic fields.

Discovery of the Antiproton

The discovery of the antielectron (positron) encouraged the belief[4] that there was a sym-

[4] Some of the more imaginative of the investigators into the structure of atoms began speculating about the symmetry of the world shortly after the electron was discovered. The discovery of the positron raised their hopes, the discovery of the proton dashed them again, then they were raised once more with the discovery of the antiproton.

metry among the elementary particles; that is, for every kind of particle there was another of the same mass but of opposite charge (if any). The search for the antiproton was intensified. Claims of discovery in cosmic rays were made—probably valid claims—but they coult not be substantiated. The first clear-cut evidence for its existence came in 1955 when the Berkeley particle accelerator was started up. Positrons had been "created" from high-energy photons, so perhaps antiprotons could be "created" in a similar way by using higher energies. Since a proton is about 1840 times as massive as the positron, it should take 1840 times more energy to create it. This meant billions of electron volts. A sheet of copper was bombarded with a proton beam with an energy of 6.2×10^9 eV. The result was proton-antiproton pairs, analogous to the electron-positron pairs. Like the positron, the antiproton can live forever in a vacuum; but in the presence of matter it soon collides with a proton and both are annihilated. The usual end result of such annihilation is one or two electrons, the same number of positrons, and radiation of gamma rays and neutrinos. If the electrons and the positrons collide, they are both annihilated, and more gamma radiation results. The then combined masses of the proton and the antiproton are converted to electromagnetic energy.

Discovery of the Neutrino

The neutrino (Italian for little neutron) is another of those elementary particles that was named before it was discovered. Belief in its existence came from a puzzling lack of energy balance that had been found in the emission of beta particles (electrons) from radioactive atoms. The energy of the emitted beta particle and the energy of the nucleus left behind did not add up to the energy of the parent nucleus

before the emission. Moreover, the emitted beta particles were not always emitted with the same energy. No physicist was willing to admit that the law of conservation of energy (or of energy and mass since $E = mc^2$) did not hold in nuclear reactions. Pauli (of Pauli's exclusion principle) suggested that the missing energy was carried away by an invisible thief, a tiny neutral particle. He was not taken seriously by many nuclear physicists; some thought the neutral particle just a "gimmick" for evading a difficulty—it had to be neutral or it would not have escaped detection. But as the years passed they began to believe in it, for the evidence, indirect as it was, mounted. Despite the many traps the physicists set for it, it evaded detection for 25 years. This is not surprising, for it is so penetrating that it can pass clear through the earth with far less than one chance in a million of being stopped. Varied methods of detection were attempted; some tried to catch it after it had escaped. Others carefully studied the process by which the electron was ejected. One possible clue was the recoil of the nucleus (Newton's third law) when it ejected an electron. If the electron was the only particle ejected, the nucleus had to recoil precisely in the opposite direction. If a neutrino was ejected with the electron, perhaps the recoil would be somewhat different. Experiments to detect this difference were difficult. World War II interrupted the work, but it was resumed when peace came. Chances of detecting the neutrino were vastly improved because uranium reactors provided radioactivity millions of times stronger than was known before. Nevertheless, Frederick Reines (an American scientist) and his collaborators spent ten years of hard work before they were able to report that neutrinos existed and behaved as predicted. It is impossible to detect any nuclear particle unless it reacts with matter in some way. The difficulty was that there were too many other particles also reacting with matter.

At any rate Pauli's guess was proved correct in 1956, about 25 years after he first made it.

Isotopes

As far back as 1815 William Prout, an English physician, was impressed by the prevalence of whole numbers and nearly whole numbers among the atomic weights. He therefore suggested that the hydrogen atom with an atomic weight of 1 was the fundamental particle; other atoms were made up of hydrogen atoms combined in some unknown way. The idea had to be abandoned as greater accuracy in atomic weight determinations were made. The idea was revived in 1912 with the discovery of isotopes.

In 1912 an English scientist, working with radioactive minerals, advanced a new concept, that of isotopes (p. 328), which are different forms of the same element, chemically identical and with the same atomic number, but having different atomic weights. This line of investigation was interrupted by World War I. The year following the war (1919) Aston built his first mass spectrograph (p. 631)—of which one type is shown in Fig. 36-1. The first isotopes Aston separated with his new instrument were those of neon. Not all the atoms of neon have either the same mass or the same random thermal velocity. The ones with the lesser mass have the greater average velocity. In a mass spectrograph the atoms are ionized by electron bombardment and then passed through electric and magnetic fields. The strengths of these fields can be regulated so that the deviation of the ions is not dependent on their speeds, but depends entirely on their mass. The deviated ions are allowed to impinge on a photographic film, which they darken much as light does, producing, when the film is developed, a spectrogram. That of neon showed three separate lines, one for each isotope. The width

and density of the lines indicate the proportions of each isotope.

About 90% of ordinary neon is Ne^{20}, which accounts for its atomic weight being close to 20 (20.2). These proportions are constant for any natural source of neon, as it is for all other elements. For oxygen there are also three isotopes with mass numbers of 16, 17, and 18. However, 99.76% of all oxygen is O^{16}. Tin has ten isotopes. Hydrogen has three, $_1H^1$, $_1H^2$ (deuterium), and $_1H^3$ (tritium); these are the only well-known isotopes with special names. The mass of any isotope can now be calculated with very great precision (to six and seven significant figures). The mass numbers of isotopes are always within less than 1% of their true masses. Chemical processes rarely separate isotopes, so that the chemist is rarely concerned with the concept.

Radioactivity

Radioactivity, as we have already indicated, involves the spontaneous disintegration of certain types of atoms to form atoms of other elements by the emission of either an electron or a helium nucleus from the nucleus of the disintegrating atom. In either case, the remaining part of the disintegrating atom is a new element. It is therefore a natural transmutation. The radioactive change of one element into another is called *decay*. Consider the emission of an alpha particle (helium nucleus) from ordinary uranium:

$$_{92}U^{238} \quad \rightarrow \quad _{90}Th^{234} \quad + \quad _2He^4 \quad \text{plus energy}$$

The emission of the helium nucleus causes a loss of two positive charges. Hence the atomic number drops from 92 to 90. The emission also causes a loss of four nucleons (2 protons and 2 neutrons) so that the mass number of the new element is 234. The thorium atom now emits an electron (beta ray):

$$_{90}Th^{234} \rightarrow {}_{91}Pa^{234} + {}_{-1}e^0$$

The mass number of the new element (proactinium) remains unchanged because the mass of the electron is negligible. The atomic number increases by one because a neutron has split into a proton and an electron; the escape of the electron leaves an additional positive charge in the nucleus.

Ejection of another electron then takes place, followed by the ejection of five helium nuclei, one after the other,

$$_{91}Pa^{234} \rightarrow {}_{92}U^{234} + {}_{-1}e^0$$
$$_{92}U^{234} \rightarrow {}_{90}Th^{230} + {}_{2}He^4$$
$$_{90}Th^{230} \rightarrow {}_{88}Ra^{226} + {}_{2}He^4$$

and so on.

In all, $_{92}U^{238}$ ejects eight alpha particles and six beta particles before the nucleus becomes stable. The final product is $_{82}Pb^{206}$, which is one of several isotopes of lead.

When atoms of $_{92}U^{235}$, one of the natural isotopes of uranium, disintegrate, the final product is also an isotope of lead, $_{82}Pb^{207}$. During the process of the disintegration of uranium-235, one or more isotopes of all the elements with atomic numbers 81 or higher are created.[5] It was Rutherford who, while working on the identification of alpha particles, conceived the idea that other elements should be present in every uranium sample, elements lighter than uranium. By long and careful work he determined the order in which the elements were created for each isotope of

uranium. This is a natural transmutation of the elements, but not a transmutation of baser elements into gold. It is much more nearly the reverse, that is, the transmutation of more valuable (to man) elements to the less valuable ones.

One should *not* get the impression, just because helium ions and electrons are ejected by radioactive atoms, that helium ions and electrons are parts of the nuclei of these atoms. The high velocities of the ejected beta particles eliminated the possibility that they came from any of the electron shells of these atoms. Other considerations showed that electrons could not exist as such within a nucleus. The fact that a neutron within a nucleus splits into a proton and an electron, the electron being ejected at that instant, does not mean that each has its own identity and that they are "tacked" together or "glued" together in the nucleus. A sculptor carves a statue out of a block of stone, but this does not mean that the statue was in the block of stone before the sculptor began his carving.

Artificial Radioactivity

The first "artificial" radioactivity was produced in 1933 by Irene and F. Joliot-Curie. They had been generating neutrons by bombarding aluminum foil with alpha particles (Fig. 36-4). The nuclear reaction for this is

$$_{13}Al^{27} + {}_{2}He^4 \rightarrow {}_{15}P^{30} + {}_{0}n^1 \quad [36\text{-}2]$$

However, they found that not only neutrons were emitted but also positrons ($_{+1}e^0$) and that the emission of positrons continued *even after the alpha particle bombardment was stopped.* Their conclusion was that $_{15}P^{30}$ was a radioactive isotope of phosphorus and that in addition to the nuclear reaction described by Eq. 36-2, there was a subsequent disintegration of the radioactive phosphorus:

---

[5] Lead is the only nonradioactive element whose atomic weight varies with the place where it is found. U^{238}, U^{235}, and Th^{232} all disintegrate radioactively into three different isotopes to form 98.5% of all lead. Since uranium and thorium do not necessarily occur together, lead from different areas may have different atomic weights.

$$_{15}P^{30} \rightarrow {}_{14}Si^{30} + {}_{+1}e^0 \quad [36\text{-}3]$$

Since that initial discovery, a thousand or more radioactive isotopes, not found in nature, have been prepared "artificially" by nuclear bombardment.

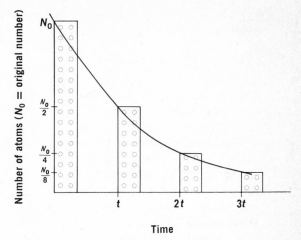

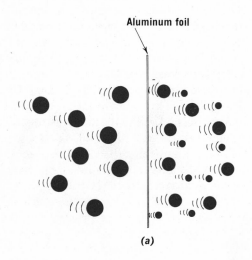

Aluminum foil

(a)

(b)

Fig. 36-4. Artificial Radioactivity. (*a*) The aluminum foil is bombarded with alpha particles (left) and emits both neutrons and positrons (right). (*b*) The foil continues to emit the small positrons even after the alpha particle bombardment has been stopped.

Fig. 36-5. Graphic Representation of Decreasing Rate of Radioactive Decay in Relation to constant Half-life of a Radioactive Element. N_0 is the number of original atoms; t is the half-life.

Half-life

Each radioactive element gives off its rays (that is, decays) at a definite rate. A definite number of particles are emitted per second *for any given quantity of the element*. This means that if we change the quantity of the element, we change the *rate* at which the particles are emitted. Consider a number of piles of widely different masses of a radioactive element. Whether the size of the pile is 1 oz, 1 lb, or 1 ton, the time for half of the atoms in each pile to decay is the same. Thus, the rate depends on the size of the pile. As the number of undecayed atoms gets less and less, the rate becomes slower and slower, so the time for complete decay to take place is infinite for each pile (Fig. 36-5).

Thus, to speak of the "life" of a radioactive element is meaningless. The half-life, however, is an actual easily determinable span of time. Nothing that man can do, either physically or chemically, to radioactive atoms can cause them to change the half-life. This half-life is

Table 36-1
Half-life of Radioactive Elements

U^{238}	4.5×10^9 yr	Po^{218}	3.05 min
U^{235}	7.1×10^8 yr	Pb^{214}	26.8 min
U^{234}	2.5×10^5 yr	At^{218}	1.5–2.0 sec
Th^{234}	24.1 days	Po^{214}	1.64×10^{-4} sec
Ra^{226}	1620 yr	Pb^{210}	22 yr
Rn^{222}	3.82 days	Pb^{207}	Stable
		Pb^{206}	Stable

a property of the atoms of a given radioactive element, and it varies enormously from element to element (Table 36-1).

Radioactivity as a Time Clock

Consider the following facts: (1) uranium has a long half-life, 4.5×10^9 years; (2) the rate at which it decays is constant for any given quantity of it; (3) it is a constituent of a mineral that crystallizes from certain magmas; and (4) it may be found in fresh, unweathered, igneous intrusive rocks that contain what is left of their original uranium plus all of the lead that is the end product of the disintegration. From these facts there arose the possibility of using the ratio of the number of atoms of lead to the number of atoms of uranium to tell the age of the sample. After long and careful work to eliminate all possible sources of error, an equation was worked out that yielded reasonably satisfactory results. Thus, the minimum age of the earth has been determined.[6]

Carbon Dating

The C^{14} method of dating is confined to more precise dating of geologic and anthro-

pologic events of the last 50,000 years.[7] C^{14} is a radioactive isotope that is formed in the atmosphere by high-energy particles from outer space (cosmic rays) striking nitrogen atoms, transmuting them to C^{14} with a half-life of 5600 years. There is an equilibrium in the atmosphere between the rate of C^{14} formation and the rate of disintegration. All living things contain carbon obtained from the atmosphere and so also contain an amount of C^{14} that is in equilibrium with that in the atmosphere. When death comes to any plant or animal, the intake ceases but the radioactive decay of C^{14} to N^{14} goes on. Thus, old dead organic matter, be it straw, wood, or bones, contains less C^{14} than new wood. By measuring the concentration of C^{14}, the time since death can be computed. By this means it has been determined that the retreat of the last great ice sheet in North America began only some 10,000 years ago.

We have left a number of questions about radioactivity unanswered. Some will have to remain that way. For others we will do what the atomic physicists of the time did; they turned to a study of the energy within the nucleus in their search for possible answers.

Exercises

1. Alpha particles ejected from radioactive atoms do not travel more than about 7 cm through air, although they are ejected at 10,000 mi/sec. Why?
2. (a) What caused Rutherford to suspect that the particles causing the long-range scintillations (in his bombardment of nitrogen with alpha particles) were smaller than alpha particles?

[6]Other methods of minimum age determinations exist, all by radioactivity of one sort or another. Their results are used as a check for the accuracy for the determinations we have listed.

[7]There are some indications that the rate of radioactive decay of C^{14} may not be constant. As of 1971, this problem is still being investigated.

(b) At that time what particles were known that were smaller than alpha particles?

(c) How did he prove what his unknown particles were?

3. The neutron was more difficult to discover and identify than the proton. Why?

4. The neutron had been postulated and named long before its discovery. Explain.

5. (a) What is an atomic mass unit (amu)?

(b) How does it differ from mass number?

6. The neutron turned out to be a more effective "bullet" with which to bombard atoms than were protons and alpha particles. Why?

7. (a) What are the decay products of neutrons?

(b) What is a neutron's half-life?

8. What is (a) a nucleon, (b) an isotope? (c) Do all atoms possess neutrons?

9. (a) How does $_8O^{16}$ differ from $_8O^{17}$?

(b) How many neutrons are present in an atom of each of the following: $_1H^1$, $_1H^2$, $_1H^3$, $_{16}S^{32}$, $_{26}Fe^{56}$, $_{82}Pb^{208}$, and $_{92}U^{238}$?

10. (a) What is a positron?

(b) What happens to it when it meets an electron?

11. Tin (Sn) has ten natural isotopes. Seven have atomic weights ranging from 113.9 to 119.9. Write the nuclear formula for each of them.

12. Natural chlorine has an invariable atomic weight of 35.45. Explain why it is not closer to 35 or 36.

13. (a) What is the underlying principle used to separate isotopes?

(b) Why can they not be separated chemically?

14. (a) What is radioactivity?

(b) What is the most important radioactive element?

15. What element is most commonly ejected from radioactive atoms?

16. Does the preceding question imply that this element is present as such in radioactive atoms? Explain.

17. Radium is a disintegration product of U^{238}. Why is it considered an element?

18. Radium disintegrates into radon and helium. The atomic number of radium is 88 and its mass number is 226.

(a) What is the atomic number of radon? (Do not look it up.)

(b) What is its mass number?

19. What happens to the atomic and mass numbers of a radioactive nucleus when it emits a beta particle? Explain.

20. (a) The ultimate end-products of all natural radioactivity are what?

(b) Are the end products of U^{238} and U^{235} the same? Explain.

21. Explain what is meant by half-life. Why is the "half-life" meaningful where the "full life" is meaningless?

22. All natural aluminum atoms have the same mass number. When aluminum is bombarded with alpha particles, Si^{30} and a proton are "created." Write the equation showing both intermediate and final products.

23. Do all natural deposits of lead minerals have their origin in the radioactive decay of uranium and other radioactive elements?

24. How is uranium used as a time clock?

25. (a) What precautions must be taken to insure a reliable result in the dating of rocks by radioactive methods?

(b) Why can C^{14} not be used to give a minimum age of the earth?

26. What advantage does carbon dating have over uranium dating?

Nuclear Energy

37

The Mass-Energy Equation

The discovery that radioactive atoms emit alpha, beta, and gamma rays with enormous amounts of energy raised the exciting possibility that man could somehow tap that rich supply. Einstein, at nearly the same time, equated mass to energy in his equation, $E = mc^2$ (c^2 in this equation being a proportionality constant). At the time (1905) this was a mere speculation, resulting from his relativity theory; there was not an experimental shred of evidence to support it. Moreover, how could mass and energy be related by the square of the velocity of light? Skepticism about the validity of the equation was not so strong when it was learned that a single alpha particle was emitted with millions of electron volts (eV),[1] whereas the energy from oxidizing carbon to

[1] An alpha particle ejected from a radioactive atom creates enormous numbers of ions in passing through 2 in. of air, at a cost of about 6×10^6 eV of energy. These ions, in returning to the neutral state, ultimately deliver this energy in the form of heat. It is therefore expected that radioactive minerals in rocks gradually cause the temperature of the rocks to rise if the heat cannot escape fast enough.

From the point of view of the physicist, a theory . . . is a policy rather than a creed; its object is to connect or coordinate apparently diverse phenomena and above all to suggest, stimulate and direct experiment.

J. J. THOMSON (1907)

CO_2 is only about 4 eV per carbon atom. We can "shoot" electrons at helium atoms in a gas discharge tube with energy high enough to strip both electrons from the helium atom (p. 423), converting it into an alpha particle. This takes only about 80 eV. Whence come the millions of electron volts with which an alpha particle is emitted from a radioactive atom?

Consider a uranium atom with its 92 protons. Ejection of an alpha particle means that two protons and two neutrons are emitted as a single particle. At the instant of ejection there is a repulsive force between 90 protons and 2 protons. Is this force great enough to eject the alpha particle with a speed of 10,000 mi/sec? Perhaps we can judge the probable size of the repulsive force if we can calculate the repulsive force between two protons in a helium nucleus. This force turns out to be about 23 million dynes—230 newtons—an enormous force for particles as small as two protons to exert on one another. Thus it seems that the repulsive forces can account for the energy of ejection of alpha particles from a uranium or other heavy atom.

This leaves us not much better off, for we are now confronted with other questions. How can any nucleus hold together even an instant in the face of such forces? Why does one uranium atom eject an alpha particle at once and another one alongside it not do so for billions of years? Where did the uranium nucleus get its energy in the first place?

Perhaps Einstein's mass-energy equation is correct, perhaps in nuclear reactions the transformation of the rest mass into energy always follows the equation proposed by Einstein; that is, the energy released by each gram of such mass when converted to energy is equal in ergs to the square of the velocity of light (in cm/sec). Thus

$$E = mc^2 = 1 \times (3 \times 10^{10})^2$$
$$= 9 \times 10^{20} \text{ ergs} \qquad [37\text{-}1]$$

The Cockcroft–Walton Experiment

The first experimental check on Einstein's theory came in 1932 when Cockcroft (England) and Walton (Ireland) bombarded lithium with high-energy protons (protons accelerated by a high voltage) in what is now called an ion accelerator. In the process alpha particles were produced.

$$_3\text{Li}^7 + {}_1\text{H}^1 \rightarrow {}_4\text{Be}^8 \rightarrow$$
$$_2\text{He}^4 + {}_2\text{He}^4 + \text{energy}$$

The energies of the alpha particles could be calculated by measuring their range in air.[2] The energy turns out to be 8.6 MeV for each, a total of 17.2 MeV for both alpha particles.[3] The lithium was at "rest" and so had no energy that concerns us here. The proton that was fired at the lithium had a kinetic energy of about 0.5 MeV. This is the input energy. How could this amount of energy impart a kinetic energy of 17.2 MeV to the alpha particles? Where did this energy come from? To say the least, this seems to be a violation of the law of conservation of energy. If the classical laws apply—that is, if no mass is converted to energy—the following equation should balance:

mass of proton + mass of Li atom
$$= 2 \times \text{mass of an alpha particle}$$

Making the proper substitutions and calculation shows that the equation does not balance. The difference is 0.0186 amu, which is far outside the limits of error, because we know

---

[2] This is analogous to measuring the energy of a bullet from a gun by measuring the thickness of a board that it will penetrate.

[3] It can be demonstrated mathematically that when 1 atomic mass unit (amu) is converted into energy, 931 MeV (million electron volts) is released.

the masses by means of Aston's mass spectrograph to five or six decimal places. In this equation we considered only the masses of the particles. Einstein's equation says that we have to consider the energies also, input and output energies expressed in amu, so that mass and energy are expressed in the same units. When we do that, the equation balances. Moreover, we can check it to see if the difference in masses—0.0186 amu—converted to energy by Einstein's equation equates with the observed energies of the alpha particles. As 1 amu is equated to 931 MeV,

$$0.0186 \times 931 = 17.3 \text{ MeV}$$

This result turns out to be in very close agreement with the measured energies of the two alpha particles, 17.2 MeV. Einstein's mass-energy equation seemed valid. To check, Cockcroft and Walton bombarded fluorine with protons, with the following result:

$$_1\text{H}^1 \ + \ _9\text{F}^{19} \ \rightarrow \ _{10}\text{Ne}^{20} \ \rightarrow$$
$$_8\text{O}^{16} \ + \ _2\text{He}^4 \ + \ \text{energy}$$

Again they measured the energies of the oxygen and fluorine atoms, set up the proper equations, and came out with an agreement between the measured and the computed values that made $E = mc^2$ no longer subject to doubt.

Stability of Nuclei

The Helium Nucleus

We still wonder how the protons and the neutrons can remain tightly packed together to form stable nuclei. Let us compare the combined masses of two free protons and two free neutrons with the mass of a helium nucleus, which consists of four such particles bound together in some way.

Mass of two free protons

$$2 \times 1.007276 = 2.014552 \text{ amu}$$

Mass of two free neutrons

$$2 \times 1.008665 = 2.017330 \text{ amu}$$
$$\text{total mass} = 4.031882 \text{ amu}$$

The mass of a helium nucleus is 4.001505 amu. The difference is 0.030377 amu. This means that when two protons and two neutrons combine to form a helium nucleus, there is a loss of mass (of 0.0304 amu). This "lost" mass is transformed into energy. How much energy? We have seen that 1 amu is equated to 931 MeV (energy), so 0.0304 amu corresponds to

$$0.0304 \times 931 = 28.3 \text{ MeV}$$

This is the energy that binds the four nucleons together to form the helium nucleus, and so is called binding energy. Formally defined, it is the difference between the total energy of the separated nucleons and the total energy of the particles in the nucleus of the neutral atom.

The Nuclear Force

Much as this may convince us that the energy to hold stable nuclei together can be accounted for, it still fails to offer any satisfying pictorial model as to how this energy overcomes the mutual repulsion of the protons or how neutrons can be attracted either to protons or to one another. Gravitational attractions are billions of billions times too small.

To better understand the problem, let us consider the nucleus of deuterium, an isotope of hydrogen ($_1\text{H}^2$). It contains one proton and one neutron and is the simplest nucleus that contains a neutron. Deuterium is a very stable isotope; like the helium nucleus, its mass is less than the combined mass of a free proton and a free neutron. There is no force of electrical attraction between the proton and the neutron in deuterium. Yet there *must* be a force of attraction between them. Whether we understand the nature of this attraction or not, we must accept the concept of very large attractive forces between protons and neutrons when they are extremely close together. Perhaps these forces are great enough to overcome the mutual repulsion between protons. This very strong attractive force between nucleons at extremely short distances is called the *nuclear force*.

The Unstable Neutron

We have used the relationship between the combined masses of free protons and free neutrons and the mass of a nucleus to explain stability of nuclei. We note that stability is increased by a decrease in mass, just as atoms with their electrons in a lower energy state are more stable than when they are in a higher energy state. Now let us see if we can also use the mass difference to explain instability. Let us begin with the neutron.

A free neutron has a mass equal to 1.008665 amu. A free proton has 1.007276 amu and an electron 0.000549 amu. Together the mass of the proton and the electron is 1.007825 amu. This is 0.000840 amu *less* than the mass of the neutron; that is, a neutron has a *greater* mass than the sum of its free parts. (We remind you that during radioactive decay a neutron breaks up into a proton and an electron—a beta ray.) The neutron may therefore be considered as existing in a *higher energy* state than the proton and the electron separately. We should suspect, then, that the neutron would be less stable than either a proton or an electron. This turns out to be the case, for the half-life of a neutron is about 13 min, whereas protons and electrons

can exist in the free state forever. The energy represented by the 0.000840 amu difference mentioned before corresponds to the energy of the emitted beta ray. Here we have another confirmation of the concept that the beta ray is ejected *from a nucleus* in radioactive atoms.

Binding Energy and the Instability of Radioactive Atoms

The instability of radioactive atoms is more complicated. We need to consider the total binding energy of nuclei—or perhaps we should say "unbinding energy," for it is defined as the energy needed from outside to tear the nucleus apart into protons and neutrons. It is calculated as the difference between the actual mass of a given nucleus and the total mass of the free protons and free neutrons of which it consists. This difference in mass is expressed either in atomic mass units or in energy units—ergs or calories or electron volts—usually electron volts.

An examination of the periodic chart reveals that as we pass from the lighter to the heavier elements, the ratio between the atomic weight and the atomic number increases. This means that the number of neutrons relative to the number of protons increases. The total binding energy necessary to hold these nucleons together in a nucleus should obviously increase as the number of nucleons increases.

More important for our purposes than total binding energy, however, is the binding energy per nucleon. If we plot this number against mass number for a variety of elements, we find that the curve at first rises sharply as the mass numbers increase, but slows as it nears a peak with a mass number close to 60. From the peak the curve very slowly declines until uranium, with a mass number of 238, is reached (Fig. 37-1). This curve reveals that the "base" elements like iron have the greatest binding energies, and so we should expect their nuclei

it that can be broken apart easily for less binding energy.

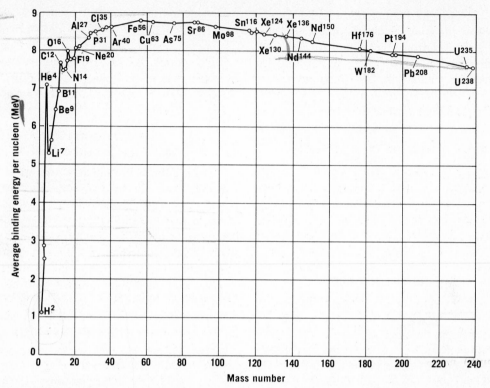

Fig. 37-1. Binding Energy per Nucleon vs. Atomic Mass Number. Note that the binding energy per nucleon (not total binding energy) ranges from about 1 MeV for deuterium ("heavy" hydrogen), H^2, with its two nucleons to a bit less than 9 MeV for iron. The elements to the left of the peak can increase their binding energies only by fusion, those to the right only by fission.

to be the most difficult to break up. Nuclear reactions, like exothermic chemical reactions, tend toward greater stability.

We need to remember that $E = mc^2$ means that in order to derive energy from atomic nuclei some mass must be lost. This loss increases the binding energy per nucleon. The binding energy per nucleon of a heavy atom like uranium is increased by splitting uranium into two atoms whose values on the above curve are higher than that of uranium. The difference in binding energy is released. To increase the binding energy per nucleon of a

light atom like deuterium, H^2 (popularly known as "heavy" hydrogen), we can cause it to fuse with another atom of H^2 to form an atom of helium. Again the difference in binding energy is released. (Why do we use heavy hydrogen instead of ordinary hydrogen?)

The graph shown in Fig. 37-1 gives us a clue to the reason for the limit to the number of naturally occurring elements. Almost all of the naturally radioactive elements are at the right in the graph. They have long half-lives. If there ever were any elements heavier than uranium-92, they must have been very unstable and so have long since disintegrated. Eleven elements beyond atomic number 92 have been artificially created by man; all are highly unstable with short half-lives compared to the age of the earth. If they ever existed they have long since decayed to the radioactive elements we find in nature or to stable lead.

Number of Protons vs. Number of Neutrons

Another clue to the stability of nuclei may be found in the relative numbers of protons and neutrons they contain. In the lighter elements the number of neutrons equals the number of protons. In iron the number of neutrons is 15% larger than the number of protons; in lead the number is just over 50% and in uranium, there are 58.7% more neutrons than protons in the nucleus. Seemingly, the more protons in a nucleus, the more neutrons necessary to maintain stability; when the number rises above 83 (that of nonradioactive bismuth), no number of neutrons can forever counteract the repulsive effect of the protons for one another. It may be that the neutrons act as a sort of nuclear cement to hold the nucleons together. Isotopes with an even number of protons and an even number of neutrons seem to be more stable than those with an odd number of one and an even number of the other, and the latter are in their turn more stable than those with an odd number of each.

We will conclude this section on stability of the nucleus by stating that whatever the attractions between neutrons and protons may be, it appears to be very strong at extremely short distances but extremely weak at any other distance, much more so than is the case with gravitational or electrostatic forces.

From this discussion and from the binding energy curve (Fig. 37-1), there emerge the two methods by which energy may be released quickly and in large amounts from the nuclei. One is by the disintegration of the heavier atoms, that is, by fission, and the other is by combination of lighter elements to form heavier ones, that is, by fusion. We will now turn our attention to these two processes.

Nuclear Fission

Nuclear physicists soon realized, as is apparent from the discussions, that large amounts of energy were stored within the atom, and that this energy was emitted naturally (by radioactivity) from the nuclei of certain atoms of high atomic weight. The problem was to learn how to release this energy artificially and to control it. The search for the means of obtaining nuclear energy and bringing it under control so as to build atomic bombs was not, as many people seem to believe, something that came about as a result of World War II. Instead, it was a conclusion to the sequence of events that began with the discoveries of Becquerel, the Curies, Thomson, Einstein, and Rutherford in the 1890's and early 1900's. The wartime research merely did on an enormous scale what scientists in their research laboratories had been doing on a small scale. Actually the war brought about little new fundamental research; that is, few additions to basic knowledge were made. Scientists were much too busy hastening to put to practical use the knowledge they already had.

The discovery of the neutron gave the nuclear physicists a new "bullet" to bombard atoms. The neutron has about the same mass as the proton and about one fourth that of the alpha particle. It had one great advantage over either in that it could penetrate into the nuclei of atoms, scoring direct hits, because it had no charge and so would experience no repulsion. Neutrons are ejected from some artificially radioactive atoms at high speeds. A typical reaction was that caused by bombarding boron with alpha particles. A radioactive isotope of nitrogen and a neutron were produced:

$$_5B^{10} + {}_2He^4 \rightarrow {}_7N^{13} + {}_0n^1$$

Neutrons lose energy in passing through matter only by direct collisions. In some of these collisions the neutron will be absorbed or captured by nuclei, especially after they have been slowed down. A neutron captured by a nucleus adds one nucleon to it, thus creating a new isotope. Isotopes that are not found in nature are always unstable—which is the reason that they are not found in nature.

Once a source of neutrons had been established, it was used to bombard other atoms. Fermi bombarded uranium with neutrons in 1934, as did Hahn and Strassman in early 1938. Presumably they caused fission, but it was not recognized as such until early in 1939. The fission was found to result in the formation of two elements near the middle of the periodic chart, barium and krypton, or antimony and niobium, or strontium and xenon, and so on. In all cases the atomic numbers of the two elements add up to 92, but their mass numbers are always larger than those of their stable isotopes; that is, they contain excess neutrons and so are radioactive. It is these radioactive isotopes that constitute the "fall-out" from nuclear explosions. A typical fission reaction is

$$_{92}U^{235} + {}_0n^1 \rightarrow {}_{92}U^{236} \rightarrow$$
$$_{54}Xe^{140} + {}_{38}Sr^{94} + 2{}_0n^1$$
$$+ \text{gamma ray} + 200 \text{ MeV}$$

U^{235} is the only isotope of uranium that can be fissioned by low-energy neutrons. This isotope is present in natural uranium only in the proportion of 1 to 140. In every case a number of neutrons are produced by the fission, the average number per fissioned atom being 2.5. This meant that the reaction could be self-sustaining; that is, neutrons from the outside would not be needed to keep it going. A chain reaction (Fig. 37-2) would be possible if not too many neutrons escaped to the outside or were absorbed. The amount of the isotope U^{235} in natural uranium was not enough to start a chain reaction; too many neutrons were absorbed by the U^{238}. It became necessary to separate U^{235} from U^{238}. This is impossible chemically because all isotopes of the same element behave exactly alike chemically. Two methods were developed, both based on the difference in mass numbers and both very expensive. Once this was done the atomic (A) bomb became possible.

If the mass of a quantity of U^{235} is below a certain critical size, the chain reaction will fail; too many neutrons escape to the outside without causing fission. Conversely, if the mass is above the critical size, the chain reaction operates spontaneously and the bomb explodes instantly. The problem is to control it. This is done by separating the U^{235} into two or more parts, each part a bit below the critical size. To set the bomb off all that has to be done is to bring the parts together. No source of neutrons is necessary to start the reaction because cosmic rays are constantly creating neutrons in the atmosphere. Despite their half-life of only 13 min, there are always enough around to start the reaction. The temperature generated in the heart of the bomb is enormous, many millions of degrees Celsius. The maximum size of the A-bomb is strictly limited by the number of masses of fissionable material, each below the critical size, that can be brought together at the same instant to form a single mass above critical size. Only a small part of each atom is converted into energy; that is, only the energy representing the difference between the mass of the uranium atom

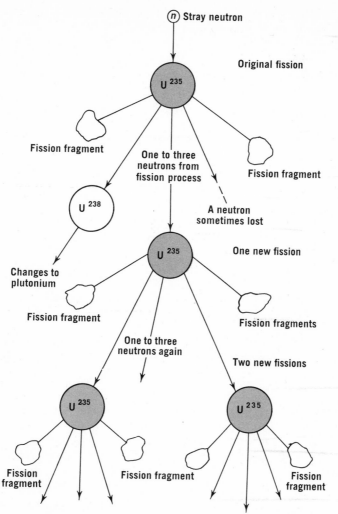

Fig. 37-2. Chain Reaction in Atomic Fission. A stray neutron starts the process by splitting a U²³⁵ atom (one of the uranium isotopes). One to three neutrons are produced, the number depending upon the kind of fission products. Suppose three are produced. There is a possibility that only one will cause a new fission, since one may strike a U²³⁸ atom to form plutonium and another may be "lost" to the chain reaction. But two may cause two new fissions, thereby giving rise to two, or possibly six, neutrons. Four of the six may produce new fissions, and from four to twelve more neutrons. Thus the number of fissions rises rapidly with each step in the chain, even though we started with one stray neutron. The process is extremely rapid; in a fraction of a second, the number of fissions is in the billions of billions. The whole quantity of U²³⁵ in a bomb is fissioned practically instantaneously. During the process some of the mass is turned into energy with the production of a fantastic amount of heat.

and the combined masses of the products is released. The amount per gram of mass converted is given by $E = mc^2$.

If we examine the graph (Fig. 37-1) we can see that the fission products with their mass numbers around 90 and 140 are nearer the top of the curve than uranium. This is always true. It is therefore not possible to fission elements at the top part of the curve. Several other radioactive elements, notably thorium-239, can be fissioned under proper circumstances.[4]

Nuclear Fusion

The discovery of atomic fission cast a new light on the source of the energy radiated from the sun. It had long been known that the enormous energy radiated could not possibly be accounted for by normal chemical processes. Could it be that atoms were undergoing fission in the sun? Analysis of the spectrum of the sun reveals comparatively few atoms that are fissionable, whereas it reveals large amounts of hydrogen and helium. Inspection of the curve in Fig. 37-1 shows that these could not be produced by fission of larger atoms. The curve does suggest that the elements to the left of the high point of the curve might be fused to form elements whose energy per nucleon is greater than either of the elements to be fused.

It was in 1939 that Hans Bethe of Cornell proposed the carbon cycle (so called because carbon serves as a sort of nuclear catalyst) to account for the source of the sun's energy. In

this cycle hydrogen is converted into helium:[5]

$$_6C^{12} + {}_1H^1 \rightarrow {}_7N^{13} + \text{energy}$$
$$_7N^{13} \rightarrow {}_6C^{13} + {}_{+1}e^0$$
$$_6C^{13} + {}_1H^1 \rightarrow {}_7N^{14} + \text{energy}$$
$$_7N^{14} + {}_1H^1 \rightarrow {}_8O^{15} + \text{energy}$$
$$_8O^{15} \rightarrow {}_7N^{15} + {}_{+1}e^0$$
$$_7N^{15} + {}_1H^1 \rightarrow {}_6C^{12} + {}_2He^4$$
$$+ \text{energy}$$

Note that the starting components were carbon and hydrogen, that the end products were the same carbon plus helium, and that the only element added during the intervening steps was hydrogen. The net effect is

$$4(_1H^1) \rightarrow {}_2He^4 + 2(_{+1}e^0) + 24.7 \text{ MeV}$$

Each of the nuclear reactions listed had been accomplished in the laboratory before Bethe proposed the cycle. It is estimated that nearly half the energy of the sun is generated via the carbon cycle. The source of the remainder is the same conversion of hydrogen to helium, but by another method, similar in principle to that of the hydrogen bomb. The details of this bomb are not available to the public, but we can make an educated guess.

There are two isotopes of hydrogen in addition to ordinary hydrogen, $_1H^2$ (deuterium) and $_1H^3$ (tritium). Tritium is radioactive, but its half-life is 12.5 yr and so it may be stored for a time. It is very rare in nature but can be transmuted from lithium at a very high cost. This reaction is

$$_3Li^6 + {}_0n^1 \rightarrow {}_1H^3 + {}_2He^4$$

The most probable reaction to produce helium is

---

[4] The most important fissionable atom is plutonium-239, an element that does not occur in nature but is made synthetically by bombarding U^{238} with neutrons. The reaction is as follows:

$$_{92}U^{238} + {}_0n^1 \rightarrow {}_{92}U^{239}$$
$$_{92}U^{239} \rightarrow {}_{93}Np^{239} + {}_{-1}e^0$$
$$_{93}Np^{239} \rightarrow {}_{94}Pu^{239} + {}_{-1}e^0$$

The intermediate element, neptunium, has a half-life of only 2.3 days, whereas Pu (plutonium) has one of about 24,000 years. It is therefore stable enough to be used. It is fissionable just as is U^{235}. It is "made" in an atomic pile under controlled conditions. Unlike U^{235} it can be separated from U^{238} by chemical means, for it is a different element.

[5] It was the English astronomer Eddington who first suggested (1927) that conversion of hydrogen to helium takes place in the sun.

$$_1H^2 \; + \; _1H^3 \; \rightarrow$$
$$_2He^4 \; + \; _0n^1 \; + \; 17.6 \text{ MeV}$$

This reaction needs a fantastically high temperature to activate it, 15 million °C at least. To fuse, hydrogen atoms must collide with extreme violence. This means they must have great speed, and this is obtained only by heating to a high temperature measured in millions of degrees. This temperature can be obtained only by use of an A-bomb. To make the H-bomb a small A-bomb is surrounded by a quantity of liquefied deuterium and tritium, which in turn is surrounded by a quantity of LiH^2. The "firing" of the A-bomb supplies the heat to start the fusion reaction. Because the activation energy of the fusion process is so extremely high, there is no upper limit to the amount of fusionable materials used in a single bomb; the H-bomb cannot explode spontaneously in the manner of the A-bomb no matter how much fusionable "fuel" is packed into it. Bombs equivalent to 50 million tons of TNT have been exploded. Any radioactive fallout from the H-bomb is due very largely to the A-bomb used to trigger it.

Note that the most usable energy that can be obtained from nuclear reactions of any kind is heat. Nuclear reactors (sometimes called piles) are simply devices in which the fission (not fusion) of uranium or plutonium atoms (footnote 4) is not allowed to reach chain reaction proportions. The heat given off is used to heat water to run a steam engine, which in turn runs a dynamo to generate electrical energy. Nuclear reactors are very large and heavy, for they must be surrounded with several tons of shielding material to absorb the deadly radiations. There is no other way at present to use nuclear power on a large scale, nor is there likely to be. Some writers have stated that the possible development of light-weight shielding will make it possible to have nuclear power plants in automobiles and airplanes. Prospects of such shielding are exceedingly dim at present. Equally dim are the present prospects of using the nuclear energy of fusion, and future prospects are not at all promising, certainly not promising enough to warrant prophecy of the kind some scientists were making some 10 or 12 years ago that success was just around the corner. Some scientists, to be sure, think that this view is too pessimistic.

Exercises

1. Einstein's mass-energy equation is a general one, and so can be applied to chemical as well as nuclear reactions. Nothing useful is learned by doing so, for the uncertainty in m (in $E = mc^2$) far exceeds the value of E. Thus, in chemical reactions, we assume that mass and energy are conserved separately. On p. 491 is the equation $2Na + Cl_2 \rightarrow 2NaCl + 196,800$ cal. Considering all that has been said so far, what is the source of the energy that appears on the right? Explain.

2. Does Einstein's mass-energy equation give us the "right" to assume that every mass can be converted to energy?

3. Approximately how many atomic mass units are there in 1 g of protons?

4. What was the significance of the Cockcroft–Walton experiment?

5. The mass of a proton is 1.007276 amu, that of a neutron is 1.008665 amu, and that of an electron is 0.000549 amu. We have already learned that a neutron may decay into a proton and an electron. How do you explain that the sum of the masses of a proton and an electron do not equal the mass of the neutron?

6. (a) What is meant by binding energy? (b) Is it released or absorbed when free

protons and free neutrons combine to form nuclei of other atoms?

(c) Is the total mass of the free protons added to the total mass of the free neutrons equal to the total mass of the protons and neutrons in the nuclei formed? Explain.

7. To explain exercise 6, how do we rewrite the law of conservation of mass and the law of conservation of energy?

8. What elements have the greatest binding energy per nucleon (Fig. 37-1)?

9. Why does the graph start with H^2 rather than H^1?

10. What relationship is there between binding energy and stability of a nucleus?

11. Which is more stable, a proton or a neutron?

12. Which is more stable, atoms that have large numbers of neutrons relative to the number of protons, or atoms that have smaller numbers of neutrons?

13. (a) How does the ratio of the number of protons to the number of neutrons in atomic nuclei change as we proceed to higher and higher atomic numbers?

(b) Can you suggest a reason for this, and relate it to natural radioactivity?

14. All atoms can be made artificially radioactive by bombardment with one sort of particle or another. There are thus hundreds of artificially radioactive isotopes. If our theories or origin of the elements from hydrogen ions, by processes like those described for our sun, are correct, then it seems likely that very large numbers of these radioactive isotopes were also made. Assuming this to be correct, how do you explain their absence (for the most part) from nature today?

15. In our previous discussions we have seen how protons, neutrons, and alpha particles have been ripped loose from atoms by nuclear bombardment. Why are these separations not referred to as nuclear fission?

16. (a) What is it that fissions certain types of atoms?

(b) What is the source (or sources) of the "fissioner"?

(c) What are the products?

17. Can you suggest a possible reason for U^{235} being fissionable but not U^{238}? (Refer to your answer to exercise 13).

18. What is a chain reaction?

19. (a) What is meant by a mass of U^{235} of critical size?

(b) Explain why there should be a critical size.

20. Suggest a reason for there being no atomic explosions in uranium mines.

21. Fermi, Cockcroft and Walton, and others obtained nuclear fission in various experiments well before 1939 but failed to recognize the new discovery because of the influence of preconceived concepts. Explain their failure.

22. Give one method (not necessarily practical) for separating U^{235} from U^{238}.

23. In what form does the great bulk of the energy in an atomic explosion appear? In what ways may this energy be used *directly*?

24. Would an automobile powered by atomic energy be practicable? Give more than one reason. Explain.

25. Nonscientists have said that the home of the future would have a small atomic power plant built into it, from which the energy to run the home could be obtained for generations at no cost and without any attention. Discuss both sides of this problem.

26. (a) In what fundamental ways do A-bombs differ from H-bombs?

(b) Which can be more destructive? Why?

27. (a) What is radioactive fallout?

(b) What is its source? (Be specific.)

The Universe Beyond the Solar System

38

Man's Place in Space and Time

It has taken man a long time to recognize his place in space and time—if we are optimistic enough to believe that he has yet done so. His universe has been an anthropocentric (man-centered) one, and still is for the vast majority of us. True, his views began to change in the early 1600's when the heliocentric hypothesis of Copernicus—as modified by Kepler—gained credence. He adjusted his thinking to a sun-centered solar system without too great difficulty, for he could still think of his solar system as being at the center of the universe. In time it seemed eminently reasonable for our heat- and light-giver to be at the center even though our eyes try to tell us that the earth is still at the center of the universe.

It is not only incorrect but unfair to say that Plato, Aristotle, Hipparchus, Ptolemy, and many other contributors to the Ptolemaic view were wrong, for their ideas were consistent with the best observations that they could

Open wide the door for us, so that we may look out into the immeasurable starry universe; show us that other worlds like ours occupy the ethereal realms; make clear to us how the motion of all worlds is engendered by forces; teach us to march forward to greater knowledge of nature.

GIORDANO BRUNO (1548–1600)

653

make. We say here what we have said else-where, perhaps in different words, that the scientists and other thinkers of the past should be judged in light of the knowledge that was available to them, not by the knowledge that is available to us. We can see farther than they could because we have their shoulders to stand on. A man may ultimately be proved to have been wholly wrong and yet deserve to be remembered as one of the greatest men of his times.

Copernicus started the first great revolution in astronomy in modern times, a revolution that resulted in the first important change from man's anthropocentric thinking. He was aided mightily by Kepler, Galileo, and others, but it remained for Newton to reveal the basic order in the universe by showing that all celes-tial motions were described by a force called gravitation, without which complete chaos would reign. Telescopic observations of the heavens started with Galileo, and in the course of time better and better telescopes and the invention of other instruments gave us higher shoulders to stand on and "eyes" that could see farther and with greater clarity than the ancients could ever dream. With them came the detection of parallax (p. 9), and one of the valid objections to the heliocentric hy-pothesis disappeared—the stars were indeed immeasurably far away. Moreover, the number of stars that could be seen increased fantastically; the naked eye can see at most 5000 to 6000 under optimum conditions,[1] a 4 in. telescope (diameter of the lens or mirror) increased the number to over 2 million, and the 200 in. giant on Mount Palomar to over 1 billion, and still much of the sky remains unsurveyed. Even prior to the installation of "the glass giant on Palomar," the volumes of

observational data would have filled a library. In the early 1920's there came the second great revolution in astronomy when Harlow Shapley of Harvard destroyed the last vestige of an-thropocentric thinking among people not handicapped by dogmas acquired from their immediate ancestors, by calculating the overall size of our galaxy, the Milky Way, and by measuring the distance from the center of our galaxy to our sun. He found the sun to be about 27,000 light years (p. 23) distant from the center of that galaxy, a galaxy containing more than 100 billion stars arranged in the form of a great disk so large that light takes 100,000 years to cross from edge to edge. With this discovery the concept that we and this earth of ours were at the center of anything completely vanished. About the same time came the realization that our galaxy did not constitute the whole universe, that there were actually millions of other galaxies, most of them smaller than ours but a few as big or bigger. These facts meant that still another adjustment in man's thinking had to take place about his importance in the universe. These facts meant the abandonment of a heliocentric universe (not the abandonment of a helio-centric solar system, however), and certainly deflated man's ego from the standpoint of his position in the material universe.

While man was adjusting his thinking to this blow to his ego, the thought came to him that perhaps in this universe of stars, space, and time he was not alone, that perhaps among all of the stars in the universe there are some that have planets revolving about them, and that perhaps some of these planets have intel-ligent life on them. With more than a hundred million million million chances, it is expectable that several million, or possibly even several billion, stars have planetary systems. Not all of them would have environmental conditions conducive to the development of life as we know it, but it seems highly probable—we

---

[1] The optimum conditions are those that exist on a high mountain top in a desert area far removed from the lights of even a small city.

might even use the word certain—that a fair percentage would have.

What should be man's response to his loss of an anthropocentric universe? This is not a scientific question, for it cannot be answered by any of the methods of investigation known to science. We will not attempt even to discuss it, let alone answer it. Suffice it to say that man has accepted the Darwinian evidence and arguments for his animal origins, for he was still left "at the top of the heap." Perhaps he still stands above all other organisms in the universe; at least he can still think so if it comforts him any, so long as there is no evidence to the contrary.

Astrophysicists have shown that the kinds of chemistry and physics that we have here on earth prevail throughout the parts of the universe that have so far been explored. Thousands upon thousands of atomic spectra—the fingerprints of atoms—have shown no atoms of elements in the stars that are not found here on earth. This is what we would expect from our study of the periodic table; if a new element were discovered in some star, where would we put it in the table? To be a *new* element it would have to be a transuranium element with a nuclear number higher than 105. No element with a number higher than 92 occurs naturally. All such elements have been synthesized in nuclear reactors or in nuclear accelerators. All are radioactive with very short half-lives, plutonium excepted (footnote 5, Chapter 37). The probability of finding such an element in any star is close to zero.

A third great revolution took place on October 4, 1957, when the first Russian *Sputnik* (the first artificial satellite) completed its orbit about the earth in about 90 min. The culmination (to date) of this revolution took place when the American astronauts landed on the moon on July 20, 1969, the first of four such landings to date.

So much for our place in the universe, a place on a small planet revolving about an average star, which is one of about 100 billion in the Milky Way, which in turn is one galaxy among millions, perhaps 100 million, of other galaxies. What about our place in time? According to Bishop Ussher (A.D. 1650) the earth (and presumably all other celestial bodies) was created in 4004 B.C. Thornton Page[2] has said

> If you accept a miracle such as this, what's wrong with creation five minutes ago? It would scarcely be more difficult for the Creator to create all of us sitting here, with our memories of events that never really happened, with our worn shoes that were never really new, with spots of soup that were never really spilled on our ties, and so on. Such a beginning is logically possible, but extremely hard to believe.

In Chapter 35 you learned that geologists have uncovered vast amounts of evidence of the worn shoes and spotted vests and ties type that indicate that the earth is a billion or more years old. You also learned in Chapter 36 that the minimum age of the earth has been calculated from the products of radioactive decay in the rocks to be at least 4 billion years. What happened earlier? We will return to this subject after learning more about stars and galaxies.

The Means of Observation

Astronomy is basically an observational science; unlike the other physical sciences, except a number of the aspects of geology, the observer has no control over the objects that he observes. Some may believe that with the advent of space vehicles of many types, astronomy may become, in part, an experimental science. Although it is true that we are using small orbiting observatories at the present

[2] Professor of Astronomy, Wesleyan University, Middletown, Conn.

time, these are used as data collectors, not for the purpose of carrying out experiments. Even if an observatory were placed on Pluto, our most distant planet, we would not be appreciably closer to any star than we are here on earth. We would have one advantage, however, on Pluto. Our atmosphere acts as an opaque blanket that blocks out most of the electromagnetic radiations coming from the sun and other stars other than ordinary light. It blocks out all the X rays, most of the ultraviolet and most of the infrared rays and all of the long radio waves. This blanket allows the rays of visible light and the short radio waves to pass through, along with a small part of the ultraviolet and of the infrared. Moreover, the blanketing effect is increased by the turbulence of the atmosphere and its content of dirt. On Pluto all types of radiation could be received without diminution of any kind, except possibly that due to distance. The atmosphere, however, has its merits, insofar as man is concerned, as a shield against lethal X rays and ultraviolet rays.

The astronomer has not only telescopes and cameras at his disposal but also photometers, spectrographs, electronic computers, and the orbiting observatory previously mentioned. There are three types of telescopes, the reflectors, the refractors, and those of the Schmidt-Type. The reflectors use curved mirrors to collect light and bring it to a focus where the observer can look at or photograph whatever is in the field of view. With a photograph he can study what he observed at any time; he can compare one photograph with another taken of the same field at another time; and so on. The glass giant of Palomar is a reflector with a 200 in. mirror. The refractors use a lens to refract (bend) the light rays so that they come to a focus. It is not feasible to make such lenses greater than 40 in. in diameter, which is the diameter in the world's largest refractor

(in southern Wisconsin). The Schmidt-Type telescope combines a thin reflecting plate with a spherical mirror to produce excellent images of large areas of the sky. The world's largest is at Mount Palomar.

One of the most important tasks of modern astronomy is the precise measurement of the color and brightnesses of stars, the most precise of which are carried out with photoelectric cells (p. 379). Some of these cells are so sensitive that when placed at the focus of the 200 in. telescope they can detect a candle at a distance of 1000 miles. The spectrograph, which is nothing more than a spectroscope used with a photographic plate, has long been the most powerful accessory to the telescope. It analyzes light from the stars just as it does light in the laboratory. The various kinds of atoms in the stars can be identified by their spectra (p. 352) and their temperatures determined by the color of the stars. The spectroscope is also used to measure the radial motion of stars; the principle involved is the Doppler effect (p. 158).

Radioastronomy

The radio waves emitted by stars and galaxies are very weak. This weakness explains the size of the radiotelescopes, for a large collecting area is needed. A very large radiotelescope in Arecibo, Puerto Rico, has a collecting surface in the form of a large parabolic dish several hundred feet in diameter. The wavelengths of the radio waves reaching us from outer space vary from $\frac{1}{10}$ in. to 25 ft. A 21 cm hydrogen radiation had been predicted theoretically before it was first observed in 1951. Radio waves have one advantage over visible light waves; they pass through the vast clouds of interstellar "dust" in our galaxy as if they were not there. There are objects (stars?) that emit very little ordinary light but do emit a high intensity of radio waves. By 1962 more than 2000 of such sources had been discovered. To best learn about the ultraviolet light and X rays emitted by stars, including our sun, the observing equipment needs to be placed at elevations of 100 mi or more; this can only be done with rockets and artificial satellites. An orbiting space observatory equipped with a telescope and other instruments, and carrying a human observer, would seem to be the answer to some of the observational problems. Actually the observer would be a liability, for if anything inside the laboratory moves, the direction of the satellite will be changed slightly. If the observer leans forward to make a correction on an instrument, the shift will change the orientation of his ship, thus introducing another error that he can never correct. An observer in an observatory on the moon would have as unshakable an observatory as one here on earth, but he would have grave difficulties living there (see Chapter 4).

The United States in November 1970 placed the third of a planned series of unmanned space observatories in orbit. The mass of one observatory is 4680 tons. The most important single objective is to study the evolution of stars by making observations of some of the young intensely hot stars in the Orion nebula (see Fig. 38-6). It is then planned to proceed to the study of somewhat older stars. In the 12 billion year (?) age of our galaxy many generations of these intensely hot massive stars have come and gone, so that stars exist in some galaxies in every stage of development.

The Source of Stellar Energy

Stars shine by their own light, that is, by the light generated within them, whereas planets shine by the light reflected from them. We have already seen how starlight (called sunlight when it comes from that star known as sun) is generated by the fusion of four hydrogen atoms into one helium atom that has a smaller mass than the sum of the four hydrogens. This process is often called the proton-proton reaction. We have also seen that a temperature of millions degrees Celsius is necessary to initiate such fusion. The important result of this fusion is that about 0.7% of the combined mass of the four hydrogens is turned into energy in accordance with the Einstein equation, $E = mc^2$. About 564 million tons of hydrogen disappears from our sun every second. All but 4 million tons of this mass is converted to helium. This 4 million tons comes from that 0.7% of the combined mass of the four hydrogens, lost by the conversion of it into energy via electromagnetic radiation. This process will continue as long as there is a sufficient supply of hydrogen atoms. This supply will probably last for at least another 5 billion years, perhaps longer, even though the conversion has been going on for some 5 billion years. The mass luminosity law states that the greater the mass of a star, the higher the temperature, and hence the greater the rate of fusion[3] of hydrogen atoms into helium and energy. Doubling the internal temperature of the star increases the rate of the proton-proton reaction by a factor of about 16. Thus the largest of the hot blue stars consume hydrogen at such a rate that their life expectancies are but very few tens of millions of years at most, despite their great mass. The above reaction is more important than the carbon cycle method (p. 650) of forming helium from hydrogen below internal temperatures of $15-16 \times 10^6°C$, whereas the carbon cycle is more important at higher temperatures.

---

[3] Some astronomers (and other scientists) speak of the fusion process as "burning" and of hydrogen as "fuel." There is absolutely no resemblance between the processes of burning and fusion except that they both produce heat.

Distances of the Near Stars

The early Greeks, despite their other achievements in astronomy, had no concept of the actual distances to the stars. This is not surprising, for even today after more than a hundred years of knowing, we still find the actual distances inconceivable. Since they could detect no parallax they concluded that the earth was stationary. Copernicus had the same difficulty; he could only state that the lack of parallax was due to their great distances. He was right, but he had no evidence. Newton made the first attempt to calculate the distance to the stars. He assumed that all the stars had about the same intrinsic brightness as the sun, and that they appeared less bright only because they were so much farther away. He knew that the intensity of light varies inversely as the square of the distance from its source (Fig. 5-1). He therefore could calculate how far away the sun would have to be to have the same *apparent* brightness as a particular star. Of course, many stars have intrinsic brightnesses that are very different from that of the sun, but a great many do have about the same brightness, and for these his estimates were reasonable.

About 1835 Bessel made the first measurement of parallax on one of the nearest stars. This is done by trigonometric methods involving the measurement of a base line and an angle (Fig. 1-4). The longest base line available to man is the diameter of the earth's orbit (186 million mi). To use the base line two observations are made on the same star six months apart. The angle is extremely small even for the nearest star, being only a small fraction of a degree. Today the measurement is made by a micrometer on photographs taken six months apart. Proxima Centauri, the nearest star, is nearly 25 trillion miles away. This is equal to 4.2 light years; a light year is the *distance* light travels in a year. Only about

forty stars are less than 16 light years away. The method of parallax can be used for stars up to 300 light years away, perhaps somewhat more with the 200 in. telescope on Mount Palomar. For those farther away indirect methods must be used; these will be described later.

Units of Stellar Distances

The largest parallax ever measured is only 0.76 sec of arc[4] for Proxima Centauri. When parallaxes are less than 0.01 sec, the unavoidable errors in measurement become as large or larger than the parallax, so that the measurement becomes useless. We have also defined the light year as the distance light travels in one year, about 6 million million mi. Proxima Centauri is 4.2 light years distant from us. Thus a parallax of 0.76 sec of arc corresponds to 4.2 light years. Smaller parallaxes mean greater distances. Another unit of stellar distance is the parsec (par for parallax, and sec for second of arc). It is the distance at which a star would have a parallax of 1 sec. It equals 3.26 light years, about 20 million million mi.

Apparent Brightness and Luminosity

About 200 B.C. Hipparchus prepared a catalogue of about 1000 stars, in which he assigned the term first magnitude to the 20 brightest stars that he could see, the term second magnitude to a fainter but larger group, and the term sixth magnitude to the faintest that he could see with the naked eye. About 2000 years later it became possible to make accurate measurements of their apparent brightnesses,

[4] One second of arc is $1/3600$ of one degree, since 60 seconds equals one minute, and 60 minutes equals one degree.

that is, the brightness of a star relative to other stars as they appear to us here on earth. (The term *magnitude* refers to brightness, not to size or mass.) These accurate measurements showed that the average of Hipparchus' 20 first magnitude stars was about 100 times as bright as his average sixth magnitude stars. Thus the greater the magnitude, the fainter the star. Astronomers wanted to keep a uniform ratio between individual magnitudes, so they set the fifth root of a hundred ($\sqrt[5]{100} \cong 2.5$) for the difference of one magnitude. Thus the brightness difference of one magnitude on this logarithmic scale is 2.5, for two magnitudes it is 6.25, for three magnitudes it is 16, for four it is 40, and for five it is exactly 100. From this scale it is seen that stars brighter than the average first magnitude star, it (the scale) has to be extended in the negative direction. Our sun has, then, an apparent magnitude of -26.7. Venus, the brightest object in the heavens aside from the sun and the moon, has an apparent brightness of -4.4. On the other hand, the apparent brightnesses of faint stars run up to $+24$. Such stars can be photographed only by our best telescopes.

Absolute Magnitudes

The astronomer is more interested in the actual brightness (absolute magnitude) of a star than in how bright it seems to be. A star may appear bright because it is very near (as is our sun), or because it is very big, or because it has a high temperature, or because of a combination of any two, or all three reasons. Absolute magnitude is sometimes called intrinsic brightness, or absolute luminosity, or absolute brightness. We will simply use the word *luminosity* instead of any of these other terms. The brightest stars have luminosities that are 10,000 times greater than our sun; the faintest stars have luminosities that are only $\frac{1}{10,000}$ that of our sun.

Luminosity

Thus one may infer that luminosity refers to the total amount of light emitted by a star. It is a property of the star itself; that is, it does not depend upon the distance. It is dependent upon surface temperature and size; the temperature determines the amount of light each square centimeter of its surface emits per second, and the size determines the number of square centimeters of the emitting surface. Stars may thus have a high luminosity either because they are very hot or very big. If they are both, their luminosity will be very high. Most giant stars have high luminosity because they are big, not because they have high surface temperature. (They are not, however, called giant stars because of their size.) Dwarf stars are, as their name indicates, stars with low luminosity, either because they are relatively cool, or small, or both. Canopus, a giant star 180 light years distant, has an intrinsic brightness 5200 times that of our sun.

Sirius, the Dog Star, has the greatest apparent brightness of any star in our night sky. It is twice as large as our sun, nearly twice as hot at the surface, and a luminosity 40 times as great. Vega has about the same properties. Most of the naked-eye stars of our winter constellation Orion are far more luminous than Sirius. The central star of Orion's belt has 10 times the volume of the sun, it is four times as hot at the surface, it is 20 times as massive, and 600 times as luminous. Rigel, a supergiant in Orion (at his heel) is 20,000 times as luminous as our sun. Betelgeuse, a cool star at Orion's shoulder, is 300 times the size of our sun.

The luminosity of a star may be calculated from the apparent brightness and its distance in those cases where the distance can be determined by parallax. All that needs to be done is to figure out, by use of the inverse-square law, how bright a star would have to be at its known distance to send us the observed amount of light. The relationship may be expressed as follows:

$$\text{apparent brightness} = \frac{\text{luminosity}}{(\text{distance})^2}$$

The proper units must be used.

This equation shows us that the distance can be calculated if the apparent brightness and the luminosity are known. As already indicated, the apparent brightness is never a problem. The problem is to use some other method for determining the luminosity. Because this other method involves the spectroscope, we will postpone discussion of it until later.

Star Temperatures and Spectra

The temperature of the surface of a star is easily measurable because precise measurements are not needed. A fair and useful estimate can be made by color alone.

Red	cool	2,000–4,000°C
Orange	warm	4,000–5,000°C
Yellow	moderately hot	6,000–7,000°C
White	very hot	10,000–12,000°C
Blue	extremely hot	15,000°C and up

Our sun is a yellow star; Vega is a white star. There are, of course, all gradations between— orange-yellow, yellow-white, blue-white, and so forth.

A more accurate determination of the temperature can be made by comparing the spectra of stars. In Chapter 20 we learned that spectra are the fingerprints of atoms. These lines show that the stars are largely composed of hydrogen (about 75% on the average). Next in abundance is helium, followed by various ionized metals. In the cooler red stars some un-ionized metals and simple compounds are present. We also learned that the spectrum of

an incandescent body also depends upon the temperature because the frequencies emitted shift from the red end of the spectrum toward the blue end as the temperature rises (Fig. 22-1a). Since there are no pronounced differences in the compositions of stars, spectral differences are due chiefly to temperature differences.

At the high temperatures of yellow, white, and blue stars, no compounds can exist; all matter is dissociated into atoms. These atoms are in "excited" states, more so in the white and blue than in the yellow stars. They emit radiation as they return to less excited states. The greater the difference between these two states, the higher the frequencies emitted. The number of possible frequencies is also increased. The excitation comes from within the star where the temperatures are vastly higher than at or near the surface. Cooler atoms at the surface absorb energy coming from within the star and reradiate it in all directions. Atoms of different substances differ in their capacities to absorb radiation at different temperatures. The effect is to produce dark (absorption) lines where the bright lines would normally appear (p. 354).

Thus, the hydrogen lines (bright or dark) in the spectrum of hydrogen or any other element in a blue star are not all exactly the same as those in the spectrum of a white star. Moreover, the intensity of the lines, bright or dark, varies with the temperature. It is therefore possible to classify the spectra into types according to the lines (bright or dark) present. The types are listed as O, B, A, F, G, K, M, R, N. Blue stars have O-type spectra. Our sun is a G-type; M, R, and N are red types. Blue stars emit 20 or more times the radiation per unit area that our sun does, whereas a red type may emit as little as $\frac{1}{20}$ as much per unit area (or even much less).

Using spectral type, the temperature may be determined by use of Wien's law. Intensity of the emitted energy is plotted against wavelength (Fig. 22-1*a*) and the curve drawn. The temperature of the star is directly proportional to the frequency (inversely proportional to the wavelength) at which most of its radiation is given off, that is, to the high point of the curve.

We can now understand how the luminosity of a star can be determined even if its distance is not known. For stars of any one spectral class whose luminosities are known, it was observed that the relative intensities of certain spectral lines depended on the luminosity. In other words, the relations among the intensities of spectral lines change as the luminosity changes. So pronounced are the differences in these relations that it was possible to predict the luminosity of a star by examining its spectrum. The validity of the method was established by applying it to the stars whose luminosities are known from the apparent brightnesses and the distances. If this is valid for *all* of them, it should be valid for the more distant stars.

Distances of the Remote Stars

We may now return to the equation,

$$\text{apparent brightness} = \frac{\text{luminosity}}{d^2}$$

Since we have developed a method for determining the luminosity that does not depend on the distance, we can now use it in conjunction with apparent brightness and thus determine the distance to those stars so far away the parallax method cannot be used. The validity of the method is, of course, tested by applying it first to those stars whose distances are known by the parallax method. If it holds for them, it should hold for those that are farther away, at least for those not more than a few thousand light years away. This is an accepted method of procedure among scientists.

Another method of calculating distances, especially useful for the most distant stars, uses the period of pulsation for certain stars called the Cepheid variables. The name comes from a pulsating star in the constellation Cepheus. These stars change in brightness more or less periodically, reaching a maximum and then fading to a minimum, over and over again. The period ranges from a day or so to a month or more. By a study of a sufficient number of stars, it was determined that the Cepheids with the longer periods had the greater apparent brightnesses. This correlation held for the few Cepheids whose distances could be readily calculated by methods already described. The problem was to correlate the period with luminosity, that is, to establish a scale by which period could be translated into luminosity. The method by which this was done is too complex for us here. Once done, however, distances to the Cepheids could be calculated.

Sizes of Stars

The stars are all so distant that even in our largest telescopes they appear as mere points of light, and so we are unable to measure their diameters of any method, direct or indirect (Fig. 38-1). If we have certain information, the diameters of stars not more than a few thousand light years distant may be calculated. The luminosity of a star is a measure of its rate of radiation. The Stefan–Boltzmann law states that the total radiant energy emitted in all directions per square centimeter per second is proportional to the fourth power of the absolute temperature, that is,

$$\frac{E \text{ (total energy)}}{\text{area}} = kT^4$$

where k is an experimentally determined constant. As the temperature can be determined from its spectrum, the star's radiating surface

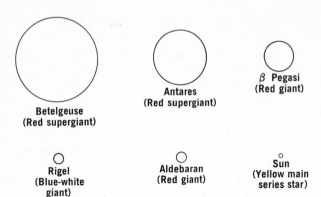

Betelgeuse
(Red supergiant)

Antares
(Red supergiant)

β Pegasi
(Red giant)

Rigel
(Blue-white
giant)

Aldebaran
(Red giant)

Sun
(Yellow main
series star)

Fig. 38-1. Some Relative Sizes of Stars. The positions of Betelgeuse and Rigel in the constellation Orion can be seen in Fig. 38-6.

in square centimeters can be determined. The surface of a sphere is 3.1416 times the square of its diameter. A little arithmetic gives us the diameter. Note that size and mass are two different things.

Calculation of the sizes of the stars yields some startling figures. Canopus turns out to have a diameter a bit greater than the radius of the earth's orbit about the sun, and Antares, a red star, has a diameter of over 400 million mi! Any astronomer would be happier if he could check this figure by some other method. This was done by Michelson, who used an ingenious method involving interference. His figure was 428 million mi. At the other end of the scale is a star that revolves about the Dog Star, Sirius. This star is a white dwarf only 25,000 mi in diameter, about the same as the planet Uranus. It is appropriately named the Pup. Some of the white dwarfs are even smaller than the earth.

Density and Mass

Despite this great range in diameters, the range in masses is remarkably small. The mass of most stars ranges from 5 times that of the sun to $\frac{1}{5}$ of it. A few masses run to as much as 100 times that of the sun. It follows that the stars with the greatest diameters (volumes) must have low densities. Antares, for example, has a density less than that of the atmosphere

here on earth. On the other hand, the density of the Pup is about 61,000 times that of water. A pint of it would weigh over 30 tons. If we remember that most of the atom is empty space, that the nucleus of a hydrogen atom occupies only a millionth of a millionth of the volume of the atom, we can begin to understand how matter could be as dense as that in the Pup.

How do astronomers ascertain the masses of stars? None of the methods so far used for investigation of stellar phenomena will give them to us. The matter would be enormously more difficult if there were not so many double stars. In all of them, each star revolves about their common center of gravity. If the period can be determined, then by the application of the law of gravitation, the mass of the system can be determined. This was done first with Sirius and the Pup. By more complex calculations the mass of each was determined. Once this was known, the Pup's density of 61,000 g/cm^3 was calculated. Some dwarf stars have vastly greater densities.

The Hertzsprung–Russell Diagram

If we plot the luminosity of stars against their spectral class, a graph like that in Fig. 38-2 results. It is called the Hertzsprung–

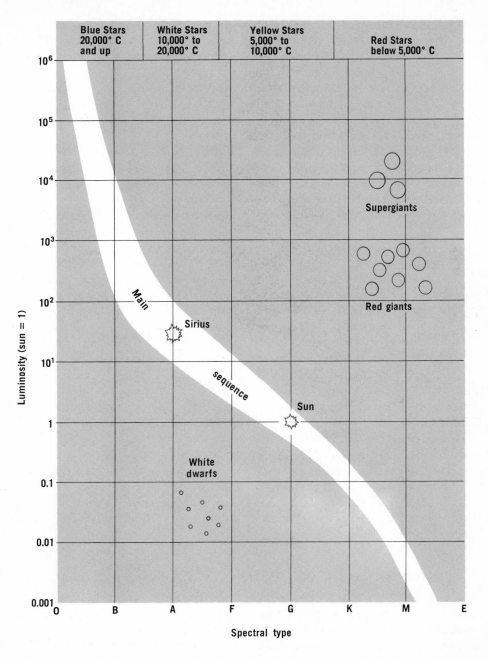

Fig. 38-2. The Hertzsprung–Russell Diagram. This diagram shows the relationship between spectral type and luminosity of stars. The red giants are extremely bright but their light is red, not white because their surface temperature is relatively low. The white dwarfs are small white stars, some with diameters not much greater than that of the earth. The sun is moderate in mass and in luminosity. Compare its mass and spectral type with those of Sirius.

Russell diagram. In such a plot a large number of stars that are in the vicinity of our sun fall along a diagonal band called the main sequence. Note that the hot stars are on the upper left, the cooler ones on the lower right. From the position of the red giants we see that they have high luminosity even though they are relatively cool. We conclude that this is possible only because they are giants in mass as well as in luminosity. From the position of the white dwarfs we see that they have low luminosity even though they are very hot. They must be dwarfs in mass as well as in luminosity. Note that neither the giants nor the dwarfs fall in the main sequence. Why do the stars other than the giants and the dwarfs fall in a band such as the main sequence? This is because there is a relationship between mass and luminosity. In general, stars that have high luminosity are massive and hot, such as the blue giants in the upper part of the main sequence. Stars that have low luminosity are relatively small and cool; they fall in the lower part of the main sequence. From these observations we can state the relationship between mass and luminosity as follows: The luminosity of a main sequence star depends on its total mass. This is sometimes called the mass-luminosity law. Note that here we have applied it only to main sequence stars. Our sun falls almost in the middle of the main sequence because it is moderate in mass, in luminosity, and in temperature.

Population I Stars

The stars described in our discussion of the Hertzsprung–Russell diagram lie in one of the arms of our galaxy as we shall see later. Stars that have the general characteristics of these stars are sometimes referred to as Population I stars. They are comparatively young stars that have converted a relatively small amount of their hydrogen to helium and energy. In places they are associated with vast clouds of gas and "dust." The full significance of Population I stars will become clearer after we have discussed galaxies, types of star clusters, and stellar evolution.

Stellar Motions

If Ptolemy were to come back to earth today he would have no trouble recognizing the constellations. In fact, he would note no differences in the positions of stars relative to one another, unless he made careful measurements. In the time since he measured Sirius, it has moved only half a degree. Other stars have moved as much as a degree. The motion of any star may be described by giving its *radial motion* (motion directly toward or away from the observer) and its *proper motion* (motion at right angles to a line between the star and an observer). The latter is obtained by direct observation. Even for stars that have high velocities, the proper motion is very small because of the great distances. Radial motion is detected by the so-called red shift of the spectral lines. The principle involved is the Doppler effect (Fig. 9-5), a principle that applies to all wave motion.

If the star is approaching the observer, the spectral lines are all shifted slightly towards the violet end of the spectrum. If the star is moving away from the observer, the shift is towards the red end. In the first case the wavelengths are apparently shorter, in the latter they are apparently longer. The amount of shift from the wavelengths as observed in the laboratory from a stationary source will give the speed towards or away from the observer. That such shifts do occur can be checked by the spectrum of the Pup as it revolves about Sirius. Along part of its orbit it is moving toward us, and in another part it is moving away. The spectral lines show corresponding shifts in position. The spectra of pulsating stars—the pulsation is caused by alternate contraction and expansion of the star—also show such shifts. From such shifts the radial motion of any star, no matter how far away, can be detected. Observation of the proper motion is limited because, as the distance increases, the amount of motion across the line of sight decreases so that it is imperceptible for most stars, unless very long periods of time are considered. One hundred thousand years from now the proper motions of the stars forming the Great Dipper will have been so great that the name, if still applied, will no longer be at all descriptive. Speeds of stars in our galaxy up to 30 or 40 mi/sec are not uncommon.

Nebulae and Galaxies

Nebulae

The term *nebula* was originally used to describe any cloud-like luminous spot in the night sky that remained fixed relative to the stars. There were three main types, the diffuse, the planetary, and the spiral. The spirals were ultimately proved by modern telescopes to be groups of stars, as many as 100 billion in a group (Figs. 38-3, 38-4, and 38-5). Some of them are spiral galaxies; our Milky Way is one. The diffuse nebulae are great clouds of interstellar gas and dust, some bright and some

Fig. 38-3. The Great Spiral Nebula in the Constellation Andomeda. Andromeda is of the order of 1 to 1.5 million light years away, yet the Great Spiral Nebula can be seen with the naked eye. It is the largest known spiral. (Photo from the Hale Observatories.)

Fig. 38-4. Spiral Nebula in the Constellation Virgo. The spirals are composed of countless stars, the brightest of which appear as definite points of light. Note the spiraling arms. (Photo from the Hale Observatories.)

Fig. 38-5. Spiral Nebula in the Constellation Coma Berenices, Seen Edge On. (Photo from the Hale Observatories.)

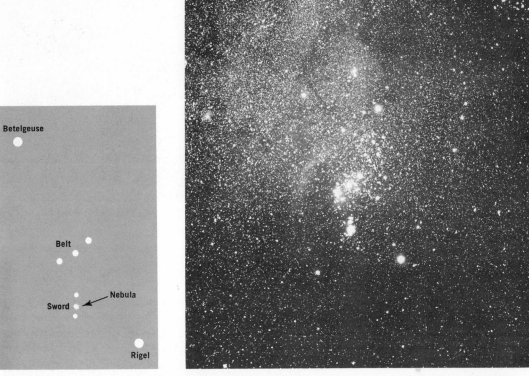

Fig. 38-6. The Diffuse Nebula in the Constellation Orion. Orion is a winter constellation easily visible in the southern sky on a clear night in the northern hemisphere. The nebulosity is the middle star in the sword. The bright stars Betelgeuse and Rigel are identified in the diagrammatic inset. See also Fig. 38-1. (Photo from the Hale Observatories.)

dark. The bright ones are illuminated by the intense radiation from one or more bright stars in the vicinity (Fig. 38-6). Spectral studies show that the light from the nebulae is in part reflected starlight and in part radiation from interstellar gases. The planetary nebulae appear to be stars with very extended and attenuated atmospheres. In some the central mass of the star can be dimly seen through its atmospheric shell, whereas in others the shells seem to be thick enough to obscure the central mass from our view. These atmospheric shells make these stars an unusual type, which so far lacks an adequate explanation.

Galaxies

The stars that we see in the sky with our naked eyes or with a relatively low-power telescope belong to a system of stars and interstellar gas and dust that make up the Milky Way (Figs. 38-7 and 38-8). We have seen that our galaxy is spread out through space in the form of a great disk that light takes 100,000 years to cross from edge to edge. The disk is comparatively thin; light takes only 10,000 years to traverse its thickness. One of the stars inside this disk is our sun (Fig. 38-8), so that we see this disk, or wheel, from a position near

Fig. 38-7. Portion of the Milky Way. (Composite photo from the Hale Observatories.)

the sun as the rim of the wheel goes right around us. Far out on this rim we see a concentration of stars in a band around the sky with our naked eyes. It looks milky so we call it the Milky Way. Some called it an island universe, and up to as late as 1920, it was commonly believed to be the whole universe. The philosopher Kant suggested as early as 1755 that certain nebulous patches, called *nebulae* at the time, were other galaxies. Herschel believed likewise about 1787, but it was not until 1923 that Kant's suggestion was firmly established. It should be realized that the identification of our galaxy as both elliptical and spiral in shape from a position well inside it (as we are) without knowing where your position is with respect to the galaxy as a whole, was an exceedingly difficult problem. Nevertheless, Harlow Shapley of Harvard did just that in 1923 when he determined that our solar system was in one of the spiral arms some 27,000 light years from the center of the galaxy. Modern research has shown that within the Milky Way, and near it, there are globular star clusters and great clouds of interstellar gas and dust, irregularly distributed, that obscure

our vision of some parts of the sky. The dark parts are being investigated by radio astronomy.

This fantastically large wheel is slowly rotating. The period of rotation of the Milky Way is between 200 and 250 million yr. The speed of our solar system due to this rotation is about 180 mi/sec. How do we know that it is rotating? Any great aggregation of matter, such as is contained in these billions of stars, would collapse because of gravitational forces into one great ball unless it were turning at a sufficient speed like a great wheel, just as our solar system would collapse if it were not turning about the sun. Other evidences of rotation of the Milky Way include the facts that it has spiral arms and that other galaxies appear to rotate. Millions of galaxies are within range of our best telescopes.

There are three general types of galaxies, the irregular, the spiral, and the elliptical. Attempts to account for the differences have led some astronomers to ascribe them to be differences in stage of development. We will defer further discussion of the ages of galaxies to the section on the evolution of stars.

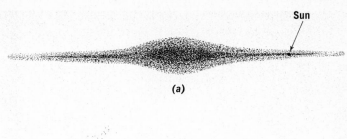

(a)

Fig. 38-8. Probable Structure of Milky Way Galaxy and Position of Our Sun in It (estimated from telescopic and radio studies). (*a*) Edge view. (*b*) "Top" view.

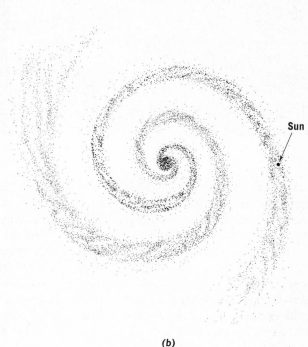

(b)

Galactic Clusters

Within our galaxy there are several hundred clusters that contain not more than a few hundred stars each. The stars in each cluster are all about the same distance from the earth and seem to have been in the cluster since birth. They have different luminosities, and as they are all about the same distance from us, they must have different masses. They also must be about the same age. They move around with the great wheel of the Milky Way with the general stream of traffic with average velocities. They are typical Population I stars.

Globular Clusters

Omega Centauri was first named as a star. Better telescopes proved it to be a gigantic ball of stars, perhaps several hundred thousand of them. These stars form a typical globular cluster, larger than most such clusters, and close enough to be seen with the naked eye (Fig. 38-9). About 120 of such clusters are known. They are remarkable not only because of their symmetry, but because they seem to consist exclusively of Population Type II stars. This means that there are no blue or white stars in them, and so the clusters must be very old, so old that such bright stars have "burned" out. There is no evidence of interstellar clouds of gas and dust such as are commonly associated with Population I stars. Moreover, they tend to be high velocity stars that are not moving with the general stream of traffic in our galaxy, but are crossing it at all angles. This suggests that they are not true parts of it; that is, they just happen to be intercepted by it as they move through space.

Stellar Evolution

In any discussion of the evolution of stars we cannot discuss the origin of the star-building materials, for there is no scientific explanation of how either matter or energy came into existence. The most that a scientist can say is, "Give us matter and energy to start with and we will attempt to give you a plausible explanation of how the present universe evolved without resorting to the supernatural." Much of any account of the evolution of an individual star cannot be proved, but all of it should be reasonable; that is, all parts of it should be in accord with the accepted principles (laws) of science. Even so, parts of any theory of stellar evolution, no matter how reasonable, may ultimately be shown to be wrong by new observations. Research astronomers will continue to make more observations, which

Fig. 38-9.   Globular Star Cluster in the Constellation Canes Venatici. The great cluster in the center is composed of tens of thousands of stars, each of which is a number of light years distant from its nearest neighbor. (Photo from the Hale Observatories.)

they will try to relate to a meaningful theory, one that is valid enough to make unnecessary the further repetition of these observations.

How does one go about the problem of stellar evolution? Man has been observing the stars scientifically and effectively for little more than 100 yr, whereas stellar evolution involves tens of millions of years at the very least. An analogy will help. Imagine a newly discovered island on which there lives a wholly unfamiliar form of life, say an unusual insect whose life cycle includes egg and adult stages and two intermediate stages that are not at all clear; it takes a full year to complete the cycle. Let us also assume that you, an expert entomologist, can stay on the island only a day or two. You wish to unravel the life cycle of the insect. Could you do it, and how? If at the time of year that you were on the island, only adult specimens could be found, you would be doomed to failure. But if all stages were present, you would simply collect numbers of live specimens of each stage, take them home, watch them develop, and arrange them in a proper sequence.

So it is with stars. If all were the same age, it would be impossible to chart their evolution. In our galaxy there is a great variety of stars; they vary in color from red through orange-yellow, yellow, and yellow-white to bluish white and to blue; they vary in surface temperature from 2000 to 30,000°C and more; they vary in mass from more than 5 to 10 times that of our sun down to less than $\frac{1}{5}$ its mass; they vary in density from less than that of our atmosphere to that where a cubic inch of its matter weighs a ton; they vary in diameter from about 25,000 mi and less to more than 100 million mi. Surely a great many different stages of development are represented; surely some are very young relatively and some are very old insofar as stages of development are concerned; they do not all age at the same rate. Naturally astronomers try to arrange them in

what seems a proper sequence. One result of such an attempt is the Hertzsprung–Russell diagram, which we have already discussed. Let us turn our attention to an earlier stage of development.

Within our galaxy (and other galaxies) there are vast masses of interstellar gas and dust, which we have already mentioned. Some astronomers have estimated that the total mass of this dust and gas in the universe is equal to, or greater than, the combined masses of all the countless billions of stars in the universe. The gases, more abundant than the dust, are chiefly hydrogen, helium, nitrogen, and oxygen, with hydrogen by far the most abundant. The dust is composed of atoms of somewhat heavier elements that can stick together to form grains of various sizes, atoms of carbon, iron, and so on.

The vast clouds of cold, extremely rarefied dust and gas seem a natural starting point for the discussion of the evolution of a star. (It is generally agreed by astronomers that the Milky Way started as a rotating flat disk of gas and dust as much as hundreds of thousands of light years across.) The individual particles would have a thermal motion of their own in the manner of gases. There would be countless small disturbances throughout, small eddies, just as there are in whirlpools of water. The particles would be subject to the law of gravitation, as are all particles in the universe. It is extremely unlikely that the density of such a gas would be uniform. Such a disk would be gravitationally unstable; that is, the forces of attraction would exaggerate any irregularities present.

The astronomer and physicist Sir James Jeans has shown that such a mass would tend to break up into a large number of smaller clouds, each of which would be 10 to 100 light years across. Again gravitation would tend to exaggerate small irregularities as the slow contraction continued. Small knots of matter would form, and numbers of them would combine to form larger knots. There might be several main centers of contraction, each one destined to form a star. We have learned (p. 212) that the compression of a gas is a heating process; the compression associated with contraction would cause the temperature to rise as gravitational energy was transformed into heat energy. In time the mass would become hot enough to shine; it would then be a full-fledged star. The contraction would continue even while the star got hotter still. The internal temperature might rise to 1 million °C in stars the size of our sun, high enough for nuclear reactions to take place, the conversion of hydrogen into helium and heat energy chief among them. The rise in temperature would cause a rise in the internal pressure. In time the pressure would be great enough to successfully oppose the gravitational contracting force. The shrinking would be slowed down, and would cease when the energy generated by the nuclear reactions balanced the radiation of energy into empty space (Fig. 38-10).

The stars forming from such huge clouds of gas and dust would have different masses. Those that have approximately the mass of our sun would settle down to a long life, a few tens of billions of years long, during which the conversion of hydrogen into helium and the output of energy would remain reasonably constant. However, for those stars that are half again as massive as our sun, the life histories are different. Because of their great mass, the internal temperatures would rise to many tens of millions of degrees Celsius. Their supply of hydrogen would not last more than a few tens of millions of years. A new source of energy would come into being by the conversion of helium into other elements. Energy production would be speeded up to fantastic rates until the star would be blown to pieces and become a supernova. There are three recorded cases of supernovae in our Milky Way in the last 1000 yr; many have been observed in other galaxies. In each case the luminosity was increased a million-fold and more for a few days. Stellar material was ejected in all directions at speeds as much as 3000 mi/sec. Thus much of the star was returned to its original condition, gas and dust, eventually to become material from which a second generation star could be created.

Within our galaxy (and others) some stars have increased in brightness a thousand to tens of thousands of times within a few days. They become dimmer as the years pass, and resume their original luminosity. These are novae, not supernovae, for they do not explode but merely expand at speeds as much as 600 mi/sec, and in doing so lose some of their mass to outer space. They therefore become smaller and more stable, perhaps a stable white dwarf.

If our reasoning about stellar evolution is correct, we should be able to extend it to the formation of galaxies. Let us return to our original vast cloud of gas and dust thousands of light years across. According to Sir James Jeans such a mass would contract and split into smaller masses that could become stars and clusters of stars such as we have in our galaxy. If big enough, a gas and dust cloud could become the source of material for all of the 100 billion stars in the Milky Way, with plenty left over for the clouds that are still in it. Such a collection of stars would have at first a very irregular shape, forming an irregular galaxy (p. 668). Somehow it began to rotate. It may have inherited a rotational movement from the original cloud. As it rotated some order would be introduced into the system. There would be a "smoothing out" process, during which spiral arms were formed in its outer parts—it would become a spiral galaxy. With still more smoothing out, the arms would tend to become incorporated into the main body of the galaxy, and in doing so it would become transformed into an elliptical galaxy.

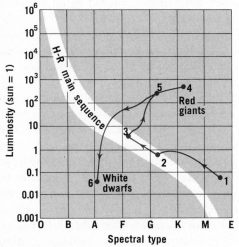

Fig. 38-10. Probable Life History of a Star of About the Mass of Our Sun, Correlated with the Hertzsprung-Russell Diagram. From 1 to 2, the star's energy is due to gravitational contraction; this phase of development has a duration of about 10^6 yr. At 2, conversion of hydrogen to helium by nuclear fusion begins. Our sun is now at the stage represented by a position slightly above 2 (see Fig. 38-2). As the star converts hydrogen to helium, over a period of about 10^{10} yr, its changing character is represented by a shift in position upward along the main sequence from 2 to 3. At point 3 most of the hydrogen has been converted into helium and that nuclear reaction becomes nearly negligible. From 3 to 4, the star's energy comes from gravitational contraction of the helium core. At the same time the outer layers expand and the star becomes more luminous—duration about 10^8 yr. At position 4 (red giant) the star's interior is at such a high temperature that the helium in the core is converted by nuclear fusion into some of the lighter elements, probably mostly carbon. This is represented on the H-R by a reversal from 4 to 5. The path from 5 to 6 (white dwarf) has not been definitely substantiated.

Population II Stars

From this account it can be seen that not all the stars in our galaxy are the same age or in the same stage of development. (Do not confuse age with stage of development. A star young in years may be in a late stage of development. The rate of aging among stars varies enormously.) We have described Population I stars (p. 664) and Population II stars (p. 669). There are no old blue stars; hot blue stars are relatively young in years but are aging fast, for they are converting hydrogen to helium at a fantastic rate compared to our sun. Even if we knew when and how the oldest stars came into existence, we would still have unanswered questions that are doomed always to remain unanswered, certainly by scientists. Somewhere here science leaves off; the only answers are those given by philosophers and theologians, answers than can never be backed by scientific evidence because the questions are not scientific questions.

The "Exploding" Universe

There are no satisfactory theories of the origin of the universe. The only one that seems to have much backing has been called the Big Bang theory—hypothesis would be a better term than theory. One of its great defects is the lack of a cause for the so-called explosion. As we have already seen, the speeds of stars that are moving towards or away from us are calculated from the Doppler shift of the spectral lines. Our previous discussion was confined to the stars within our own galaxy. When observance of the Doppler shift was extended to other galaxies, it was found that the shift *in all cases* was away from us; that is, the lines were shifted toward the red end of the spectrum. This means, if the interpretation of the shift is valid, that all galaxies are receding from us. Moreover, it was discovered that the greater the distance, the greater the velocity of recession. Double the distance and the speed was doubled.

Let us imagine their directions to be reversed so that all would move toward our galaxy, maintaining their present speeds as they do so. Given time enough they would all join together into one huge mass. Since the farther ones would be moving faster than the near ones, they would all reach this central area at the same time. That time would be some 5 billion yr from now. What does it all mean?

The evidence seems to point to the conclusion that some 5 billion yr ago, this huge mass of hot gaseous matter exploded into a vast number of huge fragments. Each one of these fragments would in time become a galaxy. Local condensations within the galaxy would give rise to stars or star systems, some of which developed into solar systems during the process. This explanation is, of course, based on the interpretation placed upon the red shift. Could something else have caused it?

A host of other questions arise at once. How did all the matter in the universe ever get together in the first place? How long had it been together before the explosion took place? How long will the universe keep expanding? Is it finite or infinite? All we can say is that the universe is probably between 10 and 15 billion yr old. Will man ever know more than that? Only time will tell.

Exercises

1. How can you prove that the stars shine by their own light, whereas the moon and the planets shine only be reflected light?
2. How bright would the sun appear to be relative to its present apparent brightness if it were removed to the position of Jupiter (about 50 times as far away)?
3. Which is brighter, a star of magnitude 1 or one of magnitude 2?
4. (a) A light year is a unit of what? (b) How far is a light second?
5. How do we calculate the distance to the nearest stars?
6. (a) What are the stars composed of? (b) How do we know?
7. How may intrinsic brightness be determined if the distance cannot be determined by parallax?
8. How may distance be determined if a star is too far away to be calculated from its parallax?
9. Explain the relationship between temperature and spectral class.
10. The intrinsic brightness of stars up to 300 light years away can be determined by the parallax method. For stars farther away intrinsic brightness can be determined from spectral class or period of variation (for Cepheid variables). Why do we feel that the latter two methods are valid?
11. Distinguish between a giant, a dwarf, and a main sequence star.
12. The spectra of the sun and the other stars show many dark lines superimposed on a continuous spectrum. What is the cause of the dark lines?
13. Explain, in terms of the Bohr theory, why the spectral lines of hydrogen in a very hot star differ from those of a cool star.
14. What are stars composed of?
15. The sun is losing mass every day by the conversion of 4 million long tons of its matter into radiation each *second*. (The same is true of every other star except that the amount may differ.) If its present mass is of the order of 10^{34} g, what percentage of its mass will be left in 5 billion yr, assuming a constant rate of loss? (There

are about 1 million g in a long ton and 31.5 million sec in a year.)

16. (a) What is a Cepheid variable?
    (b) Of what use are Cepheid variables in the study of stars?
17. How are the masses of many stars computed?
18. (a) Compare the diameters of the Pup, Antares, and the sun.
    (b) Which is nearest the average for all stars?
    (c) Compare the masses of these three stars.
19. (a) What is a double star?
    (b) What information do we need to determine the mass of a double star system?
20. Why should an aggregation of gaseous matter in space tend to contract?
21. When a contracting mass of hydrogen gas reaches a certain temperature, the hydrogen-helium fusion process is initiated. At this point, contraction stops. Why?

22. (a) What is meant by main sequence stars?
    (b) What stars lie outside the main sequence? Why?
23. How may masses of stars not in double (or triple) star systems be estimated?
24. (a) What is a galaxy? Name one besides our own.
    (b) What is a spiral nebula?
25. Galactic nebulae are great irregular masses of diffuse material (gas and fine "dust") within our galaxy that shine, probably from reflected light of nearby stars. (Do not confuse them with spiral nebulae.) What might the "dust" consist of?
26. What is the "red shift"? Explain the principle involved.
27. What inferences have been made from the red shift?
28. Does the red shift have the same significance applied to stars in our own galaxy as it does to other galaxies? Explain.

Chapter 39

Conclusion

It is not at all strange that we should conclude our explorations of the major fields of physical science in the heavens where we began them. The heavens excited early man's imagination in a way that his mundane surroundings never could. He probably became aware of such regularities of nature as the round of the seasons, the rise and fall of the tides, the phases of the moon, and the like as soon as he began to think, but centuries were to elapse before he separated the solar system from the stars. Still another score of centuries were to pass before he realized the tremendous isolation of this solar system in space.

By that time he had gained a nearly complete knowledge of planetary motions and a reasonably accurate knowledge of planetary distances, sizes, satellites, and so on, but the stars were still largely a mystery. Despite the discovery of the telescope, stellar astronomy did not advance much beyond the cataloguing stage until Fraunhofer turned his newly invented spectroscope on the sun and stars, and Bessel discovered stellar parallax. Even so, the astronomers made little progress in providing

While it is never safe to affirm that the future of Physical Science has no marvels in store ever more astonishing than those of the past, it seems probable that most of the grand underlying principles have been firmly established, and that further advances are to be sought chiefly in the rigorous application of these principles to all the phenomena which come to our notice. . . . An eminent physicist has remarked that the future truths of Physical Science are to be looked for in the sixth place of decimals.
A. A. MICHELSON
(Nobel Prize, Physics, 1907)

676

explanations until the physicists had unraveled the structure of the atom, accomplished atomic fission, reasoned the likelihood of atomic fusion, and made it a reality in the early 1950's. Stellar astronomy therefore belongs most fittingly at the end of our account just as solar astronomy belongs at the beginning.

What of the future? Will the scientists ever solve all of the mysteries of the universe? No living scientist really thinks so. But it hasn't always been that way. A. A. Michelson, the author of the epigram that heads this chapter, was a young man of 28 in 1892 when he made that prophecy. Curiously enough, at that time he was performing experiments that were laying the foundation for some of Einstein's ideas. Just three years later there began that amazing series of discoveries and new theories that revolutionized physical science; the discovery of X rays and radioactivity, the identification of the electron as a universal constituent of all matter, the creation of new and radical theories of quanta, of light, of relativity, of internal atomic structure, and far more. We remind you that the solution of every problem creates new problems. As Conant said (Chapter 10), a good theory is always fruitful. "A scientist measures a theory only by its consequences, consequences in terms of other ideas and other experiments. Thus conceived, science is not a quest for certainty; it is rather a quest which is successful only to the degree that it is continuous."

Will our present theories all be overthrown some day, to be replaced by different ones? Some will, some will undergo revision, and some will stand very much as they are. In general, the older theories stand the best chance of retention intact. The laws, however, will always hold within the limits placed upon them. Newton's laws apply to the phenomena of motion, including those of artificial satellites, just as they always have. Einstein's revision (p. 367) applies only to a very special case.

We have interwoven much history of science so that you may have a better understanding of the processes of scientific discovery, that you may see that human folly has played its part in the field of science just as it has in other fields, and that you may gain wisdom by learning how difficult it is for any man to step outside the intellectual climate of his time.

Throughout all we have kept the emphasis on principles rather than on the practical side, for this has been a course in science rather than a course about science. There is little intellectual discipline in the latter, little that will help you to see further and more dispassionately in other fields. If you now think back about the scientists mentioned in this book, you will not be able to find one of them who was trying to invent anything of practical use at the time he made his discovery. This is not to say that none of them invented anything. Perhaps they did, but, if so, none are remembered because of that. We stress the value of what has been called "useless science" over that of practical science simply because the practical scientist (Edison, for example) depends almost wholly on "useless science" for ideas. The hall of fame is replete with the names of men who made facts significant, who integrated them into a conceptual scheme, but it contains the names of few men who were mere discoverers of facts. No practical scientist ever won a Nobel prize.

One of the outstanding differences between the science of today and that before World War II is its relation to the public. Before the war the scientist and his works made little impact upon the average citizen of the United States. The role of the scientist in government was virtually nonexistent and there were practically no research grants for fundamental science. With the advent of World War II governments at last began to be vitally interested in what the scientist could do to help their side win. The center of interest was in bombing, "better" bombs, better bombers and bombsights, better ways of detecting raids, and so on. This interest culminated in the successful explosion of the A-bomb in Hiroshima.

Almost immediately a fear developed that the world might end in a great holocaust of atomic bombs. Soon the developers of the bomb were being damned for not refusing to work on it by people whose ignorance of such matters was colossal. They did not realize that the investigation that led up to the fission of atoms of U^{235} was not something that came as a result of World War II. It started as an intellectual enterprise and remained so up to the time the gentle Einstein, at the request of other scientists, suggested to President Roosevelt that U^{235} atoms might be fissioned to help win the war. For those who think that our scientists should have refused to go further, let us ask the question: Suppose they had refused, and suppose Hitler's scientists had developed the bomb before the war could be brought to an end in other ways and in our favor; what, then, would you think of our scientists?

The atomic bomb and the realization that there were enormous stores of energy within atomic nuclei excited the imaginations of people in all walks of life. Almost none had any concept of how this energy could be released and used, and so all sorts of prophecies were made, many by people who should have known better. First thoughts were in the direction of atomic power to generate electricity. One scientist had it so cheap that it would not pay to bill people for it. He failed to realize that the great part of our current bills are for distribution of electric power, and very little for its generation.

The fact that atomic energy is used to propel submarines and large ocean-going ships leads people to expect other uses that are extremely unlikely to materialize. Such people are ignorant of the fact that these atomic submarines and ships are propelled by steam just as their predecessors were. The only difference is that the heat to generate the steam is derived from an atomic reactor instead of the burning of coal or oil. In our atomic power plants the generators (dynamos) are all turned by steam turbines. In order to use atomic energy for power, man must first transform it in an atomic reactor (pile) to heat energy, heat that is usable in all the ways that heat generated in other ways is usable; there is no other way.

The advantage of atomic energy over conventional means of producing electric power is that there is no need to transport and store coal or oil. One disadvantage is the necessity of using large quantities of heavy shielding materials to protect workers from harmful radiation. For portable atomic power plants, such as an atomic rocket, the weight of the shielding material is another disadvantage.[1] The so-called nuclear rocket is merely a nuclear reactor that produces heat to raise hydrogen gas to a temperature as high as the materials composing the reactor can stand without melting. The hot gas is then ejected through a nozzle to the outside. Newton's third law takes over and the rocket is driven forward. In a rocket this requires the transportation of great quantities of hydrogen. The ion rocket requires the generation of electricity in order to ionize cesium, which is then ejected in place of the hydrogen. How this solves the transportation problem the writer fails to see. As of now our present reliance on chemically burning fuels to produce the power for our space travelers seems likely to continue indefinitely into the future.

It is true that man has been able to control atomic fission in a reactor by not allowing the heat to accumulate beyond a certain amount. If this could not be done, there would be no atomic power except in the bomb. It has been

---

[1] The disposal of atomic wastes is another problem. A dozen or two barrels of atomic wastes dumped in the western end of Lake Superior would in time pollute all of the Great Lakes, killing all animal and vegetable life.

assumed by many that some day a method of controlling atomic fusion would be found. The two situations are very different. Atomic fission takes place at ordinary temperatures. To control it one regulates the number of atoms fissioned per unit time. Fusion of H to He takes place only at temperatures that are measured in millions of degrees. Control seems out of the question, even by magnetic fields.

Even if present difficulties are all solved, our space travels are likely never to extend beyond our solar system because of our great isolation in space (see descriptions of the planets in Chapter 4). Because light travels at 186,000 mi/sec, there are those who assume that a spaceship could approach that speed and so could reach the vicinity of our nearest star in 4 to 5 yr. However, $F = ma$ still, and man's body has a limit to the amount of acceleration, positive and negative, that it can endure over a long period of time. This limit would add some months to the round trip. In addition to the air, food, and water problems, there are psychological problems that would arise from the crowding together of a number of people into cramped quarters for several years. To make the attempt would require a great deal of courage—or should we say foolhardiness?

All these considerations are relevant in varying degrees to our so-called "flying saucer" problems. Our knowledge of the other planets in our solar system indicates that the saucers could not have come from any of them. The only other source is other solar systems. The nearest star may not have one; we just do not know. Suppose it has, and one of its planets has intelligent beings on it. They would encounter the same problems in reaching us that we would have in reaching them. An adequate spaceship certainly should be far bigger than any of the saucers reported. Moreover, can you imagine beings that intelligent who would make that colossal trip (100 million times the distance to the moon) and then not make

themselves known to us? They have not, even though there have been some reports that they have. Certainly they would want to meet some of our most intelligent people—and that they have not done.

Because man has done many things that he never thought he could do, there is a tendency for many people to believe that there are no limits to what he will eventually be able to do. These people are not scientists. Many of our explanations of natural phenomena may be modified to some extent in the future; a few will be completely invalidated. But Kepler's laws, Newton's laws, and Galileo's law of free fall have stood the test of time—over 300 years. These laws and the great conservation laws may well hold forever within the limits set for them. Go back and read Chapter 10, especially the sections Uncertainty in Science and Scientific Explanation.

Now that a landing on the moon has been accomplished (and it is well to remember that none of the four trips has been powered by atomic energy), a great many prophecies have been and still are being made, mostly by unqualified people. Some expect the moon to be colonized, both for agriculture and industry. They have easy "answers" to the lack of oxygen, water, and true soil. Pulverized rock is not soil; chemical weathering is needed to turn it to soil and there is none of that on the moon. These prophets expect water to be obtained from minerals within which it is chemically bound. Such minerals are few, the percentage of water is very low, and the cost would be staggering. Mining would be confined to the primary deposits, if any.

A great many scientific problems have been solved, but the creation of new problems goes on at an ever-increasing rate. Many of these have to do with man's survival on this increasingly crowded earth. The very destructiveness of the atomic bomb may have solved the problem created by it; the probability that it will ever be used again is exceedingly small. Much has been written about the world's population and its food problem. The idea that we can continue to increase the food supply to keep pace with the increase in population is a dangerous one. One reason is that with a population increase goes a decrease in space available to produce food; new roads and streets and buildings for homes, for business and industry, for education and recreation, for airports and power stations require far more than a million acres of potentially productive land every year.

Not so much has been written about a second reason, man's too short water supply. Shortage of water is far more dangerous than shortage of food, for without adequate fresh water there can be no land-raised food. One part or another of the world discovers this peril every year because of drought. So far water for man's personal needs has not been disastrously scarce. Nor has it been for industry, largely because manufacturers and processors have refused to locate their plants in regions where a plentiful supply of relatively unpolluted water is not guaranteed them.

Perhaps the expectation of desalting sea water explains man's lack of concern to date. But the costs of desalting are prohibitively expensive at present except for personal use and in some industries. Desalination plants must be near the sea, whereas the places where the water is to be used are largely inland, and the way is always uphill. Some communities have recovered pure water (in the health sense) for local personal use from "used" waters, even sewage waters, by filtering and distillation processes. The cost is much too high for use in agriculture. The average person has no conception of how much water it takes to grow an acre of wheat (20 to 40 bu). The minimum under optimum conditions is 300,000 gal; the average under typical conditions is twice that. And what would one do with the billions of

tons of salt remaining after desalination? Dump it back into the ocean? There are strong objections to doing that on a long-term basis. Can you think of one objection?

A third reason has to do with ecology, the most publicized aspect of which concerns insecticides, fungicides, and the like, and the ban placed on the use of some of them. Man is always engaged in a never-ending battle with harmful insects and plant diseases; even now he suffers heavy losses. Scientists are continuing to develop new high-yielding strains of high-protein, high-energy foods and are introducing them into many parts of the world. But there is a danger in planting a similar strain of a single crop over broad areas of the earth, for while man is changing the course of evolution of plants by artificial methods, nature is changing the course of evolution for their enemies by her own methods. The result may be that new strains of plant enemies that are partially or wholly immune from the pesticides used to control them may develop and a probability of a famine may be set up that could take hundreds of millions of lives before relief measures could be taken.

Ecology embraces the entire household of nature—plants, animals, and their relationships with each other and their environment. There is no such thing as ecology *and* man, for man is just as much a part of nature, part of an ecosystem, as is any other animal or plant in this world, which contains at least 350,000 known species of plants and over 1 million species of animals. Ecology is worth studying because it is interesting. A more important reason is that today we are being confronted with several courses of action concerning problems that involve ecology and we are being asked which courses to take. Man has more influence over nature than any other animal. His long struggle upward from his primeval beginnings has been marked by an increasingly greater control of his environment. In a sense this control sets him apart from all other animals. Evolutionary studies indicate that these animals reached their present levels (stages of development) long before modern man reached the stage where he could exert much influence on his environment. The levels these animals reached were dictated by the environment because survival (of the species, not the individual) was impossible unless successful adaptations to that environment were made. Thus modern species are all well adapted; further evolutionary changes are unlikely to persist because such changes are apt to be for the worse unless changes occur in their environment. Man has changed the environment of a large number of species. As a result many species have become extinct, many others are on the road to extinction, and still others are undergoing, or have undergone, mutations of one sort or another that may allow them to escape extinction.

Man's ability to control his environment or to adapt quickly to changes in it has encouraged him to believe that he is not only immune from the disasters that have struck down so many species in past ages, but also immune from the consequences that he himself has made, some intentionally but many inadvertently. Today the well-informed are not so sure. More and more of them are agreeing with Dr. Albert Schweitzer, who said: "Man has lost the capacity to foresee and to forestall. He will end by destroying the earth." Until quite recently there may have been excuses for doing some ecologically unwise things but not any more; man must now conform to the rules of nature or risk disaster. He has already made large areas of the earth unproductive by his ecological ignorance.

The dangers inherent in large-scale indiscriminate spraying of insecticides were first brought to the attention of the general public some ten years ago when the late Rachel Carson published her eloquent indictment of insecticides in her book, *Silent Spring*. The impact on the ill-informed general public, including many (possibly most) conservationists, was great. However, many biologists, medical doctors, and others, who are competent to analyze the evidence and come to unprejudiced conclusions, were not wholly satisfied with the indictment. They thought that there was too much emotionalism mixed with the evidence; her picture of a world without birds was not acceptable. Far more important was the complete omission of the malaria story from the book. Malaria is spread by the anopheles mosquito, and is by far the most widespread disease on earth. The death rate in uncontrolled areas is not high, less than one in several hundred, but the debilitating effect of the disease is beyond the comprehension of those who have had no contact with it. In India alone before World War II there were some 75 million victims a year and an estimated 75,000 deaths. Today the annual toll is about 250,000 victims and almost no deaths. This vast reduction has been brought about by widespread spraying of DDT in and about the dwellings of the people. More than a billion people throughout the world who were once subject to endemic malaria, sometimes twice a year, are now free from it. Two other loathsome diseases once common in the South Pacific, filariasis (elephantiasis) and dengue, also transmitted by the anopheles mosquito, have been wiped out by DDT.

Of the hundreds of thousands of species of insects, only about 3000 destroy crops and carry diseases in anything like disastrous proportions. This is less than 1% of the total number of species, but there can be trillions of individuals of one species. What a vast swarm of locusts can do to a field of ripening grain in a few hours has to be seen to be believed. Banning DDT would bring on disastrous crop failures in many parts of the world, even in the United States.

DDT is one of a family of chlorinated hydrocarbons made from petroleum. Other members of the family are aldrin, dieldrin, and endrin. DDT was first made before the turn of the 20th century, but its insecticide properties were not discovered until 1939. Five years later its use forestalled a typhus epidemic in Naples, Italy. In 1948 Paul Müller of Switzerland won a Nobel Prize for establishing DDT as an insecticide capable of greatly increasing the food supply of a hungry world. It is a nerve poison that destroys an insect's ability to function. It kills by contact; an insect does not have to eat it. A small quantity can destroy insects over a wide area and so is cheap; it is the poor man's insecticide. Substitutes, none as efficient in controlling malaria according to the World Health Organization of the United Nations, cost far more. The profits of chemical companies making insecticides would be increased if the manufacture of DDT were banned.

Why defend DDT? Dr. Thomas Jukes, Professor of Medical Physics at the University of California at Berkeley, gives an answer: "Because disease and hunger debase mankind, and halt man's upward struggle towards freedom of the spirit." Put another way, a ban "would be against a most basic human right—the right to be protected against deadly disease." Moreover, there is no evidence at present that DDT is harmful to man; no human being has ever died from it or even become seriously ill from it even though as much as 5 to 6 grams of it have been ingested. The American Medical Association says there is no evidence that DDT can cause cancer in humans. It will take years of research before we can be certain about what DDT and the other chlorinated hydrocarbons can do or cannot do to man. In the meantime both scientists and laymen are wondering if the benefits are worth the environmental price that has to be paid. This question cannot be resolved by any of the methods known to science. How can you balance increased crop yields and control of malaria against the near extinction of many species of animal life, particularly birds?

Regardless of what we have said, neither DDT nor any other insecticide is likely to be the final answer to these problems of food and disease. This is because the genes of all kinds of organisms do not always faithfully replicate as described in Chapter 29. A few of them mutate, giving rise to individuals that are different in some significant way from the parents. Thus some individual anopheles mosquitos are "born" with a natural resistance to DDT, and they pass this resistance on to their descendants. This development of immunity steadily decreases DDT's usefulness. Other methods of insect control range from the introduction of predators, most commonly another insect, to tampering with reproductive systems (for example, sterilizing enormous numbers of males raised in captivity by radioactive rays, and then releasing them to mate as usual) or to applying a juvenile hormone to insect larvae, which prevents them from metamorphosing completely into adults. These methods kill by using what may be termed a "rifle" technique, since they can be made to apply to one particular species only, whereas insecticides kill by a "shotgun" technique, for they kill beneficial species as well as pest species, and often other forms of life.

Intelligent and knowledgeable protesters against DDT do not wish to get rid of all pesticides. They are encouraging the development of pesticides that are very toxic when first sprayed but which break down quickly to harmless substances, something that DDT does not do until several years have elapsed.

Many communities have commissions or boards appointed by governmental authorities whose sole purpose is to regulate the use of pesticides. Such boards are subjected to pressures from two groups, one of farmers and pesticide manufacturers, and the other of conservationists. One great criticism of these boards is their personnel; too many appointees are "prominent" citizens who have no scientific background, no ecological expertise, and possibly no training in the gathering of the needed information. Consequently, the activities of many boards are likely to be determined by one or another pressure group and/or by the member who can arouse the local public through appeals to emotion and prejudice. Tampering with the ecology of a region is an activity that is best left to experts. Some wholly unexpected and unpleasant surprises have occurred because a man with a little knowledge thought he knew the whole story.

Pollution, a word that to many is more or less synonymous with ecology, has many facets. There is little that an average lone individual can do about most of the facets, but one—that of the littering of the landscape—he can do something about. But how many do anything about it? A brief time ago we were hopeful that America would become more beautiful, but the enthusiasm of our people, particularly our young people, soon waned. For many it was only a fad, and it is fast going the way of all fads. Increase of the amount of litter in some of our parks, recreation areas, and even our cemeteries has come about by sheer vandalism, perpetrated chiefly by young people for whom the recreation areas were established. Various governmental units spend a total of over $100 million annually to dispose of the litter so thoughtlessly and carelessly spread by man.

The problem of solid waste disposal has been with man ever since he began community living. For thousands of years the problem was essentially that of human wastes. In his tribal days, when he could no longer put up with his own filth, the tribe could pick up and move to a new site. Much later, when he first built large cities, and continuing down even into the 18th and 19th centuries, human and other wastes flowed down some streets in open sewers, which commonly led into streams. In time the stench forced the covering of the sewers, and later cess pools, septic tanks, and underground conduits solved the local aspects of the problem. A rapidly developing industrial society created new problems that we will always have with us. We can eliminate the problems completely only by closing down all plants and factories that pollute our environment. That, of course, would bankrupt the nation in short order. Given time, most plants and factories will find acceptable solutions.

All power plants except the atomic reactor ones pollute the atmosphere. The worst are the coal-burning plants; coal from many mines contains sulfur in objectionable amounts which burns off as sulfur dioxide (SO_2), probably the worst of the air pollutants. The same objection can be made of the oil-burning plants but to a lesser degree in most cases. Natural gas is relatively free of pollutants, but in most areas it is too expensive.

The atomic reactor plants are entirely free of air pollutants, but they have another potential danger, that from radioactive rays. Actually the danger is almost nonexistent; it exists only in the minds of ill-informed people, some of whom occupy positions of responsibility, state governors, for example. There isn't a single atomic power plant in existence that gives off as much radioactivity as the residents of New York City or of Denver experience every day of their lives. All rocks emit radioactive rays, some more than others. Some rays reach us from outer space. The maximum permissible radiation that man can experience without danger to his health is more than 2 million times that which a worker in such a plant receives. The danger of an atomic explosion is nil; atomic reactors are not atomic bombs. Moreover, the waste fission products are mixed with cement or fused glass, and then stored in deep abandoned salt miles, all of which are completely free of groundwater. (How do we know that?) The big problem is to overcome the ignorance and the prejudice of the people.

We will concern ourselves with only one more facet of the pollution problem, that of thermal pollution, some aspects of which involve atmospheric pollution and water pollution. As commonly applied, thermal pollution refers to waste heat in the generation of electric power. The only pollution-free plant is the hydroelectric plant, for which few desirable or practical sites are left. Plants that burn fossil fuels (coal, oil, natural gas) and atomic reactor plants generate steam to run steam turbines, which in turn run electric generators. After passing through the turbine, the steam is condensed to hot water. This is the source of the thermal pollution. Poured into streams, it warms their waters, and may have disastrous effects on the life of the streams. On the other hand, if the hot water is partially cooled before it enters the streams (and it almost always is), it can have beneficial effects. Many species of fish grow faster in these warmed waters. In some areas the hot waters are put to good use to provide heat for housing developments, factories, greenhouses, and such.

There is one facet of thermal pollution of which the general public is completely ignorant. All of the energy we use, no matter what its source, is eventually degraded to heat in accordance with the second law of thermo-dynamics (p. 200). And by all energy we include all human activities, from metabolism to driving and stopping an automobile. No scientific breakthrough on this problem is possible by any stretch of the imagination or otherwise. This degradation of other forms of energy to heat can be reduced only by manipulating the number of consumers or by limiting the per capita consumption of energy. Much has been written about the possible climatic effects of increasing the amounts of CO_2 and dust in the atmosphere. We will not add to it.

The central problem about which all other ecological problems may be grouped is that of keeping the population within limits. Advocates of population control have just formed a new Coalition for a National Population Policy headed by Milton S. Eisenhower. They will attempt to stabilize population by voluntary means. Even if their goal of 2.1 children a family could be realized immediately, it would take 70 years for the population to stabilize. The problem of birth control is hedged about by social custom, by tribal taboos, by religious and moral prohibitions. Birth control, either voluntary or enforced by law in every country, is the only permanent solution. Those who would prevent this would condemn hundreds of millions now living to death by starvation. The harsh ecological truth is that our greatest and most intractable problem is man himself.

Appendix

Units of length (metric system):

10 millimeters (mm) = 1 centimeter
  (1 mm = approx. 0.04 in.; 1 cm = approx. 0.4 in.)
100 centimeters (cm) = 1 meter (39.37 in.)
1000 meters (m)   = 1 kilometer (0.62 mi)
  Note: 1 in. = 2.54 cm; 1 ft = about 30 cm.

Units of volume (metric system):

1 cubic centimeter (cm^3) = 1 milliliter (ml)
1000 cm^3 = 1 liter
  Note: 1 liter is slightly more than one quart (1.06 qt).

Units of weight (metric system):

1 gram (g) = very nearly the mass of 1 cm^3 (1 ml) of water at 4°C. The difference is
             in the 6th decimal place.
1000 g   = 1 kilogram (2.20 lb)
  Note: 1 ton = 909 kg; 1 long ton = 1000 kg.

Other units based on metric system:

1 micron (μ)   = 1 millionth (10^{-6}) meter = 1 thousandth (10^{-3}) millimeter
1 millimicron (mμ) = 1 millionth (10^{-6}) millimeter
1 Ångström (Å)   = 10^{-8} cm, the order of magnitude of the diameter of an atom.

685

Index

The letter n means a footnote.